Register Now for
to Your

DSM-5® AND FAMILY SYSTEMS

Jessica A. Russo, PhD, LPCC-S, NCC, is a core faculty member of Walden University's College of Social and Behavioral Sciences. She is a licensed professional counselor in Ohio, a school-based mental health therapist, and co-owner of a private practice, Summit Therapy Group, Inc., in Akron, Ohio. Dr. Russo has over 15 years of clinical experience with individuals, couples, and families. Her areas of practice include working with couples and families, disadvantaged youth, and families impacted by substance abuse. She has presented at local, regional, and national professional conferences, such as the Association for Counselor Education and Supervision (ACES) and the American Counseling Association (ACA), as well as numerous professional development workshops to mental health clinicians, school counselors, teachers, and college faculty. Among her written contributions are chapters to books including *The Group Therapist's Notebook* and *Casebook for the DSM-5*.

J. Kelly Coker, PhD, has worked as a drug prevention/intervention counselor for children and adolescents in a K–12 setting as well as for at-risk and adjudicated youth in outpatient and group home settings. Dr. Coker has also worked in private practice with children, adolescents, adults, and couples and families with a variety of issues, including depression, anxiety, eating issues, and self-harming behavior. She has worked as an assistant and associate professor in Council for Accreditation of Counseling and Related Educational Programs (CACREP)-accredited counseling programs as well as a core faculty member and administrator in online CACREP-accredited counseling programs. Dr. Coker serves as a CACREP board member and site team reviewer. She has presented at numerous national conferences, including the American Counseling Association (ACA) and Association for Counselor Education and Supervision (ACES), and has been published in several professional journals and edited books. She is the assistant dean for the School of Counseling at Walden University.

Jason H. King, PhD, CMHC, is a core faculty member and student development coordinator, School of Counseling Programs, Walden University. Dr. King owned and clinically directed an outpatient mental health and substance abuse treatment clinic that collected data for the American Psychiatric Association's Routine Clinical Practice field trials that informed the *Diagnostic and Statistical Manual of Mental Disorders, Fifth Edition (DSM-5)* revision process. Because of this role he is listed on page 914 of the *DSM-5* as a Collaborating Investigator. He served as a *DSM-5* Revision Task Force committee member for the American Mental Health Counselors Association (AMHCA) and ACA and has given over 190 national and international trainings on the *DSM-5* since its publication in May 2013. Dr. King completed a podcast and webinar on the *DSM-5* with the ACA and wrote 19 monthly articles on the *DSM-5* in ACA's *Counseling Today*. He composed a journal article on the *DSM-5* published in the National Board for Certified Counselors' (NBCCs') *The Professional Counselor* (www.tpcjournal.nbcc.org/wp-content/uploads/2014/07/Pages-202 -215-King.pdf) and authored a 100-page online continuing education course on the *DSM-5* (www.ContinuingEdCourses.Net). He is also the *DSM-5* specialist for the PIMSY Electronic Health Record (EHR) practice management mental/behavioral health advisory board. Dr. King is the *DSM-5* content editor for the textbook *Diagnosing Children and Adolescents: Guide for Mental Health Practitioners*.

DSM-5® AND FAMILY SYSTEMS

Jessica A. Russo, PhD, LPCC-S, NCC
J. Kelly Coker, PhD
Jason H. King, PhD, CMHC

SPRINGER PUBLISHING COMPANY
NEW YORK

Springer Publishing Company, LLC
11 West 42nd Street
New York, NY 10036
www.springerpub.com

Acquisitions Editor: Sheri W. Sussman
Compositor: Westchester Publishing Services

ISBN: 978-0-8261-8398-9
e-book ISBN: 978-0-8261-8399-6

17 18 19 20 21 / 5 4 3 2 1

The author and the publisher of this Work have made every effort to use sources believed to be reliable to provide information that is accurate and compatible with the standards generally accepted at the time of publication. The author and publisher shall not be liable for any special, consequential, or exemplary damages resulting, in whole or in part, from the readers' use of, or reliance on, the information contained in this book. The publisher has no responsibility for the persistence or accuracy of URLs for external or third-party Internet websites referred to in this publication and does not guarantee that any content on such websites is, or will remain, accurate or appropriate.

Library of Congress Cataloging-in-Publication Data

Names: Russo, Jessica A., editor. | Coker, J. Kelly, editor. | King, Jason H., editor.
Title: DSM-5 and family systems / [edited by] Jessica A. Russo, J. Kelly Coker, and Jason H. King.
Other titles: Diagnostic and statistical manual of mental disorders-5 and family systems
Description: New York, NY : Springer Publishing Company, LLC, [2017] | Includes bibliographical references and index.
Identifiers: LCCN 2017000293 (print) | LCCN 2017001039 (ebook) | ISBN 9780826183989 (hard copy : alk. paper) | ISBN 9780826183996 (ebook)
Subjects: | MESH: Diagnostic and statistical manual of mental disorders. 5th ed | Mental Disorders—diagnosis | Family Therapy—methods
Classification: LCC RC337 (print) | LCC RC337 (ebook) | NLM WM 430.5.F2 | DDC 616.890072/7—dc23
LC record available at https://lccn.loc.gov/2017000293

Contact us to receive discount rates on bulk purchases.
We can also customize our books to meet your needs.
For more information please contact: sales@springerpub.com

Printed in the United States of America by McNaughton & Gunn.

CONTENTS

CONTRIBUTORS

Carrie Alexander-Albritton, PhD, NCC, LPC, CADC
Associate Professor, Department of Counselor Education
Western Illinois University
Moline, Illinois

Roxanne Bamond, PhD, LMFT, AAMFT Approved Supervisor
Core Faculty, Counselor Education
Marriage and Family Counseling/Therapy Program
Capella University
Minneapolis, Minnesota

Esther Benoit, PhD, LPC, NCC
Core Faculty, Marriage and Family Counseling
Walden University
Minneapolis, Minnesota

Danielle A. Black, PhD, LCP
Director, Child, Adolescent, and Family Services
The Family Institute at Northwestern University
Assistant Clinical Professor
Department of Psychology
Northwestern University
Evanston, Illinois

Matthew R. Buckley, EdD, LPC, LMHC, NCC, ACS, DCC
Core Faculty, Clinical Mental Health Counseling
Walden University
Minneapolis, Minnesota

Anne S. Cabanilla, PsyD, LP, LPC
Core Faculty, Mental Health Counseling
Capella University
Minneapolis, Minnesota

Trevon Clow, PhD, LMHC
Faculty Member
Capella University
Minneapolis, Minnesota

Deb Coolhart, PhD, LMFT
Assistant Professor
Syracuse University
Syracuse, New York

Kelly Dunbar Davison, PhD, LPC-S, NCC
Core Faculty, Clinical Mental Health Counseling
Walden University
Minneapolis, Minnesota

Kristen Eldredge, EdD, LPC, ACS, NCC
Core Faculty, Clinical Mental Health Counseling Program—Online
The Chicago School of Professional Psychology
Chicago, Illinois

Joelle P. France, EdD, MBA, MSW, LCSW (CO)
Core Faculty, Clinical Mental Health Counseling
Walden University
Minneapolis, Minnesota

Brandy L. Gilea, PhD, LPCC-S, NCC
Core Faculty, Clinical Mental Health Counseling
Walden University
Minneapolis, Minnesota

Marilyn Haight, PhD, LPC, NCC
Core Faculty, Clinical Mental Health Counseling
Walden University
Minneapolis, Minnesota

Brooks Bastian Hanks, PhD, LCPC
Core Faculty, Clinical Mental Health Counseling
Walden University
Minneapolis, Minnesota

Nicole R. Hill, PhD, LPC
Professor and Department Chairperson
Syracuse University
Syracuse, New York

Aaron Hugh Jackson, PhD, LPC
Core Faculty, Marriage, Couples, and Family Counseling Program
Walden University
Minneapolis, Minnesota

Jennifer Jancsin, MA, LPCC-S
Director of Behavioral Health Counseling
Zepf Center and the University of Toledo
Toledo, Ohio

Christie Jenkins, PhD, LPCC-S
Core Faculty, Clinical Mental Health Counseling
Walden University
Minneapolis, Minnesota

Joel A. Lane, PhD, LPC
Assistant Professor and Coordinator of Clinical Mental Health Counseling
Portland State University
Portland, Oregon

Amber Lange, PhD, LPC, CAADC
Core Faculty, Department of Counseling
Capella University
Minneapolis, Minnesota

John Laux, PhD, LPCC
Associate Dean of the College of Health and Human Services
The University of Toledo
Toledo, Ohio

Jan Lemon, PhD, LPC-S, NCC, NCSC
Assistant Professor and Coordinator of School Counseling
Mississippi College
Clinton, Mississippi

Brianna Mason, MA
Syracuse University
Syracuse, New York

Candace M. McLain-Tait, EdD, LPC, ACS
Core Faculty, Clinical Mental Health Counseling
Walden University
Minneapolis, Minnesota

Carol Pfeiffer Messmore, PhD, LMFT
Core Faculty, Marriage and Family Counseling/Therapy Program
Capella University
Minneapolis, Minnesota

Emily Meyer-Stewart, MEd, NCC, LPC
Licensed Professional Counselor
Gestalt Therapist
Private Practice
Pittsburgh, Pennsylvania

Rosanne Nunnery, PhD, LPC-S, NCC
Core Faculty, Mental Health Counseling
Capella University
Minneapolis, Minnesota

Rachel M. O'Neill, PhD, LPCC-S (OH)
Core Faculty, Clinical Mental Health Counseling
Walden University
Minneapolis, Minnesota

Katarzyna Peoples, PhD, LPC, LMHC
Core Faculty
Counselor Education and Supervision
Walden University
Minneapolis, Minnesota

Carol Podgorski, PhD, MPH, LMFT
Associate Professor of Psychiatry
University of Rochester School of Medicine and Dentistry
Rochester, New York

Torey Portrie-Bethke, PhD, NCC
Core Faculty, Clinical Mental Health Counseling
Walden University
Minneapolis, Minnesota

Juan A. Lopez Prida, Medical Student
Universidad Autonoma de Baja California
Tijuana, Baja California, Mexico

Alyssa Weiss Quittner, PhD, LMFT
Core Faculty, Marriage and Family Counseling/Therapy Program
Capella University
Minneapolis, Minnesota

Amanda Rovnak, PhD, PCC-S, LISW-S, LICDC-CS
Core Faculty, Clinical Mental Health Counseling
Walden University
Minneapolis, Minnesota

Stephanie K. Scott, PhD, LMHC
Core Faculty, Clinical Mental Health Counseling
Walden University
Minneapolis, Minnesota

Annabelle Shestak, MS, NCC
Doctoral Student
University of Massachusetts, Lowell
Lowell, Massachusetts

LoriAnn Stretch, PhD, LPC-S, NCC, ACS
Department Chair of CMHC-Online Campus
The Chicago School of Professional Psychology
Chicago, Illinois

Lee A. Teufel-Prida, PhD, LPCC, LMHC, NCC
Assistant Director of Training and Clinical Assistant Professor
The Family Institute at Northwestern University
Northwestern University
Evanston, Illinois

Kaisha A. Thomas, PhD, LMFT, LMHC, NCC, CCMHC
Faculty, Marriage and Family Counseling/Therapy Program
Capella University
Minneapolis, Minnesota

Carrie VanMeter, PhD, LPCC, LSC
Associate Professor
Coordinator of School Counseling Professional Practice
Walsh University
North Canton, Ohio

Holly H. Wagner, PhD, LPC, NCC
Assistant Professor
Southeast Missouri State University
Cape Girardeau, Missouri

Margaret Clark Zappitello, EdD, LPC, LMFT, LAC, MAC, NCC
Core Faculty, Clinical Mental Health Counseling
Walden University
Minneapolis, Minnesota

FOREWORD

*I*t has been well over half a century since Von Bertalanffy's *General Systems Theory* was introduced and early family therapy pioneers began to discuss and treat families from a systemic orientation. The assessment and diagnosis of a family system required systemic thinking; it became clear that attempts to address identified problems from a linear modality often created new resultant problems in some other area of the family system. Family systems research, training, and conceptualizations have evolved since the advent of family therapy, yet an important reality remains: Each new generation of helpers must develop as systemic thinkers. *A key question remains: To what degree have today's clinicians become systemic thinkers?*

For the new clinician in the field, questions about systemic clinical work often take more practical forms. How can I understand and use the *Diagnostic and Statistical Manual of Mental Disorders, Fifth Edition (DSM-5)*, from a relational and cultural perspective? What are the current systemic-oriented assessments I can use to help couples and families? How can I avoid ethical dilemmas when counseling couples and families? How do individual diagnoses affect my family treatment planning?

This text arose out of a desire by Drs. Russo, Coker, and King to help systemically oriented clinicians answer critical questions about diagnosis and the *DSM-5* as they counsel families from diverse communities. Although this is an inexhaustible topic, the text demonstrates how to use the *DSM-5* as an aid for assessment, diagnosis, treatment planning, and intervention while dialectically fusing both systemic-focused wellness and pathology considerations. As many clinicians are still shifting from the *Diagnostic and Statistical Manual, Fourth Edition, Text Revision (DSM-IV-TR)* to the *DSM-5*, a focus on clinical applications helps the reader identify and clarify how revisions in the *DSM-5* affect family system views. *DSM-5 and Family Systems* can help clinicians in their goal to develop as systemic thinkers, which, if accomplished to some degree, will help clients in a most natural fashion from their lived experience and context.

Mark D. Stauffer, PhD, NCC
Author: *Foundations of Addictions Counseling;*
Foundations of Couples, Marriage, and Family Counseling;
and *Human Development Across the Life Span: Applications for Counselors*

PREFACE

$\mathcal{S}$ystemic-oriented clinicians may have an innate aversion to the linear-focused syndrome approach to conceptualizing mental health disorders within individuals. Just as oil and water are two immiscible liquids, systemic-oriented clinicians may struggle with how to properly mix seemingly opposing concepts from the *Diagnostic and Statistical Manual of Mental Disorders, Fifth Edition* (*DSM-5*), with their circular causality approach to relational problems. Fortunately, this book offers practical strategies for systemic-oriented clinicians to harmonize the perceived mutual incompatibility between an individual's dysfunction and commonly used systemic theories and techniques.

Users of this book will appreciate the clarification provided on understanding relational problems associated with the onset, progression, and expression of psychiatric symptoms—while incorporating an understanding of parent–child, sibling, extended family, and significant-other relationship issues in overall clinical formulation. This book also advances the discussion about relational and cultural features, family systems assessments, family systems interventions, and ethical and legal implications when working with clients and their family members with identified *DSM-5* disorders.

Each chapter in this book focuses on a specific diagnosis or category of diagnoses from the *DSM-5*. Seven sections in each chapter guide the reader to explore how best to integrate *DSM-5* diagnoses from a systems perspective:

- *DSM-5* **and Family Systems**: Each chapter opens with an overview of the diagnosis from a systemic perspective. Using recent and relevant research from the literature, authors describe the disorders and diagnoses that are the focus of the chapter, and explore how a systemic framework is applied in working with patients with these disorders.
- **Relational and Cultural Features**: Authors share the application of *DSM-5* diagnoses, including specific disorders, relevant to understanding the role of relationships and culture in working systemically with the *DSM-5*. This context addresses the systemic complexities of working with couples and families from a diagnostic framework, and the potential impact of cultural considerations in the treatment of specific disorders.
- **Family Systems Assessments**: In this section, chapter authors describe relevant and empirically validated assessments that can be used when diagnosing clients within a systemic context. Often, assessments designed to aid with diagnosis are designed to assess the individual. Systemically focused counselors also need tools to support working within a systemic framework with diagnoses and treatment planning.
- **Family Systems Interventions**: Once a diagnosis is made, systemically focused counselors need to design treatment plans and interventions that address the disorder within a systemic framework. This section provides specific tools, therapies, and counseling strategies to support clinical work with clients and their families once the *DSM-5* diagnosis has been identified.

- **Ethical and Legal Implications**: In this section, authors present relevant ethical codes and guidelines as well as any legal implications of work with clients and their families when working with particular diagnoses. The ethical codes and guidelines of both the American Counseling Association (ACA) and the American Association for Marriage and Family Therapy (AAMFT) are explored, and relevant legal precedents and implications are presented and discussed in context to the disorder of focus.
- **Case Conceptualization**: In this section, the authors also present detailed case studies to help bring together the practice of assessment, diagnosis, and systemic interventions to support clients, couples, and families. Additionally, each case conceptualization provides a series of discussion questions for further exploration.
- **Summary**: Each chapter concludes with a summary of the relevant points, providing a focused understanding of the presented disorder and how to address it systemically.

It is our hope that this textbook will assist the systemic clinician in working from a relational perspective to provide accurate and consistent diagnoses that guide treatment plans to effectively help clients and their families.

Jessica A. Russo, PhD, LPCC-S, NCC
J. Kelly Coker, PhD
Jason H. King, PhD, CMHC

ACKNOWLEDGMENTS

The authors would like to express their thanks, first and foremost, to all chapter-contributing authors as this book would not be possible without their expertise. A special thank you goes to Drs. Mark Stauffer, David Capuzzi, and Mike Bishop for providing ongoing support, encouragement, and wisdom throughout the process of writing this textbook.

Additionally, the authors would like to extend their gratitude to the editorial team at Springer Publishing Company, who believed in the importance and need of this textbook for the mental health profession. Finally, on a personal note, the authors would like to thank their families and friends who have supported them during this time-consuming project with patience and understanding. We are grateful for their unconditional support and companionship.

SYSTEMIC LEVELS IN NEURODEVELOPMENTAL DISORDERS

Lee A. Teufel-Prida and Juan A. Lopez Prida

Neurodevelopmental disorders are broadly defined as disorders that manifest or appear in the developmental period. More specifically, neurodevelopmental disorders can be defined as a series of complex traits that emerge as a result of genetic determinants interacting with various poorly understood environmental components resulting in a diverse clinical presentation (Cristino et al., 2014). This broad category of disorders is a new introduction to the *Diagnostic Statistical Manual of Mental Disorders* (5th ed.; *DSM-5*; American Psychiatric Association [APA], 2013) and represents significant attention and focus to the area of neurodevelopment. Because neurodevelopmental disorders are generally associated with the developmental period, this group of disorders is associated with infancy, childhood, and adolescence. Most commonly, the onset and diagnosis of a neurodevelopmental disorder occurs in childhood. Despite the onset of neurodevelopmental disorders appearing in childhood, one should note that these disorders rarely experience a remission or relapse and are considered to be a stable set of symptoms over time (World Health Organization, 2014), and thus neurodevelopmental disorders appear throughout the individual's life span.

DSM-5 AND FAMILY SYSTEMS

Neurodevelopmental disorders impact not only the individual diagnosed with the disorder, but also the family of the individual diagnosed. Because neurodevelopmental disorders are commonly diagnosed in childhood, it is the parent or caregiver of the individual with a neurodevelopmental disorder who seeks assistance through a physician, psychologist, counselor, social worker, or teacher. Parents and family members are often the first to notice differences in their child. Parents are also asked to regularly monitor their children's development through scheduled pediatric well-child care visits at developmentally critical periods in a child's growth and development. See the Periodicity Schedule for a comprehensive schedule of well-child care visits, specifically recommendations for preventive pediatric health care at American Academy of Pediatrics' (2015) website. The American Academy of Pediatrics' (2010) recommendation that all pediatricians screen for developmental delays serves to increase awareness about developmental issues and preventative measures that may be taken early in a child's life to increase the likelihood of developmental milestones being achieved. However, the reality is that few pediatricians use standardized assessments when assessing for developmental delays (Sand et al., 2005). Thus, parents and caregivers need to be able to accurately and regularly communicate with medical providers to ensure care for their child in need and advocate for services to assist their child.

Neurodevelopmental Disorders as Significant Focus of Attention

The *DSM-5* represents a shift in clinical and research focus toward neurodevelopment. Systemic clinicians are now regularly asked questions about the assessment, diagnosis, and treatment of neurodevelopmental disorders, whereas, in the past, neurodevelopmental disorders were treated primarily by medical professionals in neurology or pediatrics or perhaps a psychologist with expertise in neuropsychology. The Children's Health Care Act of 2000 represented a specific shift in attention by authorizing the Centers for Disease Control and Prevention (CDC) to create the Autism and Developmental Disabilities Monitoring Network. This network, which is funded by the CDC, works to estimate the number of children with Autism Spectrum Disorder (ASD) and other developmental disabilities in the United States. For example, research from tracking estimated prevalence rates from 1991 to 2010 in the Greater Atlanta, Georgia metropolitan area suggests that the incidence of Intellectual Disability and hearing loss among 8-year-old children remained about the same with some minor increase in vision impairment. Similarly, in the same population of 8-year-olds with cerebral palsy in Atlanta, the incidence remained about the same from 1993 to 2010. In sharp contrast, the estimated incidence of ASD among 8-year-olds in Atlanta increased 269% from 1996 to 2010 (CDC, 2015). Even more specifically, the National Institutes of Health (NIH) estimates that in 2012 Autism received approximately $192 million in science, actual research projects funded, and NIH budget, whereas in 2012 Attention Deficit Hyperactivity Disorder (ADHD) received approximately $60 million in science, actual research projects funded, and NIH budget. The trend to fund and research Autism continues with $216 million estimated to be spent in 2017 for science, actual research projects funded, and NIH budget compared to $43 million for ADHD, $33 million for Fetal Alcohol Syndrome, $40 million for Fragile X syndrome, and $5 million for Tourette syndrome. Given the increase in research and treatment attention on neurodevelopmental disorders and neurodevelopment in general, the role of family members is a factor to consider in systemic treatment.

The Role of Neurodevelopment in Families

Parents are impacted by the increased attention on neurodevelopment. Due to research in the area of neurodevelopment and efforts to ensure that children meet developmental milestones, parents are increasingly aware of the importance of healthy and unobstructed neurodevelopment. As the definition of neurodevelopment evolves, emerging research continues to show that neurodevelopment is the interaction between genetic inheritance and the environment. Ultimately, genes and the environment are refereed by nongenetic influences to make up the brain from conception to adulthood (Fine & Sung, 2014). Because of this interaction between genes and the environment, parents have a crucial part to play in the likelihood of neurodevelopmental disorders whether they are conscious or aware of the part they play or not. For example, a parent with a Specific Learning Disorder, Impairment in Reading (otherwise known as Dyslexia; APA, 2013, p. 67), may be aware that his or her child is at increased likelihood of also having a Specific Language Disorder due to the genetic components of the disorder (Fisher & DeFries, 2002). The biological origination of specific learning disorders according to the APA (2013) is the interaction of genetic, epigenetic, and environmental factors. Dyslexia's behavioral manifestation is difficulty in learning specifically printed words (APA, 2013), and a person would be aware of challenges given school reports and possible educational or psychological assessments. A person with dyslexia may also be aware that a biological relative also struggled in school. Yet, parents with no known neurodevelopmental disorder may be concerned about ASD due to increased media or research attention around this disorder. In addition, there are multiple nonspecific risk factors for ASD. The lack of clear risk factors may lead a parent to wonder about his or her role in ASD. Both parent examples display the role that neurodevelopment and neurodevelopmental disorders, risk factors specifically, play in families.

Families may be curious about how to promote healthy neurodevelopment. Likewise, families may wonder what causes abnormal neurodevelopment. To understand the root cause of the neurodevelopmental disorder or the etiology of the neurodevelopmental disorder is a key element to understanding neurodevelopment as a whole (Thome, Drossos, & Hunter, 2013). Families play a role in the etiology of neurodevelopmental disorders given that most neurodevelopmental disorders have multiple causal sources, including genetics. The etiological contributors include genetic, biological, psychosociological, and environmental (Environmental Protection Agency, 2015). See Table 1.1 for a list of various contributors or causes of neurodevelopmental disorders. Families and counselors have an opportunity to impact these contributors in a positive or negative fashion.

Neurodevelopmental Versus Neurocognitive

Neurodevelopmental disorders can be mistaken for neurocognitive disorders. The important distinction between neurodevelopmental and neurocognitive disorders is that neurodevelopmental disorders emerge in the developmental period of life versus neurocognitive disorders, which are acquired during the life span (APA, 2013). Counselors should make careful assessment of the behaviors associated with the disorder and the age of onset when making a diagnosis. For example, a traumatic brain injury (TBI) can occur at any age with prevalence being high in childhood (Faul, Xu, Wald, & Coronado, 2010), but the associated symptomatology and the fact a TBI is acquired make it a neurocognitive disorder and not a neurodevelopmental disorder. TBI in children may appear as issues in cognition or challenges academically and even meeting developmental milestones. More specifically, a TBI is the direct result of an accident or is an acquired impairment, whereas a neurodevelopmental disorder is not acquired; rather it is part of a person's innate biological and behavioral makeup. Thus, when making a differential diagnosis, an understanding of when the symptoms appeared and if an injury occurred is an important factor in final diagnosis.

Neurodevelopmental Disorders in the *DSM-5*

The chapter in the *DSM-5* on neurodevelopmental disorder categories includes Intellectual Disability (intellectual developmental disorder), Communication Disorder, Autism Spectrum Disorder, Attention Deficit Hyperactivity Disorder, Specific Learning Disorder, and Motor Disorders. See Table 1.2 for a list of all the disorders associated with neurodevelopmental category. In the *DSM-5*, there are notable changes associated with some of the

TABLE 1.1 *Neurodevelopmental Disorder Causes*

	Genetic causes	Fragile X syndrome
		Down's syndrome
		Rett's syndrome
		ICF syndrome
		ATR-X syndrome
		Angelman syndrome
		Other single genetic lesion syndromes
	Biological causes	Prenatal disorders
		Arrested hydrocephalus
		Perinatal disorders
		Prematurity
		Peripartum ischemic
		Encephalopathy
		Fetal distress syndrome
		Postnatal disorders
		Anoxemia at birth
		Postnatal infection
		Primary neoplasm
	Illness or disease	
	Nutritional factors	
	Psychosocial	Emotional trauma
		Neglect abuse
		Abuse/maltreatment
		Antenatal maternal stress
	Environmental	Exposure to toxins known and unknown
		Alcohol, tobacco, drugs
		Mercury
		Lead
		Polychlorinated biphenyls
		Dioxins
		Pesticides
		Ionizing radiation
		Aluminum[a]
		Acetaminophen[a]
		In utero exposure to toxins known and unknown
		Poverty
Family life	Emotional	Lack of attachment
		Poor family dynamics
		Divorce and remarriage
		Foster care

[a]Causality questioned; empirical evidence may be biased.

TABLE 1.2 Neurodevelopmental Disorders

Category/Disorder	Subtype/Disorder

Intellectual Disability	• Intellectual Disability (intellectual developmental disorder)
	  ▪ Mild
	  ▪ Moderate
	  ▪ Severe
	  ▪ Profound
	• Global Developmental Delay
	• Unspecified Intellectual Disability (intellectual developmental disorder)

Communication Disorders	• Language Disorder • Speech Sound Disorder • Childhood-Onset Fluency Disorder (Stuttering) • Social (Pragmatic) Communication Disorder • Unspecified Communication Disorder
Autism Spectrum Disorder	• Specify if: associated with medical or genetic condition or environmental factor; associated with neurodevelopmental, mental, or behavioral disorder • Specify severity: amount of support required • Specify if: with or without intellectual impairment, with or without accompanying language impairment, with catatonia

Attention-Deficit/ Hyperactivity Disorder	• Combined presentation
	• Predominantly inattentive presentation
	• Predominantly hyperactive/impulsive presentation
	  ▪ Specify: in partial remission
	  ▪ Specify severity: mild, moderate, severe
	• Other Specified Attention-Deficit/Hyperactivity Disorder
	• Unspecified Attention-Deficit/Hyperactivity Disorder

Specific Learning Disorder	• Specify if:
	  ▪ With impairment in reading
	  ▪ With impairment in written expression
	  ▪ With impairment in mathematics
	• Specify severity: mild, moderate, severe

Motor Disorder	• Developmental Coordination Disorder
	• Stereotypic Movement Disorder
	  ▪ Specify if: with self-injurious behavior, without self-injurious behavior
	  ▪ Specify if: associated with known medical or genetic condition, neurodevelopmental disorder, or environmental factor
	  ▪ Specify severity: mild, moderate, severe

(continued)

TABLE 1.2 *Neurodevelopmental Disorders* (continued)	
Category/Disorder	**Subtype/Disorder**

	• Tic Disorders
	  ▪ Tourette's Disorder
	  ▪ Persistent (Chronic) Motor or Vocal Tic Disorder
	  ▪ Provisional Tic Disorder
	  ▪ Other Specified Tic Disorder
	  ▪ Unspecified Tic Disorder

Other Neurodevelopmental Disorders	• Other Specified Neurodevelopmental Disorder • Unspecified Neurodevelopmental Disorder

disorders within the neurodevelopmental chapter. Specifically, the term *mental retardation* has been replaced with intellectual disability (intellectual developmental disorder). The shift to intellectual disability comes as a result of use by persons in the medical community, counselors, educators, and advocacy groups. In addition, the term *intellectual disability* aligns with a federal statue in the United States (Rosa's Law, 2010). Rosa's law removed terms such as mental retardation and mentally retarded from educational, federal health, and labor policies. These terms were replaced with the deemed people-first language of "individual with an intellectual disability" and "intellectual disability." The noted additional terminology (Intellectual Developmental Disorder) is associated with the *ICD-11*, which recognizes disorders.

In addition, the *DSM-5* disorders under the Communication Disorders subsection include Language Disorder (LD), Speech Sound Disorder, Childhood-Onset Fluency Disorder (Stuttering), and the new disorders: Social (Pragmatic) Communication Disorder, and Unspecified Communication Disorder.

In a similar move to combine disorders into overarching and theoretical categories, the specific learning problems from the *Diagnostic and Statistical Manual of Mental Disorders* (4th ed.; *DSM-IV*; APA, 1994)—reading, math and writing, as well as learning disorder not otherwise specified—were replaced with a category called "Specific Learning Disorder." One can still acknowledge the more common types of describing reading deficits as dyslexia and specific types of mathematics deficits as dyscalculia. The *DSM-5* continues to recognize motor disorders as Developmental Coordination Disorder, Stereotypical Movement Disorder, Tourette's Disorder, Persistent (Chronic) Motor or Vocal Tic Disorder, and Other Specified and Unspecified Tic Disorder. The criterion for tic disorders is standardized. Major attention is paid to the description for stereotypical movement disorder. This reflects the importance the motor disorders category has in the diagnosis of self-injurious behavior. Nothing in particular changed from the *DSM-IV* to *DSM-5* regarding motor disorders; the *DSM-5* did add a new Z code of personal history of self-injury. When making this diagnosis of stereotypic movement disorder, the system clinician is required to specify with or without self-injurious behavior and to specify any associated medical or genetic condition, neurodevelopmental disorder (e.g., intellectual disability/intellectual developmental disorder), or associated environmental factors (e.g., intrauterine drug exposure).

In a parallel move to combine and focus the classification, APA (2013) in the *DSM-5* notes ASD as encompassing the previous *DSM-IV* Autistic Disorder (Autism), Asperger's Disorder, Childhood Disintegrative Disorder, and Pervasive Developmental Disorder Not Otherwise Specified. ASD is a single condition with severity of symptoms noted in two core domains. These two domains that are measured for symptom severity are deficits in social communication and social interaction, and restricted, repetitive behaviors, interests, and activities, otherwise known as restrictive, repetitive behaviors (APA, 2013).

ADHD is a neurodevelopmental disorder due to the brain developments associated with ADHD, such as impulse control, attention, planning, and stimulation. Specifically, individuals with ADHD exhibit delays in brain maturation (Sripada, Kessler, & Angstadt, 2014). It appears that the lag in connection development may help to explain the reason for distractibility and behavioral inhibition in persons with ADHD. The previous *DSM-IV* associated ADHD with disruptive behavior disorders. APA (2013) notes several important distinctions for ADHD in the *DSM-5*:

- Multiple examples are provided to the criterion items to assist in the diagnosis of ADHD throughout the life span, with examples of symptoms expressed in adults now provided for 15 of the 18 possible symptoms compared to three of the 18 possible symptoms.
- The latest age of onset for ADHD noted in the *DSM-5* is symptoms being present prior to the age of 12, instead of age 7 in the *DSM-IV*.
- There are no longer subtypes of ADHD; instead there are presentation specifics that map to the prior subtypes. These specifics then designate combined, predominately inattentive, and predominately hyperactive/impulsive presentations. The content of the diagnosis has not changed from *DSM-IV* to *DSM-5*; this was a semantic change.
- The comorbid diagnosis of Autism Spectrum Disorder is now permitted.
- The symptoms required for diagnosis in persons 17 and older is at least five symptoms, instead of the six symptoms required for persons under the age of 17.

There continues to be the major symptom domains for ADHD: inattention and hyperactivity impulsivity and combined inattention and hyperactivity impulsivity. Similarly, there remain 18 primary symptoms that are possible for ADHD in the *DSM-5* as there were in the *DSM-IV*.

RELATIONAL AND CULTURAL FEATURES

Neurodevelopmental disorders exist in society through the cultural lens, which, in turn, encompasses the relational customs that could play a role on a neurodevelopmental disorder setting. Culture affects how people relate and cope with neurodevelopmental disorders, and defines neurodevelopmental disorders to such an extent that cultural differences among people act as barriers for the proper assessment and treatment of neurodevelopmental disorders throughout the world. Once this is taken into account, it becomes evident that a family systems approach is the most adequate treatment option because, in family systems, the family's views, goals, relationships, and value systems are the main point of interest for therapy.

Culture and Neurodevelopmental Disorders

Culture is an important denominator in the discussion of neurodevelopmental disorders. Often information about disorders is generalized to individuals in the rest of the world with little consideration on the diverse cultural factors. For example, some studies have shown that Eastern cultures manifest autistic behavioral traits to a greater extent than Western cultures; that Eastern cultures score higher (or lower) on some subscales than Western cultures on the Autistic-Spectrum Quotient (AQ; Baron-Cohen, Wheelwright, Skinner, Martin, & Clubley, 2001); and that, furthermore, some Eastern countries differ on scores on subscales from other Eastern countries (Freeth, Sheppard, Ramachandran, & Milne, 2013). These multicultural studies have inspired thought on whether some of the subscales should be modified or discarded to be able to properly evaluate a more diverse group of people with ASD. Thus, intentional thought and consideration must be paid to culture and family makeup when discussing and treating neurodevelopmental disorders. This is very important for countries with eminent cultural diversity, such as the United States and the United Kingdom (Norbury & Sparks, 2013).

Regarding the diagnosis of LD, there are some important culture-related implications that should be taken in account and that will be discussed further on, such as the nature of the language that a person with LD natively speaks or how a language suffers dialectical modifications in the different communities in which it is spoken. And not only have Western cultures been compared with Eastern cultures, but also Western countries have been compared among themselves, taking in account their culturally diverse population (when applicable). Continuous research with a cultural approach on neurodevelopmental disorders will, as it has already been shown, broaden the understanding on said disorders and will shed greater light on how neurodevelopmental disorders can manifest differently in the innumerable cultural settings throughout the world.

Language Disorder (LD) and Culture

When assessing LD and other neurodevelopmental disorders in developing countries, it is noted that a lack of any formal education or lack of exposure to visual representations of objects (i.e., people who have seen only physically present objects and have never seen a photograph, drawing, or other visual representation of an object) makes applying standardized tests an unreliable way of diagnosing neurodevelopmental disorders (Carter et al., 2005). It is important to explore culture and language of origin when addressing LD. A non-English speaker or English-as-a-second-language speaker may have challenges that can be accounted for by regional, social, and/or cultural variations of language. Considering these factors is important in the diagnosis of LD along with, for example, potential hearing or sensory impairment, intellectual disability, neurological disorders, and language regression associated with ASD.

Most of the LD standardized tests are made by and for White middle-class, English-speaking people (Hirsh-Pasek, Kochanoff, Newcombe, & de Villiers, 2005). It would be understandable that said tests would not correctly evaluate non–English-speaking people. Even if the tests are translated, elemental differences between English and other languages make English-speaking people with LD manifest deficiencies in certain aspects of language where people who speak another language and also have LD do not manifest impediments (Bedore & Leonard, 2005; Leonard, 2009).

Comprehensibly, different ways of diagnosing LD must be developed for people depending on the language they speak—but not only for people who speak different languages but also for people who speak the same language in different countries. The dialectal differences are another border between countries that speak the same language (Norbury & Sparks, 2013). An example of this is British English when compared to American English (e.g., soccer, football; flashlight, torch; French fries, chips).

Language is not only spoken differently in different countries, but it is also spoken differently in different parts of a same country, and, furthermore, by different people in the same place within a country. An example of this can be seen in the differences between "mainstream American English" and native speakers of African American English (Seymour, Roeper, & de Villiers, 2005). The *Diagnostic Evaluation of Language Variation* is an example of an assessment design that works to evaluate LD in native speakers of African American English. It has been designed to evaluate LD based on similar (noncontrasting) features instead of utilizing different (contrastive) features of African American English when compared to mainstream American English (Seymour et al., 2005). Assessment designs with this same philosophy are being developed for other dialects in the United States, but many dialects still lack standardized assessments (Norbury & Sparks, 2013).

Autism Spectrum Disorder (ASD) and Culture

The AQ (Baron-Cohen et al., 2001) is a widely used test to score the degree of autism in people. It is divided into five subscales: imagination, attention to detail, attention switching, social skill, and communication. The AQ was designed from traits that are relevant to and present in Western cultures. This is evident on the imagination subscale, where people from Eastern cultures tend to score higher than people in Western cultures. Imagination is not cultivated in the same way in Western and Eastern cultures (Freeth et al., 2013), being so that in Eastern cultures, a perceived low imagination may not be an autistic trait, but, in fact, be the outcome of the cultural setting in which the individual develops.

People with ASD tend to be highly aware of details and proficient at identifying patterns. Although this trait may prove to be true in people with ASD around the globe, the items used to score this trait may be biased. One item in which Eastern cultures generally score higher than Western cultures is "I usually notice car number plates or similar strings of information" (Freeth et al., 2013, p. 2577). In some Eastern cultures, some numbers convey a significant meaning, such that people would want certain numbers in their car number plates and avoid others (Pandiyan, 2012; Paul, 2011). Easterners are more prone to notice car number plates than Westerners, and it should not be correlated with the degree of autism, but rather with the beliefs inherent in some Eastern cultures.

These and other differences have been noted between Eastern and Western cultures regarding the AQ, but there are some findings that are constant in both cultures. Females have been reported to score lower than males in the AQ. Also, science students score higher than nonscience students (Freeth et al., 2013).

Furthermore, in some Eastern cultures it is deemed rude to look at another's eyes, so it would be normal for them to perpetuate this conduct upon being examined for ASD. It has been shown that people from Asian cultures usually fixate on the nose area of the face (Blais, Jack, Scheepers, Fiset, & Caldara, 2008; Kelly et al., 2011). This cultural difference is evident from 9 months of age (Liu et al., 2011). Hence, false positives would be common in certain cultures when relying on the area of fixation for assessment.

The overarching differences between people from different cultures (even when residing in the same geographical space) cannot be ignored when diagnosing neurodevelopmental disorders that are so heavily influenced by the social and cultural components of specific populations. Failure to consider these factors will undoubtedly result in false data that will deter progress on the understanding of neurodevelopmental disorders and their undeniable cultural aspects.

Family Systems

Systems theories are derived from general systems theory, an interdisciplinary approach that has been conceptualized as a weltanschauung or "unique worldview." General systems theory proposes that events, situations, and people should be interpreted within their environment rather than in isolation (Von Bertalanffy, 1950). Bearing this in mind, when applying general systems theory, a mental health professional, for example, would treat families coping with ASD together with all the systems and subsystems with which they interact and not as ASD individuals in isolation (Cridland, Jones, Magee, &

Caputi, 2013). Family systems approaches consider families as unique interactive and reactive units that possess a basic social system of rules, values, and goals (Edwards, 2011). Some of the main concepts that are relevant to family-focused ASD research are macroscopic approach, microscopic approach, boundaries, ambiguous loss, and traumatic growth (Cridland et al., 2013).

Macroscopic approaches focus on the way families interact with other systems, such as the community, other families, schools, and social groups. Microscopic approaches examine relationships within the family, such as maternal, marital, and/or sibling subsystems. Both approaches should be taken into consideration when researching ASD families, for they address external and internal family interactions that shape the disorder with which the family lives. Similarly, boundaries encompass the limits to which the roles of a family (as a whole) and the roles of each family member (as individuals) can reach (Cridland et al., 2013). It is important for the well-being of families to be flexible about their boundaries when life event changes such as in employment or residence ensue (Seligman & Darling, 2007), and families that are able to do this have high "permeability" of their boundaries (Cridland et al., 2013, p. 215). The most resilient ASD families are able to be flexible in role and responsibility changes as well as communicate with each other about personal needs (Bayat, 2007).

Families coping with ADHD, as expected, present higher levels of stress than families with children who have no neurodevelopmental disorders, but it has also been shown that these families may present higher levels of stress than families with ASD and families with ASD and ADHD comorbidity. Parents of ADHD children presented higher levels of stress than families with ASD and families with ASD and ADHD due to a lack of emotional closeness and affective bonding with their children and a lower capacity to understand their feelings and needs. This can be explained by the parents' belief that the ADHD child's behavioral problems are caused by factors that are modifiable by the child, whereas parents with ASD children tend to more easily accept that children may not control their behavior due to the nature of the disorder itself (Miranda, Tarraga, Fernandez, Colomer, & Pastor, 2015).

Parents with children diagnosed with ADHD also manifested a higher degree of stress related to feelings of sadness, unhappiness with oneself, and discontent with one's life circumstances than parents with ASD. Finally, ADHD parents perceived, to a greater extent than ASD parents, that they were not competent as parents regarding management of the child's behavior and discipline, and felt a lack of skills and knowledge to appropriately parent their ADHD child (Miranda et al., 2015).

Bearing in mind not only the aforementioned aspects but all the ways that neurodevelopmental disorders affect the family as a whole and its systemic and subsystemic interactions, it is clear that a therapy in which the individual with a neurodevelopmental disorder is treated in isolation would not provide the impact that family systems therapy might attain. Failing to consider the ways families impinge on the family member with a neurodevelopmental disorder, and vice versa, would amount to a partial treatment in which its success would be minimal in comparison to that of a therapy that actively works on goals for the whole family.

Value Systems

An intrinsic part of any family is its value system. Value systems affect the way families see their neurodevelopmental disorder and the goals they have, not only regarding their family member with a neurodevelopmental disorder, but also in other aspects of their lives as a family and as individuals. Some value systems trends have been identified among families with neurodevelopmental disorders (Carona, Silva, Crespo, & Canavarro, 2014). Also, there are studies that show how certain aspects of said value systems affect families.

It is important, as part of an integral treatment for families with a neurodevelopmental disorder, to assess their value systems and to work on them to better improve the family's quality of life.

It has been shown that parents of children with neurodevelopmental disorders are more likely than parents of children without such disorders to adopt coping strategies that reduce the family's quality of life (Raina et al., 2005). One of these deleterious coping strategies is *disengagement behavior*. Disengagement behavior consists of renouncing life goals and other aspects that gave meaning to life (Carona et al., 2014). In this scenario, the caregiving burden experienced by parents was overencumbering (Garner et al., 2011) and led them to feelings of helplessness (Taft, Resick, Panuzio, Vogt, & Mechanic, 2007). Disengagement behavior makes the family's value system change into an unhealthy state, which makes caregiving not only the number one priority, but also makes any other activity, project, or goal something not worth considering anymore (Carona et al., 2014). Although it may appear congruent that setting everything aside to take care of a child with a neurodevelopmental disorder would render better results, it actually impacts on the child in a negative way (Duffy, 2011). A possible explanation is that, because disengagement behavior diminishes the parents' quality of life (Guðmundsdóttir, Guðmundsdóttir, & Elklit, 2006), the stress experienced by parents directly impinges in a deleterious manner on the child's quality of life (Carona et al., 2014). This is an example of why the family's value systems need to be considered when treating families with a neurodevelopmental disorder. In this case, parents should be refocused on their goals and valued directions in life, by encouraging them to pursue meaningful activities that they have been avoiding or abandoning, while assessing the underlying processes that have led to a maladaptive coping behavior (Veale, 2008). Leaving this aspect of the family untouched could prove to be an impasse in the process of a family successfully coping with a neurodevelopmental disorder.

FAMILY SYSTEMS ASSESSMENTS

When it is suggested that an individual has a neurodevelopmental disorder, it is essential to obtain an accurate diagnosis. Many times, the children, teens, and adults dealing with a suspected diagnosis are confused and find themselves confronting time-consuming and costly processes. It is important that family members, especially parents and guardians of children and teens thought to have a neurodevelopmental disorder, locate qualified personnel who are able to determine if their children or teens meet the criteria for a disorder.

Counselors and/or a medical doctor with training and expertise in neurodevelopmental disorders may do an initial assessment for a neurodevelopmental disorder. In many cases, an initial or preliminary diagnosis will require further and more involved assessment and observation. An accurate diagnosis by a clinician is based on specific observable behaviors and characteristics across a variety of environments and situations, in addition to a comprehensive history of early development. Because neurodevelopmental disorders are complex and multifaceted, it is recommended that family members of the person experiencing symptoms be involved in the diagnostic process. Oftentimes, the family must coordinate numerous care providers and clinicians to achieve an accurate diagnosis and/or treatment approach. Specifically, family members of persons with a neurodevelopmental disorder often engage in the assessment process to obtain a diagnosis from not only a mental health professional and a medical doctor, but also assessments from physical and occupational therapists, neurologists, psychiatrists, and speech and language pathologists (SLPs). Similarly, if the individual suspected of having a neurodevelopmental disorder is in a school program, an educator with knowledge of the individual's academic performance should be involved in the assessment process to determine if educational support is warranted.

Parents of a child with a suspected neurodevelopmental disorder should be encouraged to discuss concerns with their child's pediatrician and contact individual providers/ centers to identify their assessment options. In addition, for infants or toddlers prior to their third birthday, parents can investigate early intervention programs in their locale or a First Steps program via their local health department for early intervention services. If children are ages 3 (children approaching the age of prekindergarten) through 5 (children of kindergarten age) or even up to 21, and in need of assessment, parents can contact their local school district for information. School districts employ psychologists and other trained professionals to assess school-aged children. In order to be eligible for special education and related services, typically a team of qualified professionals must complete an educational assessment to determine suitability. The educational assessments done via the school system are typically at no cost to the family. Parents, guardians, or advocates have a legal right to request that the assigned public school evaluate a child for special education. Federal law, the Individuals with Disabilities Education Act (IDEA) as amended in 2004, gives parents, guardians, and advocates this legal right. States, through local school districts, must "identify, locate, and evaluate every child who may have a disability requiring special education services." This is called "Child Find." When there is suspicion that a child has a disability, parents and educators have a responsibility and a right to request a full, individual, comprehensive, multidisciplinary evaluation. However, some families may want a second opinion or second evaluation. In this scenario of second opinion or second evaluation, parents can contact their insurance company to determine how much and what portions of the assessment will be covered by insurance or whether or not they accept Medicaid. Also, if the school district refuses to evaluate the child, the parents may be able to have an evaluation still done at the school's expense. IDEA requires schools to have procedures in place to ensure evaluation of children in need and resolution of disputed cases.

Because neurodevelopmental disorders appear in the developmental period, associated assessment typically occurs in childhood. For example, in the majority of ASD cases, a diagnosis is possible before or around a child's second birthday (Chawarska, Klin, Paul, Macari, & Volkmar, 2009). Early and accurate diagnosis of a neurodevelopmental disorder can help families access appropriate services, provide a common treatment objective for professionals working with the client and family, and establish a context for families and caregivers to understand the client's challenges. Any diagnosis of a neurodevelopmental disorder should be periodically reviewed for changes in the child's development or revisions to diagnostic categories. Collaboration across an interdisciplinary team of professionals with training and expertise specific to the neurodevelopmental disorder in question and family involvement are essential in assessment and diagnosis of specific neurodevelopmental disorders. More so, it is important that clinicians agree with the assessment results and believe assessment results are consistent with respective diagnostic characteristics of a given disorder.

Assessments Tools or Techniques Commonly Used for Neurodevelopmental Disorders

There are numerous assessments to diagnose a neurodevelopmental disorder. In general, historical information is initially reviewed with the parent(s) and the clinician. There are typically subsequent visits to assess medical, developmental, behavioral, or neurological factors impacting functioning. All of the following might be included in the assessment process:

- Child and parent interviews
- Biopsychosocial assessment with a complete family history

- Genogram
- Parent and teacher self-completed rating scales of child behavior
- Self-reported information from parent or caregivers
- Observation of child behavior at home, school, and in the office
- Psychological tests
- Medical record review
- School record review
- Intelligence testing and achievement testing
- Pediatric examination for medical conditions
- Neurodevelopmental screening
- Vision, hearing, and speech and language assessments

Given the multitude of potential assessments, exams, and tests, the most commonly used measures that are administered by a clinician trained and expert in neurodevelopment are summarized in Table 1.3.

TABLE 1.3 Neurodevelopmental Disorders and Associated Assessments

Category/Disorder	Assessment
Intellectual Disability	The Wechsler Preschool and Primary Scale of Intelligence—Revised Edition (WPPSI-R; Wechsler, 1989)
	Wechsler Intelligence Scale for Children—Fifth Edition (WISC-V; Wechsler, 2014)
	Differential Ability Scales (DAS; Elliott, 1990)
	Stanford–Binet Intelligence Scale—Fourth Edition (SBIS-IV; Thorndike, Hagen, & Sattler, 1986)
	Wide Range Achievement Test 3 (WRAT3)
	Test of Nonverbal Intelligence—Third Edition (TONI-3; Brown, Sherbenou, & Johnsen, 1997)
Communication Disorders	Sequenced Inventory of Communication Development—Revised Edition (SICD-R; Hedrick, Prather, & Tobin, 1984)
	Nonspeech Test (Huer, 1988)
	Assessing Semantic Skills Through Everyday Themes (ASSET; Barrett, Zachman, & Huisingh, 1988)
	Expressive One-Word Picture Vocabulary Test—Revised Edition (Gardner, 1990)
	Receptive One-Word Picture Vocabulary Test—Revised Edition (Gardner, 1990)
	Clinical Evaluation of Language Fundamentals—Preschool (CELF-P; Wiig, Secord, & Semel, 1992)
	ECOScales Manual (MacDonald, Gillette, & Hutchinson, 1989)
	Peabody Picture Vocabulary Test—III (PPVT-III; Dunn & Dunn, 1997)
	Reynell Developmental Language Scales (Reynell, 1977)

(continued)

TABLE 1.3 Neurodevelopmental Disorders and Associated Assessments (continued)	
Category/ Disorder	**Assessment**
	Preschool Language Scale—Third Edition (PLS-III; Zimmerman, Steiner, & Pond, 1992)
Autism Spectrum Disorder	Ages and Stages Questionnaire—Third Edition (ASQ-3; Squires & Bricker, 2009)
	Modified-Checklist for Autism in Toddlers—Revised With Follow-Up (M-CHAT-R/F; Robins, Fein, & Barton, 2009)
	Autism Diagnostic Interview—Revised (ADI-R; Lord, Rutter, & Le Couteur, 1994)
	Gilliam Autism Rating Scale (GARS; Gilliam, 1995)
	Childhood Autism Rating Scale, Second Edition (CARS2; Schopler, Van Bourgondien, Wellman, & Love, 2010)
	Autism Diagnostic Observation Schedule (ADOS; Lord, Rutter, DiLavore, & Risi, 1999)
Attention-Deficit/ Hyperactivity Disorder	Vanderbilt ADHD Teacher Rating Scale (VADTRS) and Vanderbilt ADHD Parent Rating Scale (Wolraich, Feurer, Hannah, Baumgaertel, & Pinnock, 1998)
	Behavior Assessment System for Children—Second Edition (BASC-2; Reynolds & Kamphaus, 2005)
	Child Behavior Checklist/Teach Report Form (CBCL; Achenbach, 1991)
	Conners' Parent and Teacher Rating Scales
Specific Learning Disorders	Reading
	Scholastic Reading Inventory (SRI)
	Woodcock Reading Mastery Test—Third Edition (WRMT-III)
	Gray Oral Reading Test—Fifth Edition (GORT-5)
	Test of Word Reading Efficiency—Second Edition (TOWRE-2)
	Test of Early Reading Ability—Third Edition (TERA-3)
	Math
	KeyMath-3 Diagnostic Assessment
	Test of Mathematical Abilities—Third Edition (TOMA-3)
Motor Disorders	Beery–Buktenica Developmental Test of Visual Motor Integration
	Peabody Developmental Motor Scales——Seond Edition (PDMS-2)
	Pediatric Evaluation of Disability Inventory (PEDI)
	Functional Independence Measure for Children (WeeFIM)
	Vineland Adaptive Behavior Scales (VABS)
	Bayley Scales of Infant Development II (BSID-II)
	Movement Assessment of Infants (MAI)

FAMILY SYSTEMS INTERVENTIONS

There is a plethora of intervention approaches for individuals and families coping with neurodevelopmental disorders. Ultimately, the intervention approaches differ in the method used to address goals. Interventions can range from behavioral therapies to social–emotional strategies to developmental techniques. Also, the goals of the intervention program can differ from individual treatment of the person with a neurodevelopmental disorder to comprehensive interventions involving parents and caregivers with an interdisciplinary team to address a wide range of skills or behaviors. Since neurodevelopmental disorders are multifaceted and the needs of persons with neurodevelopmental disorders are complex, families often become educators, advocates, and interventionists themselves.

Comprehensive intervention programs work with parents and caregivers to develop effective strategies for the given client and provide feedback for the growth and development of treatment goals and objectives. Clinicians should be aware of the social contexts of home, school, vocation, and community when choosing interventions. In addition, clinicians should incorporate culture, gender, and language when deciding on specific treatment activities. Finally, clinicians should be aware that over time family interactions and relationships will change, and thus the needs of the family for specific interventions will change over time. Ultimately, when planning interventions, careful attention must be paid to family priorities and concerns (Marshall & Mirenda, 2002).

There are a number of different treatment interventions for neurodevelopmental disorders that are systemic in nature. When a clinician is selecting an intervention, the clinician can match the intervention with the treatment goals and objectives for the family and their current functioning around the disorder. The developmental stage and diagnosis of the individual with the neurodevelopmental disorder is always considered. For instance, an intervention that is evidence based for families coping with ASD may not be evidence based for families coping with ADHD. The following is a summary list of family-oriented interventions used for neurodevelopmental disorders.

Intellectual Disability

Intellectual Disability is characteristically a deficit in general mental abilities (APA, 2013). Specifically, families may notice minimal-to-slow-motor skills, language skill, and self-help skill development in comparison to peers. Similarly, there may be failure to develop intellectually or problems maintaining expectations in school. Some parents may also notice social challenges, such as difficulty adapting to new situations and difficulty understanding and following common rules. Individuals with an intellectual disability are most commonly served via the educational system via an Individualized Education Plan (IEP). However, prior to school age, family interventions or services for the family and individual may be the best ones. Familial interventions include but are not limited to the following types.

Individualized Family Service Plan

An individualized family service plan details the child's specific needs and the services that will help the child thrive. Early interventions may be numerous and could include speech therapy, occupational therapy, physical therapy, family counseling, or nutritional services. Counselors can assist in the development and coordination of such plans.

Stress Intervention

Services associated with intellectual disabilities are often associated with educating parents on how to best promote child development and assist parents in their well-being

(Blacher, Neece, & Paczkowski, 2005). Because parents of children with intellectual disabilities are at increased risk for stress and other mental health issues, a stress intervention for parents is suggested. Specifically, cognitive behavioral group interventions designed to reduce the stress of mothers show the strongest research evidence for success (Hastings & Beck, 2004).

Communication Disorders

A communication disorder is a deficit in receiving, sending, processing, and/or comprehending concepts or verbal, nonverbal, and graphic symbols. The specific disorders within the communication disorder domain include LD, speech sound disorder, childhood-onset fluency disorder (stuttering), social (pragmatic) communication disorder, and unspecified communication disorder. Common family interventions may include the following, but are not limited to these interventions.

Parent-Mediated Interventions

Parents are encouraged to use individualized intervention approaches at home with their child. Using the learned interventions from a session(s) with an SLP or other trained professional such as teachers, special educators, and/or counselors can increase learning outcomes for the child. Parents can also assist in the coordination of various professionals.

Speech Therapy

There are many options for speech therapy. An SLP is able to work with the child and parents to formulate the best treatment approach. Under the umbrella of speech therapy, an SLP may use various modalities or treatment options.

Autism Spectrum Disorder (ASD)—Family-Oriented Interventions

There are multiple other interventions for ASD and emerging interventions for ASD. Interventions range from traditional behavioral interventions to social communication interventions. Clinicians are encouraged to do additional research on techniques and treatment approaches that might support the child and family with whom they are working. This is not an exhaustive list.

Pivotal Response Treatment (PRT)

Derived from applied behavioral analysis, PRT is play based and child initiated. PRT addresses what are called "pivotal" areas in development, such as motivation, response to various cues, self-management, and social interaction initiation. The result is improvements across a variety of areas and skills (Koegel & Koegel, 2006). Parents and caregivers and everyone involved in the child's life are encouraged to adopt the skills and techniques used in PRT; more specifically, parents can lead PRT (Minjarez, Williams, Mercier, & Hardan, 2010). PRT is considered one of the most heavily researched and efficacious treatments for ASD (Mohammadzaheri, Koegel, Rezaee, & Rafiee, 2014).

SCERTS© Model

The Social Communication, Emotional Regulation, and Transactional Support (SCERTS) Model involves using various interventions to achieve child-initiated communication and authentic progress, that is, the ability to learn and apply skills in a spontaneous functional way in a variety of settings (SCERTS, 2016). The SCERTS Model (2016) was derived from empirical and clinical work, and as such is noted to be consistent with evidence-based practice in ASD and other neurodevelopmental disorders commonly related to or diagnosed with ASD (National Research Council, 2001; Prizant & Rubin, 1999).

Early Start Denver Model

The Early Start Denver Model (ESDM) is designed to address ASD through child-led, play-based treatment that zones in on the development of social communication skills via individual counseling, peer interactions in a school or care setting, and home-based psychoeducation (Dawson et al., 2010). ESDM is rooted in deep parental involvement and shared engagement in activities. Children engaged in ESDM for a 2-year span showed improvement in cognitive and language abilities and adaptive behavior, in addition to few autism symptoms (Dawson et al., 2010). Clinicians can become certified in ESDM.

Attention-Deficit/Hyperactivity Disorder—Family-Oriented Interventions

There are numerous interventions for ADHD. Interventions range from psychopharmacological interventions to school-based interventions. Often parents feel pulled to seek the assistance of medication and can neglect the efficacy of other interventions. Clinicians are encouraged to seek interventions that work with the family and create wellness for the child in all areas of his or her life.

Parent Behavior Training

Parent behavior training for ADHD primarily includes four manualized programs of behavior training interventions for parents (of preschoolers). These manualized programs involve assisting parents in managing problem behaviors and developing effective parenting strategies. The programs include the Triple P (Positive Parenting of Preschoolers program), Incredible Years Parenting Program, Parent–Child Interaction Therapy, and the New Forest Parenting Program. All four programs are considered efficacious for treating ADHD (Charach et al., 2011). These programs are also evidence based for disruptive behaviors in general (Charach et al., 2011) and may be beneficial for other neurodevelopmental disorders that present with disruptive behaviors (i.e., intellectual disability and ASD).

Teacher-Training Programs

Teacher programs offer teachers the opportunity to learn behavioral strategies to better the classroom environment. Children and Adults With Attention-Deficit/Hyperactivity Disorder is an organization that conducts numerous trainings for teachers interested in improving their interaction with children who have ADHD. Also, the American Academy of Pediatrics offers multiple suggestions of what teachers can do to help students with ADHD.

Specific Learning Disorder

In the *DSM-5*, a specific learning disorder is a single overarching diagnosis with specifiers for deficits in reading, mathematics, and written expression. Characteristics of a specific learning disorder are noted based on a client's medical, developmental, educational, and familial history. The broad approach to specific learning disorder diagnosis is an effort to ensure that persons with deficits in learning are provided appropriate services.

Family Support

Treatment for learning disorders tends to focus on assisting the child or adolescent in classroom performance, teaching the child how to advocate for him- or herself at school, identifying the learning strengths of the child or adolescent, enhancing self-esteem and general confidence, and finally improving the child's social and behavioral skill set. There are many mediating factors that can impact the success of a person with learning disorders. Self-esteem may be influenced by what a person with a learning disorder perceives is family support (Nalavany & Carawan, 2011). A supportive parent or family member can make a difference by supporting a child to identify his or her strengths and improve his or her classroom performance. In addition, a supportive parent or family member can help advocate for the child at school, thus modeling appropriate self-advocacy for educational needs.

School Resource Room

A child may qualify for part-time or full-time assistance at school depending on what is recommended by his or her IEP. Specialized services can be provided in a resource room for specific academic subjects. Typically, students maintain a "mainstream" schedule for some subjects and activities depending on the specific learning disorder specifier(s).

Motor Disorders

Motor disorders are associated with developmental coordination impairment, repetitive movement, or the various tic disorders. With motor disorders, an individual can feel embarrassed. Support groups and psychoeducation around these disorders are often a positive addition to any familial intervention.

Early Intervention

Identifying and treating motor developmental concerns early in a child's life is associated with facilitating developmental gain in motor development (Blauw-Hospers, de Graaf-Peters, Dirks, Bos, & Hadders-Algra, 2007; Blauw-Hospers & Hadders-Algra, 2005). The type of intervention that might be beneficial for a preterm child should be differentiated from a child who was born full term (Blauw-Hospers & Hadders-Algra, 2005). Although the outcomes for early intervention on motor development may not exceed what can be accounted for by maturation, early intervention does assist with cognitive development in at-risk groups (Orton, Spittle, Doyle, Anderson, & Boyd, 2009). In addition, an early enriching environment that stimulates and facilitates cognition, motor, and sensory development is key for successful motor abilities (Morgan, Novak, Dale, Guzzetta, & Badawi, 2014) to develop.

Occupational Therapy

Expanding on the idea and importance of early intervention, occupational therapy can be beneficial for children with motor disorders. Occupational therapy is not just for adults with occupations. Children with motor disorders can work with occupational therapists to improve fine-motor and gross-motor development, along with addressing the various social, environmental, and psychological factors that might impact physical functioning and well-being.

ETHICAL AND LEGAL IMPLICATIONS

The legal and ethical issues associated with neurodevelopmental disorders range from informed consent of parents and minors to the legal implications of disorders in childhood. Counselors are called on to service and advocate for children and families in multiple systems from home environments to school classrooms. Thus, it is essential to be aware of the legal and ethical implications of neurodevelopmental disorder diagnosis.

Ethical

In order to receive services, as is often the case with neurodevelopmental disorders, a diagnosis is required. The ethical consideration of treatment needs and current disability may or may not be considered until a diagnosis is reached. This lag in time between assessment and qualifying for services can be critical given the developmental level and need for early intervention as it relates to neurodevelopmental disorders. More specifically, certain programs or services may have restrictive diagnostic criteria for admission or age limitations or geographic catchment areas. Clinicians can assist with the need for service by providing opportunities for intake, referrals for services that are available while waiting for assessment, and advocating for services that are "needs driven." The aforementioned should be discussed in the informed consent process. The American Counseling Association (ACA) outlines informed consent in the *Code of Ethics* (2014; Section A.2.a: Informed Consent). Similarly, Section B.2.a of the ACA *Code of Ethics* outlines the counselor's responsibility to minors or adults who lack the capacity to give voluntary, informed consent. Also, informed consent, according to the ACA and the American Association for Marriage and Family Therapy (AAMFT) *Code of Ethics*, is an ongoing process, and as treatment, services, or diagnosis is deemed appropriate, so should the informed consent be reviewed.

Given that neurodevelopmental disorders typically continue throughout the life span, it is important to consider "quality of life" care and services versus curative treatments. Clinicians, parents, family members, and clients can benefit from understanding the lifetime experience of a disorder and what services will look like over time. Similarly, parents and the identified person with a neurodevelopmental disorder can work to share responsibilities of care with various care providers and family members instead of a single parent or the person with the disorder assuming all care responsibilities for a lifetime. Clinicians can assist greatly with diagnosis acceptance and long-term treatment planning.

Clinicians and parents may feel challenged by the overwhelming amount of information about neurodevelopment and what does or does not impact development. Sorting through what is evidence based and is causative for neurodevelopmental disorders may also be a dilemma. Given easy access to the Internet and alternative therapies for neurodevelopmental disorders, parents, caregivers, and clinicians alike may be tempted to pursue untested and biased approaches or even consider explaining disorders via untried causes. However, parents and caregivers should not ignore warnings about the risk factors, precipitating behaviors, and known causes of neurodevelopmental disorders when conceiving and caring for children.

Legal

Children and adolescents with a neurodevelopmental disorder such as intellectual disability or ASD are covered under the IDEA. IDEA is a law-ensuring service to children with disabilities throughout the nation, including infants, toddlers, children, and youth with disabilities. Infants and toddlers with disabilities (birth to 2 years) and their families receive early intervention services under IDEA Part C. Children and youth (ages 3–21) receive special education and related services under IDEA Part B (www2.ed.gov/about/offices/list/osers/osep/osep-idea.html, n.d.). There are six pillars under IDEA to which children with disabilities are entitled: an individualized plan, free appropriate public education, least restrictive environment, appropriate evaluation, parent and teacher participation, and procedural safeguards (www2.ed.gov/about/offices/list/osers/osep/osep-idea.html, n.d.). These six pillars are extremely important during the assessment and intervention processes. Parents and families should work closely with schools and care providers around the services provided under IDEA.

Confidentiality and educational records as they relate to the IEP can be confusing for parents and some school personnel. The IEP is considered part of the educational record. The Family Educational Rights and Privacy Act (FERPA; 1974) is a federal law that protects the privacy of student educational records. It is important to note that schools must have written permission from the parent or eligible student to release any information from the student's educational record. However, FERPA allows schools to disclose those records, without consent, under several different conditions (34 CFR § 99.31); specifically school officials with legitimate educational interest can access the school record. Thus, a teacher working with a child who has an IEP can have access to this record (www2.ed.gov/policy/gen/guid/fpco/ferpa/index.html, n.d.). Understanding the legal limits of confidentiality under FERPA is especially important as parents work to coordinate with school personnel, teachers, and care providers the most effective treatment plan for their child.

CASE CONCEPTUALIZATION

In order to further conceptualize working with families impacted by neurodevelopmental disorders, a case example is provided. The following case example discusses Ren and his family as they navigate the various systems associated with the diagnosis and treatment of ASD.

Presenting Concerns

Ren is a biracial (Mexican American) child and his age is 5 years and 3 months. His parents, Anna (26) and Sam (31), report a family history of a learning disorder for the father, Sam. The parents are concerned because Ren is mostly fussy and the mom, Anna, continues to "baby" Ren who does not like the texture of most baby food. He refuses to eat crunchy foods such as pretzels or carrots. Ren is large for his age (reportedly in the 98th percentile for height and weight per his pediatrician). He was slow to walk, starting at 20 months old, but even now he is clumsy and frequently has difficulty running without falling, or manipulating smaller objects with his hands. Ren was also slow to talk, starting at age 18 months, and even now he communicates in simple sentences. Ren does make verbal sounds and will regularly grunt repeatedly when he is frustrated. Ren also is very focused on his large Lego set and does not like other toys. Similarly, Ren will fixate on the ceiling fans in the family home and is soothed to sleep by a spinning night light near his bed.

More specifically, Ren regularly grabs his mom's hand to do things for him or uses her hand to point at what he wants. Yet, Ren also does initiate conversation and responds to his own name. During time with other children, Ren is reluctant to share and becomes emotional if his preferred toys are not in his possession. Ren's mom notes that she feels Ren can be "distant" but that he does respond to her kisses and hugs for soothing, even noting that Ren will initiate physical touch from her.

The family lives paycheck to paycheck. Sam, the father, works in construction and regularly gets work. However, his job does not allow for regular time at home. Anna, the mother, is the primary caregiver to Ren and she is now pregnant with her second child. Anna feels strained to care for Ren sometimes due to his size and difficulty communicating. Despite Anna being bilingual (Spanish and English), only English is spoken in the home.

Concurrent Problems (Treatments and Services Received)

Ren regularly sees his pediatrician. Ren is up-to-date on all of his vaccinations. Ren is rarely if ever sick per the mother. The pediatrician referred the family for a developmental assessment due to the lack of emotional reciprocity, deficits in verbal and nonverbal communication, repetitive interest in objects, and sensory hyperactivity to food textures and potentially touches. The pediatrician also referred Ren to a physical therapist for his gross- and fine-motor development to assist him in meeting his milestone of walking.

The parents were aware of this referral after Ren's 18-month-old developmental screening and routine well-child visit. However, they delayed seeing a counselor because they believed he would grow out of motor challenges and difficulty communicating. But now at his 5-year-old well-child care visit with the pediatrician, he is still experiencing challenges with his development. The pediatrician recommended that the mother and father take the child to a clinician who specializes in child development and consider also following up with an SLP depending on what the clinician recommended.

Background History and Stressors

The mother, Anna, reports that she had a normal pregnancy with Ren and that he was a full-term baby delivered vaginally. The mother reports that there were no complications at birth and that she started taking her prenatal vitamins as soon as she knew she was pregnant around month 2 of the pregnancy. Both mother and father report that they live in a suburban area not far from a large farming community. Anna, who was born in Mexico, grew up on a farm in the United States and regularly helped her parents who were migrant workers. Anna worries that she was exposed to large amounts of pesticides, but is unsure and tries to not think about this impacting her children. Sam grew up in an urban area and reports that he was also slow to walk and had difficulty in school, saying that he has dyslexia.

Sam believes nothing is wrong with his son and he believes that Anna worries too much and "babies" Ren due to her Mexican heritage. Anna identifies strongly with her Mexican heritage and regularly involves her family in the care of Ren. The family reports that they eat an "all-American" diet and love pizza and pasta and anything that is quick and easy. Anna reports that she knows she should eat healthy for herself and her children but doesn't know how and feels strained for time to prepare food. Anna feels very concerned about Ren's development and worries that he might be autistic after looking at the behaviors Ren exhibits online.

Strengths

Both Anna and Sam love their son Ren. They are eager to assist Ren and determine what is "going on" with him. Anna is open to improving her parenting and willing to do things to assist Ren. Both Anna and Sam are self-sufficient and report strong family support from grandparents and siblings. Sam shows resilience from his identified learning disorder and shows empathy for his son not yet walking.

DSM-5 Impressions and Implications

Autism Spectrum Disorder—requiring substantial support for restricted repetitive behavior, interests, and activities (level 2-moderate); requiring support for social communication and social interaction (level 1-mild); without accompanying intellectual impairment; with accompanying language impairment, speaks in simple sentences and regularly uses nonverbal sounds to communicate; associated with Developmental Coordination Disorder; without catatonia.

Relational Problems

The amount of care that Ren requires and Anna's pregnancy have resulted in increased verbal arguments between Anna and Sam. Anna feels overwhelmed and stressed. Sam is working extra to pay for recommended physical therapy and assessments with various clinicians, such as a counselor specializing in development and an SLP. It is noted that the family is eating a high gluten and casein diet. And the family may be exposing themselves to unknown environmental toxins.

Assessments

The recommended assessments for Ren and his parents could be numerous. Initially, a neurodevelopmental assessment should be completed involving an interview of the parents to gather detailed information about Ren and the family along with an observation of Ren. An Ages and Stages Questionnaire—Third Edition (ASQ-3; Squires & Bricker, 2009) and a Childhood Austim Rating Scale—Second Edition (CARS2; Schopler et al., 2010) are also recommended. Given that Ren is school aged, an assessment from a school psychologist would be requested based on the aforementioned assessments and findings. Depending on the outcome of the assessment from the school psychologist, an IEP would be initiated and followed by school personnel in contact with Ren.

Interventions

The suggested intervention would be PRT. Additional interventions are recommended by the physical therapist and SLP to be coordinated by parents via a parent-mediated intervention approach. The adjunctive services of nutrition and environmental wellness counseling are recommended as needed. The parents would also collaborate on the completion of the IEP and follow-up meetings with school personnel to ensure that school interventions are working well for Ren.

Ethical and Legal Implications

The required parental informed consent as outlined in Sections A.2.a and A.2.d of the ACA *Code of Ethics* and Standard 1.2 of the AAMFT *Code of Ethics* is to be discussed with the parents and child prior to the start of assessment and intervention. Also the counselor should review the limits of confidentiality per Sections B.1.d and B.5.c of the ACA *Code of Ethics* and Standard 2.1 of the AAMFT *Code of Ethics*. Given the likely collaboration between multiple clinicians and caregivers, releases of information should be completed to coordinate services. How to disclose information to third parties is outlined in Section B.6.g of the ACA *Code of Ethics* and Standard 2.3 of the AAMFT *Code of Ethics*. It is also important to explain how IDEA and FERPA relate to Ren.

DISCUSSION

As you continue to reflect on the case study and the overall approach, contemplate these questions:

- How might you coordinate with the various service providers in this case, such as the pediatrician, physical therapist, SLP, and potential nutritionist?
- What recommendations would you make for the family as a sibling is born and becomes part of the family system?
- How would you build on the strength of Mexican family heritage in this family?
- What are the identified gender roles of this family and how do they impact the success of interventions chosen? How will you assist in reducing the stress of the parents and building parental wellness?
- What might be some values of this family and how might their value system impact treatment outcomes?

Ren is a 5-year-old male child with ASD. He also has the comorbid diagnosis of a Developmental Coordination Disorder given that he is slow to walk, struggles to run more than a few steps, and he is large with somewhat awkward gross motor movements. At this juncture, it is not believed that Ren has any intellectual deficits to constitute an intellectual disability. Ren's parents are actively involved in his life. Anna, his mother, is currently pregnant with her second child and still provides constant care and attention for Ren. Sam, his father, is understanding his delay in walking and is working extra to pay for the services Ren is currently in need of. The family is eager to understand what is going on with Ren and how to best assist him.

The family is open and honest in the sharing of all developmental and historical information as it relates to Ren. They are also willing participants in the observation of Ren in the home. Observed behaviors are repetitive vocalization, that is, grunting and fixation on certain toys and home objects. Ren also demonstrates minimal to no flexibility with food and textures of food. He is similarly sensitive to the textures of toys, preferring smooth to rough. Yet, Ren does provide eye contact with his parents and regularly seeks emotional comfort from the mom. His parents are attentive, but noticeably anxious and stressed in their desire to help.

After the completion of assessment, the family is eager to begin interventions to assist Ren and improve the wellness of the family. All persons involved is in agreement that PRT is the intervention to proceed with at this time. The family also agrees to pursue the pediatric recommendations of physical therapy (PT) and speech and language pathology (SLP) as well. The prognosis for this family is overall good, given the early diagnosis, willingness of the parents to participate in treatment, and the additional clinical services being provided.

SUMMARY

Neurodevelopmental disorders can appear throughout the life span, but they are characteristically associated with the developmental period or childhood. The onset of neurodevelopmental disorders is most commonly seen in childhood. Individuals with neurodevelopmental disorders do not typically experience a remission or relapse, and the disorders are considered to be stable over the course of a lifetime. Given the onset of symptoms occurring in childhood, parents and families are also impacted and involved in the diagnostic and treatment process. Similarly, the value systems and culture of an individual can greatly impact the therapeutic course of neurodevelopmental disorders. Systemic clinicians must be aware of the legal and ethical implications of working with said families while also using evidence-based interventions that are relational in nature. The case illustration of Ren and his family highlights the importance of early intervention and family inclusion in treatment interventions and assessment.

REFERENCES

Achenbach, T. M. (1991). *Manual for the child behavior checklist and 1991 profile.* Burlington: University of Vermont Department of Psychiatry.

American Academy of Pediatrics. (2015). Periodicity schedule: Schedule of screenings and assessments recommended at each well-child visit from infancy through adolescence. Retrieved from https://www.aap.org/en-us/professional-resources/practice-support/Pages/PeriodicitySchedule.aspx

American Academy of Pediatrics, Council on Communications and Media. (2010). Policy statement: Media education. *Pediatrics, 126*(5), 1012–1017. doi:10.1542/peds.2010-1636

American Association for Marriage and Family Therapy. (2014). *AAMFT Code of Ethics.* Alexandria, VA: Author. Retrieved from http://aamft.org/imis15/aamft/Core/ContactUs/ContactUs.aspx

American Counseling Association. (2014). *ACA code of ethics.* Alexandria, VA: Author.

American Psychiatric Association. (1994). *Diagnostic and statistical manual of mental disorders* (4th ed.). Washington, DC: Author.

American Psychiatric Association. (2013). *Diagnostic and statistical manual of mental disorders* (5th ed.). Arlington, VA: American Psychiatric Publishing.

Baron-Cohen, S., Wheelwright, S., Skinner, R., Martin, J., & Clubley, E. (2001). The Autism-Spectrum Quotient (AQ): Evidence from Asperger syndrome/high-functioning autism, males and females, scientists and mathematicians. *Journal of Autism and Developmental Disorders, 31*(1), 5–17.

Barrett, M., Zachman, L., & Huisingh, R. (1988). *Assessing semantic skills through everyday themes.* East Moline, IL: LinguaSystems.

Bayat, M. (2007). Evidence of resilience in families of children with autism. *Journal of Intellectual Disability Research, 51*(9), 702–714. doi:10.1111/j.1365-2788.2007.00960.x

Blacher, J., Neece, C. L., & Paczkowski, E. (2005). Families and intellectual disability. *Current Opinion in Psychiatry, 18,* 507–513.

Blais, C., Jack, R. E., Scheepers, C., Fiset, D., & Caldara, R. (2008). Culture shapes how we look at faces. *PLoS One, 3*(8), 1–8. doi:10.1371/journal.pone.0003022

Blauw-Hospers, C. H., de Graaf-Peters, V. B., Dirks, T., Bos, A. F., & Hadders-Algra, M. (2007). Does early intervention in infants at high risk for a developmental motor disorder improve motor and cognitive development? *Neuroscience and Biobehavioral Reviews, 31*(8), 1201–1212.

Blauw-Hospers, C. H., & Hadders-Algra, M. (2005). A systematic review of the effects of early intervention on motor development. *Developmental Medicine and Child Neurology, 6,* 421–432.

Brown, L., Sherbenou, R. J., & Johnsen, S. K. (1997). *Test of nonverbal intelligence* (3rd ed.). Austin, TX: Pro-Ed.

Carona, C., Silva, N., Crespo, C., & Canavarro, M. (2014). Caregiving burden and parent–child quality of life outcomes in neurodevelopmental conditions: The mediating role of behavioral disengagement. *Journal of Clinical Psychology in Medical Settings, 21*(4), 320–328. doi:10.1007/s10880-014-9412-5

Carter, J. A., Lees, J. A., Muria, G. M., Gona, J., Neville, B. G. R., & Newton, C. R. J. C. (2005). Issues in the development of cross-cultural assessments of speech and language for children. *International Journal of Language and Communication Disorders, 40,* 385–401. doi:10.1080/13682820500057301

Centers for Disease Control and Prevention. (2015, June). Developmental disabilities, key findings: Trends in the prevalence of autism spectrum disorder, cerebral palsy, hearing loss, intellectual disability, and vision impairment, metropolitan Atlanta, 1991–2010: Estimates of funding for various research, condition, and disease categories. Retrieved from https://www.cdc.gov/ncbddd/developmentaldisabilities/features/dev-disability-trends.html

Charach, A., Dashti, B., Carson, P., Booker, L., Lim, C. G., Lillie, E., . . . Schachar, R. (2011, October). *Attention deficit hyperactivity disorder: Effectiveness of treatment in at-risk preschoolers; long-term effectiveness in all ages; and variability in prevalence, diagnosis, and treatment* (Report No. 12-EHC003-EF). Rockville, MD: Agency for Healthcare Research and Quality. Retrieved from http://www.effectivehealthcare.ahrq. gov/search-for-guides-reviews-and-reports/?pageaction=displayproduct&productid=814

Chawarska, K., Klin, A., Paul, R., Macari, S., & Volkmar, F. (2009). A prospective study of toddlers with ASD: Short-term diagnostic and cognitive outcomes. *Journal of Child Psychology and Psychiatry, 50*(10), 1235–1245.

Cridland, E., Jones, S., Magee, C., & Caputi, P. (2013). Family-focused autism spectrum disorder research: A review of the utility of family systems approaches. *Autism, 18*(3), 213–222. doi:10.1177/136236131 2472261

Cristino, A. S., Williams, S. M., Hawi, Z., An, J-Y., Bellgrove, M. A., Schwartz, C. E., . . . Claudianos, C. (2014). Neurodevelopmental and neuropsychiatric disorders represent an interconnected molecular system. *Molecular Psychiatry, 19*, 294–301. doi:10.1038/mp.2013.16

Dawson, G., Rogers, S., Munson, J., Smith, M., Winter, J., Greenson, J., . . . Varley, J. (2010). Randomized, controlled trial of an intervention for toddlers with autism: The Early Start Denver Model. *Pediatrics, 125*(1), e17–23.

Duffy, L. (2011). Parental coping and childhood epilepsy: The need for future research. *Journal of Neuroscience Nursing, 43*(1), 29–35. doi:10.1097/jnn.0b013e3182029846

Dunn, L. M., & Dunn, L. M. (1997). *Peabody Picture Vocabulary Test* (3rd ed.; PPVT-III). Bloomington, MN: PsychCorp, Pearson Education.

Edwards, J. (2011). *Working with families: Guidelines and techniques* (2nd ed.). Hoboken, NJ: Wiley.

Elliott, C. D. (1990). *Differential ability scales*. San Antonio, TX: The Psychological Corporation.

Environmental Protection Agency (2015). *Rosa's law: Report (to accompany S. 2781)*. Retrieved from https:// www.epa.gov/sites/production/files/2015-10/documents/ace3_neurodevelopmental.pdf

Family Educational Rights and Privacy Act. 20 U.S.C. § 1232g (1974); 34 CFR Part 99. Retrieved from http://uscode.house.gov/view.xhtml?req=granuleid:USC-prelim-title20-section1232g&num=0&edit ion=prelim

Faul, M., Xu, L., Wald, M. M., & Coronado, V. G. (2010). *Traumatic brain injury in the United States: Emergency department visits, hospitalizations, and deaths 2002–2006*. Atlanta, GA: Centers for Disease Control and Prevention, National Center for Injury Prevention and Control.

Fine, J. G., & Sung, C. (2014). Neuroscience of child and adolescent health development. *Journal of Counseling Psychology, 61*(4), 521–527.

Fisher, S. E., & DeFries, J. C. (2002). Developmental dyslexia: Genetic dissection of a complex cognitive trait. *Nature Reviews Neuroscience, 3*, 767–780.

Freeth, M., Sheppard, E., Ramachandran, R., & Milne, E. (2013). A cross-cultural comparison of autistic traits in the UK, India, and Malaysia. *Journal of Autism and Developmental Disorders, 43*(11), 2569–2583.

Gardner, M. F. (1990). *Expressive one-word picture vocabulary test* (Rev. ed.). Novato, CA: Academic Therapy Publications.

Garner, R., Arim, R., Kohen, D., Lach, L., MacKenzie, M., Brehaut, J., & Rosenbaum, P. (2011). Parenting children with neurodevelopmental disorders and/or behavior problems. *Child: Care, Health and Development, 39*(3), 412–421. doi:10.1111/j.1365-2214.2011.01347.x

Gilliam, J. E. (1995). *Gilliam autism rating scale*. Austin, TX: Pro-Ed.

Guðmundsdóttir, H., Guðmundsdóttir, D., & Elklit, A. (2006). Risk and resistance factors for psychological distress in Icelandic parents of chronically ill children: An application of Wallander and Varni's disability-stress-coping model. *Journal of Clinical Psychology in Medical Settings, 13*(3), 295–302. doi:10 .1007/s10880-006-9025-8

Hastings, R. P., & Beck, A. (2004). Practitioner review: Stress intervention for parents of children with intellectual disabilities. *Journal of Child Psychology and Psychiatry, 45*(8), 1338–1349. doi:10.1111/j.1469 -7610.2004.00357.x

Hedrick, D. L., Prather, E., & Tobin, A. (1984). *Sequenced inventory of communication development* (Rev. ed.). Los Angeles, CA: Western Psychological Services.

Hirsh-Pasek, K., Kochanoff, A., Newcombe, N., & de Villiers, J. (2005). Using scientific knowledge to inform preschoolers: Making the case for "empirical validity." Society for Research in Child Development, *Social Policy Report, 19*, 3–19.

Huer, M. B. (1988). *The nonspeech test for receptive/expressive language*. Lake Zurich, IL: Don Johnston Developmental Equipment.

Kelly, D. J., Liu, S., Rodger, H., Miellet, S., Ge, L., & Caldara, R. (2011). Developing cultural differences in face processing. *Developmental Science*, 14, 1176–1184. doi:10.1111/j.1467-7687.2011.01067.x

Koegel, R., & Koegel, L. (2006). *Pivotal response treatments for autism: Communication, social, and academic development*. Baltimore, MD: Brookes.

Leonard, L. (2009). Cross-linguistic studies of child language disorders. In R. Schwartz (Ed.), *Handbook of child language disorders* (pp. 308–324). New York, NY: Psychology Press.

Liu, S., Quinn, P. C., Wheeler, A., Xiao, N., Ge, L., & Lee, K. (2011). Similarity and difference in the processing of same- and other-race faces as revealed by eye tracking in 4- to 9-month-olds. *Journal of Experimental Child Psychology*, 108, 180–189. doi:10.1016/j.jecp.2010.06 .008

Lord, C., Rutter, M., DiLavore, P., & Risi, S. (1999). *Autism diagnostic observation schedule manual*. Los Angeles, CA: Western Psychological Services.

Lord, C., Rutter, M., & LeCouteur, A. (1994). Autism Diagnostic Interview-Revised: A revised version of a diagnostic scale for caregivers of individuals with possible pervasive developmental disorders. *Journal of Autism and Developmental Disorders*, 24, 659–685.

MacDonald, J. D., Gillette, Y., & Hutchinson, T. A. (1989). *ECO scales manual*. San Antonio, TX: Special Press.

Marshall, J. K., & Mirenda, P. (2002). Parent-professional collaboration for positive behavior support in the home. *Focus on Autism and Other Developmental Disabilities*, 17, 216–228.

Minjarez, M. B., Williams, S. E., Mercier, E. M., & Hardan, A. Y. (2011). Pivotal response group program for parents of children of autism. *Journal of Autism and Developmental Disorders*, 41, 92–101. doi:10.1007/s10803-010-1027-6

Miranda, A., Tarraga, R., Fernandez, M. I., Colomer, C., & Pastor, G. (2015). Parenting stress in families of children with autism spectrum disorder and ADHD. *Exceptional Children*, 82(1), 81–92.

Mohammadzaheri, F., Koegel, L. K., Rezaee, M., & Rafiee, S. M. (2014). A randomized clinical trial comparison between pivotal response treatment (PRT) and structured applied behavior analysis (ABA) intervention for children with Autism. *Journal of Autism and Developmental Disorder*, 44, 2769–2777. doi:10.1007/s10803-014-2137-3

Morgan, C., Novak, I., Dale, R. C., Guzzetta, A., & Badawi, N. (2014). GAME (goals-activity-motor enrichment): Protocol of a single blind randomized controlled trial of motor training, parent education and environmental enrichment for infants at high risk of cerebral palsy. *BMC Neurology*, 14, 203. doi:10.1186/s12883-014-0203-2

Nalavany, B. A., & Carawan, L. W. (2011). Perceived family support and self-esteem: The meditational role of emotional experience in adults with dyslexia. *Dyslexia*, 18, 58–74.

National Research Council, Division of Behavioral and Social Sciences and Education, Committee on Educational Interventions for Children with Autism. (2001). *Educating children with autism*. Washington, DC: National Academies Press.

Norbury, C. F., & Sparks, A. (2013). Difference or disorder? Cultural issues in understanding neurodevelopmental disorders. *Developmental Psychology*, 49(1), 45–58.

Orton, J., Spittle, A., Doyle, L., Anderson, P., & Boyd, R. (2009). Do early intervention programs improve cognitive and motor outcomes for preterm infants after discharge? A systematic review. *Developmental Medicine and Child Neurology*, 51, 851–859. doi:10.1111/j.1469-8749.2009.03414.x

Pandiyan, V. (2012). Having too much on our plates. Retrieved from http://www.thestar.com.my/opinion/letters/2012/06/21/having-too-much-on-our-plates

Paul, J. L. (2011). What's in a number? *The Hindu*. Retrieved from http://www.thehindu.com/todays-paper/tp-national/tp-kerala/whats-in-a-number/article2472179.ece

Prizant, B. M., & Rubin, E. (1999). Contemporary issues in interventions for autism spectrum disorders: A commentary. *Journal of the Association for Persons with Severe Handicaps*, 24, 199–217.

Raina, P., O'Donnell, M., Rosenbaum, P., Brehaut, J., Walter, S. D., Russell, D., . . . Wood, E. (2005). The health and well-being of caregivers of children with cerebral palsy. *Pediatrics*, 115(6), e626–e636. doi:10.1542/peds.2004-1689

Reynell, J. (1977). *Reynell developmental language scales*. Windsor, UK: NFER Publishing.

Reynolds, C. R., & Kamphaus, R. W. (2005). Introduction to the Reynolds Intellectual Assessment Scales and the Reynolds Intellectual Screening Test. In D. P. Flanagan & P. L. Harrison (Eds.), *Contemporary intellectual assessment: Theories, tests, and issues* (2nd ed., pp. 461–483). New York, NY: Guilford Press.

Robins, D. L., Casagrande, K., Barton, M. L., Chen, C., Dumont-Mathieu, T., & Fein, D. (2014). Validation of the Modified Checklist for Autism in Toddlers-Revised with Follow-Up (M-CHAT-R/F). *Pediatrics*, 133(1), 37–45.

Rosa's Law. S. Rept. 111-244 (2010). Retrieved from https://www.congress.gov/congressional-report/111th-congress/senate-report/244/1

Sand, N., Silverstein, M., Glascoe, F. P., Tonniges, T., Gupta, B., & O'Connor, K. (2005). Pediatricians' reported practices regarding developmental screening: Do guidelines work? Do they help? *Pediatrics, 116*(1), 174–179.

Sattler, J. M. (1991). Normative changes on the Wechsler Preschool and Primary Scale of Intelligence—Revised Animal Pegs subtest. *Psychological Assessment: A Journal of Consulting and Clinical Psychology, 3*(4), 691–692. doi:10.1037/1040-3590.3.4.691

Schopler, E., Van Bourgondien, M. E., Wellman, G. J., & Love, S. R. (2010). *Childhood autism rating scale* (2nd ed.). Torrance, CA: Western Psychological Services.

Seligman, M., & Darling, R. (2007). *Ordinary families, special children* (3rd ed.). New York, NY: Guilford Press.

Seymour, H. N., Roeper, T., & de Villiers, J. (2005). *Diagnostic evaluation of language variation*. San Antonio, TX: Psychological Corporation.

Social Communication, Emotional Regulation, and Transactional Support. (2016). The SCERTS Model. Retrieved from http://www.scerts.com

Squires, J., & Bricker, D. (2009). *Ages and Stages Questionnaires®: A parent-completed child monitoring system* (3rd ed.). Baltimore, MD: Brookes.

Sripada, C. S., Kessler, D., & Angstadt, M. (2014). Lag in maturation of the brain's intrinsic function architecture in attention-deficit/hyperactivity disorder. *Proceedings of the National Academy of Sciences of the United States of America, 111*(39), 14259–14264. doi:10.1073/pnas.1407787111

Taft, C., Resick, P., Panuzio, J., Vogt, D., & Mechanic, M. (2007). Examining the correlates of engagement and disengagement coping among help-seeking battered women. *Violence and Victims, 22*(1), 3–17. doi:10.1891/vv-v22i1a001

Thome, J., Drossos, T., & Hunter, S. J. (2013). Neurodevelopmental disorders and associated emotional/behavioral sequalae. In L. A. Reddy, A. S. Weissman, & J. B. Hale (Eds.), *Neuropsychological assessment and intervention for youth: An evidence-based approach to emotional and behavioral disorders* (pp. 271–298). Washington, DC: American Psychological Association.

Thorndike, R. L., Hagen, E. P., & Sattler, J. M. (1986). *Technical manual for the Stanford-Binet Intelligence Scale* (4th ed.). Chicago, IL: Riverside.

Veale, D. (2008). Behavioural activation for depression. *Advances in Psychiatric Treatment, 14*(1), 29–36. doi:10.1192/apt.bp.107.004051

Von Bertalanffy, L. (1950). An outline of general system theory. *British Journal for the Philosophy of Science, 1*(2), 134–165. doi:10.1093/bjps/i.2.134

Wechsler, D. (1989). *The Wechsler Preschool and Primary Scale of Intelligence* (Rev. ed.) (WPPSI-R). San Antonio, TX: The Psychological Corporation.

Wechsler, D. (2014). *Wechsler intelligence scale for children* (5th ed.). Bloomington, MN: NCS Pearson.

Wiig, E. H., Secord, W., & Semel, E. M. (1992). *Clinical evaluation of language fundamentals: Preschool*. San Antonio, TX: The Psychological Corporation.

Wolraich, M. L., Feurer, I. D., Hannah, J. N., Baumgaertel, A., & Pinnock, T. Y. (1998). Obtaining systematic teacher reports of disruptive behavior disorders utilizing *DSM-IV. Journal of Abnormal Child Psychology, 26*(2), 141–152.

World Health Organization. (2014). Mental disorders. Retrieved from http://www.who.int/mediacentre/factsheets/fs396/en

Zimmerman, I. L., Steiner, V. G., & Pond, R. E. (1992). *PLS-3: Preschool language scale-3*. San Antonio, TX: The Psychological Corporation.

SYSTEMS-FOCUSED THERAPY WITH SCHIZOPHRENIA AND OTHER PSYCHOTIC DISORDERS

Joel A. Lane

Some of the most severe and debilitating mental illnesses involve the experience of psychosis—a set of symptoms characterized by a loss of contact with reality. The most common of these illnesses include Schizophrenia, Schizoaffective Disorder, and some severe cases of Depressive and Bipolar Disorders. Although schizophrenia is rare, affecting approximately 1.1% of the general population (Schizophrenia and Related Disorders Alliance of America [SARDAA], 2008), its economic burden is substantial. The estimated annual economic cost of schizophrenia in the United States is $65 billion (SARDAA, 2008), including both direct (e.g., treatment) and indirect (e.g., lost wages) costs. Based on this estimate, schizophrenia accounts for nearly 4% of total U.S. health care expenditures (Muñoz, Muñoz, & Wise, 2010).

Given the debilitating nature of psychosis and its economic impact, it is not surprising that an enormous amount of funding is devoted to research about the etiology and treatment of schizophrenia (Bentall, 2009; Montgomery et al., 2004). What is, perhaps, more surprising is that schizophrenia, unlike other mental illnesses, seems to display significantly better prognoses for individuals in developing countries than those in industrialized nations (Bugra, 2006; Harrison et al., 2001; Hopper, Harrison, & Wanderling, 2007). That is, an individual with schizophrenia living in a country such as the United States, despite a presumably stronger therapeutic infrastructure, is more likely to experience worse treatment outcomes, more impairment, and a higher likelihood of future episodes of psychosis than someone experiencing the condition in a developing country. Although some authors have questioned the conclusions of this research (Cohen, Patel, Thara, & Gureje, 2008), the scholarly consensus—based on decades of longitudinal research—is that people with schizophrenia in Westernized countries are worse off than those in developing countries (Bugra, 2006; Harrison et al., 2001; Hopper et al., 2007).

Can you think of any explanations for these findings? One possibility is that the pace of life and emphasis on individual achievement may be different in the United States than a place such as Nigeria (one of the developing countries with better outcomes), for example. Similarly, poorer countries may offer more employment opportunities such as day labor (Fields, 2010), making it easier for people with schizophrenia to make a living and lead a meaningful life. With this explanation, psychosis would be more debilitating in the United States because it would interfere more prominently with highly valued aspects of U.S. society. However, a contrasting explanation is that Westernized and developing countries have different cultural and societal values regarding the role of the family in people with mental illness (Harrison et al., 2001). In the United States, the common process for people with severe mental illness is individual treatment, often in the form of psychotropic medication and inpatient hospitalization. Although few would question the efficacy of antipsychotic medications to manage acute and ongoing psychosis symptoms, schizophrenia relapse rates remain high (Leucht et al., 2012), suggesting the importance of incorporating additional treatment approaches along with pharmacotherapy. However, it appears that many of the countries with better schizophrenia outcomes emphasize family support and deemphasize psychiatric intervention. Though this explanation needs additional empirical support (Cohen et al., 2008; Kulhara, Shah, & Grover, 2009), it suggests that family is an important concept in the topic of psychosis. Indeed, current psychosis treatment approaches in the United States are increasingly incorporating the family system into the treatment process, with promising results (e.g., Walker & Gowen, 2011). In light of these trends, this chapter examines Schizophrenia Spectrum and Other Psychotic Disorders through a family systems lens, applying a systemic framework to conceptualizing the experience, etiology, and treatment of these conditions.

DSM-5 AND FAMILY SYSTEMS

Before applying a family systems perspective to the schizophrenia spectrum disorders, it is first necessary to understand the experience of and relevant diagnoses associated with psychosis. This section describes the psychosis symptoms, discusses their episode nature, and defines the various schizophrenia spectrum diagnoses.

Psychosis Symptoms

Symptoms of psychosis include delusions, hallucinations, disorganized thinking and speech, grossly disorganized or abnormal behavior, and negative symptoms. Delusions are disturbances of thought content. People with delusions have thoughts that other people either would not have or would be able to know are fantasy, and yet for the person with delusions, the thoughts seem so real that they are accepted as reality. People with delusions might believe others are plotting to harm them, that the newscaster was talking directly to them, or that they can hear messages from God. Delusions can be difficult not only for the individual but also for family members. If you were attempting to provide emotional support to a loved one experiencing psychosis, can you imagine how difficult it would be to distinguish reality from fantasy and how to appropriately respond to them?

Hallucinations are another symptom of psychosis: They are disturbances of experiences involving the five senses. Auditory hallucinations, in which people hear things for which there are no identifiable stimuli, are the most common type. Auditory hallucinations commonly involve voices, either of real people the individual knows or of aliens, deities, or other imagined individuals. Sometimes the content of auditory hallucinations is benign, but in more severe cases the voices can convey harmful messages about the individual's self-worth or the intentions of others. Visual hallucinations are the second most common type of hallucinations, and refer to seeing things for which there are no identifiable stimuli. Like with auditory hallucinations, common examples include seeing people, deities, aliens, and monsters. Though far less common, people can also have tactile (i.e., sense of touch) hallucinations, olfactory (sense of smell) hallucinations, and gustatory (i.e., sense of taste) hallucinations. These latter three types are much more common in cases of substance- or medication-induced psychosis (Keshavan & Kaneko, 2013); otherwise, auditory and visual hallucinations are the most prevalent in actual cases of schizophrenia and related disorders. A common tactile hallucination, for example, is the sensation that bugs are crawling inside one's body under the skin.

Disorganized thinking and speech is another symptom of psychosis. In persons with this symptom, thought and speech patterns are distorted in one of several ways, making it difficult to understand or follow their communication. One common instance of this symptom is referred to as *loose associations*, where two or more thoughts might be communicated at the same time due to some arbitrary or vaguely connected commonality. Thought and speech can also be disorganized in the form of tangential speech. In this pattern of disorganization, one's train of thought is difficult to follow because it meanders through many unrelated thoughts, often never returning to the initial topic. Many clinicians have had the experience of asking a question to someone with schizophrenia and receiving a response as if an entirely different question had been asked, which could be an example of tangential speech. Still another form of disorganized speech is incoherence, in which speech is unintelligible, involves made-up words, or word choices do not flow together in any meaningful way.

The next symptom of psychosis is grossly disorganized or abnormal behavior. This symptom refers to a wide range of unusual behaviors—an individual with disorganized behavior may appear childlike, hostile, or engage in behavior that others would consider situationally inappropriate (examples include dressing inappropriately for the weather or undressing in public places). Or, behavior can be disorganized because of its repetitive quality (e.g., continuously and frantically twirling one's hair) or through its absence of movement entirely. These latter cases are examples of Catatonia: a type of disorganized behavior characterized by unresponsiveness to external cues and either repetitive motions or motor immobility. People exhibiting catatonia often assume a bizarre body posture and will maintain that posture for long periods of time, appearing unresponsive to environmental stimuli. If you were to try to move a person within a catatonic stance, most likely he or she would either resist your attempt, return to his or her original posture once you stopped trying to move him or her, or simply maintain the new body position he or she finds himself or herself in as a result of your forced movement.

Finally, *negative symptoms* is an umbrella term for a group of symptoms; namely, thoughts, feelings, or behaviors that are diminished or absent. Examples of these symptoms may include flat affect, amotivation, dramatically slowed movement and speech, and avolition (i.e., a lack of motivation to perform any self-directed purposeful activities). Sometimes it is difficult to distinguish negative behaviors from certain types of disorganized behaviors, and the differentiation of the two symptoms is not of critical importance given the similar impacts each type of symptom can have on the individual and on the family. In fact, disorganized behavior and negative symptoms also share in common their resistance to treatment: These symptoms are generally less responsive (and often unresponsive entirely) to antipsychotic medications (King, 1998). These symptoms are considered to be the most difficult on the individual's family members, even more so than delusions, hallucinations, and disorganized speech. One of the primary difficulties for family members is that negative symptoms frequently impact activities of daily living, such as hygiene behaviors, eating, and sleeping. Imagine how difficult it would be to have a family member exhibiting one or more forms of disorganized behavior or negative symptoms, and the impact it would have on the entire family. Whose responsibility would it be to ensure the family member was fed, washed, and appropriately clothed? If the family member's pattern of disorganized behavior resulted in endangerment (e.g., running out into traffic), would you be comfortable with that person being left alone? If not, whose responsibility would it be to monitor that family member? If your family made the difficult decision that your loved one should live in a residential setting where they could be more closely monitored, would you have any feelings of guilt? These are the difficult realities of the family impact of schizophrenia spectrum conditions.

Variations in Symptom Presentation

The presentation of psychosis symptoms can vary dramatically from one individual to the next. There are several reasons for this variation. First, the individual symptoms have a wide range of severities, and not all symptoms will exist at the same severity level in an individual case of psychosis. For this reason, the current edition of the *Diagnostic and Statistical Manual of Mental Disorders* (5th ed.; *DSM-5*; American Psychiatric Association [APA], 2013) includes a clinician-rated assessment for each schizophrenia spectrum diagnosis that measures the severity of each individual symptom. Second, the individual symptoms have many different presentations. For example, the most common theme of delusions in the United States is paranoia, usually in the form of people believing that someone is trying to hurt or spy on them. However, another common theme of delusion is grandiosity. People with grandiose delusions might believe that they are a deity, or that they are a messenger sent from God. You can probably imagine how different two people would seem if one was experiencing paranoid delusions and the other one was experiencing grandiose delusions! And yet, they would both be considered the same symptom of psychosis. A final reason for the variation in psychosis presentations is one's specific collection of symptoms. People with psychosis generally do not display all of the symptoms; thus, the combination of present versus absent symptoms can lead to seemingly countless variations of clinical presentations. Imagine working with a client who is experiencing grandiose delusions and visual hallucinations, but is otherwise unaffected with regard to speech, movement, affect, and behavior. Now imagine a different client who displays signs of paranoid thinking mixed in with bizarre speech patterns, flat affect, and whose arms are perpetually stretched upward (an example of catatonia). Both of these individuals would likely have the same diagnosis (most likely schizophrenia, depending on the time frame of the symptoms) despite having little else in common regarding their symptom presentations.

Can you imagine how these differences in presentations could lead to difficulties in making treatment decisions? If so, you are not alone. In fact, some authors have suggested that one of the reasons for the aforementioned poor prognosis of schizophrenia is that the diagnosis is too broad (e.g., Bentall, 2009). These same authors have suggested that an alternative approach could be to diagnose individual psychosis symptoms (e.g., someone could be diagnosed with delusions and disorganized speech). This a la carte approach, it is argued, could lead to more specific diagnoses as well as treatment decisions. This idea was a contributing factor in the inclusion of the aforementioned individualized symptom severities in the *DSM-5*.

The Ebb and Flow of Psychosis Symptoms

In addition to the person-to-person variability in psychosis, the severity of an individual's psychosis symptoms often fluctuates, sometimes dramatically. It is common for the onset of these symptoms to occur in the late teens or early 20s. However, it is also common for these individuals to exhibit personality characteristics that are precursors to the active phase (i.e., the period of time during which symptoms are acute and clearly observable by others) symptoms of psychosis. Individuals might display magical thinking (e.g., believing that one's thoughts can harm someone else), social isolation (e.g., self-identifying as a "loner" and having few friends), paranoid thinking (e.g., believing that one is being followed while driving in front of another car), or other eccentricities that are not quite sufficiently severe to be considered delusional. We refer to these less severe precursor symptoms as *prodromal symptoms*. Similarly, after an active phase of psychosis has subsided, functioning may be completely restored, or it may return to the level of these precursor symptoms. We refer to the less severe symptoms in this period as *residual symptoms* since they occur after an active phase of psychosis. However, despite the different terminology, there is often little difference between prodromal and residual symptoms; rather, they are distinguished only by their sequencing around an active phase of psychosis.

Psychosis Diagnoses

In the *DSM-5* (APA, 2013), the mental illnesses involving psychosis are conceptualized mostly within the category Schizophrenia Spectrum and Other Psychotic Disorders. A unique feature of these diagnoses relative to other mental health conditions is that they consist mostly of the same set of symptoms (i.e., the psychosis symptoms described earlier), but differ with regard to the onset and duration of the symptoms. The hallmark of these diagnoses is schizophrenia. It involves a minimum of 1 month of active phase symptoms and a total of 6 months of symptoms including prodromal and residual phases. Schizophreniform Disorder involves the same set of symptoms as schizophrenia (though often at a less severe level of impairment), though its time frame indicates somewhere between 1 month and 6 months of total disturbance. The duration of Brief Psychotic Disorder is even shorter: with this diagnosis, symptoms last between 1 day and 1 month. Another distinguishing characteristic of Brief Psychotic Disorder is that psychosis symptoms often have a more rapid onset with this diagnosis compared to Schizophrenia and Schizophreniform Disorder, and often the onset occurs directly following a highly stressful event. Because these three conditions are differentiated primarily by time frame, some clinicians consider it a best practice to first either provide a provisional diagnosis or use Other Specified Schizophrenia Spectrum and Other Psychotic Disorder at the onset of the symptoms, and to wait until an entire symptom cycle has occurred before formerly diagnosing the specific mental illness.

A less severe form of psychosis can be found in instances of Delusional Disorder. This condition differs from other conditions on the schizophrenia spectrum in that it involves only one psychosis symptom: delusions. People experiencing Delusional Disorder do not experience disruptions in speech, behavior, movement, or affect, and they do not experience hallucinations. Rather, these individuals generally function without disruption other than the presence of one of more prominent delusions. As previously discussed, the nature of these delusions may be paranoia (e.g., believing others are plotting to harm you), grandiosity (e.g., believing that you have special powers), or any number of other themes. One theme that is much more common in Delusional Disorder than in other schizophrenia spectrum disorders is *erotomania*, in which individuals believe that someone else (usually a famous person) is in love with them or has a special relationship with them. In fact, many of the notorious cases of celebrity stalkers demonstrate classic presentations of Delusional Disorder, Erotomanic Type. Although less severe than other psychoses, a difficulty of working with cases of Delusional Disorder is that it can be more difficult to parse truth from delusion when the individual is otherwise high functioning. In schizophrenia, for example, delusions are usually accompanied by disorganized speech and behavior, making it clearer that a disturbance is present. Imagine working with someone who is fully oriented and whose presentation is otherwise unremarkable, but who tells you he or she is being stalked by an ex-lover. How would you handle that situation? Would you be able to know whether he or she was describing reality or delusional content? If you determined that the client was experiencing delusions, how would you share this determination with him or her? Therein lies the unique difficulty in working effectively with Delusional Disorder.

In another direction on the schizophrenia spectrum, sometimes psychosis and mood disorders can be experienced concurrently. Schizoaffective Disorder involves an active phase of psychosis combined with either a major depressive or manic episode. People with this diagnosis first experience symptoms of psychosis, and eventually the contents of those symptoms trigger mood symptoms. For example, consider an episode of psychosis involving paranoia or other themes that negatively impact self-worth (e.g., hearing voices that criticize you). With such content, could you imagine feeling depressed the longer the delusions persisted? It certainly seems reasonable that this might happen. If this were to happen to you, and you later experienced a major depressive episode as a result, you would meet the basic criteria for Schizoaffective Disorder, Depressive Type. Now, suppose the content of your psychosis was entirely different, and instead of voices criticizing you, suppose they were grandiose in nature, telling you that you were God-like (or maybe even God himself). If these symptoms were to elevate your mood to the point of affecting your energy, sleep, thought patterns, and impulsivity, you would likely meet the criteria for Schizoaffective Disorder, Bipolar Type. In either case, you can see how the addition of depressive symptoms compounds the severity of an already debilitating condition. Indeed, although suicide risk is already elevated in schizophrenia (Jamison, 2000), it is even higher with concurrent depressive episodes (Harkavy-Friedman, Nelson, Venarde, & Mann, 2004).

Psychosis Etiology: The Role of Family Systems

Since these symptoms and conditions were first identified, researchers and clinicians have been asking questions like, *What is the etiology of schizophrenia? Why do people develop these symptoms?* Presently, the scientific consensus is that psychosis is a brain disorder caused largely by genetic predisposition. This consensus has its basis in longitudinal research of twins from the 1960s and 1970s (e.g., Gottesman & Shields, 1972). In these studies, researchers tracked identical and fraternal twins, finding that the risk of schizophrenia was much higher if an identical twin had the condition (nearly 50%) than if a fraternal twin had it (around 20%; Gottesman, 1991). The implication of these findings is that genetics must play a larger role in schizophrenia than environmental factors, since the genetics of identical twins are identical. schizophrenia and its related disorders also have a high rate of heritability, meaning that the risk of developing the illness is significantly elevated when family members also have the illness. In recent years, brain and genetic research has grown in sophistication, and we now know that certain regions of the brain are shaped differently for people with schizophrenia (Haijma et al., 2013) and that the presence of certain genes can increase risk (e.g., Kwon, Wang, & Tsai, 2013). One recent study even found that certain forms of a gene that impacts the development of the immune system increase risk of schizophrenia by contributing to an overactive "pruning" of neurons and synapses during adolescence (Sekar et al., 2016).

Despite these findings, many researchers and clinicians contend that environmental factors, such as family relationships and stressful life experiences, are important contributing or exacerbating factors to schizophrenia etiology. They criticize the overapplication of the aforementioned research by pointing to the growing field of *epigenetics*: the study of the role of environmental factors in gene expression (cf., Holliday, 2006). This neuroscience field has yielded exciting evidence suggesting that significant life experiences, such as the accumulation of many stressful life events, can actually shape the activation of certain genes. Epigenetics raises important etiological questions: Are the neurocognitive and genetic differences found in people with schizophrenia the *cause* of the illness? Or are they the *result* of significantly stressful life experiences? After all, life stress is a risk factor for schizophrenia, as people living in poverty and people from traditionally marginalized racial and ethnic backgrounds are at an increased risk (Boydell et al., 2001; Sharpley, Hutchinson, McKenzie, & Murray, 2001; Tandon, Keshavan, & Nasrallah, 2008). Even the aforementioned heritability of schizophrenia could be interpreted in different ways: Are relatives more likely to develop schizophrenia solely because of inherited genes? Or, is it possible that the increased risk is due, at least in part, to the interpersonal challenges of living with someone with the illness? Imagine how scary and chaotic it might be to have a parent with schizophrenia—how might his or her recurrent episodes of psychosis shape your relationship with him or her, the stability of your home life, your sense of attachment security, your outlook on the world?

Regardless of whether or not the family environment plays a causal role in schizophrenia, it is clear that the family environment plays a role in the course, prognosis, and treatment of the illness. Consider the research regarding psychosis in industrialized and developing nations discussed at the beginning of this chapter. Why is it that industrialized nations—where schizophrenia is treated primarily with antipsychotic medications—display a higher incidence of relapse into future episodes? Such medications are highly effective at reducing most of the psychosis symptoms (e.g., Kahn et al., 2008), so the high relapse rates are a possible indication of the importance of additional, nonmedical, treatment considerations. In the proceeding section, we explore the role of the family in the experience and prognosis of the schizophrenia spectrum disorders. In particular, a wealth of existing research demonstrates that the nature of emotional expression among family members is a significant factor in the prognosis and relapse rate of schizophrenia.

RELATIONAL AND CULTURAL FEATURES

Next, we consider relational and cultural features of psychosis. One of the most well-researched systemic features associated with psychosis is emotional expression within the family, which is discussed in this section. We also examine the impact of psychosis on the family, cultural differences in symptom presentation, and racial disparities in diagnosis and treatment of psychosis.

How Psychosis Impacts and Is Impacted by Others

Now that we have examined the impact of psychosis on the individual, let us consider its impact on the entire family system. Caring for relatives with schizophrenia can be an enormous burden for family members, both emotionally and financially (Caqueo-Urízar & Gutiérrez-Maldonado, 2006). In particular, the first episode of psychosis is a risk factor for distress, depression, and anxiety among family members (Martens & Addington, 2001), both during and after the episode (Tennakoon et al., 2001). This first episode can be especially difficult for family members because it is unexpected, and this feeling of unpreparedness compounds an already difficult challenge (Addington, Collins, McCleery, & Addington, 2005).

Among these challenges, there are numerous transitions that relatives must navigate in order to adequately support a family member with psychosis. Any role transition within a family has corresponding impacts on each individual within the family (Caqueo-Urízar & Gutiérrez-Maldonado, 2006), and in the case of psychosis, these impacts are enormous. Schedules may need to be adjusted to ensure the relative is adequately monitored and can attend numerous therapy appointments, family roles may need to be adjusted (e.g., children may be "parentified" and assume caretaking responsibilities for a parent experiencing psychosis; Jurkovic, 2014), and finances may need to be constrained to afford medications and other treatments (Melamed, Friedberg, & Zoldan, 1998). Further difficulties can be experienced in the form of transference of the psychosis symptoms. At times, the content of the psychosis can involve the family members. For example, people who suffer from side effects of antipsychotic medications may develop a delusion that family members are conspiring against them by attempting to ensure they regularly take their medications. In a small percentage of cases, acts of violence can be directed at family members (Walsh, Buchanan, & Fahy, 2002). However, one should be careful not to overgeneralize this information, as one of the common negative stereotypes and sources of stigma against people with schizophrenia is that they are dangerous (Hinshaw & Cicchetti, 2000). Rather, violence occurs in a small percentage of cases (Walsh et al., 2002), and it is much more likely to occur in the form of self-harm rather than harm against others (Jamison, 2000).

To better understand the systemic difficulties of psychosis, imagine you are a parent to a boy whom you perceive as problematically different from others of his age—how would you try to help? You probably would be aware of his many positive qualities, and how from the time he was born you were daydreaming about the person he would grow up to become: what he would do for a living, with whom he would settle down, and so forth. Imagine how difficult it would be to watch him exhibit prodromal symptoms. Would you blame yourself for these eccentricities? If so, could you imagine the resulting sense of guilt, and how that guilt would impact your sense of urgency to help him? You might continually ask yourself: "Why can't he just be more like everyone else?" You might, in your moments of guilt, reassure yourself by thinking: "My other children turned out well, so it cannot possibly be my fault that he is the way he is. It must be that he isn't applying himself." Can you imagine how all of these desires and emotions might result in being quick to correct him when he says something unusual? How you might pressure him to join the football team at school, thinking it might help him fit in with his peers?

Now, think about the same scenario from the child's perspective. You have a sense that you are different from others. Perhaps your eccentricities result in difficulties making friends. You also have a strong sense that your family does not understand you and wishes you were different. They criticize seemingly everything you say and every decision you make. You can tell they wish you were more like your siblings. How would this awareness shape how you see the world? Can you imagine it resulting in significant self-doubt? How it might cause you to wish you were different? Can you imagine how this self-doubt might grow in severity to the point where you even question your own perceptions of the world around you? How you might retreat into an inner world as an escape from the rejection and criticism of the real world? Can you imagine how all of these factors combined could grow in severity to the point that you eventually lose contact with reality?

If you can empathize with both the parents *and* the child in this scenario, you are closer to understanding psychosis from a family systems perspective. A basic systemic perspective of psychosis suggests that these symptoms can serve as a catalyst for reciprocal and systemic impacts on the family. Such a perspective effectively explains the aforementioned scenario—perhaps something in the child's genes contributed to some of his eccentricities. These eccentricities, in turn, make it difficult for him to fit in at school and cause his parents to worry. Their sense of worry, combined with all of their aforementioned guilt and confusion, cause them to criticize their child. Their criticism, in turn, causes him to doubt and question himself, and the repeated occurrence of these factors eventually causes the child to spiral into a state of psychosis.

This scenario might also help us appreciate another significant complication of psychosis on the family system: internalized stigma. The term *stigma* refers to negative attitudes about a person or personal characteristic. There exists significant societal stigma against people with mental illnesses, especially conditions such as schizophrenia that are severe and persistent. Negative stereotyping of these individuals can result in rejection and ridicule due to beliefs that they are "crazy," "weird," or dangerous. Stigma can add to the already difficult experience of psychosis, both for the individual and the family. It can result in rejection and social isolation for the individual, and it can be a problem for the relatives of someone with schizophrenia, as well. Despite current scientific evidence that mental illnesses are the result of a combination of genetic, familial, and nonfamilial environmental risk factors, a negative stereotype that dysfunctional family environments are the cause of mental illness continues to exist (Miklowitz, 2004). The self-blame and guilt parents can experience when their child suffers from schizophrenia are significant. It is easy to imagine this shame being internalized in a way that contributes to the patterns of criticism we saw in the above example. The irony in the scenario is that, if family criticism and rejection truly stems from an unfounded belief that their dysfunction caused their loved one to be different, it could actually result in worsening the course and prognosis of the illness, an idea we explore in the next section.

Expressed Emotion in the Family

The primary way in which family dynamics are thought to impact the experience and prognosis of psychosis is through *expressed emotion*, which refers to the nature of one's family environment, specifically how family members talk to and about the individual. Note that expressed emotion is an entirely different construct than emotional expression, which refers to one's ability to understand and talk about one's emotional experience. Families high in expressed emotion are critical, emotionally overinvolved, intolerant, and sometimes hostile toward one another (Amaresha & Venkatasubramanian, 2012; Barrowclough, Tarrier, & Johnston, 1996). When it comes to individuals with mental illness, family members with high expressed emotion often believe that these behaviors are helping the individual. Despite this belief, a wealth of evidence has demonstrated that high expressed emotion in the family increases symptom severity and rates of relapse for many mental illnesses (Butzlaff & Hooley, 1998; Leucht et al., 2012), especially schizophrenia. The problem of high expressed emotion is so well documented that the *DSM-5* (APA, 2013) now includes it among the "Other Problems that May be a Focus of Clinical Attention" (p. 731). High Expressed Emotion Level Within Family can be used as supplemental diagnostic information for any primary diagnosis, and it is frequently added in cases where the primary diagnosis involves psychosis.

To better understand the problem of high expressed emotion, imagine you have a friend or family member who is in an active state of psychosis and is currently telling you about the content of his or her delusional beliefs. How would you try to help him or her understand that his or her beliefs are unfounded? For many people, the "obvious" answer would be to directly challenge the beliefs. You might say, "Snap out of it! That's not real! You're being delusional!" all in the hopes that the other person will have a moment of clarity and realize that he or she is losing contact with reality. Although it is easy to understand the good intentions of such an approach, this type of intervention is likely to backfire and add to the person's sense that he or she is dysfunctional. Now imagine that *you* are the one experiencing psychosis and a friend or family member is trying to help you. First, remember to imagine not only the state of psychosis itself, but also its resulting emotions. Could you imagine feeling highly confused and disoriented? Would you feel scared, perhaps even terrified? If so, what do you think would be the best possible way your loved one could respond to you? Would it be through confrontation, as we previously explored? Or would it be through compassion? Though perhaps counterintuitive, it seems that trying to comfort the individual and provide some empathy (perhaps by saying "That must be such a scary experience you are having right now.") can be more effective at alleviating psychosis symptoms than actually trying to challenge the symptoms (Bentall, 2009). In a powerful illustration of this idea, research psychologist Eleanor Longden (2013) disclosed her own experience with psychosis, describing how her initial auditory hallucinations were benign in nature. This changed, however, when she began disclosing to others that she was hearing voices. She noticed that the content of the voices became increasingly hostile and problematic as she received negative responses from others. Such responses communicated to her that she was "crazy," and in turn the content of the voices changed to similar messages.

Cultural Differences in Psychosis Symptoms

This idea—that our responses to people with psychosis can modify the content and severity of their psychosis symptoms—suggests that the content of psychosis symptoms are socially constructed. Indeed, there exists considerable cross-cultural variation in the content and prevalence of the various psychosis symptoms (Bauer et al., 2011; Brekke & Barrio, 1997; Kim, 2006; Luhrmann, Padmavati, Tharoor, & Osei; 2015). A prominent factor in this variation is the sociocentricity of ethnic and cultural groups worldwide (Banerjee, 2012). *Sociocentricity* refers to a continuum with collectivism on one end and individualism on the other end. This continuum can be useful in considering a given cultural group's societal and relational values. These values seem to shape the themes of psychosis symptoms (Bauer et al., 2011; Kim, 2006; Luhrmann et al., 2015). For example, in an anthropological study of hallucinations in the United States, India, and Ghana (Luhrmann et al., 2015), people in the United States reported that the voices were violent in nature, and were more likely to view their hallucinations as a sign that they were mentally ill. In India, most participants reported hearing the voices of deceased family members giving them advice and encouragement, and they were much more likely to report that the nature of the voices was playful and entertaining. In Ghana, most participants reported hearing the voice of God, and participants were evenly divided with regard to whether the hallucinations were positive or negative experiences. Another study demonstrated differences in the prevalence of the various types of hallucinations across cultures. Among the interesting findings, Austrian patients had the lowest rates of auditory hallucinations but were among the highest in rates of visual hallucinations, whereas virtually none of the Pakistani patients reported visual hallucinations (Bauer et al., 2011).

Racial Disparities in Schizophrenia Diagnosis and Treatment

Although the primary focus of this chapter is a family systems perspective on psychosis, there exist broader sociopolitical implications as well. As previously mentioned, episodes of psychosis are often preceded by significant life stressors (Myin-Germeys, van Os, Schwartz, Stone, & Delespaul, 2001). Accordingly, individuals living in poverty are, unfortunately, at a higher risk for schizophrenia (Tandon et al., 2008). So too are victims of abuse, neglect, and other forms of trauma (Darves-Bornoz, Lempérière, Degiovanni, & Gaillard, 1995; Gil et al., 2009). Thus, relevant information in a client's diagnosis may often include housing and economic problems (e.g., Extreme Poverty or Homelessness) or abuse and neglect (e.g., Child Physical Abuse, Confirmed, Subsequent Encounter). There are also significant racial disparities in schizophrenia prevalence, with nonmajority racial groups experiencing higher risk in various countries (Boydell et al., 2001; Sharpley et al., 2001; Zolkowska, Cantor-Graae, & McNeil, 2001). In the United States, African Americans are two-and-a-half times more likely than Whites to receive a diagnosis of schizophrenia (Barnes, 2008; Bresnahan et al., 2007). Some research has also linked schizophrenia with the acculturation difficulties people from various countries face when emigrating to the United States (Tandon et al., 2008). In cases like this, the inclusion of Acculturation Difficulty in the client's diagnosis is warranted.

In an attempt to better understand these racial and ethnic disparities in schizophrenia prevalence, some researchers have sought possible genetic differences passed down from different ethnic ancestries (Lin, Anderson, & Poland, 1995). However, a different explanation that, sadly, possesses significant empirical support is that these disparities may be due to systemic inequalities. Consider that people of color in the United States are more likely to experience poverty compared to Whites (Lichter, Qian, & Crowley, 2005). Some researchers have reported evidence that social class mediates the relationship between race and schizophrenia prevalence. That is, these findings suggest that poverty is a primary reason that minority groups are more likely to experience psychosis. In fact, these researchers found that, when controlling for social class, nonminority groups were actually *more* symptomatic than minority groups (Brekke & Barrio, 1997).

Another important study (Eack, Bahorik, Newhill, Neighbors, & Davis, 2012) suggests that racial prejudice may contribute to disparities in psychosis diagnoses. The researchers in this study diagnostically interviewed a large group of inpatient residents. Similarly, to overall estimates, they found that African American patients were approximately three times as likely as White patients to be diagnosed with schizophrenia. However, the clinicians conducting the interviews were also asked to rate the perceived honesty of each patient immediately following the interview. The researchers found that perceived honesty predicted these racial disparities much more strongly than other sociodemographic variables. After controlling for perceived honesty, the racial disparities were no longer statistically significant. In other words, the main reason that African Americans were more likely to be diagnosed with schizophrenia was that clinicians were less likely to trust them compared to the White patients.

As if these problems were not sufficiently troubling, there is also evidence of racial disparities in the quality of treatments for people with schizophrenia. As background, there are two general classifications of antipsychotic medications. Older antipsychotic medications are referred to as *typical* antipsychotics (e.g., Chlorpromazine). Although these medications are generally considered efficacious, they have intense, sometimes permanent, side effects that often resemble the effects of Parkinson's disease (Leucht, Pitschel-Walz, Abraham, & Kissling, 1999). Thus, they are generally used only as a last resort, mostly in inpatient treatment settings. Newer drugs are referred to as *atypical* antipsychotics, and are similarly effective while also having a much safer side-effect profile. In one large-scale study of people receiving outpatient treatment for schizophrenia (Kreyenbuhl, Zito, Buchanan, Soeken, & Lehman, 2003), African American patients were three times less likely to receive atypical antipsychotic medications than White patients, and they were more likely to be placed on anti-parkinsonian medications often used to treat the side effects of typical antipsychotics. These disparities persisted even after controlling for other demographic factors. Although it is not clear whether these differences are due to racism or ethnic differences in psychopharmacological response to antipsychotics (Lin et al., 1995), significant evidence exists suggesting that systemic inequalities contribute to the racial disparities in schizophrenia diagnosis and treatment. In cases where racism or other forms of oppression are present, clinicians are encouraged to add Target of (Perceived) Adverse Discrimination or Persecution to the diagnostic information.

FAMILY SYSTEMS ASSESSMENTS

Now that we have examined the impact of psychosis on the family system, and the role of family systems in psychosis symptoms, let us turn our attention to assessing and treating psychosis using a family systems lens. There are numerous family characteristics to consider when assessing for psychosis, as well as numerous family-focused assessment tools. When assessing for psychosis, it is important to consider both the impact of the psychosis on the family, and also the impact of the family on the person with psychosis.

Assessing the Impact of Psychosis on the Family

As previously discussed, caring for a loved one with schizophrenia can be an enormous challenge for family members. Accordingly, most family assessments in this regard are developed using a stress-coping paradigm (Lazarus & Folkman, 1984; Ritsner et al., 2003), which conceptualizes the experience of stress as involving two components: (a) the specific, situational stressor, and (b) the individual's appraisal of the resources necessary to either tolerate or eliminate the stressor. Applying this framework to the experience of psychosis within the family system elucidates several important assessment considerations. Given the impact family members can have on the prognosis of schizophrenia, it is important to assess their experience of their loved one's mental illness, experiences with previous mental health services, and relevant family patterns of coping with stress, and overall well-being (Pharoah, Mari, Rathbone, & Wong, 2010; Szmukler et al., 1996). Doing so helps clinicians better understand the family's experience of the illness, anticipate potential difficulties family members may have with treatment based on previous experiences, and target treatment strategies that will optimize family functioning toward the support of the person experiencing psychosis. In considering the assessment of these areas, try to imagine how each area might inform next steps. For example, because disorganized speech patterns might increase the difficulty of accurately understanding a client's symptoms, the usefulness of hearing the entire family's experience of those symptoms can aid in your own understanding. Suppose that, in your assessment, you discover a long history of negative experiences with previous treatment providers—can you imagine how that information would be useful in considering how you might work to build the family's trust in you and the treatment process? And certainly, assessing family well-being and coping patterns will illuminate important intervention directions during the treatment process.

Several useful family assessments exist to assess such areas. One such assessment is the Experiences of Caregiving Inventory (ECI; Szmukler et al., 1996). The ECI was developed using an extensive interview-based procedure, distilling hundreds of family interviews several times into a 66-item self-report inventory. The items ask family members to rate the frequency of various experiences over a 1-month period (e.g., "During the past month, how often have you thought about [your family member's] risk of committing suicide?"), on a 5-point scale (0 = *never*, 4 = *nearly always*). The items coalesce into subscales including problematic family experiences of the mental illness (including difficult behaviors, negative symptoms, sense of loss, dependency, and the overall impact on the family), stigma, difficulties with prior treatment providers, and positive family experiences (including personal and relational experiences). The clinician can use these subscales to anticipate potential family assets and areas of difficulty and to follow up with family members about specific item responses where appropriate. The ECI demonstrates impressive reliability and validity, and it is a widely used family assessment for psychosis and other mental illnesses (McCleery, Addington, & Addington, 2007).

Another useful assessment for families is the Caregiver Burden Inventory (CBI; Novak & Guest, 1989). Though initially developed to assess the family impact of Alzheimer's Disease, it also demonstrates salient reliability and validity as an assessment of family impact during the first episode of psychosis (McCleery et al., 2007). The CBI assesses the objective and subjective impacts of the illness on the caregiver's life. Its item structure and scoring method are similar to the ECI, though it is a briefer instrument, with only 24 items. Subscales include time-dependence burden (i.e., the amount of time needed to care for the person), developmental burden (i.e., the perceived disruption to the caregiver's life and social trajectories), physical burden (i.e., the health impacts on the caregiver, such as reduced sleep), the social burden (i.e., the negative impact on various life roles within the family, social environment, and career), and emotional burden (i.e., negativity toward the person or the situation).

There are numerous benefits to incorporating self-report instruments such as the ECI and CBI into work with families. First, they are relatively quick and easy to administer and score. Second, they can yield useful information about specific difficulties and resources present within the family. Third, they can be used to track progress over time; for example, one could administer the CBI at quarterly intervals to assess the efficacy of family therapy for a given family member. Each of these assessments also has specific advantages over the other. The CBI, for example, is significantly shorter than the ECI and takes less time to administer and score. It also focuses on one specific family member, and there may be instances where such a focus is preferred. The ECI, on the other hand, is a more comprehensive assessment, and it focuses on the family as a whole. One other advantageous difference is that it assesses negative *and* positive impacts on the family, whereas the CBI assesses only negative impacts. In fact, the ECI authors specifically avoid the term *burden* within the assessment to emphasize the potential positive aspects of caring for someone with mental illness (Szmukler et al., 1996). Thus, the CBI and ECI may each appeal to different clinicians on the basis of needs and theoretical orientation.

Assessing the Impact of the Family on the Person With Psychosis

In addition to assessing the impact of psychosis on the family system, it is also important to assess the impact of the family on the person with the mental illness. Doing so will provide valuable information about family resources and challenges that may impact the recovery process. Given that family history of psychosis and other mental illnesses is a significant risk factor, assessing this history can provide information invaluable to making accurate diagnostic decisions. Another useful direction of family assessment, given the aforementioned role of cultural values in the experience of psychosis, is the cultural patterns learned through the family, and how those patterns shape an individual's experience with his or her mental illness.

One important area of family assessment is to learn about family patterns that might impact the experience of and recovery from psychosis. Considering that high expressed emotion within the family typically involves criticism, hostility, and emotional overinvolvement, assessing for these qualities is essential. Such an assessment can occur informally or through one of several semistructured assessments (Hooley & Parker, 2006). Perhaps the most popular semistructured approach is the Camberwell Family Interview (Leff & Vaughn, 1985). This interview involves separate conversations with each family member (without the presence of the other family members) and contains questions about the patient's symptom experience and history, as well as the degrees of participation, tension, and irritability within the household. Although the Camberwell Family Interview is considered an ideal assessment of expressed emotion, it can be cumbersome to administer, as each administration requires 1 to 2 hours and separate administrations are required for each family member. The Camberwell Family Interview also requires prior training to administer and score. Other alternatives include the Five-Minute Speech sample (Magaña et al., 1986), which involves a family member talking for five uninterrupted minutes about the patient. The speech sample is later coded for evidence of emotional overinvolvement, criticism, and overall expressed emotion. There also exist self-report measures that are even easier to administer and score, such as the Level of Expressed Emotion Scale (Cole & Kazarian, 1988).

A second important area of family assessment is obtaining a detailed family history of mental illness. A history of psychosis in first-, second-, and third-degree relatives substantially increases one's risk of schizophrenia. Although approximately 1.1% of the general population experiences schizophrenia (SARDAA, 2008), that number rises to approximately 6.0% of the population with a family history of schizophrenia and 27.1% of the population with a family history of any mental illness (Mortensen, Pedersen, & Pedersen, 2010). Thus, obtaining a detailed family history of mental illness can be helpful in correctly identifying instances of schizophrenia. This can be achieved by asking the client directly, or by interviewing the client's immediate family if the client is not able to answer such questions. It can be useful to ask about family members who may have been formally diagnosed and also those whom others have suspected of being symptomatic despite never receiving a formal diagnosis. It can also be useful to create a family genogram with the client to obtain this information; such an activity provides the clinician with needed information while also providing a more creative outlet for the client than standard diagnostic interview questions (McGoldrick, Gerson, & Petry, 2008).

A final area of family assessment is understanding the multicultural values of the family as they pertain to mental illness. As previously discussed, there are numerous implications of cultural values for the experience of psychosis, and both cultural and family factors impact an individual's openness to various treatment approaches (Shea & Yeh, 2008). Accordingly, one of the major changes in the *DSM-5* (APA, 2013) was the addition of the Cultural Formulation Interview, an open-ended interview protocol to assist clinicians in understanding culturally relevant beliefs and practices that could shape diagnosis and treatment planning. This interview protocol can facilitate communication around topics that are sometimes difficult to initiate. There are separate versions for the client and for informants of the client. Many of the questions pertain to cultural values within the family, including "What do others in your family . . . think is causing your problem?"; "Are there any kinds of support that make your problem better, such as support from family . . .?"; "Are there any kinds of stresses that make your problem worse, such as . . . family problems?"; and "Are there other kinds of help your family . . . has suggested would be helpful for you now?" (pp. 752–754). Thus, using the Cultural Formulation Interview may help clinicians understand relevant cultural and family dynamics for their clients.

FAMILY SYSTEMS INTERVENTIONS

Increasingly, family therapy is being incorporated into psychosis treatment plans as a way of reducing symptom severity and relapse rates. In fact, family therapy is now considered an evidence-based treatment for schizophrenia (Lehman et al., 2004). Numerous family therapy modalities have been developed for psychosis (cf., Addington et al., 2005; McCleery et al., 2007). These models generally share common intervention strategies, including psychoeducation, emotional support, crisis intervention, and training healthy coping strategies (Lehman et al., 2004). Such an approach, when combined with pharmacotherapy, has demonstrated reduced relapse rates at multiple time intervals when the family therapy lasts at least 9 months (Pitschel-Walz, Leucht, Bauml, Kissling, & Engel, 2001). Although these interventions are likely to address high expressed emotion within the family, clinicians are also encouraged to assess for related problems and, when necessary, use specific interventions that target the family's emotional boundaries, criticism, hostility, inflexibility, and internalized stigma.

A family systems conceptualization of high expressed emotion emphasizes the reciprocal influences of each family member: it is not as simple as family members expressing emotion in dysfunctional ways, but rather it is also mindful of the strain placed on the entire family due to the mental illness, and how this strain can exacerbate the problem of high expressed emotion (Miklowitz, 2004). Such a conceptualization is not only useful, but may also help increase collaboration among all members in a given family system. A difficulty in addressing expressed emotion without a family systems lens is that family members can hear that they are at fault for their loved one's illness (Wasserman, Weisman de Mamani, & Suro, 2012).

Family Psychoeducation

For numerous reasons, family psychoeducation is important in treating psychosis. This intervention can teach the family to better understand the symptom experiences of their loved one, help them create more realistic expectations for the loved one's capabilities and prognosis, and learn strategies for managing medications. Each of these pieces, in turn, can help the family better support the client in a way that will improve outcomes. One intervention that seems especially useful is to teach about the risks of using critical language when discussing the client's symptoms. Instead, the family can be taught the importance of using affirming, compassionate language that responds to the underlying emotion rather than the symptom itself. Systems-oriented psychoeducation can also normalize the common role changes that occur within the family due to mental illness, and it can help family members make intentional decisions about these changes in the best interest of the family (Miklowitz, 2004).

Crisis Intervention

Because crisis risk is elevated for people with psychosis, crisis assessment and intervention skills are important skills for any clinician working with schizophrenia and related conditions. These skills have useful implications in family systems work as well. First, periods of crisis are likely to disrupt family patterns and result in chaotic interactions and behaviors between and among family members (Cicchetti & Toth, 1992). Thus, clinicians can work with the family through these periods to mitigate problematic interactions and maintain stability as much as is possible. Second, crisis assessments and safety plans are more likely to be effective when the entire family is involved (Stanley & Brown, 2012). Safety planning within family therapy can increase collaboration and establish a healthy sense of responsibilities and boundaries for each family member. Crisis intervention can help the entire family navigate times of extreme stress and potential relapse (James & Gilliland, 2012).

Emotional Support and Healthy Coping

A third consideration for family work involving psychosis is enhancing emotional support and healthy coping patterns within the family (Lehman et al., 2004). Emotional support in this case refers both to providing support to the family through therapy and also helping the family learn healthy ways of emotionally supporting one another outside of therapy (Miklowitz, 2004). By addressing patterns of coping within the family (both adaptive and maladaptive), clinicians can help ensure that the family is working together to positively support their loved one. This focus can also help families improve management of both everyday problems and stressful life events in a healthy way (James & Gilliland, 2012). Combined with psychoeducation, families can learn and implement healthy communication and problem solving, foster a realistic sense of the controllable and uncontrollable aspects of psychosis, and proactively plan for fluctuations in the loved one's illness (Miklowitz, 2004). These interventions, while important for all family work involving psychosis, are especially salient during the first episode of psychosis (Addington et al., 2005; Szmukler et al., 1996), a time in which the family is likely to be surprised by their loved one's symptoms and unsure of how to adequately provide support.

Family Boundaries

Another important consideration is enhancing autonomy and independence for the individual with mental illness, and healthy interpersonal boundaries for the entire family (Kins, Beyers, & Soenens, 2012). One developmental theory of the contributions of high expressed emotion to psychosis is that it can interfere with the development of self-schema and identity development during childhood, which in turn can lead to problems with emotional regulation (Peris & Miklowitz, 2015). Thus, when working to enhance emotional support within the family, some potential challenges could be family enmeshment and difficulties processing negative affect. Helping the family work through these issues is critical to modifying expressed emotion. It is also important to help the person with psychosis establish appropriate autonomy and mastery, which can be challenging given that psychosis can impact activities of daily living and increase one's dependence on others. Working through such challenges can help the family be supportive but also differentiated, and it can help the individual pursue a meaningful life in the midst of his or her mental illness.

ETHICAL AND LEGAL IMPLICATIONS

A final point of consideration in psychosis and family systems is that of ethical and legal implications. Many of these implications resemble those of other mental illnesses. From an ethical standpoint, determining the appropriate level of care is essential to ensuring treatment efficacy and client protection. This is especially true for the schizophrenia spectrum, where inpatient stays and intensive outpatient modalities are often necessary during active phases of the psychosis. Moreover, from an ethical and legal standpoint, working to reasonably ensure safety during periods of suicidality is important for both client safety and clinician liability, and it is particularly relevant in this case given that suicide risk is elevated during psychosis (Kelleher et al., 2013). One challenge that can emerge in some cases of psychosis is how to handle clients who should be receiving inpatient treatment but do not consent to this level of care. Every state has different laws regarding involuntary hospitalizations, so it is important for clinicians to familiarize themselves with the laws of their state so they are adequately prepared to respond ethically and legally in such situations.

Although these considerations are relevant for nearly all mental illnesses, recent empirical and treatment directions have created a new ethical discussion specific to schizophrenia. Recent research has suggested that early detection and treatment of prodromal symptoms is associated with positive outcomes (Morrison et al., 2012), and that the duration of untreated psychosis is associated with negative outcomes (Addington, Van Mastrigt, & Addignton, 2004). Undoubtedly, this focus on early detection and treatment has many positive implications. Related community-based treatment programs have demonstrated a sixfold decrease in future hospitalization rates and corresponding increases in school and work participation when intervention occurs at the first sign of potential psychosis (Sale, 2008; Sale & Melton, 2010). While emphasizing early detection is clearly efficacious, it also warrants important ethical conversations. For example, some estimates suggest that approximately 13% of adolescents who display prodromal symptoms later develop active psychosis (Haroun, Dunn, Haroun, & Cadenhead, 2006). The inverse of this statistic, of course, is that the vast majority of prodromal adolescents do not end up experiencing psychosis. The resulting ethical question, then, revolves around appropriate levels of treatment during this early period. Some clinicians have advocated for the use of antipsychotic medication during this period or in instances where a person is at risk of developing schizophrenia in the future (Miller et al., 2003). Preventative prescriptions are referred to as *prophylactic* interventions, and they are common in other branches of medicine. However, in the case of antipsychotic medications, which often involve intense and sometimes permanent side effects, such an approach carries substantial risk, particularly in light of the fact that more than 80% of adolescents with prodromal symptoms do not later develop active psychosis. Haroun and colleagues (2006) provide an ethical decision-making model for pharmacological treatment of prodromal psychosis that incorporates the number of present risk factors, the client's ability to consent to pharmacological treatment, and the importance of enhancing autonomy during psychosis. Collectively, this issue further supports the use of family- and community-based therapy at any stage of psychosis.

CASE CONCEPTUALIZATION

In order to further conceptualize working with families impacted by schizophrenia spectrum disorders, a case example is provided. The case example presents a fictional family in which one of the members is experiencing a first episode of psychosis. We examine relevant presenting and historical factors, assessment and diagnostic information, treatment considerations, and ethical implications.

Presenting Concerns

Michael is an 18-year-old, first-generation Taiwanese American male in his first semester of college. When Michael first arrived at college, he initially felt encouraged by the new beginning. He had always experienced social difficulties at school and criticism from his parents, both of which stemmed from his "eccentricities," including his interests in abstract art, relative disinterest in social interaction, and occasional magical thinking. His parents also expressed concern that he was too "Americanized," wishing that he would align more closely with their Taiwanese values and that he would use his Taiwanese birth name, Chih-ming. Contrary to his high school experience, people in his dorm were friendly and welcoming, and some even shared his interests. This feeling of encouragement quickly changed, however, when classes started. All of a sudden, Michael was bombarded with readings and homework, and he felt like he could barely keep up in class, let alone keep up with groceries, laundry, and all of the unexpected responsibilities that came with finally moving away from home. After the first 3 weeks of classes, Michael was incredibly stressed, which affected his sleep and hygiene. He began noticing people giving him strange looks as they walked past him, and all of a sudden he felt just as isolated from the people in his dorm as he had felt from high school classmates. As he sat in his dorm room, he was sure he could hear them through the walls talking about how weird he was and laughing. He began to notice that everywhere he went, he could hear the voices of people in his dorm room mocking him. Over time, their voices grew louder and louder, even drowning out the voices of his professors during class sessions. He stopped bathing entirely because, for some reason, their voices were loudest when Michael was in the shower. The voices grew increasingly hostile over time, and he could even hear the voices of his parents joining in at times. Sometimes the voices were all saying different things at once, and sometimes they were shouting in unison, saying things like "You're a worthless piece of trash" and "Why can't you just be normal like everyone else?" He stopped going to class, partly because he couldn't understand his professors over the voices and partly because sitting in the classroom made him uncomfortable. He would look around at the other students and suspect that they were plotting to kill him. One day he was watching television and was horrified when the newscaster began talking directly to him, saying: "In other news, Michael is a worthless piece of trash and would be doing the rest of the world a favor if he would just kill himself already." Michael was contemplating how he might go about attempting suicide when he noticed an e-mail he had recently received from a college counselor on campus. The counselor said she had received a referral from one of Michael's professors, who was worried about him. The counselor asked if Michael would be willing to come in to talk with her to see how she might be able to help him. Through meeting with the counselor, Michael applied for a medical leave from the university and was admitted to a nearby inpatient treatment facility. Michael was prescribed an atypical antipsychotic medication and participated in individual, group, and family therapy during his inpatient stay. His family would come to the facility once per week for 90-minute sessions, while individual sessions occurred twice weekly and group sessions occurred daily.

Concurrent Problems

Notice that several relevant factors are present in this scenario that modify the experience and complexity of psychosis for Michael. Although he had a long-standing history of social difficulties and family pressures, the stresses of transitioning into college life seemed to provide the final "push" that sent him spiraling into active psychosis. In a similar vein, Michael's academic difficulties are a relevant part of his clinical picture. As is often the case, there seemed to be a reciprocal relationship with these academic struggles and Michael's psychosis—that is, the stress caused by struggling academically likely exacerbated the psychosis symptoms, which in turn led to further academic difficulty, and so on. Another likely important factor in this case is Michael's cultural heritage. Recall that he was a first-generation Taiwanese American and felt the tension of these two cultures. Finally, Michael experienced significant interpersonal difficulties both socially and with regard to his family (each of these interpersonal difficulties will be explored later in this case example). All of these factors seemed to impact his experience with psychosis and are relevant to Michael's diagnosis and treatment.

Background History and Stressors

Some early themes that emerged in individual and family therapy centered around Michael feeling like an outcast on multiple levels. As a first-generation American, he felt like he did not fully fit in with American society nor his Taiwanese heritage. He often felt ill-prepared to interpret social cues from peers at school, and he perceived that his parents wished he shared their cultural values. Making matters worse, his older brother Chia-hao was the "golden child" of the household and identified more strongly with his family's Taiwanese heritage, which further added to Michael's sense of pressure. He was teased often at school and quickly developed a reputation as a "loner," and he felt equally out of place at home. This concern often resulted in Michael feeling criticized and judged by his family. They would make suggestions about how he could make friends at school, try to talk him into trying out for the football team, and discourage his interests, which they told him were "weird" and would not lead to any meaningful vocation later in life. Michael felt like his parents were always "on his case" and were disinterested in trying to understand him. He both looked up to his brother and also was jealous of how everything seemed to come easily to Chia-hao, often wishing he shared Chia-hao's interests and talents. With all of the rejection he experienced at school and at home, Michael wondered whether or not he would ever find anything at which he was truly skilled or anyone with whom he connected.

Strengths

Despite Michael's condition, there exist several signs of strength and resilience. First, prior to the onset of active phase symptoms, Michael displayed progress in his social functioning, and he felt encouraged by his ability to make friends at college and find people who shared his interests. Second, there is reason to believe that his family relationships were soon to improve. It is common for conflict between children and their parents to increase throughout adolescence and peak just before leaving the parental household (Seiffge-Krenke, Overbeek, & Vermulst, 2010), and leaving the parental household is associated with increased relational satisfaction (Seiffge-Krenke, 2006). Finally, despite the pressures he felt due to comparisons to his brother, Michael also looked up to Chia-hao and valued their relationship. Thus, despite the presence of family difficulties, Michael had an ally within the family and may be likely to experience more positive relations with his parents in the future.

DSM-5 Impressions and Implications

By the time Michael was admitted to inpatient treatment, he had experienced more than 1 month of active phase symptoms and a total of 6 months of disturbance when including prodromal symptoms. Thus, he was diagnosed with schizophrenia, First Episode, currently in Acute Episode. Supporting symptoms included auditory hallucinations (i.e., hearing the voices of dormmates and his parents), delusions (i.e., suspecting that others were plotting to kill him and believing that the newscaster was talking directly to him), disorganized behavior (i.e., changes in hygiene habits), and possible negative symptoms in the form of withdrawal from nearly all social and academic activity.

Relational Problems

Due to Michael's perceived criticism from his family members, his diagnosis included High Expressed Emotion Level Within the Family. Because the active phase of symptoms seemed to stem from transitioning to university life, another relevant addition to his diagnosis could be Phase of Life Problem. His academic and social difficulties also warranted the addition of Academic or Educational Problem and Unspecified Problem Related to Social Environment, respectively (if Michael were still experiencing bullying and teasing like he did in high school, adding Social Exclusion or Rejection would also be useful). Finally, given the relevance of Michael's status as a first-generation immigrant, Michael's diagnosis also included Acculturation Difficulty.

Assessments

In the *DSM-5* (American Psychiatric Association, 2013), Schizophrenia Spectrum symptom severity is assessed using the Clinician-Rated Dimensions of Psychosis Symptom Severity, in which each symptom is rated on a 5-point scale ranging from 0 (not present) to 4 (present and severe). In Michael's case, hallucinations would likely be rated as 3, delusions would be rated as 4, disorganized speech would be rated as 0, abnormal psychomotor behavior would be rated as 2, negative symptoms would be rated as 2 or 3, impaired cognition would be rated as 2, depression would be rated as 1, and mania would be rated as 0. Two other assessments that would be useful for Michael and his family include the

Camberwell Family Interview and the Cultural Formulation Interview. The Camberwell Family Interview would be useful to better understand patterns of high expressed emotion within the family, as well as to better understand the dynamics and potential strengths and resources of the family system. The Cultural Formulation Interview could be used to better understand Michael's beliefs about his symptoms and about the treatment process, and it could help establish a multicultural dialogue between clinicians and patients.

Interventions

Michael was treated with a combination of atypical antipsychotic medication, group therapy with other residents, individual therapy, and family therapy. For family therapy, his parents and brother traveled to the facility twice per week for 90-minute sessions. One of the initial interventions used in family therapy was psychoeducation. Michael's family learned about the nature of psychosis symptoms and how best to support Michael once discharged. Topics included managing medications, expectations, and household stressors. The family also learned about the importance of calm, emotionally supportive language. This latter piece created some difficulty, as Michael's parents seemed to interpret this psychoeducation as criticism of their parenting style. Thus, the clinician used systems interventions centered around helping the family communicate emotional support needs and boundary preferences to one another. Michael was able to articulate to his parents that he felt overly pressured and constantly measured against the standard set by his older brother. For the first time, Michael's parents realized that their expectations—though well meaning—may be contributing to an impossible standard and preventing Michael from fully exploring his own identity. Michael, in turn, was better able to understand the importance his parents placed on preserving their cultural heritage as a way of honoring all they left behind in order to move to the United States. In this way, family therapy led to a shared understanding, healthier communication patterns, and appropriate boundaries among family members, all of which led to significant progress in Michael's symptoms and sense of self. The family collectively decided that Michael should try college again, and that his chances for success could be improved by maintaining his medication and attending counseling through the university. They also created a plan for monitoring Michael's emotions and symptoms so that they could continue to reevaluate the decision to integrate back into the college environment.

Ethical and Legal Implications

In this case, the primary ethical and legal implications involved implementing the appropriate level of care to ensure Michael's safety. Although Michael was initially contacted by a college counselor at his university, it would not have been appropriate for Michael to receive only outpatient counseling given his active psychosis and intense suicidal ideation. Helping Michael enter inpatient treatment was the most appropriate course of action to provide him with monitoring and intensive, multifaceted treatment options.

DISCUSSION

As you continue to reflect on the case study and the overall approach, contemplate these questions:

- If you were the college counselor in this situation, how would you have talked to Michael about inpatient treatment? What if he had initially declined your suggestion?

- Do you think allowing Michael to return to college was the right thing to do? Why or why not?
- Family therapy in the case example focused primarily on Michael and his parents. What role should Chia-hao have in the family therapy?
- If Michael's symptoms had included communication difficulties due to disorganized speech, how would that have impacted the family sessions?
- In light of the previous section on ethical and legal implications, do you think Michael should have been treated for psychosis as a teenager, when his symptoms were prodromal?

SUMMARY

Schizophrenia and related conditions involve symptoms of psychosis, in which the distinguishing characteristic is a loss of contact with reality. Symptoms of psychosis include delusions (i.e., distortions of thought content), hallucinations (i.e., distortions of the five senses), disorganized speech, disorganized behavior, and negative symptoms (including flat affect, restricted social behavior, and restricted goal-oriented behavior). Psychosis symptoms generally occur in phases, including prodromal, active, and residual phases. There are numerous challenges placed on the family system when a family member develops psychosis, and a wealth of research suggests that high expressed emotion within the family system can negatively impact the experience and prognosis of psychosis. Psychosis symptoms also seem to be culturally constructed, with differing themes occurring in different cultures worldwide. There are also significant racial disparities in schizophrenia prevalence and treatment. When treating schizophrenia and related conditions, a combination of family and pharmacological therapies has demonstrated efficacy. Family systems can be incorporated into psychosis assessment through measuring the impact of psychosis on the family as well as the impact of the family on the person with psychosis. Many useful family systems interventions exist for psychosis, including providing psychoeducation, managing risk, addressing emotional support and coping, and fostering healthy family boundaries. Finally, ethical and legal considerations include selecting an appropriate level of care, adequately ensuring client safety, and selecting appropriate treatments for adolescents displaying early signs of psychosis.

REFERENCES

Addington, J., Collins, A., McCleery, A., & Addington, D. (2005). The role of family work in early psychosis. *Schizophrenia Research, 79,* 77–83. doi:10.1016/j.schres.2005.01.013

Addington, J., Van Mastrigt, S., & Addington, D. (2004). Duration of untreated psychosis: Impact on 2-year outcome. *Psychological Medicine, 34*(2), 277–284.

Amaresha, A. C., & Venkatasubramanian, G. (2012). Expressed emotion in schizophrenia: An overview. *Indian Journal of Psychological Medicine, 34*(1), 12–20. doi:10.4103/0253-7176.96149

American Psychiatric Association. (2013). *Diagnostic and statistical manual of mental disorders* (5th ed.). Arlington, VA: American Psychiatric Publishing.

Banerjee, A. (2012). Cross-cultural variance of schizophrenia in symptoms, diagnosis, and treatment. *The Georgetown Undergraduate Journal of Health Sciences, 6*(2), 18–24.

Barnes, A. (2008). Race and hospital diagnoses of schizophrenia and mood disorders. *Social Work, 53,* 77–83.

Barrowclough, C., Tarrier, N., & Johnston, M. (1996). Distress, expressed emotion and attributions in relatives of schizophrenia patients. *Schizophrenia Bulletin, 22,* 691–702.

Bauer, S. M., Schanda, H., Karakula, H., Olajossy-Hilkesberger, L., Rudaleviciene, P., Okribelash-vili, N., . . . Stompe, T. (2011). Culture and the prevalence of hallucinations in schizophrenia. *Comprehensive Psychiatry, 52,* 319–325.

Bentall, R. P. (2009). *Doctoring the mind: Is our current treatment of mental illness really any good?* Washington Square: New York University Press.

Boydell, J., van Os, J., McKenzie, K., Allardyce, J., Goel, R., McCreadie, R. G., & Murray, R. M. (2001). Incidence of schizophrenia in ethnic minorities in London: Ecological study into interactions with environment. *British Medical Journal, 323*(8), 1336–1339. doi:10.1136/bmj.323.7325.1336

Brekke, J. S., & Barrio, C. (1997). Cross-ethnic symptom differences in schizophrenia: The influence of culture and minority status. *Schizophrenia Bulletin, 23*(2), 305–316.

Bresnahan, M., Begg, M. D., Brown, A., Schaefer, C., Sohler, N., Insel, B., . . . Susser, E. (2007). Race and risk of schizophrenia in a US birth cohort: Another example of health disparity? *International Journal of Epidemiology, 36*(4), 751–758. doi:10.1093/ije/dym041

Bugra, D. (2006). Severe mental illness across cultures. *Acta Psychiatrica Scandinavica, 113*, 17–23.

Butzlaff, R. L., & Hooley, J. M. (1998). Expressed emotion and psychiatric relapse: A meta-analysis. *Archives of General Psychiatry, 55*, 547–552.

Caqueo-Urízar, A., & Gutiérrez-Maldonado, J. (2006). Burden of care in families of patients with schizophrenia. *Quality of Life Research, 15*(4), 719–724. doi:10.1007/s11136-005-4629-2

Cicchetti, D., & Toth, S. L. (1992). The role of developmental theory in prevention and intervention. *Development and Psychopathology, 4*, 489–494.

Cohen, A., Patel, V., Thara, R., & Gureje, O. (2008). Questioning an axiom: Better prognosis for schizophrenia in the developing world? *Schizophrenia Bulletin, 34*(2), 229–244. doi:10.1093/schbul/sbm105

Cole, J. D., & Kazarian, S. S. (1988). The Level Of Expressed Emotion Scale: A new measure of expressed emotion. *Journal of Clinical Psychology, 44*, 392–397.

Darves-Bornoz, J. M., Lempérière, T., Degiovanni, A., & Gaillard, P. (1995). Sexual victimization in women with schizophrenia and bipolar disorder. *Social Psychiatry and Psychiatric Epidemiology, 30*(2), 78–84.

Eack, S. M., Bahorik, A. L., Newhill, C. E., Neighbors, H. W., & Davis, L. E. (2012). Interviewer-perceived honesty mediates racial disparities in the diagnosis of schizophrenia. *Psychiatric Services, 63*(9), 875–880. doi:10.1176/appi.ps.201100388

Fields, G. S. (2010). *Labor market analysis for developing countries.* Retrieved from http://digitalcommons.ilr.cornell.edu/workingpapers/157

Gil, A., Gama, C. S., de Jesus, D. R., Lobato, M. I., Zimmer, M., & Belmonte-de-Abreu, P. (2009). The association of child abuse and neglect with adult disability in schizophrenia and the prominent role of physical neglect. *Child Abuse and Neglect, 33*, 618–624. doi:10.1016/j.chiabu.2009.02.006

Gottesman, I. I. (1991). *Schizophrenia genesis: The origins of madness.* New York, NY: W. H. Freeman/Times Books/Henry Holt & Co.

Gottesman, I. I., & Shields, J. (1972). *Schizophrenia and genetics: A twin vantage point.* New York, NY: Academic Press.

Haijma, S. V., Van Haren, N., Cahn, W., Koolschijn, P. C. M. P., Hulshoff Pol, H. E., & Kahn, R. S. (2013). Brain volumes in schizophrenia: A meta-analysis in over 18,000 subjects. *Schizophrenia Bulletin, 39*(5), 1129–1138. doi:10.1093/schbul/sbs118

Harkavy-Friedman, J. M., Nelson, E. A., Venarde, D. F., & Mann, J. J. (2004). Suicidal behavior in schizophrenia and schizoaffective disorder: Examining the role of depression. *Suicide and Life-Threatening Behaviors, 34*(1), 66–76.

Haroun, N., Dunn, L., Haroun, A., & Cadenhead, K. S. (2006). Risk and protection in prodromal schizophrenia: Ethical implications for clinical practice and future research. *Schizophrenia Bulletin, 32*(1), 166–178.

Harrison, G., Hopper, K., Craig, T., Laska, E., Siegel, C., Wanderling, J., . . . Wiersma, D. (2001). Recovery from psychotic illness: A 15- and 25-year international follow-up study. *British Journal of Psychiatry, 178*(6), 506–517. doi:10.1192/bjp.178.6.506

Hinshaw, S. P., & Cicchetti, D. (2000). Stigma and mental disorder: Conceptions of illness, public attitudes, personal disclosure, and social policy. *Development and Psychopathology, 12*, 555–598.

Holliday, R. (2006). Epigenetics: A historical overview. *Epigenetics, 1*(2), 76–80.

Hooley, J. M., & Parker, H. A. (2006). Measuring expressed emotion: An evaluation of the shortcuts. *Journal of Family Psychiatry, 20*(3), 386–396. doi:10.1037/0893-3200.20.3.386

Hopper, K., Harrison, G., & Wanderling, J. A. (2007). Chapter 3: An overview of course and outcome in ISoS. In K. Hopper, G. Harrison, A. Janca, & N. Sartorius (Eds.), *Recovery from schizophrenia: An international perspective* (pp. 23–38). New York, NY: Oxford University Press.

James, R. K., & Gilliland, B. E. (2012). *Crisis intervention strategies* (7th ed.). Independence, KY: Cengage.

Jamison, K. R. (2000). Suicide and bipolar disorder. *Journal of Clinical Psychiatry, 61*(9), 47–56.

Jurkovic, G. J. (2014). *Lost childhoods: The plight of the parentified child.* London, UK: Routledge.

Kahn, R. S., Fleischhacker, W. W., Boter, H., Davidson, M., Vergouwe, Y., Keet, I. P. M., . . . Grobbee, D. E. (2008). Effectiveness of antipsychotic drugs in first-episode schizophrenia and schizophreniform disorder: An open randomised clinical trial. *Lancet, 371,* 1085–1097.

Kelleher, I., Corcoran, P., Keeley, H., Wigman, J. T. W., Devlin, N., Ramsay, H., . . . Cannon, M. (2013). Psychotic symptoms and population risk for suicide attempt: A prospective cohort study. *JAMA Psychiatry, 70*(9), 940–948. doi:10.1001/jamapsychiatry.2013.140

Keshavan, M. S., & Kaneko, Y. (2013). Secondary psychoses: An update. *World Psychiatry, 12*(1), 4–15. doi:10.1002/wps.20001

Kim, K. I. (2006). Delusions and hallucinations in East Asians with schizophrenia. *World Cultural Psychiatry Research Review, 1,* 37–42. Retrieved from http://www.wcprr.org/pdf/jan06/jan063742.pdf

King, D. J. (1998). Drug treatment of the negative symptoms of schizophrenia. *European Neuropsychopharmacology: The Journal of the European College of Neuropsychopharmacology, 8*(1), 33–42.

Kins, E., Beyers, W., & Soenens, B. (2012). When the separation-individuation process goes awry: Distinguishing between dysfunctional dependence and dysfunctional independence. *International Journal of Behavioral Development, 37*(1), 1–12.

Kreyenbuhl, J., Zito, J. M., Buchanan, R. W., Soeken, K. L., & Lehman, A. F. (2003). Racial disparity in the pharmacological management of schizophrenia. *Schizophrenia Bulletin, 29*(2), 183–193.

Kulhara, P., Shah, R., & Grover, S. (2009). Is the course and outcome of schizophrenia better in the "developing" world? *Asian Journal of Psychiatry, 2*(2), 55–62. doi:10.1016/j.ajp.2009.04.003

Kwon, E., Wang, W., & Tsai, L.-H. (2013). Validation of schizophrenia-associated genes CSMD1, C10orf26, CACNA1C and TCF4 as miR-137 targets. *Molecular Psychiatry, 18,* 11–12. doi:10.1038/mp.2011.170

Lazarus, R. S., & Folkman, S. (1984). *Stress, appraisal, and coping.* New York, NY: Springer Publishing.

Leff, J. P., & Vaughn, C. E. (1985). *Expressed emotion in families.* New York, NY: Guilford Press.

Lehman, A. F., Kreyenbuhl, J., Buchanan, R. W., Dickerson, F. B., Dixon, L. B., Goldberg, R., . . . Steinwachs, D. M. (2004). The schizophrenia Patient Outcomes Research Team (PORT): Updated treatment recommendations 2003. *Schizophrenia Bulletin, 30*(2), 193–217.

Leucht, S., Pitschel-Walz, G., Abraham, D., & Kissling, W. (1999). Efficacy and extrapyramidal side-effects of the new antipsychotics olanzapine, quetiapine, risperidone, and sertindole compared to conventional antipsychotics and placebo: A meta-analysis of randomized controlled trials. *Schizophrenia Research, 35*(1), 51–68.

Leucht, S., Tardy, M., Komossa, K., Heres, S., Kissling, W., Salanti, G., & Davis, J. M. (2012). Antipsychotic drugs versus placebo for relapse prevention in schizophrenia: A systematic review and meta-analysis. *Lancet, 379*(9831), 2063–2071. doi:10.1016/S0140-6736(12)60239-6

Lichter, D. T., Qian, Z., & Crowley, M. L. (2005). Child poverty among racial minorities and immigrants: Explaining trends and differentials. *Social Science Quarterly, 86*(5), 1037–1059.

Lin, K.-M., Anderson, D., & Poland, R. E. (1995). Ethnicity and psychopharmacology: Bridging the gap. *Psychiatric Clinics of North America, 18,* 635–647.

Longden, E. (2013). Eleanor Longden: The voices in my head [video file]. Retrieved from https://www.ted.com/talks/eleanor_longden_the_voices_in_my_head?language=en

Luhrmann, T. M., Padmavati, R., Tharoor, H., & Osei, A. (2015). Differences in voice-hearing experiences of people with psychosis in the USA, India, and Ghana: Interview-based study. *British Journal of Psychiatry, 206*(1), 41–44. doi:10.1192/bjp.bp.113.139048

Magaña, A. B., Goldstein, J. M., Karno, M., Miklowitz, D. J., Jenkins, J., & Falloon, I. R. (1986). A brief method for assessing expressed emotion in relatives of psychiatric patients. *Psychiatry Research, 17,* 203–212.

Martens, L., & Addington, J. (2001). Psychological well-being of family members of individuals with schizophrenia. *Social Psychiatry and Psychiatric Epidemiology, 36,* 128–133.

McCleery, A., Addington, J., & Addington, D. (2007). Family assessment in early psychosis. *Psychiatry Research, 152,* 95–102. doi:10.1016/j.psychres.2006.07.002

McGoldrick, M., Gerson, R., & Petry, S. S. (2008). *Genograms: Assessment and intervention* (3rd ed.). New York, NY: W. W. Norton.

Melamed, E., Friedberg, G., & Zoldan, J. (1998). Psychosis: Impact on the patient and family. *Neurobiology, 52*(7), S14–S16.

Miller, T. J., Zipursky, R. B., Perkins, D. O., Addington, J., Woods, S. W., Hawkins, K. A., . . . McGlashan, T. H. (2003). The PRIME North America randomized double-blind clinical trial of olanzapine versus placebo in patients at risk of being prodromally symptomatic for psychosis: II. Baseline characteristics of the "prodromal" sample. *Schizophrenia Research, 61,* 19–30.

Miklowitz, D. J. (2004). The role of family systems in severe and recurrent psychiatric disorders: A developmental psychopathology view. *Development and Psychopathology, 16*, 667–668. doi:10.10170S0954579404004729

Montgomery, J. H., Byerly, M., Carmody, T., Li, B., Miller, D. R., Varghese, F., & Holland, R. (2004). An analysis of the effect of funding source in randomized clinical trials of second generation antipsychotics for the treatment of schizophrenia. *Controlled Clinical Trials, 25*(6), 598–612. doi:10.1016/j.cct.2004.09.002

Morrison, A. P., French, P., Stewart, S. L. K., Birchwood, M., Fowler, D., Gumley, . . . Dunn, G. (2012). Early detection and intervention evaluation for people at risk of psychosis: Multisite randomised controlled trial. *British Medical Journal, 344*, 1–14. doi:10.1136/bmj.e2233

Mortensen, P. B., Pedersen, M. G., & Pedersen, C. B. (2010). Psychiatric family history and schizophrenia risk in Denmark: Which mental disorders are relevant? *Psychological Medicine, 40*(2), 201–210. doi:10.1017/S0033291709990419

Muñoz, E., Muñoz, W., & Wise, L. (2010). National and surgical health care expenditures, 2005–2025. *Annals of Surgery, 251*(2), 195–200. doi:10.1097/SLA.0b013e3181cbcc9a

Myin-Germeys, I., van Os, J., Schwartz, J. E., Stone, A. A., & Delespaul, P. A. (2001). Emotional reactivity to daily life stress in psychosis. *Archives of General Psychiatry, 58*, 1137–1144.

Novak, M., & Guest, C. (1989). Application of a multidimensional caregiver burden inventory. *The gerontologist, 29*(6), 798–803.

Peris, T. S., & Miklowitz, D. J. (2015). Parental expressed emotion and youth psychopathology: New directions for an old construct. *Child Psychiatry and Human Development, 46*(6), 863–873.

Pharoah, F. M., Mari, J. J., Rathbone, J., & Wong, W. (2010). Family intervention for schizophrenia. *Cochrane Database of Systematic Reviews, 4*(CD000088). doi:10.1002/14651858.CD000088.pub2

Pitschel-Walz, G., Leucht, S., Bauml, J., Kissling, W., & Engel, R. R. (2001). The effect of family interventions on relapse and rehospitalization in schizophrenia: A meta-analysis. *Schizophrenia Bulletin, 27*(1), 73–92.

Ritsner, M., Ben-Avi, A., Ponizovsky, A., Timinsky, I., Bistrov, E., & Modai, I. (2003). Quality of life and coping with schizophrenia symptoms. *Quality of Life Research, 12*(1), 1–9.

Sale, T. (2008). EAST helps people with psychosis out west. *Behavioral Healthcare, 28*(6), 28–31.

Sale, T., & Melton, R. (2010). Early psychosis intervention in Oregon: Building a positive future for this generation. *Focal Point: Youth, Young Adults, and Mental Health, 24*, 25–28.

Schizophrenia and Related Disorders Alliance of America. (2008). *About schizophrenia: DSM-5 schizophrenia spectrum disorder.* Retrieved from http://www.sardaa.org/resources/about-schizophrenia

Seiffge-Krenke, I. (2006). Leaving home or still in the nest? Parent-child relationships and psychological health as predictors of different leaving home patterns. *Developmental Psychology, 42*(5), 864–876. doi:10.1037/0012-1649.42.5.864

Seiffge-Krenke, I., Overbeek, G., & Vermulst, A. (2010). Parent-child relationship trajectories during adolescence: Longitudinal associations with romantic outcomes in emerging adulthood. *Journal of Adolescence, 33*(1), 159–171. doi:10.1016/j.adolescence.2009.04.001

Sekar, A., Bialas, A. R., de Rivera, H., Davis, A., Hammond, T. R., Kamitaki, N., . . . McCarroll, S. A. (2016). Schizophrenia risk from complex variation of complement component 4. *Nature, 530*, 177–193. doi:10.1038/nature16549

Sharpley, M., Hutchinson, G., McKenzie, K., & Murray, R. M. (2001). Understanding the excess of psychosis among the African-Caribbean population in England: Review of current hypotheses. *British Journal of Psychiatry, 178*(40), 60–68. doi:10.1192/bjp.178.40.s60

Shea, M., & Yeh, C. J. (2008). Asian American students' cultural values, stigma, and relational self-construal: Correlates of attitudes toward professional help seeking. *Journal of Mental Health Counseling, 30*(2), 157–172.

Stanley, B., & Brown, G. K. (2012). Safety planning intervention: A brief intervention to mitigate suicide risk. *Cognitive and Behavioral Practice, 19*(2), 256–264. doi:10.1016/j.cbpra.2011.01.001

Szmukler, G. I., Burgess, P., Herrman, H., Benson, A., Colusa, S., & Bloch, S. (1996). Caring for relatives with serious mental illness: The development of the experience of caregiving inventory. *Social Psychiatry and Psychiatric Epidemiology, 31*(3), 137–148.

Tandon, R., Keshavan, M. S., & Nasrallah, H. A. (2008). Schizophrenia, "just the facts": What we know in 2008. 2. Epidemiology and etiology. *Schizophrenia Research, 102*(1–3), 1–18. doi:10.1016/j.schres.2008.04.011

Tennakoon, L. D., Fannon, D. G., Doku, V. C., Ceallaigh, S. O., Kuipers, E., & Sharma, T. (2001). Experience of caregiving: A prospective follow-up study among the relatives of first-episode psychotic clients. *Schizophrenia Research, 49*, 277–278.

Walker, J. S., & Gowen, (2011). *Community-based approaches for supporting positive development in youth and young adults with serious mental health conditions.* Portland, OR: Research and Training Center for Pathways to Positive Futures, Portland State University.

Walsh, E., Buchanan, A., & Fahy, T. (2002). Violence and schizophrenia: Examining the evidence. *British Journal of Psychiatry, 180*(6), 490–495. doi:10.1192/bjp.180.6.490

Wasserman, S., Weisman de Mamani, A., & Suro, G. (2012). Shame and guilt/self-blame as predictors of expressed emotion in family members of patients with schizophrenia. *Psychiatry Research, 196*(1), 27–31. doi:10.1016/j.psychres.2011.08.009

Zolkowska, K., Cantor-Graae, E., & McNeil, T. F. (2001). Increased rates of psychosis among immigrants to Sweden: Is migration a risk factor for psychosis? *Psychological Medicine, 31*, 669–678.

RELATIONAL FUNCTIONING: UNDERSTANDING BIPOLAR AND RELATED DISORDERS

Matthew R. Buckley and Stephanie K. Scott

Success in working effectively with how mental illness manifests itself in individuals is greatly enhanced when clinicians are oriented to how mental illness impacts families. Mental illness does not operate solely in an individual, but appears in relationships with disturbing and often destructive force. This is especially evident in individuals and families impacted by Bipolar and Related Disorders. It is especially important for clinicians to understand the course of Bipolar Disorder (BD) so that they can help promote understanding within a family when one of their members experiences mania and depression as part of their normal way of living. Developing an understanding of the manifestation and the course of BD helps all concerned to approach treatment and management of the disorder more realistically and lessens potential despairing due to unmet expectations. This chapter helps to acquaint clinicians with how BD occurs, its course, and its impact on families and individuals, and to respond with resiliency and effective problem-solving orientations.

DSM-5 AND FAMILY SYSTEMS

When individuals are challenged by mental illness, often the challenge is shared by their families in complex ways. Family systems also impact the course and treatment of mental illness by how family members respond to the affected members, how much support is offered, how healthy the family system is at any given time, the stressors the family system sustains and how it responds, and larger support systems that may impact family functioning. BD affects and is affected by the family system and successful treatment is enhanced when family members understand the course and treatment of the illness, respond in supportive ways, and stay patient and empathic within the context of constructive communication and problem solving. BD is a daunting condition to face alone and even more challenging when a family system is not aligned on some level with a carefully crafted treatment plan. Conversely, as families are supported to learn, accept, and adapt to the needs of the affected member, treatment gains can be multiplied and affected members can find renewed hope for fulfilling and productive lives. Thus, understanding BD from a systems perspective can help clinicians effectively conceptualize how families can be incorporated into treatment, what types of family support to offer, and how the disorder can develop over the life span.

Overview of Bipolar Disorder

BD is a personal and family crisis. As a mental illness, BD takes a significant toll on personal efficacy and self-worth and is often bewildering to family members as they try to manage the symptoms of the illness and support their affected loved ones in the midst of frustrating and competing interpersonal, social, and logistical factors. The emergence of BD as manifested by intense periods of mania, often followed by periods of deep depression, disrupts peace, tests relationships, clouds future dreams and aspirations, and often destroys marriages and family relationships. It is extremely useful to take a family systems approach in conceptualizing BDs, as family relationships are where the fallout of this disorder has the greatest impact.

Primary Features of Bipolar Disorder

The primary feature distinguishing bipolar and related disorders from all other mental disorders is the presence of *mania* (as manifest in Bipolar I Disorder) *or hypomania* (as manifest in Bipolar II Disorder; American Psychiatric Association [APA], 2013), which is a state of intense, energized mood, cognition, and behavior, resulting in an increased capacity for creativity and clarity of thought (rational and irrational), rapid ideas and racing thoughts, sometimes irritability and impatience with others, reduced need for sleep, distractibility, an objective-focused activity, and/or energy present most of the time during the episode (APA, 2013; Carr, 2009; Goodwin & Jamison, 1990; Jamison, 2011; Miklowitz, 2008; Rusner, Carlsson, Brunt, & Nystrom, 2009). For example, a young college student who was a blues guitarist had the strong impression during a manic episode that he could create a device that, connected to his guitar, would enhance the resonance from strumming the strings, vibrating through his arm, up the shoulder, through the neck, and up onto the scalp of the person playing to stimulate hair growth; anyone playing the guitar with this device would be positively impacted with a healthy head of hair. He described the concept with passionate clarity and intense emotion because thousands of his friends (friends whom he had not yet met) who struggled with hair loss were all on the verge of financial and social ruin because of their lack of hair. He perseverated on figuring out the mechanism, thinking he was just on the brink of discovery. His invention never materialized and, luckily, he did not have access to the financial resources to make an investment in the venture.

With mania and hypomania, there is a decreased need for sleep, increased sexual desire, and a need for stimulation, which can involve risk-taking behaviors resulting in painful and/or harmful consequences. The subjective experience of mania is also characterized as paradoxical where there is lightning-fast epiphany beyond the vision of all others, which produces a feeling of grandiosity and power. Many who experience mania describe feeling frustrated at their limited capacity to experience and carry forward these creative insights, like drinking water from a fire hose (Rusner et al., 2009). For example, a successful attorney experiencing a manic episode was able to borrow $50,000 against her retirement when she flew to Las Vegas and walked up and down the strip, cheerfully and enthusiastically distributing hundred-dollar bills to passersby until, within a matter of minutes, the money was gone. She was ecstatic and believed that many were blessed by her efforts and that money would continue to flow to her and she would be the means whereby many more would receive blessings from God, through her. When she came to herself, she realized what she had done and felt deep and pervasive shame. Mania, but not hypomania, is also sometimes accompanied by delusional thinking and psychosis, which mimic symptoms of Schizophrenia (APA, 2013). Hypomania contains similar symptoms manifest in mania, but of a lesser duration and lesser intensity (National Institute of Mental Health [NIMH], 2016a) and is a characteristic of Bipolar II Disorder (APA, 2013).

The most frightening time for those experiencing mania is when it begins to dissipate because for many it signals the descent into depression. Another complex manifestation of depression is Bipolar With Mixed Episodes (see APA, 2013, pp. 149–150). These depressive episodes are characterized by deep sadness, hopelessness, feelings of emptiness, fatigue, lack of energy, loss of appetite, listlessness, dysphoria, and apathy for a minimum of 2 weeks (APA, 2013). Depressive episodes are often attended by shame and embarrassment for the consequence of manic actions, a lack of pleasure in activities once enjoyable, the need to isolate from others, a sense of worthlessness, guilt, somatic aches and pains, troubled sleep, and thoughts of death. Whereas in mania, the risk of death is typically from thrill seeking, in depressed individuals, the primary risk of death is suicide. Many who suffer from bipolar depression describe the subjective feeling of depression as intense as is the feeling of mania (Rusner et al., 2009). Mania is characterized as the "highest of highs," whereas depression is characterized by the "lowest of lows" (Miklowitz, 2008, p. 23). Suicide is a very real concern for the bipolar client, family, and friends, and those treating bipolar persons. In the course of antidepressant treatment of BD, or depression, the first symptoms that respond to treatment are a lack of energy (i.e., people become more energized) and sleep (i.e., people tend to sleep better when on antidepressants), and one of the last symptoms to clear up is mood. This makes people with BD especially susceptible to suicide because they actually have the energy to kill themselves. States of high energy along with depression increase suicidal risk (Jamison, 2011).

The *Diagnostic and Statistical Manual of Mental Disorders* (5th ed.; *DSM-5*; APA, 2013) categorizes Bipolar and Related Disorders as: Bipolar I Disorder characterized by a manic episode lasting 7 days or longer; Bipolar II Disorder characterized by a hypomanic episode lasting no more than 4 days; Cyclothymic Disorder characterized by hypomanic symptoms that would not meet the full diagnostic criteria for a hypomanic "episode" and depressive symptoms that would not meet the full symptom criteria for a depressive "episode" (this includes a lower level of intensity of both extremes, a lower level of frequency with symptoms occurring 4 days compared to 7 days for a manic episode, and a subthreshold of symptoms necessary to meet the disorder); Substance/Medication-Induced Bipolar Disorder characterized by symptoms of mania precipitated by a particular medication or substance; and Bipolar Disorder Related to a Medical Condition, in which symptoms of mania can be precipitated by a health-related condition (APA, 2013). Mania becomes the primary symptom distinguishing BD from other depressive disorders and causes significant "impairment in social and occupational functioning" (APA, 2013, p. 124) as well as a disruption to family relationships and functioning, which is the general standard that distinguishes problematic behavior from a mental disorder.

Associated Features of Bipolar Disorder

Prevalence rates for all BDs for adults are 3.9% over the lifetime with 2.6% of the adult population meeting diagnostic criteria in a given year and 2.5% of adolescents over the lifetime with 2.2% of the population meeting criteria in a given year. Approximately 1.7% of adolescents report having mania alone during the lifetime and 1.3% report having manic symptoms in a given year (APA, 2013; NIMH, 2016a). These data are significant because it appears that adolescent manifestation of BD approaches that of adults and it is important for mental health clinicians to identify, diagnose, and treat BD early in affected individuals. Additionally, 50% to 67% of adults affected reported the onset of BD before the age of 18 and 15% to 28% reported experiencing symptoms before 13 years (Perlis et al., as cited in Miklowitz, 2012). Men and women experience BD equally although there is some evidence suggesting that women experience Bipolar II Disorder at a higher rate (APA, 2013; Miklowitz, 2008; NIMH, 2016a). Women also tend to experience higher "rapid cycling" (i.e., four or more mood episodes within a single year) and more "mixed states" (i.e., mixed symptoms or "features" of mania and depression within a single episode) than men (APA, 2013, p. 130). BD With Mixed Features is especially difficult to treat with psychotropic medications because of the nature of simultaneous manic and depressive symptoms (Miklowitz, 2008). There is a strong hereditary component in BD; "a family history of bipolar disorder is one of the strongest and most consistent risk factors for bipolar disorders" (APA, 2013, p. 130). Goodwin and Jamison (1990) and Jamison (2011) reviewed the research on risk factors and also indicated the strong connection to family members who have had BD and noted that careful assessment as to the course and treatment of the illness is helpful in making predictions to the course of the disorder in newly diagnosed individuals. Over 90% of those experiencing a manic episode eventually have recurring episodes and roughly 60% of individuals having a manic episode also have a depressive episode; so the likelihood is high that mania persists within individuals with multiple episodes, including episodes of depression. The persistence of symptoms within the interepisode phases of the illness indicates that, for many, there is never a break within this chronic condition (Goodwin & Jamison, 1990; Jamison, 2011; Miklowitz, 2008). Miklowitz (2008) noted that depressive episodes in the bipolar cycle are much more difficult to treat and that individuals spend much more time in depressive states than manic ones; research suggests as much as three times more weeks during the year with depressive symptoms versus symptoms of mania (Judd et al., as cited in Miklowitz, 2008). It is clear that BD is a chronic, often debilitating condition that requires a multifaceted treatment approach to manage effectively (Goodwin & Jamison, 1990; Jamison, 2011; Miklowitz, 2007, 2008, 2012).

For both adults and adolescents, symptoms of BD can be comorbid with a wide variety of other disorders including Anxiety Disorders (including specific phobias), Attention-Deficit/Hyperactivity Disorder, Personality Disorders, Substance Use Disorders, serious and often untreated medical conditions, and for adolescents, Disruptive and/or Conduct Disorders, and "disorders with prominent irritability" (APA, 2013, p. 132), which need to be carefully assessed in order not to misdiagnose children as bipolar (Carr, 2009). This vulnerability of comorbidity adds to the complex environmental and family factors that influence treatment outcomes for affected individuals.

Treating Bipolar Disorder Symptoms

The primary treatment of BD is psychopharmacological and typically starts with lithium bicarbonate and other mood stabilizers, antidepressants, and atypical antipsychotics and anxiolytics that are often prescribed in the acute phase of the illness (Goodwin & Jamison, 1990; Miklowitz, 2008, 2012). Because bipolar individuals often have sleep disturbance, sleep medications are often prescribed to regulate circadian rhythms. Good sleep hygiene is one of the easiest and best ways to help prevent triggering mania (Jamison, 2011). The use of electric convulsive therapy is an option for entrenched, severe, and persistent depressive symptoms (NIMH, 2016b). Other treatment modalities are being researched including deep brain stimulation, the use of optogenetics, and genetic mapping (Detroit Public Television, 2016). A common and frustrating feature of medication treatment for bipolar individuals is medication compliance (Goodwin & Jamison, 1990; Jamison, 2011). Individuals affected with BD often find the effects of drug therapy as blunting the euphoric effects of the experience of mania, and develop abhorrence to the side effects of the medication. They are also often resistant to the idea that they will be taking medications for the rest of their lives in order to maintain a balanced mood, to help them make reasoned choices, maintain their interpersonal relationships and support systems, and lower the incidence of additional and severe episodes. The trade-off of life stability (which is a relative term) with experiencing intense feelings of euphoria, clarity, and power is often a difficult dynamic for individuals to negotiate, and those treated for BD are forced to confront the losses associated with this challenging condition. Approaching assessment, diagnosis, and treatment within grieving framework can help bipolar individuals cope with the significant changes attendant to their disorder and become more open to living a life with the disorder. Understanding how family systems impact and are impacted by BD provides enhanced insight into developing therapeutic leverage in the treatment of BD.

Family Systems and Bipolar Disorder

The impact of BD on families is hard to fully measure, but the consequences are clearly tragic and often corrosive to close family relationships, friendships, and other support systems. Individuals experiencing manic and depressive symptoms reflect the bewilderment, anger, hopelessness, and existential despair often felt in family members who struggle to support their loved one while at the same time try to make sense of what is difficult to accept: that their loved one has a chronic condition that will persist throughout her or his life and, as family members, they too travel a parallel path.

Practical and Emotional Consequences

There are both tangible and intangible impacts for families of an individual with BD. The tangible consequences include being introduced into the legal system with adolescent or adult family members who may act out during a manic episode and violate the law (Hyde, 2001). Hiring legal counsel for an arrest and interfacing with the legal system become stressful. Other potential, practical consequences include unemployment resulting from inconsistent or poor job performance; impulsive and poor financial decisions resulting in loss of income, savings, or retirement resources; loss of social status within the community; interfacing with mental health agencies and social services, and a wide variety of mental health personnel; and often being marginalized by a mental health system that does not recognize the legitimate burden family members carry and the inability to access important treatment information on behalf of their affected loved one because of right to privacy and confidentiality constraints (Rusner, Carlsson, Brunt, & Nystrom, 2012). Numerous inpatient hospitalizations and intensive outpatient programs, encountering resistance from the affected family member to comply with medication and other forms of treatment, the emergence and persistence of substance use disorders comorbid with BD, dealing with younger family members who may be more vulnerable to the effects of this condition and who may be wondering what is wrong with mommy, daddy, brother, or sister are all lived experiences for family members where BD is prevalent. Sometimes partners of spouses, sons and daughters of parents, and parents of children may cut off and/or leave or divorce the impacted relative because of the stress attendant to this condition. These life disruptions cast a pall on other family and social activities and center the collective energy and family resources on addressing the problem. It is difficult to maintain hope in the future.

Intangible Consequences

The intangible or emotional fallout for the family is a real and felt experience and centers on working to accept the disorder and attendant consequences. Miklowitz (2008) noted that when an affected individual is in a manic state, family members may initially find the observed behavior as interesting or exciting, but soon turn to distress and anxiety as their loved one becomes more impulsive, unpredictable, and erratic; the family member may leave and not return home for days. If the manic episode is new to family members, there is often confusion about how to respond and about the immediate need for perspective. Often, family members seek to discern differences between the illness and the characteristics of the affected loved one in an attempt to make sense of their behaviors. If the affected individual is a parent, children and other family members need reassurance; if a child, parents may seek to discipline or reason with their loved one with little success. Some affected individuals become violent, destructive, and/or manifest delusional and psychotic symptoms that are frightening and family members are faced with having to protect and be protected from the affected family member. If the manic episode is repeated as part of the course of the illness, family members become retraumatized to the episode and may seek equilibrium through a variety of behaviors ranging from acting out themselves (mostly in children) to calmly responding to the situation and following a predetermined plan. Often family members try to reason with the affected member with little success. During episodes of depression, family members seek to motivate and instill hope within their family member and often face their own sense of hopelessness and despair when attempts to support, encourage, and offer solutions are rejected or treated with indifference. Motivating someone who is depressed is extremely challenging and sometimes family members wonder which is worse, the mania or depression. Rusner et al. (2012) summarized the effects of BD on the family:

> Being closely related to a person with bipolar disorder means a paradox of both being needed and rejected, (i.e., vitally necessary but simultaneously also excluded), whilst being overshadowed by bipolar disorder. It means living in a state of constant pressure and existential exposure, periodically being exposed to huge distress without means of getting away from it. Life is overshadowed by the illness. One's attention is focused on the well-being of the person with [bipolar disorder] in such a way that one's own needs take second place. In a desperate struggle for survival, the close relatives are stretched to the limits of their ability. Being closely related to someone with bipolar disorder also means simultaneously foreseeing and following the often sudden and unexpected changes of the person with [bipolar disorder]. (p. 202)

This lived experience in family members as well as the affected relative signals clearly that BD is a family illness and the need for family intervention and support cannot be overestimated.

RELATIONAL AND CULTURAL FEATURES

There is little empirical evidence of cultural differences in the incidence and manifestation of BD across cultural groups (APA, 2013; Goodwin & Jamison, 1990; Miklowitz, 2008), but clinicians are best advised to maintain a cultural perspective when diagnosing and treating BD, including uses of assessment instruments, diagnosis, and treatment of individuals diagnosed with bipolar and other disorders. Of particular importance is the recognition that the *DSM* system is based on a medical model and is inherently limited in validating treatment approaches other than medical (Jacob et al., 2013). However, the *DSM-5* does provide an important assessment tool, the *Cultural Formulation Interview,* which provides a framework to assist clinicians in assessing the cultural identity of the affected individual, perceptions of the distress (including how the cultural group of the client would view the problem), psychosocial stressors and "cultural features of vulnerability and resilience" (APA, 2013, p. 750), and cultural aspects of both the client and the clinician that might impact treatment (APA, 2013). Viewing culture therapeutically includes a perceptual expansion of cultural groups to include age, gender, sexual orientation, religion, language, occupation, military service, social networks, substance use, migration status, geographical region, relationship status (i.e., married or divorced), and not simply race and ethnicity (American Counseling Association [ACA], 2014; APA, 2013).

Closely connected to culture is how relational variables impact and are impacted by BD. These relational factors largely constitute how family and friends interact with their affected loved one(s) and how counselors interact supportively with bipolar individuals and their families and support networks. In the following discussion, we discuss key ways in which counselors can approach bipolar clients constructively to help decrease resistance to treatment and help set the stage for effective treatment. The discussion regarding how families communicate, interact, and create environments that positively or negatively impact affected individuals falls under the section "Vulnerability–Stress Model."

The importance of developing an empathic, accepting, supportive, and validating therapeutic alliance has been well supported in the research literature (Havens & Ghaemi, 2005; Hersoug, Høglend, Monsen, & Havik, 2001; Horvath, 2001; Jamison, 2011; Kress & Paylo, 2015; Lambert & Barley, 2001; Meyers, 2014; Norcross & Hill, 2004). As it pertains to work with bipolar clients, Havens and Ghaemi (2005) advocated for clinicians to use empathy and authenticity when working with BD clients and to not be afraid of conflict within the process of making therapeutic contact. "The meeting and initial work with manic persons is often complicated. When we meet with them, we collide with them. We have to confirm the collision, not deny it" (p. 142). Demonstrating empathy for paranoid and grandiose thinking is not only critical for a successful therapeutic alliance, but gives the clinician a more accurate assessment as to the extent of the client's delusions, grandiosity, and paranoia. Counselors modeling for clients a sense of humor and often a playful attitude in their interactions together help clients learn to more realistically view themselves and reality-test relationships. Humor, appropriately and skillfully used, also helps reinforce for clients that their counselors do not view them as a culmination of their manic and depressive episodes, but as people who can be related to, which is empowering to them. Bipolar-affected clients often know that they negatively impact loved ones and others, and as a result, feel deep shame and guilt for what is often irritating and offensive behavior; having a place that is safe for them to explore different ways of seeing themselves is important. Finally, Havens and Ghaemi (2005) noted the corrective therapeutic effect this type of encounter has on the client:

> The job of the clinician is twofold initially: first, to seek to existentially be with manic patients and then, to counterprojectively give perspective to those patients about their manic worldview, without completely denying it. This twofold approach then can lead to a healthy therapeutic alliance, which itself has a mood-stabilizing effect. Along with mood-stabilizing medications, this alliance can then lead patients toward full recovery. (p. 146)

Clients experiencing the effects of BD can benefit greatly from the "stabilizing effect" of a strong therapeutic alliance that sets the basis for all other work. The therapeutic relationship provides a place where the bipolar client can experience acceptance and the family can receive real and targeted support. Jamison (1996), herself bipolar, put into perspective the importance of the therapeutic relationship in her own treatment:

> Lithium . . . gentles me out, keeping me from ruining my career and relationships, keeps me out of a hospital, alive, and makes psychotherapy possible. But, ineffably,

psychotherapy heals. It makes some sense of the confusion, reigns in the terrifying thoughts and feelings, returns some control and hope and possibility of learning from it all. Pills cannot, do not, ease one back into reality. . . . Psychotherapy is a sanctuary, it is a battleground, it is a place where I have been psychotic, neurotic, elated, confused and despairing beyond belief. But, always, it is where I have believed—or have learned to believe—that I might someday be able to contend with all of this. (Goodwin & Jamison, 1990, p. 725)

Miklowitz (2012) noted the importance of family therapists showing patience and adaptability in working with bipolar patients and their families. Even from a psychoeducational perspective where there are often established protocols toward the goal of educating clients on the disease, its course, and the impacts on individuals and families, being aware of topics that may be highly emotional and aware of the need to address these issues with empathy and sensitivity is paramount for family counselors.

Jamison (2011) noted that an important implication for family treatment is for counselors to involve the family directly in the treatment of the identified bipolar family member. Family members can often provide much more accurate and rich perspectives regarding what happens when the bipolar member is manic and/or severely depressed. Often, the bipolar member is not a completely reliable source of information for these events; she or he can certainly comment on how it feels to be manic or depressed, or how specifically these states manifest herself or himself in daily living, but she or he may not be fully aware of the consequences of her or his actions while in these extreme states. Jamison (2011) also recommended that counselors and therapists can help bipolar clients develop "advanced directives" (p. 31) that may include signed consent from clients about how the illness is to be addressed or treated, including being treated against their will if they are in a full-blown manic or depressed episode. The rationale is that we want bipolar clients to be thinking about the course of their illness and making decisions about treatment when they are balanced, lucid, and making rational judgments rather than when they are manic or depressed. This can best be accomplished within the context of supportive family members who can express understanding and empathy, while at the same time express clearly the consequences of clients' manic and depressive behaviors and advocate strongly for responsive and responsible action to be taken. Family-focused treatment (FFT) is discussed later as an effective approach within this context of the therapeutic alliance.

Vulnerability–Stress Model

In treating BD and related disorders, it is helpful to conceptualize the condition as comprehensively as possible in order to capture essential facets of the disorder including the associated genetic, biological, and environmental factors and how these manifest in individuals. Miklowitz (2008) noted that these factors do not appear independent of each other but all "interact in bringing about episodes of mood disorder or in protecting against their occurrence" (p. 49). Understanding how these factors mutually impact and are impacted by each other over the course of the disorder can help manage episode occurrence and develop resilience in affected individuals and their families. The Vulnerability–Stress Model (Miklowitz, 2008) is a useful tool in helping clinicians conceptualize the disorder and, in turn, help affected individuals and their families understand the origin, course, and prognosis of the illness. Later in the chapter we discuss how this model provides the foundation for effective treatment approaches.

Genetic and biological vulnerability includes the manifestation of the disorder in members of an affected person's family (i.e., who in the family has or has had the bipolar or related disorders, including parents, grandparents, siblings, or extended relatives), brain functioning (i.e., to what level may there be structural or brain abnormalities and quality of functioning and dysfunction in neurotransmitters—this is obviously difficult for counselors to determine without reliance on medical evaluation), and other biological factors (e.g., chemical imbalances, changes in hormonal and immune system functioning, sleep regulation). When vulnerability is high in these areas, the amount of environmental stress needed to trigger a manic or depressive episode tends to be low (e.g., a simple, but unexpected schedule change at work or an unexpected and isolated conflict with a spouse or other family member); those with high vulnerability have a low tolerance for and little protection from events that others without the disorder might manage quite well. Those with low vulnerability to genetic, neurological, and biological factors would likely not be vulnerable to mood episodes unless there were high social stressors at play (e.g., death of a close friend or family member, an eviction from a dwelling, a significant financial event or other crisis, or chronic conflict and stress). Thus, low environmental stress acts as a protective factor from the occurrence and reoccurrence of mood episodes. Because the nature of genetic or biological vulnerability may be hard to detect and determine, managing environmental stress becomes a high priority in treating and managing bipolar episodes and their severity.

One primary manifestation of environmental factors is the quality of interpersonal relationships within the family and the consequent level of stress in the home environment. These factors are referred to as *psychosocial provoking agents* (Miklowitz, 2008, p. 50) that largely impact vulnerability and the manifestation of manic and depressive states. Because BD impacts individuals and families in often unpredictable and disorienting ways, and because of the real and felt consequences of BD in the family (e.g., loss of employment, social stigma, loss of support systems, financial problems), family members often assume patterns of responding that range from being long-suffering, helpful, and supportive to being critical, blaming, and sometimes uncooperative. These reactions contribute significantly to the emotional climate within the home and impact the perpetuation of continued episodes. Miklowitz (2008) suggested that these "cause and effect relationships between mood disorder symptoms and family environmental factors are bidirectional: Families are affected by bipolar disorder as much as they affect it" (p. 51). Like many family interventions and models of family therapy, the Vulnerability–Stress Model was developed from research on family interactions with patients with schizophrenia. Miklowitz (2008) and his team began researching how this model applied to bipolar-disordered individuals and their families. He built upon the existing research around a fundamental construct related to family functioning: *emotional expression* (EE). EE is "a measure of emotional attitudes among relatives (usually parents or spouses) of a psychiatric patient" (Miklowitz, 2008, p. 53) and is defined as critical, hostile, or emotional overinvolvement statements and attitudes family members communicate overtly or indirectly to the member(s) affected by the disorder. The *DSM-5* has a new Z code that captures this dynamic: High Emotional Expression Level Within Family (Z63.8). Elevated or high EE becomes the primary vehicle for socioenvironmental stressors within the family (Miklowitz, 2007, 2008, 2012). Bipolar-disordered individuals are two to three times more likely to deteriorate into a manic or depressive episode in families where high EE exists and experience prolonged and more severe manic or depressive states. There is no evidence to suggest that high EE families cause BD, but the evidence is clear that high EE causes stress that contributes significantly to the perpetuation of mood episodes (Miklowitz, 2008). Miklowitz (2007) described how EE develops and is perpetuated between the affected child and his or her parents and how the child reinforces high EE reactions within parents, which impacts overall relationship functioning. Children who exhibit behaviors and attitudes consistent with a low tolerance for stress, unstable mood, elevated anxiety, irritability, and problematic cognitive functioning largely meet the criteria for high biological and genetic vulnerability. Miklowitz noted that generational influences within high EE families can significantly impact the vulnerabilities of family members who may be predisposed to BD and vulnerable to criticism toward their condition.

These parent–child dynamics along with the "vulnerabilities" noted create a perfect storm for the development and perpetuation of unstable mood states that often evolve into adulthood and throughout the developmental life span. The Vulnerability–Stress Model helps clinicians assess and further understand not only the relationships between genetic, biological, and socioenvironmental factors, but helps focus attention on the emotional expression and the quality of interpersonal reactions in the home that could be either provoking manic or depressive mood states or protecting affected individuals from their recurrence.

FAMILY SYSTEMS ASSESSMENTS

Accurate assessment of BD is essential to the formulation of an accurate and workable diagnosis, which can lead to targeted treatment in areas of need. When conducting formal and informal assessment, it is vital to remember that data generated from assessment can be revelatory (thus opening new areas of inquiry) or confirmatory of a diagnosis. Each assessment acts as an individual data point, like a mosaic of a larger picture. Assessment for BD could be characterized as the individual assessment and diagnosis of the disorder while family assessment addresses essential aspects of the family environment including the quality of family interactions.

Individual Assessment

A thorough biopsychosocial assessment should be conducted on the client upon the initial intake (or shortly thereafter) to capture a comprehensive context in which the presenting problems occur. There are numerous models of biopsychosocial assessments, but the primary domains in which they all converge include identifying information, presenting problem, history of the presenting problem including a mental health history, medical history, family history, personal history that includes a developmental timeline, conducting a mental status exam (i.e., appearance, behaviors/psychomotor activity, attitudes, affect and mood, speech and thought, perceptual disturbances, orientation and consciousness, memory and intelligence, and reliability, judgment, and insight (Kress & Paylo, 2015). Other domains of inquiry essential to the biopsychosocial history include legal problems, substance use, spirituality/religion, cultural/ethnic background, suicidal ideation (including ideation, plan, and attempts), financial concerns and socioeconomic status, and resources and resilience factors. Utilizing the Level 1 and Level 2 Cross-Cutting Symptom Measures associated with the DSM-5 can also provide a targeted assessment of symptoms, including the Altman Self-Rating Mania Scale (Altman, Hedeker, Peterson, & Davis, 1997) that was modified for use as a DSM-5, Level 2 Cross-Cutting Symptom Measure for both adults and children. This can be self-administered or administered to a parent or guardian (APA, 2013; see also www.psychiatry.org/psychiatrists/practice/dsm/dsm-5/online-assessment-measures). Another helpful measure that can detect both threshold and subthreshold levels of mania is the Composite International Diagnostic Interview BD Screening Scale (Kessler & Ustun, 2004). This is a clinician-administered assessment that was created and validated as helping to generate conservative diagnoses of BD. For an assessment of general disability, the World Health Organization Disability Assessment Schedule 2.0 is a self-administered (or an informant version) instrument that is also part of the DSM-5 offering (APA, 2013, pp. 745–748). The goal of individual assessment is to obtain a differential diagnosis and it is important to (a) administer formal assessments ethically and according to the protocols specified in specific instruments including being trained in the administration and interpretation of data; (b) gather and make sense of the data and share the results with clients in a manner that is comprehensible, clearly explaining the limitations of assessment and assessment results; and (c) use the data to confirm existing clinical impressions and/or to generate new clinical directions. The importance of counselors adhering to the diagnostic criteria and being familiar with disorder specifiers (e.g., mixed features, rapid cycling, seasonal pattern) and associated features of each diagnostic category cannot be overstated. Consultation with other professionals including those of a treatment team is essential. Kress and Paylo (2015) reminded clinicians of the importance of understanding clients within the context of their families and social systems, which means that the family can provide important context for the counselor in diagnosis and treatment, which leads to the process of family assessment.

Family Assessment

Family assessment becomes essential in understanding how BP affects and is affected by factors environmental and relational in nature. Previously we discussed areas of assessment related to the *Vulnerability–Stress Model* including assessing the EE within a family environment. Assessment of EE for research purposes was a matter of extensive training and coding family responses within a 60- to 90-minute interaction between a family or multiple family members and the affected member. Specific benchmarks would distinguish high from low EE. For example, families would be classified as being high EE families when, during the interaction, there were six or more critical comments made (e.g., "If he keeps sleeping in, he is going to lose this job just like he has all the others."); if there were signs of hostility in the interactions (e.g., "He acts like he can't control this behavior, but I know he can; he makes me so angry!"); and if there was evidence of emotional over-involvement between a family member (or members) and the bipolar individual (e.g., "I can't manage to sleep if he doesn't come home when he says that he will." or "I'm afraid that if I leave on this trip, she's going to burn the house down."; Miklowitz, 2007, 2008, 2012; Miklowitz et al., 2008). These same criteria can be used by counselors in family therapy settings. Miklowitz (2008) recommended that, as part of the protocol of a comprehensive family assessment with all willing family members present, the counselor have the family (or a family member and the affected bipolar member) engage in a conversation regarding their relationships or how they have attempted to solve problems they experience for 5 to 10 minutes and to observe and note the number of EE statements that are generated within the interaction and what the statements are. This not only gives important data about the level of EE, but sensitizes counselors to what family members value, what they may be struggling with, and process and context of their conversations. Developing sensitivity to the quality and types of interactions family members have can give counselors useful information in designing treatment, including areas of interpersonal functioning on which to focus. A very useful family assessment tool is the *genogram,* which can be used to develop an understanding of where BD (and other mental health problems) has occurred within the family (Watson, Poon, & Walters, 2005). A genogram is a multigenerational family tree that symbolically represents different dynamics related to family and individual functioning that is psychological, cultural, and interpersonal in nature. This comprehensive assessment can include medical issues, symptomatology, treatment, and outcome, as well as family context and patient experience. Genograms have the ability to leverage a clearer understanding of the Vulnerability–Stress Model as applied to individuals affected by BD and their families. Other related areas of family assessment are important in helping counselors understand how family members have been affected by BD and quality of life for the bipolar member. The Mood Disorder Burden Index (Martire et al., 2009) was developed to assess caregiver perceptions and experiences in three core domains: patients' mood symptoms, caregivers' worries about the future, and caregivers' interpersonal difficulties with the patient. This is consistent with supporting caregivers in their experience with BD family members. The Quality of Life in Bipolar Disorder Scale (Michalaka, Murray, & CREST.BD, 2010) is also a self-administered instrument designed as an alternative to psychiatric measures that fail to assess for treatment outcome and recovery and well-being for those afflicted with BD. This instrument can give counselors insight into how the bipolar individual has been impacted by the disorder and indirectly, how the family has been impacted. An important additional source of assessment is in the *DSM-5* under "other conditions that may be a focus of clinical attention" or Z codes (APA, 2013, pp. 715–727). Formerly known as *V codes*, these conditions are accompanied by focused descriptions of individual and family conditions that impact and are impacted by bipolar and other mental disorders. Referencing these conditions helps provide a richer context for assessment and treatment. General headings for these codes include Relational Problems, Abuse and Neglect, Educational and Occupational Problems, Housing and Economic Problems, and Other Problems Related to the Social Environment, among others. Specific Z codes include Parent–Child Relational Problem, Child Physical Abuse Suspected and/or Confirmed, High Emotional Expression Level Within Families, Disruption of Family by Separation and Divorce, Child Neglect Suspected and/or Confirmed, and Social Exclusion or Rejection (APA, 2013).

Just as developing and maintaining the quality of the therapeutic relationship is important in treatment of BD, counselors should always be mindful of being client centered, empathically inquisitive, and validating of the subjective experience of clients and their families as information is gathered during the assessment process. Assessment is not a singular event that occurs upon intake, but a continuous process of measuring symptom reduction, improvement in family communication and problem solving, acceptance, and self-efficacy in living with BD.

FAMILY SYSTEMS INTERVENTIONS

As previously stated, traditional treatments for BD have been grounded primarily in pharmacologic intervention with an integration of individual psychotherapy; in fact, this combination has been found to be more effective than either protocol alone (Carr, 2014; Geddes & Miklowitz, 2013; Miklowitz & Scott, 2009; West et al., 2014). In addition, the goals of treatment for BD have historically focused on symptom reduction and prevention of future episodes (Leboyer & Kupfer, 2010). However, a more contemporary view has recognized the integral role of psychosocial variables—including significant relationships and life stressors— on the exacerbation of bipolar symptomology. In fact, while the biological etiology of BD remains unchallenged, the course and severity of the disorder cannot be separated from the individual's psychosocial context and influences (Miklowitz, 2008; West & Weinstein, 2012). As was discussed earlier in this chapter, psychosocial stressors can directly contribute to, or even catalyze, the occurrence of a bipolar episode. Similarly, the occurrence of an episode can aggravate psychosocial stressors. For example, marital discord can cause significant stress on individuals with BD, making them more susceptible to a bipolar episode. The occurrence of an episode, in turn, can increase marital discord due to the changes in the individuals' behaviors and affect regulation. Thus, a cycle can develop of constant challenge and crisis, which may self-perpetuate without the disruption of systemic treatment.

There has been considerable research evaluating the efficacy and outcomes of pharmacological treatment for BD as a stand-alone treatment, compared with both individual and combination (individual and family) psychotherapy. This effort to determine the "optimal" treatment for BD has yielded mixed results (Justo, Soares, & Calil, 2007). Some studies have found a significant impact from the integration of family therapy, while others found little or no differences in outcomes. Such discrepancies may be accounted for by small sample sizes and variations in study designs. Moreover, it is important for clinicians to remember that BD actually comprises a *group* of heterogeneous disorders, with significant variations in etiology, manifestation, and severity. In addition, the relative influences of psychosocial factors can vary widely in individuals with BD. It should be considered, then, that the question become not whether family systems treatment *is or is not* effective for BD, but *how and when* it can be applied and adapted according to the needs of the client and family. In this section, a selected family systems approach for BD is discussed, including some of the unique considerations and challenges of family treatment for BD.

Family-Focused Treatment for Bipolar Disorder

Family-focused treatment (FFT) is an integrative approach to treatment of BD, which combines psychoeducation and family therapy (Miklowitz, 2008). FFT begins with a thorough assessment of individual symptomology and family systems dynamics, and proceeds through a structured and preset treatment, with specific goals throughout the duration. While the detail and depth of family relationships are often not fully understood until well into treatment, it is important for the counselor to gather as much information during intake as possible. For example, a key goal in assessment would be to identify family conflicts that may be contributing to the stress across the system, which in turn can exacerbate BD symptomology in the identified client. Conversely, it is equally vital to understand the strengths and protective factors across the system, which can support the emotional regulation of the individual with BD, as well as the overall health of the family system. This information informs both the psychoeducation and therapy components of treatment, as it guides both specific goals and interventions. Of course, adaptions may need to be made along the way, depending on the observed progress of the client and family.

As part of a thorough assessment, the counselor should have a firm understanding of the cultural beliefs, practices, and influences on the family system. This is important not only to provide a context to the experiences and dynamics of the system, but also to provide the counselor with a perspective on how FFT may need to be adapted somewhat to maximize efficacy. For example, some cultures stress oral over written communication, which would impact the homework and other written assignments that are part of the general FFT protocol (Ozerdem, Oguz, Miklowitz, & Cimilli, 2009). These important elements can be adapted, however, and awareness of this on the front end of treatment can improve the structure and experience for the clients.

Another important element of assessment prior to FFT is the determination of appropriateness of this type of intervention. For example, not all individuals diagnosed with BD have the support of family members willing to participate in treatment. Miklowitz (2008) noted that 46% of adults diagnosed with BD do not have family members participate in treatment. There can be many reasons for this, including geography and access to services; it may also be that the very reasons for family members to *not* participate in treatment are the reasons they *should*. That is, often the extremes of bipolar episodes cause significant conflict in family systems, and may make some or all members unwilling to participate. In addition, not all individuals are appropriate for the FFT protocol. Persons who are in acute phases of BD, have developmental disabilities or other biological conditions that impact cognition, refuse to adhere to medication protocols, or have a comorbid active substance use disorder are among those for whom FFT is not recommended (Miklowitz, 2008). Furthermore, counselors will find that the efficacy of FFT is not necessarily predictable across viable treatment groups (Fristad & MacPherson, 2014). Adolescents diagnosed with BD, for example, are positively impacted by FFT, but less so than adults (Miklowitz et al., 2008); further, the degree of efficacy in such cases may differ minimally from psychoeducation alone (Miklowitz et al., 2014). This could be due a variety of factors, including developmental stage considerations and the differing role of family dynamics in the treatment. Still, the majority of extant research supports the assertion that FFT is an effective adjunct for treatment of BD, and can significantly impact relapse of the disorder (Miklowitz, 2008; Miklowitz, 2012; Reinares et al., 2016).

Another rationale for the use of FFT is its impact on caregivers. Studies have found higher rates of anxiety, depression, and general distress in caregivers of those diagnosed with BD (Goosens, Van Wijngaarden, Knoppert-Van Der Klein, & Van Achterberg, 2008; Martire et al., 2009; Perlick et al., 2016; Steele, Maruyama, & Galynker, 2010). Family-based interventions improve illness outcome and caregiver well-being (Reinares et al., 2016). In fact, FFT has been found to have a positive impact on the mental health of caregivers, even when the diagnosed family member is not participating in the treatment (Perlick et al., 2010).

The course of treatment of FFT for BD is fairly structured, and is based on three distinct treatment stages: (a) psychoeducation, (b) communication enhancement training (CET), and (c) problem solving (Miklowitz, 2008). Each stage builds on the previous one, although counselors may find themselves integrating pieces or reviewing elements of the previous stages as treatment progresses, based on the needs of the family system. Treatment using FFT usually lasts approximately 9 months, and is structured around 21 sessions that generally begin following an acute phase of BD (Miklowitz, 2012). Clinical sessions are conducted weekly for the first 3 months, followed by a step-down to biweekly, then once per month. The underlying philosophy of FFT is that BD is experienced *by the family*, not just by the diagnosed client. As such, BD episodes are viewed as "disaster" experiences shared by the family system, which in turn cause disequilibrium (Miklowitz, 2008, p. 12). Thus, the treatment focus is on reestablishing balance and harmony to the system, which in turn supports the health and wellness of the diagnosed client.

General Goals

Although specific goals depend on the information gathered at intake, and often modified during the course of treatment, FFT for BD has six general goals that outline and guide the overall process (adapted from Miklowitz, 2008, pp. 7–12):

1. *Assist the client and relatives in integrating the experiences associated with episodes of BD.* This goal focuses on understanding the diagnostic features of BD, as well as the experience of it from the perspective of the diagnosed individual. It also helps the family system better understand and accept both the severity and significance of the diagnosis.

2. *Assist the client and relatives in accepting the notion of a vulnerability to future episodes.* The focus of this goal is in the recognition that BD is a chronic, persistent, lifelong diagnosis that requires continual support. The diagnosed individual—as well as the family—may believe that the condition can be "cured" and thus have an unrealistic expectation of treatment. The periods of stability that occur between episodes can often contribute to this assumption.

3. *Assist the client and relatives in accepting a dependency on mood-stabilizing medication for symptom control.* Most clinicians specializing in the treatment of BD can attest to the importance of medication compliance; consistent use of mood-stabilizing medications can minimize the intensity of BD episodes, and prevent future occurrences. While BD cannot be "cured" with a medication regimen, the impact of consistent pharmacotherapy is considerable. Clients diagnosed with BD and their families must understand the importance of this component, which can be especially challenging to convey between episodes when the need for medication is less obvious. Furthermore, the undesirable

side effects of many medications can make the client less willing to maintain this portion of the treatment protocol.

4. *Assist the client and relatives in distinguishing between the client's personality and his or her BD.* Often with BD, there develops a trend with the diagnosed individual and his or her family system to view the individual's behaviors solely through the lens of the diagnosis. This can lead to inaccurate assumptions about the meaning and importance of behaviors. For example, if the diagnosed client becomes angry, this is not necessarily "the illness talking" nor is it always a sign of an impending episode; in fact, it may very well be a natural and appropriate reaction to a situation. This goal can be particularly challenging for both the diagnosed individual and the family system, as often BD episodes are marked by intensification of what may otherwise be normal traits and behaviors.

5. *Assist the client and family in recognizing and learning to cope with stressful life events that trigger recurrences of BD.* FFT is based on the Vulnerability–Stress Model discussed previously in this chapter. This model includes both an understanding of preexisting biological conditions that create vulnerability and the environmental stimuli that trigger or catalyze reactions based on this vulnerability. It is essential for the client and family to understand how these two elements interact. While the biological components cannot be altered, clients and families should understand how psychosocial stressors such as conflictual relationships and major life changes can impact the vulnerability of an individual with BD.

6. *Assist the family in reestablishing functional relationships after the episode.* The behavioral extremes associated with BD episodes can be challenging for families to cope with. The before, during, and after phases of BD episodes can be aggravated by the conflicts that arise across family systems in response to the situation. Thus, a key focus for treatment is in enhancing communication patterns and providing families with coping skills. Improving communication across the system is essential, as is helping the family members develop supportive relationship behaviors.

Psychoeducation

In the initial stage of treatment using the FFT model, the primary goal is psychoeducation. This stage, in turn, is broken down into phases with focus on different informational needs. In the beginning, the clinician imparts a great deal of vital information to the family system; it is important for this to be done in a warm, interactive manner. Clinicians using FFT must be wary of the potential for this stage to devolve into a solely instructional experience, much like a classroom environment. Continually checking in with family members and encouraging discussion about the material can minimize this risk and enhance rapport with family members. Clinicians may find handouts helpful to illustrate key points (Miklowitz, 2008).

In the beginning of the psychoeducation stage, the clinician should provide an overview of the FFT protocol, reasons for family participation, and his or her role as a clinician (Miklowitz, 2008). Treatment goals should also be addressed, both the more broad general goals and specifics for the family system. This is also a good time to provide an overview of BD symptomology, as well as prodromal symptoms and environmental triggers. It is important during such discussions that the clinician take time to explore the unique experiences and perspectives of each family member, as often it is the associated meaning for the system members that impacts the manner in which they cope with and react to a BD episode. Furthermore, discussions around environmental triggers are an important way for families to better understand the blind spots they may have regarding the diagnosed family member's vulnerabilities. That is—events that may be considered minor, benign, or otherwise simply normal life events to some family members may prove to be substantially more stressful for the family member with BD. For example, starting a new job is generally an exciting event, marked by optimism and hope. However, it can also be a source of anxiety, as it may trigger fear of failure or insecurities associated with the unknown. For individuals with BD, these emotions are often intensified, and may be difficult to manage. A lack of empathy for the different experience of the family member with BD may also create conflict, as the affected family member may feel unsupported and misunderstood. While such a circumstance may not itself trigger a BD episode, it can contribute to the likelihood of one occurring.

This leads to another important element in the psychoeducation stage of FFT—understanding etiology, course, and prognosis. The reality that almost any life event can contribute to the occurrence of a BD episode may be overwhelming to both the diagnosed client and the family system. As such, it is important for all members to have a basic understanding of the nature of BD, from the genetic foundations to the biological triggers to the environmental influences. As part of this discussion, it is vital for counselors to explain the Vulnerability–Stress Model, as well as how both risk and protective factors impact outcomes. Family members should understand that *knowledge is power*, and may be their greatest protective factor.

When discussing the genetic and biological influences on BD, it is also crucial for counselors to address "gene guilt" (Miklowitz, 2008, p. 136) and the related topic of inevitability. Conversations around the genetic and biological components of BD may be comforting for some, who are soothed by viewing the disorder as an illness outside their control. Others may focus solely on this piece, raising fears about genetic transmission and the "inevitable" passing of BD genes. It is essential for counselors to tread lightly during these discussions, validating the individual fears and concerns while also educating family members on the multiple influences that impact the development of BD. There is no single etiological pathway, nor one single treatment modality. Family members would benefit most from understanding risk and vulnerability, rather than focusing on responsibility for the existence of the disorder in the family system.

Counselors should wrap up this stage of treatment with a review of topics covered, an opportunity for family members to ask questions they may have about the information, and a plan of support for both the diagnosed individual and the family system. For example, the counselor might suggest a family group activity such as making a plan for how each member can support the success of the individual with BD, as well as steps they can take as a group to improve potential environmental stressors. Such an activity would segue well into the next stage of treatment, which focuses on communication across the system.

Communication Enhancement Training

Following the psychoeducation stage of treatment, family members should have a firm grasp of the basics of BD, as well as recognition of the importance of family dynamics and relationships on the course and severity of BD. The primary goal of this stage is to improve communication strategies, particularly those associated with psychosocial stressors (Miklowitz, 2008). Attention may also need to be given to communication patterns during relatively calm periods, as negative interaction patterns tend to persist during these times as well; however, they are also less obvious, so the clinician may find the focus to be mainly on precrisis, crisis, and postcrisis interactions. There is some degree of psychoeducation to this stage as well, though it is much more interactive with family members, as the clinician uses demonstration and practice to help change communication patterns in the system. The theme throughout this stage is to create supportive communication in which family members become more comfortable with expressing their beliefs and feelings, and more effectively listen to each other.

The CET stage normally begins about 8 weeks into treatment, after psychoeducation has been completed and the diagnosed family member has achieved a degree of stability (Miklowitz, 2008). This is an important consideration, and the time table may need to be adjusted. While this stage generally positively impacts family dynamics, should tensions still be too high or the diagnosed family member not be stable, efforts to enhance family communication may not only be unsuccessful, they may also be counterproductive. Further, while this stage normally lasts for about seven sessions according to the FFT model, the counselor may find that the emotional traits or developmental stages of family members necessitate a need for some adjustment. For example, families with high emotional expression (EE) in a few or all members may resist the structured communication exercises, and have more difficulty altering their patterns. The counselor will likely be aware of this issue already, however, as a result of the previous 8 weeks of psychoeducation. As such, the counselor should be able to adapt the presentation and practice of CET for the family members.

Four basic communication skills underscore the work of this stage, and provide the foundation for the practice and role-playing demonstrations. It is important to present these in the order listed, as each builds on and supports the next (adapted from Miklowitz, 2008):

1. **Expressing positive feelings.** This is an exercise focused on sharing accolades, kudos, or otherwise positive feedback for the purpose of conveying approval and positive regard. This helps diffuse existing negativity in the system and makes members more amenable to future requests for change. An example of this might be "I was so thankful that you made dinner for me when I had to work late last week."
2. **Active listening.** This is an essential skill for family members, as it not only supports greater understanding, but can also convey respect and validation. Counselors should demonstrate the components of this skill to help clarify the fundamentals. Examples of active listening include maintaining eye contact with the speaker, nodding head while the other person is speaking, verbalizations such as "uh-huh" or "sure," and reiterating or paraphrasing pieces of what was said.
3. **Making positive requests for change.** This skill should be introduced as a means of de-escalating tensions as well as fostering growth across the system. Again, this skill is best demonstrated first by the counselor, to include important elements such as making "I" statements and ensuring the request is not a veiled criticism. An example of this might be "I would really appreciate if you would call me and let me know when you are going to work late."
4. **Expressing negative feelings about specific behaviors.** The goal of this skill is to clearly identify an undesirable behavior, describe the associated feelings, and make a specific request for change. As with the previous skill, it can also foster positive growth across the system. However, it can also be very challenging to implement as it can give rise to defensiveness, or reveal additional conflicts in the system. Counselors should be prepared to intervene and redirect if necessary during practice. An example of effective use of this skill might be "I felt a little disrespected when you came home late last night and never called. I would appreciate it if you would let me know beforehand next time."

When providing both the instruction and feedback for the CET stage, counselors should remember that these skills may feel forced and unnatural—in many ways, they *are*. Family members view this stage as learning new "building blocks," although they ultimately construct their own "house." The family should also recognize the strengths and skills already in the system, as well as pieces that are less conducive to effective communication. Throughout the practice exercises, the counselor's encouragement and support, as well as identification of ways CET can improve understanding and dynamics, can go a long way in supporting the efficacy of this stage. Furthermore, it is helpful for the family members to understand that while practice does not make perfect, it can and will improve interactions during times of stress. That is, the more the family members practice these skills, the more comfortable and natural they will become—which will be especially important during times of stress and conflict.

A secondary benefit of CET can be found in changing patterns of family dynamics (Miklowitz, 2008). That is, training family members to communicate in a more open, positive, and supportive manner can alter existing patterns of interaction that are less beneficial. Whether the family relationships are marked with rapid escalation or avoidance, structured communication can buffer the negative effects of these habits by forcing the individuals to create new patterns of communication. This change often requires a lot of practice, and can be met with resistance; however, the counselor can facilitate this change through consistent practice, and by encouraging family members to raise the more difficult topics in clinical sessions. That way, the counselor can offer feedback and redirection as needed, and more effectively coach the family members toward success in their new communication efforts.

Lastly, a third—and also indirect—benefit of the CET stage is found in its impact on EE. In short, EE is a measure of the emotional attitudes and beliefs conveyed in family dynamics (Miklowitz, 2008). Families that are high in EE often display negative and critical communication, criticisms, hostility, and emotional overinvolvement. These behaviors are observed in response to BD episodes, and can be predictors of future relapse (Fredman, Baucom, Boeding, & Miklowitz, 2015; Fredman, Baucom, Miklowitz, & Stanton, 2008). Thus, it is clear that improved communication patterns can have a positive impact on these behaviors and improve relationships across the system. Furthermore, the resulting improvements in family dynamics observed in this stage help provide a more positive foundation for the next stage of treatment: dealing with problems.

Problem Solving

Once family members have a solid understanding of BD and have demonstrated improvement in their communication and dynamics, they are ready to move into more directly addressing issues that persist. Usually introduced at around the 15th session of FFT, this stage focuses on (a) recognizing and discussing problems and (b) developing a plan to address these problems (Miklowitz, 2008). A significant aspect of this stage can also be found in the empowerment of the family system; that is, helping the family learn experientially that they can and will be able to handle issues that arise. The counselor facilitates this through practice in addressing current issues, and by helping the family develop a proactive pattern of addressing these. The success of this stage is directly impacted by the successes of previous stages; thus, the counselor may find the need to go back and review materials or exercises previously covered, depending on the family's responsiveness to interventions in this stage.

As with the CET stage, the problem-solving stage is best begun with a structured approach, which essentially teaches the integration of previous stage skills while providing a forum for effective family therapy. The approach to problem solving is broken down into five elements (adapted from Miklowitz, 2008):

1. **Define the problem.** It is important for all family members to contribute to the description of the problem, to share perspectives, and to feel heard. This is facilitated by skills acquired in the previous stages.
2. **Identify possible solutions.** Any potential, reasonable solutions should be noted, without any discussion of feasibility. As with problem definition, all family members should contribute with ideas of how the problem might be solved.
3. **Discuss pros and cons of different solutions.** In this step, family members should discuss the benefits and costs of each idea, and select the best solutions. It is possible that more than one solution may be chosen in response to the problem.

4. **Implement selected solution(s).** Based on the selected solution(s), family members carry out efforts to achieve the desired goal.
5. **Evaluate effectiveness.** Family members reflect on the effectiveness of the chosen solutions, give each other recognition for efforts, and discuss ways to improve in the future.

As with the structured approach of the CET stage, family members may be initially resistant to this approach to problem solving. It is important to remember that they are learning new skills, which is most effectively accomplished by breaking pieces down and understanding what does and does not work. Furthermore, the structured nature of this problem-solving approach supports involvement of all family members, which in turn reinforces positive relational dynamics.

It is recommended that families practice problem-solving skills between sessions using this structured format (Miklowitz, 2008). The counselor should consider providing a worksheet to help families follow the steps, and to support their internalization of the related skills. Furthermore, the families should be encouraged to bring their worksheets to sessions, so that the counselor can review the steps and outcomes with them. If additional intervention by the counselor is needed, this is an optimal time for it. However, counselors should also remember that they are essentially trying to work themselves out of a job. That is, their goal is to teach the family skills for solving their own problems, rather than becoming a necessary part of the equation.

Challenges in Family Systems Treatment of Bipolar Disorder

As with any mental health treatment, there can be challenges and considerations unique to the individual diagnosed with BD, as well as to the family system. For example, there is considerable social stigma attached to the BD diagnosis, which may make both the diagnosed individual and the family less comfortable with participating in treatment. In addition, family systems work necessitates the coordination of multiple family members' schedules, involves a high degree of openness and vulnerability, and requires them to embrace change. Some individuals and families may feel pressured by the expectations of family treatment, which can present a great challenge to the process. While it is impossible to predict all potential hurdles the counselor may encounter, some common issues are discussed in the following sections.

Denial

Denial may be present in the diagnosed member of the family system, the family members, or both. This may be as obvious as complete rejection of the diagnosis, or a more subtle minimization of the severity and significance of the disorder. Regardless, counselors should be sensitive to the reasons behind the denial, and focus treatment on the issues at hand. For example, rather than engaging in what could essentially become an argument as to whether a diagnosis is valid, it is better for interventions to emphasize growth and improvement, and to de-emphasize labels. Although acceptance of the diagnosis is important, the label itself may be contributing to the denial present in the family system—perhaps due to the stigma of mental illness in society as a whole. It is also possible that various members of the family system have differing perceptions about the diagnosis or its severity, making it more likely that there may be some denial regarding the necessity of family treatment. It is helpful for counselors to remember that they treat *people* not *diagnoses*, and to let that philosophy guide their empathy and validation of the family members' experiences and beliefs.

Resistance

Resistance is, in many ways, the more active and mobilized form of denial. That is, it is often the presence of denial that drives resistance behaviors. When individuals with BD and their families are mired in denial, it is far more likely that they will be resistant to treatment. Resistance may be as overt as refusing to attend sessions or to comply with medication protocols, or more subtle as observed in chronic tardiness or failure to fully participate in treatment. Resistance may also be present in the form of verbalized blame or defensiveness. Sometimes, family members resent the need to participate in treatment, and may feel as though they are being "punished" for the diagnosis of one family member. As with denial, it is important to focus on the issues at hand rather than the labels, and encourage family members to be open to improving relationships and communication across the family system.

Crises

It would be unfair to assume that crises are inevitable in families with one or more members having BD, but it *is* essential to plan for them. Even with the most effective treatment, relapse episodes are likely to occur at some point in time, and families should have a plan in place to address these. Planning for crises may be unpleasant and elicit additional resistance, but, if presented properly, it can also empower and calm fears of what may lie ahead. The nature of acute BD episodes, whether mania or depression, can make it difficult for the diagnosed family member to have an objective, realistic view of what is happening for him or her. Therefore, identifying evaluative behaviors and a plan of action to ensure the safety of the individual and family are important aspects of crisis management.

Relapse of acute BD states may be accompanied by additional crises, such as suicidal ideation, substance abuse, aggression/violence, or other self-destructive behaviors. Again, a plan to address these issues, should they arise, is an essential part of minimizing impact and improving outcomes. Discussing the topics *before* they happen in a nonjudgmental, objective, solution-focused way can help family members better deal with the crises when they do occur.

ETHICAL AND LEGAL IMPLICATIONS

Clinicians working with families in which one or more members is diagnosed with BD must follow, though arguably more complex, ethical, and legal considerations. Basic ethical foundations of beneficence, nonmaleficence, justice, fidelity, and autonomy apply across all clinical fields, including family therapy. In addition, practice standards pertaining to consent, confidentiality, competence, assessment, disclosure, record keeping, and other parameters underpin foundations of practice for family treatment, just as they do in individual work. However, working with multiple members of a family system can make the challenges common to enforcing such standards increase exponentially. That is, the more family members participating in treatment, the more challenging ethical and legal issues can become.

Whether a counselor focuses on individual or family work, it is imperative to have a solid knowledge of ethical and legal requirements and guidelines to which the counselor must adhere. A thorough understanding of local, state, and federal laws can provide an effective foundation. The counselor should also be familiar with ethical decision-making models upon which to rely for more complex circumstances. Still, it is nearly impossible to plan for all potential situations that may present an ethical or legal quandary. Therefore, this section focuses on some of the *more common* ethical and legal considerations in daily practice as they may specifically pertain to family work with individuals diagnosed with BD.

Informed Consent

The most immediate concern when working with clients diagnosed with BD lies in their capacity for informed consent. For example, common issues with acute mania include impaired judgment and lack of insight (Appelbaum, 2007). It can be argued, then, that clients with BD who are experiencing an acute stage do not have the capacity to ethically and legally consent to treatment (Misra, Rosenstein, Sochermann, & Ganzini, 2008). To complicate matters, assessment of an individual's manic state may not be immediately reliable, as lower levels of mania are often difficult to detect, and only clearly evident in retrospect. Furthermore, the existence of an acute state does not necessarily equate to inability to consent. Thus, accurate appraisal of competence for consent may be challenging with individuals diagnosed with BD (Borkosky & Smith, 2015).

Another important consideration pertaining to informed consent relates to systems work in which a minor is included. While legally most states allow parents to sign consent on their minor children's behalf, the family counselor should consider whether ethically this documentation is sufficient. It can be argued that while children rarely choose to participate in treatment on their own accord (Koocher, 2008), if they *do* participate, they should understand the process and goals of treatment. Furthermore, it may be prudent to have minor children sign informed consent agreements along with parents, even if their signatures are not legally binding. In doing so, the counselor includes the minor child in the process of agreeing to treatment; as such, the minor child may feel empowered and be more engaged.

Confidentiality

As with consent, an immediate concern over confidentiality relates to an individual's mental state and capacity. Individuals in acute stages of BD may exhibit potentially harmful behaviors that require intervention of external support, such as hospitalization. All family members should understand prior to beginning treatment that safety is first and foremost—and as such, the clinician may need to take steps to ensure safety of one or all members, potentially compromising confidentiality. Such measures should be outlined clearly in the confidentiality disclosure reviewed prior to treatment.

Another common issue in working with family systems lies in the potential for "secrets" to be revealed, compromising the confidentiality of one or more members. This may occur accidentally during a session, or result from the sharing of information outside the clinical environment. For example, stigmatized behaviors such as hypersexuality, gambling, and substance use are common issues with BD; it may be very embarrassing to the client or family members to have such information be shared outside the family system. Counselors and clients should be aware of the potential damage to relationships should such information be revealed, and be clear on the boundaries and practice of treatment.

Counselors should also consider that confidentiality and consent are "parallel and corollary rights" (Borkosky & Smith, 2015, p. 20)—the issues, limitations, and requirements for these considerations are intertwined and interrelated. In other words, ethical and legal concerns that pertain to one of these aspects likely affect the other. As such, it may be in the counselor's best interest to discuss them concurrently with clients' families.

Identifying the "Client"

A core philosophy in family systems work is that the family itself is the "client." The counselor's focus is on relationships and dynamics, which in turn impact the mental health and wellness of the individuals in the system. However, because most third-party payers do not reimburse for treatment without an identified client (Kress, Hoffman, Adamson, & Eriksen, 2013), it becomes necessary to select one person in the system as the "client," with other family members participating in the treatment of that individual. This can present an issue not because this is an unethical decision for the counselor, but because this practice keeps the focus on one individual in the system as the "problem." This, in turn, can perpetuate some of the very issues the family system seeks to remedy.

Because caregivers and other family members may also be exhibiting mental health issues, counselors might choose to identify more than one client among family members. This practice may "level the playing field" somewhat, but can also be a slippery slope in practice. Diagnoses often become part of an individual's medical record; as such, family members should be fully informed of the implications of additional diagnoses among family members.

Identifying the "Family"

The "client" in family counseling is the family itself; however, how "family" is defined may vary among participants or even with the attending counselor. Some individuals may consider "family" to mean only legal or biological relatives; others consider meaningful relationships to be the defining aspect of "family." The individual with the BD diagnosis may wish to include a best friend or intimate partner in family sessions; this may not be acceptable to other participants. Some amount of discussion, or even negotiation, may be needed to maximize the benefit to the individual and to the family system as a whole. It should be agreed upon at the outset of treatment who will participate in the family sessions, whether or not they are legal relatives of the individual with the BD diagnosis.

Counselor Competence

Counselors are bound to practice within the scope of their competence (Sori & Hecker, 2015). It is widely recognized that working with families effectively requires specialized training. Knowledge of family system theory is essential, as is an understanding of the developmental adaptations often necessary for successful family therapy. A counselor working primarily with individuals, even if specializing in the treatment of BD, should not assume that interventions and techniques can be extrapolated to family systems work. Conversely, even the most skilled family therapist should seek consultation and supervision when working with the first clients in which BD is a diagnosis in the family system. Further, it would behoove the family therapist to obtain additional training in empirically supported interventions specific to BD and to have an in-depth understanding of the development, course, and prognosis for the disorder.

Treatment Adherence Versus Coercion

The most prominent issue when considering the topic of treatment adherence versus coercion relates to psychopharmacology. As was noted previously in this chapter, medication is usually an important part of effective treatment of BD. Failure to adhere to a medication regimen can have disastrous effects—not only on the diagnosed individual, but also on the family system. Clients who refuse to take prescribed medications may be deemed "resistant" to treatment; however, counselors should consider the impact of such labels.

Clients with a BD diagnosis may feel coerced into taking medications if they believe failure to do so will cause them to be discharged from treatment. Furthermore, the participation of a caregiver or other family member in medication monitoring (often a recommended part of family treatment) may cause the diagnosed individual to feel pressured to adhere to the medication regimen. It is important for clients with a BD diagnosis to understand that they have the *right* to refuse medications, but should empower themselves to choose the pharmacological support, as it enhances their treatment outcomes. It is also important to frame the family participation in a positive way, and to minimize the potential perception of coercion.

Legal Issues

It is always important, as an aspect of the confidentiality review with clients, for counselors to address the potential for legal issues and how information might be handled. Clients who are court ordered for treatment may actually be *required* to share information from treatment, which can result in violation of confidentiality for the participating family members. Furthermore, individuals with a BD diagnosis tend to have higher rates of legal problems than the general population (Frank et al., 2008), which makes conversations about information disclosure in such situations especially imperative. Addressing the topic at the outset of treatment could not only clarify any future questions about legal disclosure, but also foster important conversations between the counselor and participating family members. In fact, it may be wise to include an addendum to the standard consent form that is specific to legal issues (Borkosky & Smith, 2015).

Counselors may also be called to testify or otherwise share information should the family system experience divorce or other legal dissolution of the household. Considering that the divorce rate for individuals with BD is two to three times higher than in the general population (Granek, Danan, Bersudsky, & Osher, 2016), it is important to address this very real possibility at the outset of treatment. Some counselors try to eliminate this involvement by including an agreement in the intake paperwork stating that the clients will not call the counselor to testify in any legal proceedings; however, this rarely holds up in court (Perlman, 2012). It is quite common, in fact, for family counselors to become involved when there are issues of custody of minor children (Borkosky & Smith, 2015; Boumil, Freitas, & Freitas, 2012).

There may also be legal considerations that do not involve the disclosure of information, but rather how the events impact family members. As noted previously, individuals with a BD diagnosis tend to have higher rates of legal involvement. It is important to address the impact of these events not only on the diagnosed individual, but also the rest of the family system. Disclosures of such information—whether preexisting or occurring during treatment—should be agreed upon and limitations made clear prior to the start of treatment.

CASE CONCEPTUALIZATION

Throughout the chapter we have provided some brief examples of how BD manifests in people and impacts families. Practice in working with individuals and families often occurs within training programs, most specifically in internship experiences. The following case of Simon is presented to help you flesh out the concepts we have introduced in the chapter and to prompt you to think carefully about how you would approach working with someone like Simon and members of his immediate and extended family.

Presenting Concerns

Simon was a 46-year-old Caucasian male who was first diagnosed with BD in his early 20s. Simon had been in and out of treatment for BD since age 23. However, he had not experienced a consistent severe onset of symptoms until late into his 20s, which made him believe that his illness could someday be "cured." Still, he had four prior hospitalizations, two of which had been for depressive episodes so severe that he had been suicidal. Simon had been inconsistent with outpatient psychotherapy, and had only participated in family therapy briefly during hospitalizations. Recently Simon had experienced a relapse, resulting in his needing brief inpatient treatment for stabilization and medication adjustment. Prior to hospitalization, Simon had experienced an acute manic episode that included his withdrawing a significant amount of money from the retirement account he shared with his wife, Bridget (44). Simon had decided that he wanted to pursue his hang-gliding hobby full time, and needed the money for a custom rig and supplies. During this period, Simon was also experiencing reduced sleep, sometimes staying awake for as long as 3 to 4 days at a stretch while he worked on building the motorized component of the rig. Simon had believed he could use the rig to set a world distance hang-gliding record, and dismissed his wife's disagreement as "not supporting [his] dreams."

Concurrent Problems

Simon had a history of Bipolar I Disorder, and had experienced multiple inpatient and outpatient treatment episodes, with the most recent being inpatient treatment following an acute manic episode. Simon's absence from work due to hospitalization, combined with poor work performance and issues about getting along with peers, caused him to be fired from his job. Bridget worked full time as the manager of a small medical practice, but her income was not sufficient to fully support the family. Simon was actively seeking employment at the time he and his family came in for family counseling; the topic of finances remained a source of stress for him and his wife. Bridget shared that they fought about money often, as well as about Simon's aversion to taking his medications. Although Simon reported he was compliant with medications at the time of intake, Bridget noted that he had a history of stopping his medications because he did not like their side effects, and that he had done so shortly before the onset of the last acute manic episode.

Background History and Stressors

Despite multiple treatment episodes, Simon has been inconsistent with medication management and psychotherapy. He is currently unemployed and experiencing some financial stress. Simon and Bridget had been married for 21 years, and had two teenage children—Danielle (17) and Trevor (15)— who also attended the first family session. The children reported that they loved their father very much, but that he was difficult to live with and that they generally avoided being at home. Danielle also admitted that she was embarrassed by her father's illness and hospitalizations, and could not wait to go away to college so she could "get away from the craziness" at home. Trevor had a less critical view of his father's illness, but did admit that "it would be nice to have a peaceful household for once." Both teenagers reported that their biggest complaint at home was how often and loudly their parents fought. The family did not report any significant religious or cultural affiliations, and had no extended family in the area.

Strengths

Simon expressed a determination to improve and a willingness to adhere to participation in family therapy. The family included his wife and children, all of whom expressed a commitment to participate. At the time of intake, there appeared to be a relatively low emotional expression (EE) in this system, which indicated a more open and supportive communication.

DSM-5 Impressions and Implications

Simon was the identified client in this case. The initial diagnosis was Bipolar I Disorder, most recent episode manic, partial remission. Simon did not present acute symptomology at the time of intake, as he was consistently taking medications to help manage the disorder. At the time of his previous acute manic episode, which resulted in a hospitalization, Simon exhibited abnormally elevated mood, decreased need for sleep, flights of ideas, and excessive spending. The behaviors caused significant impairment at both work and home, and were not due to other factors or influences. Simon reported that in retrospect he could recognize manic symptoms, but at the time of the episode felt incredibly energized and motivated.

Relational Problems

Simon had a history of resisting feedback from his wife regarding her observations of his behaviors, which led to more conflict in the marital and familial dynamics. Bridget had threatened to leave Simon multiple times over the course of their marriage, usually after or during a manic episode. At the time of intake, Bridget expressed that she wanted her marriage to work and still loved Simon very much, but that she had "grown weary" after all the years of conflict and turmoil with Simon. Bridget also noted that the children were almost out of the house, which lessened her motivation to "put up with (Simon's) antics." With this in mind, Relationship Distress With Spouse was included in the initial diagnostic impression. In addition, Child Affected by Parental Relationship Distress applied in this case, based on the reported impressions of the two teenage children. Lastly, because Simon was currently unemployed and the family experiencing financial stress, Other Problems Related to Employment and Unspecified Housing or Economic Problem were added.

Assessments

A biopsychosocial assessment was completed during intake; this provided not only a summary of presenting concerns, but the context—both historical and contemporary—needed for effective treatment. In addition, to better understand the interactive systemic influences across the system, a genogram was constructed. This assessment focused on the immediate family system—Simon, Bridget, Danielle, and Trevor—and their relational dynamics. The genogram also included extended family members and their systemic influences. Because Simon's most recent episode was manic, the Altman Self-Rating Mania Scale (Altman et al., 1997) was chosen both as a starting point for the clinician and as a help to monitor progress during treatment.

Interventions

The recommended systemic approach for this family system was FFT (Miklowitz, 2008). This protocol included interventions focusing first on psychoeducation to help the family members understand the diagnosis, as well as the need to adhere to treatment (including medications). The next step was to address the stressors associated with relational dynamics across the system by improving communication patterns. Although family members exhibited a relatively low EE, they did report conflicts associated with parental arguments and a general avoidance of interaction. The CET component of FFT addressed these issues. Lastly, as the family members moved into the problem-solving phase of FFT, they developed their ability as a system to recognize and address issues, and were able to address these together. This last stage of treatment was particularly essential as it not only reinforced the progress gained from the CET stage, but also empowered the family. This, in turn, supported cohesiveness and wellness across the system.

Ethical and Legal Implications

In accordance with *ACA Code of Ethics*, informed consent was obtained from all family members, including the minor children. It was vital for all family members to understand the scope and limitations of confidentiality, and that the focus of treatment was on the system as a whole. Furthermore, while there was no reported history of domestic violence in this family system, it was prudent to review this piece carefully, as physical abuse is a common issue with BD. This sensitive topic was approached in a manner that was supportive and nonjudgmental, while also setting clear boundaries regarding family safety and the counselor's duty to report.

DISCUSSION

As you continue to reflect on the case study and the overall approach, contemplate these questions:

- A genogram is a vital assessment tool for family work. How can you integrate the Vulnerability–Stress Model into this assessment, and why is it such an essential component for this family?

- Z codes identify other conditions that may be the focus of clinical attention. Based on the information in the section "Case Conceptualization", what additional possible Z codes may apply to this case? What more do you need to know to determine the accuracy of these, and how can you integrate these into treatment?

- How do the psychosocial stressors in Simon's life impact his level of functioning at this time?

- An important aspect of psychoeducation would be to ensure that Simon and his family accept and commit to a consistent medication regimen. How can you approach this with the family system without coercion?

- How does the low EE of this family system impact the CET and problem-solving stages of treatment? How might these, in turn, support Simon's recovery and the overall wellness of the family system?

SUMMARY

BD affects individuals and families in profound and important ways. It is important to understand that primary treatments for bipolar symptoms also include a family systems perspective in putting into context how manic and depressive symptoms occur, including how the therapeutic relationship impacts affected individuals and families. Family-focused treatment (FFT) provides an effective, evidence-based model of supporting families. It is also vital to maintain a strong ethical stance when incorporating treatment options to ensure that ethical principles (e.g., beneficence, fidelity, autonomy, etc.) are preserved. The meaningful inculcation of these concepts and practices is an individualized process where counselors are faced with practicing effectively and being mindful and intentional about how they personalize effective interventions. We encourage counselors to be thoughtful, intentional, and intelligent in their consumption and integration of the treatment research. Counselors have as much potential to learn about themselves, their values, biases, and how they contextualize their own personal life experiences from working with clients and families as they have to learn about the clients and families they seek to help. This awareness is essential in gaining a true and empathic understanding of how people deal with BD as a challenging, life-disrupting condition. Clients and their families can easily become resilient heroes instead of ineffective victims through the challenging and often uncertain process of treatment.

REFERENCES

Altman, E. G., Hedeker D., Peterson, J. L., & Davis, J. M. (1997). The Altman Self-Rating Mania Scale. *Biological Psychiatry, 42*, 948–955.

American Counseling Association. (2014). *ACA code of ethics.* Alexandria, VA: Author.

American Psychiatric Association. (2013). *Diagnostic and statistical manual of mental disorders* (5th ed.). Arlington, VA: American Psychiatric Publishing.

Appelbaum, P. S. (2007). Assessment of patients' competence to consent to treatment. *The New England Journal of Medicine, 357*, 1834–1840. doi:10.1056/NEJMcp074045

Borkosky, B., & Smith, D. M. (2015). The risks and benefits of disclosing psychotherapy records to the legal system: What psychologists and patients need to know for informed consent. *International Journal of Law and Psychiatry, 42–43*, 19–30.

Boumil, M. M., Freitas, D. F., & Freitas, C. F. (2012). Waiver of the psychotherapist-patient privilege: Implications for child custody litigation. *Health Matrix, 22*(1), 1–31.

Carr, A. (2009). Bipolar disorder in young people: Description, assessment and evidence-based treatment. *Developmental Neurorehabilitation, 12*(6), 427–441.

Carr, A. (2014). The evidence base for family therapy and systemic interventions for child-focused problems. *Journal of Family Therapy, 36*, 107–157.

Detroit Public Television. (2016). Ride the tiger: A guide through the bipolar brain. Aired April 13, 2016. Retrieved from http://www.pbs.org/ride-the-tiger/resources/life-with-bipolar-disorder/

Frank, E., Soreca, I., Swartz, H. A., Fagiolini, A. M., Mallinger, A. G., Thase, M. E., . . . Kupfer, D. J. (2008). The role of interpersonal and social rhythm therapy in improving occupational functioning in patients with bipolar I disorder. *American Journal of Psychiatry, 165*, 1559–1565.

Fredman, S. J., Baucom, D. H., Boeding, S. E., & Miklowitz, D. J. (2015). Relatives' emotional involvement moderates the effects of family therapy for bipolar disorder. *Journal of Consulting and Clinical Psychology, 83*(1), 81–91.

Fredman, S. J., Baucom, D. H., Miklowitz, D. J., & Stanton, S. E. (2008). Observed emotional involvement and overinvolvement in families of patients with bipolar disorder. *Journal of Family Psychology, 22*(1), 71–79.

Fristad, M. A., & MacPherson, H. A. (2014). Evidence-based psychosocial treatments for child and adolescent bipolar spectrum disorders. *Journal of Clinical Child and Adolescent Psychology, 43*(3), 339–355.

Geddes, J. R., & Miklowitz, D. J. (2013). Treatment of bipolar disorder. *Lancet, 381*(9878), 1672–1682.

Goodwin, F. K., & Jamison, K. R. (1990). *Manic Depressive Illness.* New York, NY: Oxford University Press.

Goosens, P. J. J., Van Wijngaarden, B., Knoppert-Van Der Klein, E. A. M., & Van Achterberg, T. (2008). Family caregiving in bipolar disorder: Caregiving consequences, caregiver coping styles, and caregiver distress. *International Journal of Social Psychiatry, 54*(4), 303–316.

Granek, L., Danan, D., Bersudsky, Y., & Osher, Y. (2016). Living with bipolar disorder: The impact of patients, spouses, and their marital relationship. *Bipolar Disorders, 18*(2), 192–199.

Havens, L. L., & Ghaemi, N. (2005). Existential despair and bipolar disorder: The therapeutic alliance as a mood stabilizer. *American Journal of Psychotherapy, 59*(2), 137–147.

Hersoug, A. G., Høglend, P., Monsen, J. T., & Havik, O. V. (2001). Quality of working alliance in psychotherapy: Therapist variables and patient/therapist similarity as predictors. *Journal of Psychotherapy Practice and Research, 10*(4), 205–216.

Horvath, A. O. (2001). The alliance. *Psychotherapy, 38*(4), 365–372.

Hyde, J. A. (2001). Bipolar illness and the family. *Psychiatric Quarterly, 72*(2), 109–118.

Jacob, K. S., Kallivayalil, R. A., Mallik, A. K., Gupta, N., Trivedi, J. K., Gangadhar, B. N., . . . Sathyanarayana Rao, T. S. (2013). Diagnostic and statistical manual-5: Position paper of the Indian Psychiatric Society. *Indian Journal of Psychiatry, 55*(1), 12–30.

Jamison, K. R. (1996). *An unquiet mind.* New York, NY: Vintage Books.

Jamison, K. R. (2011). *Assessment and psychological treatment of bipolar disorder.* Mill Valley, CA: Psychotherapy .net.

Justo, L., Soares, B. G. D. O., & Calil H. (2007). Family interventions for bipolar disorder. *Cochrane Database of Systematic Reviews, 4,* CD005167. doi: 10.1002/14651858.CD005167.pub2

Kessler, R. C., & Ustun, T. B. (2004). The World Mental Health (WMH) survey initiative version of the World Health Organization (WHO) Composite International Diagnostic Interview (CIDI). *International Journal of Methods in Psychiatric Research, 13*(2), 93–121.

Koocher, G. P. (2008). Ethical challenges in mental health services to children and families. *Journal of Clinical Psychology: In session, 64*(5), 601–612.

Kress, V. E., Hoffman, R. M., Adamson, N., & Eriksen. K. (2013). Informed consent, confidentiality, and diagnosing: Ethical guidelines for counselor practice. *Journal of Mental Health Counseling, 35*(1), 15–28.

Kress, V. E., & Paylo, M. J. (2015). *Treating those with mental disorders: A comprehensive approach to case conceptualization, and treatment.* New York, NY: Pearson.

Lambert, M. J., & Barley, D. E. (2001). Research summary on the therapeutic relationship and psychotherapy outcome. *Psychotherapy, 38*(4), 357–361.

Leboyer, M., & Kupfer, D. J. (2010). Bipolar disorder: New perspectives in health care and prevention. *Journal of Clinical Psychiatry, 71*(12), 1689–1695. doi:10.4088/JCP.10m06347yel

Martire, L. M., Hinrichsen, G. A., Morse, J. Q., Reynolds, C. F., III, Gildengers, A. G., Mulsant, B. H., . . . Kupfer, D. J. (2009). The Mood Disorder Burden Index: A scale for assessing the burden of caregivers to adults with unipolar or bipolar disorder. *Psychiatry Research, 168,* 67–77.

Meyers, L. (2014, August). Connecting with clients. *Counseling Today.* Retrieved from http://ct.counseling .org/2014/08/connecting-with-clients/

Michalaka, E. E., Murray, G., & CREST.BD. (2010). Development of the QoL.BD: A disorder-specific scale to assess quality of life in bipolar disorder. *Bipolar Disorder, 12,* 727–740.

Miklowitz, D. J. (2007). The role of the family in the course and treatment of bipolar disorder. *Current Directions in Psychological Science, 16*(4), 192–196.

Miklowitz, D. J. (2008). *Bipolar disorder: A family-focused treatment approach.* New York, NY: Guilford.

Miklowitz, D. J. (2012). Family-focused treatment for children and adolescents with bipolar disorder. *Israeli Journal of Psychiatry and Related Sciences, 49*(2), 95–103.

Miklowitz, D. J., Axelson, D. A., Birmaher, B., George, E. L., Taylor, D. O., Schneck, C. D., . . . Brent D. A. (2008). Family-focused treatment for adolescents with bipolar disorder. *Archives of General Psychiatry, 65*(9), 1053–1061. doi:10.1001/archpsyc.65.9.1053

Miklowitz, D. J., Schneck, C. D., George, E. L., Taylor, D. O., Sugar, C. A., Birmaher, B., . . . Axelson, D. A. (2014). Pharmacotherapy and family-focused treatment for adolescents with bipolar I and II disorders: A 2-year randomized trial. *The American Journal of Psychiatry, 171*(6), 658–667.

Miklowitz, D. J., & Scott, J. (2009). Psychosocial treatments for bipolar disorder: Cost-effectiveness, mediating mechanisms, and future directions. *Bipolar Disorders, 11*(s2), 110–122.

Misra, S., Rosenstein, D., Sochermann, R., & Ganzini, L. (2008). Bipolar mania and capacity to consent: Recommendations for investigators and IRBs. *Ethics and Human Research, 32*(1), 7–15.

National Institute of Mental Health. (2016a, March 13). Bipolar disorder. Retrieved from http://www .nimh.nih.gov/health/topics/bipolar-disorder/index.shtml#part_145403

National Institute of Mental Health. (2016b, April 11). Rate of bipolar symptoms among teens approaches that of adults. Retrieved from http://www.nimh.nih.gov/news/science-news/2012/rate-of-bipolar-symptoms-among-teens-approaches-that-of-adults.shtml

Norcross, J. C., & Hill, C. E. (2004). Empirically supported therapy relationships. *The Clinical Psychologist*, *57*(3), 19–24.

Ozerdem, A., Oguz, M., Miklowitz, D., & Cimilli, C. (2009). Family-focused treatments for patients with bipolar disorder in Turkey: A case series. *Family Process*, *48*(3), 417–428.

Perlick, D. A., Berk, L., Kaczynski, R., Gonzales, J., Link, B., Dixon, L., . . . Miklowitz, D. J. (2016). Caregiver burden as a predictor of depression among family and friends who provide care for persons with bipolar disorder. *Bipolar Disorders*, *18*(2), 183–191.

Perlick, D. A., Miklowitz, D. J., Lopez, N., Chou, J., Kalvin, C., Adzhiashvili, V., & Aronsons, A. (2010). Family-focused treatment for caregivers of patients with bipolar disorder. *Bipolar Disorders*, *12*, 627–637.

Perlman, G. L. (2012). A judicial perspective on psychotherapist-client privilege: Ten practical tips for clinicians. *Journal of Child Custody*, *9*(1–2), 126–152.

Reinares, M., Bonnin, C. M., Hidalgo-Mazzei, D., Sanchez-Moreno, J., Colom, F., & Vieta, E. (2016). The role of family interventions in bipolar disorder: A systematic review. *Clinical Psychology Review*, *43*, 47–57.

Rusner, M., Carlsson, G., Brunt, D., & Nystrom, M. (2009). Extra dimensions in all aspects of life: The meaning of life with bipolar disorder. *International Journal of Qualitative Studies on Health and Well-being*, *4*, 159–169.

Rusner, M., Carlsson, G., Brunt, D. A., & Nystrom, M. (2012). The paradox of being both needed and rejected: The existential meaning of being closely related to a person with bipolar disorder. *Issues in Mental Health Nursing*, *33*, 200–208. doi: 10.3109/01612840.2011.653037

Sori, C. F., & Hecker, L. L. (2015). Ethical and legal considerations when counselling children and families. *Australian and New Zealand Journal of Family Therapy*, *36*(4), 450–464.

Steele, A., Maruyama, N., & Galynker, I. (2010). Psychiatric symptoms in caregivers of patients with bipolar disorder: A review. *Journal of Affective Disorders*, *121*, 10–21.

Watson, W. J., Poon, V. H. K, & Walters, I. A. (2005). Genograms: Seeing your patient through another window. *Patient Care Canada*, *16*, 67–75.

West, A. E., & Weinstein, S. M. (2012). A family-based psychosocial treatment model. *Israeli Journal of Psychiatry and Related Sciences*, *49*(2), 86–94.

West, A. E., Weinstein, S. M., Peters, A. T., Katz, A. C., Henry, D. B., Cruz, R. A., & Pavuluri, M. N. (2014). Child- and family-focused cognitive behavioral therapy for pediatric bipolar disorder: A randomized clinical trial. *Journal of the Academy of Child and Adolescent Psychiatry*, *53*(11), 1168–1178.

FAMILY PROCESS IN DEPRESSIVE DISORDERS

Rosanne Nunnery and Jan Lemon

*P*art of exploring families and depression includes evaluating relational and cultural features that are unique. Prior to a diagnosis of depression in a family, professionals need to utilize proper assessments to ensure the diagnosis fits the criteria for a depressive disorder. Once a thorough diagnosis has been made, interventions should be considered in light of the needs of the family. Of course, no diagnosis or treatment should be considered without an eye on the ethical and legal implications that are inherent in the profession of marriage and family therapy, mental health counseling, and other ethical codes that apply to those working with families diagnosed with depression.

When one considers diagnosis, it is less of a challenge to focus on an individual versus the family diagnostic evaluation. How can a family be depressed? If there is depression in a family system, how can one pinpoint exactly how to focus on the assessment process? There are debates about how to approach diagnosis of the family since the *Diagnostic and Statistical Manual of Mental Disorders* (5th ed.; *DSM-5*; American Psychiatric Association [APA], 2013a) is not specifically designed to do a collective diagnosis. One element of understanding depressive disorders in relation to families is to have a brief exploration of the etiological aspects shaping the development of depression along with historical integration of depression in the diagnostic manuals (APA, 1968, 2013a; Hyman, 2010). A depressive disorder is a severe illness that has a great impact on the lives of those affected and specifically has bearing on their family systems. As a result, if one is to focus on diagnosis of depression from an individual perspective, there is no doubt that the family system is greatly impacted by one member's diagnosis of depression. To get a broader understanding of the *DSM-5* diagnostic process and how it relates to family systems, there will be a thorough explanation of depressive disorders and how these diagnoses impact family systems. This will include Disruptive Mood Dysregulation Disorder (DMDD), Major Depressive Disorder (MDD), Persistent Depressive Disorder (dysthymia), Premenstrual Dysphoric Disorder (PDD), Substance/Medication-Induced Depressive Disorder (SIDD), Depressive Disorder Due to Another Medical Condition, Other Specified Depressive

Disorder, Unspecified Depressive Disorder, and consideration of the specifiers for depressive disorders (APA, 2013a).

DSM-5 AND FAMILY SYSTEMS

Depression and the *DSM-5*

With the vast list of depressive disorders outlined in the *DSM-5* (APA, 2013a), breaking down each of the diagnoses into smaller segments helps formulate an understanding of the characteristics. Some of these symptoms will be clearly evident whereas others will require a thorough intake or biopsychosocial evaluation. With use of assessments, one can effectively evaluate symptoms, explore the impact of these symptoms on the individual and family life, and learn about the impact on daily functioning. While evaluating and assessing, a systemic clinician should maintain close attention to age, developmental factors, and applicable criteria.

Disruptive Mood Dysregulation Disorder

Stepping back and viewing Disruptive Mood Dysregulation Disorder (DMDD), the reader needs to take on the lens of a young person likely between the ages of 6 and 17. The etiology of this disorder begins in infancy but progresses into early childhood with symptoms of anger outbursts, tantrums, irritability, and the inability to regulate emotions (Brown University, 2013; Margulies, Weintraub, Basile, Grover, & Carlson, 2012). To be diagnosed, the child must be at least 6 years of age and the onset of the symptoms should be evident prior to age 10 and persist for at least 12 months (APA, 2013a; Brown University, 2013).

Developmental literature articulates that children and adolescents within this age range will experience a vast array of types of development, emotions, social and peer interaction, caregiver engagement, and development of the ability to cope with stressful situations (Insel, 2007; Newman & Newman, 2015a). As part of this developmental process for those with DMDD, these individuals are attempting to navigate their world and often express their needs through behavior. Sometimes this behavior is not totally understood by the outside world, especially the caregiver, but it provides some relief to the emotions individuals experience (Newman & Newman, 2015a; Rasmussen, 2010). All behaviors have an intention to achieve a desired goal and thus reducing the incentive to abandon the behavior. (Newman & Newman, 2015a; Pryor, 1999; Rasmussen & Aleksandrof, 2014). This diagnosis is not merely suggesting a normal emotional and behavioral response to a stressor. In evaluating DMDD, a caregiver or systemic clinician will report severe and ongoing temper outbursts that are exhibited by rages that come out of nowhere three to four times per week. When the child is not having these outbursts, there is an intense and persistent level of irritability toward others, such as friends, parents, and/or teachers without just cause. There is a consistent nonepisodic irritable mood that is underlining within the child and is a core element of the diagnosis. There are genetic and environmental links to this disorder with evidence suggesting deficits with information processing that can impact decision making, cognitive processing, and difficulties with regulating emotions causing severe disruption with the child and the family (Dickstein et al., 2010; Guyer et al., 2007; Rich et al. 2008).

As a result of these links, the child may scream or be erratic with behavior that is outwardly expressed to others. This causes the caregiver to intervene with a desire to get the child to calm down. A child may become angry in his school and immediately begin to scream out in anger for the teacher to change the grade with words such as "Change my grade," "I hate you," "I'll show you if you don't change my grade." The teacher may relent to get the child to calm down. If the adult does not relent, the child's irritability will escalate leading to volatility resulting in possible destruction of property. What separates this from merely a behavioral disorder is that with DMDD a child has a persistent and severe irritable mood with the overlap of destructive/volatile outbursts that can happen several times a week without an intention of control or manipulation (APA, 2013a). This disorder is not prevalent in all children and is more commonly diagnosed with boys and is included in the new *DSM-5* (APA, 2013) due to the high level of overdiagnosed bipolar disorder in children (Roy et al., 2013).

Major Depressive Disorder

Major Depressive Disorder (MDD) extends far beyond the blues and is not a normal reaction to what is perceived as loss or an event that is stressful. Major depression is considered a clinical depression that is far more severe and chronic and greatly impacts an individual's life (APA, 2013a). When considering this diagnosis, it is important to know the difference between clinical and situational depressions. Situational depression is short term and linked back to a life change or adjustment and its symptoms subside overtime. Clinical depression can occur for a wide array of reasons such as an adjustment or change, but there is the heightened consideration of genetics and suicidal ideation and depression that persists (APA, 2013a; Blazek, Kazmierczak, & Besta, 2015).

There are three large factors when considering the diagnosis of major depression. One must consider genetics, which includes the physiological responses, impact on daily functioning, cognitive deficits, and the inability to merely shake off the feelings of depression (APA, 2013a; Nolen-Hoeksema, 2014b). The *DSM-5* indicates that individuals with MDD will experience depressive mood, loss of interest in activities, sadness, emptiness, and overall hopelessness. There is a requirement that at least five of the nine MDD criteria areas be considered with an occurrence of experiencing the symptoms every day for at least 2 weeks. For Criterion A to be met, this disorder must have an indication of depressed mood and loss of interest in pleasurable activities (APA, 2013a). As noted, there are various symptoms with which a client might present for a diagnosis of MDD to be met. There might be depressed mood, which includes intense feelings of sadness and emptiness and notably diminished pleasure in activities for most of nearly every day. For MDD to be considered, a clinician must observe his or her client's weight to see if there is significant weight loss or gain and check for insomnia or hypersomnia, psychomotor agitation before proceeding to look at other symptoms. In addition, other symptoms are feelings of extreme fatigue, loss of energy, feeling worthless, experiencing guilt almost every day, and difficulty concentrating and making decisions. For some clients, there are recurrent thoughts of death or dying. It is critical to note whether the symptom causes major distress and impairment in various aspects of life and is not linked to a substance abuse or an other medical condition (APA, 2013a). When one's life is a plethora of MDD symptoms, there is a direct impact on peer, familial, and other relationships due to the abrupt disengagement, communicating, and engaging in previous activities that were typical of the individual. It is important to note that there are specifiers to help narrow down whether it is a single episode, recurrent, in remission, or present with psychotic features, but the first goal is to narrow down the symptom criteria.

Major Depression Bereavement Exclusion

Some systemic clinicians continue to feel there is not a place in the new *DSM-5* (APA, 2013a) for a systemic approach much less a focus on relational considerations (Denton & Bell, 2013). However, other systemic clinicians could argue that the bereavement exclusion allows for more focus on family and relationship factors in the diagnosis process. Clinicians are required to follow the *DSM-5* (APA, 2013a) classification process that includes not only the primary codes for depressive disorders but also consideration of

Z codes outlined in the *DSM-5* (APA, 2013a). There was much debate regarding the consideration of major depression bereavement exclusion due to caution about pathologizing a central process of one's human experience, the death of a loved one (Wakefield, 2013). For the current *DSM-5* (APA, 2013a), the bereavement exclusion was eliminated and some systemic clinicians argue that it was "replaced by a vague note suggesting that clinical judgment is needed in distinguishing normal grief and reactions to other stressors from depressive disorder" (Wakefield, 2013, p. 149). However, the *DSM-5* (APA, 2013a) intention with the removal of the bereavement exclusion was to fully help characterize bereavement as a psychological stressor that could possibly ignite a major depressive episode. However, when the exclusion was used (*Diagnostic and Statistical Manual of Mental Disorders,* 4th ed.; *DSM-IV*; APA, 1994), there was a specific intent to exclude individuals who exhibited depressive symptoms that might have lasted a couple of months after the death of a loved one so they would not be inadvertently diagnosed with major depression. The new *DSM-5* (APA, 2013a) has an uncomplicated bereavement option when the focus of clinical attention is the normal grief response associated with the death of a loved one. An individual or family may seek out treatment due to symptoms associated with grief that may appear as major depression but are a response to a loss. It is important to recognize this grief response as normal and that reactions vary depending on cultural groups (APA, 2013a). It is critical to have a careful eye on the difference between major depression and symptoms that are a response to grief. Grief can include a varied range of emotions from emptiness, sadness, and anger to moments of positive emotional response and even humor. There will be times when there is a preoccupation with thoughts surrounding the deceased, but with major depression there is a pervasive level of unhappiness, being self-critical, and loathing that could manifest into suicidal thoughts (APA, 2013a). Individuals experiencing grief that develops into a major depressive episode (five of nine symptoms for at least 2 weeks), due to the death of a loved one, can receive needed treatment 6 weeks earlier as compared to previous diagnostic criteria (APA, 2013a).

Persistent Depressive Disorder (Dysthymia)

Persistent Depressive Disorder (Dysthymia) in the *DSM-5* (APA, 2013a) includes a combination of what was formerly considered chronic MDD and dysthymic disorder (*DSM-IV*; APA, 1994). Looking at the criteria, individuals are required to exhibit a persistent depressed mood that lasts all day, almost every day for at least 2 years in adults and 1 year in children. This is a primary criterion with there being at least two other symptoms that persist during this period of time for a minimum of at least 2 months within the 2 years (adults) and 1 year (children). This criterion includes a change in eating patterns with either over- or undereating, insomnia or hypersomnia, low self-esteem, difficulty making decisions, and feelings of hopelessness. As with all symptoms, one needs to rule out the presence of a medical condition or substance addiction (APA, 2013a). Individuals who are persistently depressed have a tendency to feel overwhelmed by the demands of life, although there may be a desire to achieve greater accomplishments. The individuals might err on the side of caution with pursuing these goals because of an overarching dark cloud of concern that they lack the skills necessary and prefer not to be highlighted as not fully achieving these goals leading to a disconnect from others (Rasmussen & Aleksandrof, 2014). Specifiers should be evaluated based on the clients most intense presenting symptoms and can provide specific detail regarding how to proceed with treatment.

Premenstrual Dysphoric Disorder

Premenstrual Dysphoric Disorder (PDD) was added to the new *DSM-5* as a result of investigating severe and persistent manifestation of premenstrual syndrome that a majority of women experience as part of their menstrual cycle (Matsumoto, Asakura, & Hayashi, 2013). Matsumoto et al. (2013) articulate that there are no uniform biological factors, physical characteristics, or specific blood tests that fully articulate premenstrual syndrome, but diagnostic guidelines were established to help articulate the difference between the two with PDD having more severe and persistent symptoms with mental impairment impacting a woman's quality of life. Braverman (2007) and Clayton (2008) indicate that the prevalence rate among women who might potentially be diagnosed with PDD ranges from 2% to 9%. Familial risk for PDD has been examined along with genetic factors with results indicating that PDD symptoms are strongly linked with genetics versus familial environment with a strong link to specific hormones and the body's reaction to them in women with this diagnosis (Epperson et al., 2012). The *DSM-5* (APA, 2013a) highlights that one must consider environmental risk factors associated with stress in one's life, trauma exposure, and genetic markers.

There are many specific features of PDD that need to be fully assessed by the client and clinician to verify the diagnosis (Craner, Sigmon, Martinson, & McGillicuddy, 2014). The *DSM-5* (APA, 2013a) reiterates the use of a credible scale with specific focus on daily ratings of symptoms for at least two symptomatic cycles. Once assessed and tracked for approximately 1 year, the essential features of PDD include three broad areas of symptoms: cognitive, affective, and physical. In most of the menstrual cycles, there are five primary symptoms that must be present in the final week before the onset of menses and it is important to note that the symptoms begin to improve a few days after the onset of menses and then become more minimal or almost absent in the week to postmenses in Criterion A of the diagnosis (APA, 2013a; Hartlage, Brandenburg, & Kravitz, 2004). During the specifically assessed time frame, the individual must exhibit at least one symptom demonstrating unstable mood. The symptoms may include marked lability that can be presented as mood swings, sadness, or tearfulness. There will be marked problems with feeling rejected, feeling irritable and angry, and having depressed mood with possible feelings of hopelessness and irrational thoughts. There can be symptoms of anxiety that can be exhibited by tension and agitation. Another consideration of PDD, where at least one criterion must be met, is the specific behavioral and somatic symptoms with decreased interest in activities, difficulty concentrating, feeling lethargic and having low energy, sleeping problems, feeling overwhelmed, and experiencing physical symptoms of muscle aches, feeling bloated, and having breast tenderness and swelling. For evaluating the categories for this appropriate diagnosis, at least five symptoms need to be present to meet the criteria for PDD (APA, 2013a).

Substance/Medication-Induced Depressive Disorder

Substance use commonly co-occurs with depressive disorders. As a result, a challenge arises when attempting to narrow down the specific Substance/Medication-Induced Depressive Disorder (SIDD; Magidson, Wang, Lejuez, Iza, & Blanco, 2013). The use of assessment is critical when attempting to narrow down the criteria for SIDD. Magidson et al. (2013) as explored by Hasin, Samet, and Nunes (2006) indicated that "depressive symptoms that only occur in the context of substance use and exceed the expected pharmacological effects of the particular substance are typically diagnosed as SIDD" (p. 539). Knowing this, to determine this diagnosis, systemic clinicians should look closely at persistent disturbance in mood and loss of interest in activities as indicated in Criterion A. Systemic clinicians should evaluate all symptoms with evidence from a full psychosocial history, physical examination, and laboratory test as needed to meet Criterion B. The symptoms must be evident either during or right after the medication or alcohol is consumed and have a clear link to the symptoms in Criterion A. It is important that other depressive disorders are ruled out and that symptoms persist in relation to Criterion A for at least 1 month postcessation of the ingestion of the medication or alcohol (APA, 2013a).

Depressive Disorder Due to Another Medical Condition

Evaluating whether an individual has Depressive Disorder Due to Another Medical Condition a systemic clinician must specifically review Criteria A and B in the *DSM-5* (APA, 2013a). An individual with depression linked to a medical condition will initially appear as having a depressed mood with a clear lack of interest in most, if not all, activities of previous interest (Criterion A). Along with these features, the symptoms will have a direct relationship to the physiological effects of another medical condition (Criterion B; APA, 2013a). To narrow down the specific medical condition, a systemic clinician will need to conduct a further biopsychosocial evaluation, obtain medical records, or have a physiological examination completed to support the diagnosis (APA, 2013a; Nolen-Hoeksema, 2014b). This will help to solidify that the depression and mood disturbance is directly linked to the medical condition. Criteria C, D, and E (APA, 2013a) require that other mental disorders are ruled out, that there exists no indication of delirium, and that the symptoms cause distress in various aspects of an individual's life. Research has shown that there is a direct link between some medical conditions and depression. In fact, depression can exacerbate medical symptoms along with depression being linked to specific medical conditions (Bhattacharya, Chan, & Sambamoorthi, 2014; Katon, 2011; Patten et al., 2014).

Other Specified Depressive Disorder/Unspecified Depressive Disorder

When evaluating for Other Specified Depressive Disorder, consider a likelihood of a short duration of symptoms. There remains marked impairment in functioning that is clinically distressing to an individual, but there are not enough criteria to categorize one having a specified depressive disorder such as MDD. The specifiers of recurrent brief depression, short-duration episode (4–13 days), or depressive episode with insufficient symptoms provide detailed guidance to narrow down what a client is experiencing (APA, 2013a). In an Unspecified Depressive Disorder, there is indication of symptoms that cause clinically significant distress and impairment in social, occupational, or other areas of life but do not meet full criteria for the other depression diagnosis, and there is not a specific reason for the symptoms as noted in Other Specified Depressive Disorder (APA, 2013a).

Specifiers

There are multiple specifiers for depressive disorders with subcategories to help truly highlight what may be occurring in the presence of a specific depression diagnosis. These specifiers can be further evaluated in the *DSM-5* (APA, 2013a) and are clearly identified to review depending on the depressive diagnosis. These specifiers help narrow down and define the types of features that are present with an individual with a specific diagnosis. From these features, one can more closely evaluate the level of severity. The specifiers are linked to the depressive disorder chosen. These include specificity for anxiety, distress, mixed variation of depressive features, traits of melancholy, atypical pattern of mood and behavior, consideration of psychotic features, and assessing mood in relation to a consistent seasonal pattern (APA, 2013a). Systemic clinicians select a specifier and must adhere to the standards outlined to the chosen depressive diagnosis. There are three severity levels with a specific number of symptoms, severity of those symptoms, and overall marked functional impairment: mild, moderate, and severe (APA, 2013a).

Depressive Symptoms and Family Systems Theory

The *DSM-5* (APA, 2013a) provides the foundation by which to evaluate symptoms that are present at the onset of treatment. Diagnoses are important to help determine treatment plans and specific interventions to assist individuals diagnosed with a disorder. When approaching diagnoses from a systemic perspective, there are varied theoretical perspectives and options to treat the specified needs of each individual, couple, or family. With the array of evidence-based treatments, clinicians can guide clients with management of symptoms, integration of appropriate and relevant tools to effectively cope, and consideration of the larger relational impact of those diagnosed with a specified depressive disorder.

Bowen's Theory

"We are born into families. They are the foundation of our first experiences of the world, our first relationships, and our first sense of belonging to a group" (McGoldrick, Preto, & Carter, 2016, p. 1). For most individuals, life unfolds within the context of a family structure. This structure includes culture, which reinforces values, beliefs, and ideals connected to kinship ties, and development of an identity embedded within a larger social context (McGoldrick et al., 2016). There are varied family systems theories that provide a framework to understand the interaction between members in a family unit. Bowen's theory explored how individuals within the context of a family seek to find and maintain an identity while creating a sense of togetherness for the benefit of the unit (Bowen, 1966, 1976). Part of this theory includes defining individuality, togetherness, attachment, and triangulation (Bowen, 1976; Kerr & Bowen, 1988). When there is unresolved emotional attachment, where an individual has a hard time differentiating self from the family by making individualized decisions, then one is impacted both physically and psychologically (MacKay, 2012). Triangulation can occur naturally in a family system as children and adults are placed in the role as third-party decision makers. When one is unable to make decisions, there is a likelihood that some form of depression or anxiety has set in, rendering one to have problems with decisions leading to asking a third family member to provide insight versus a couple or two family members communicating about the problem (MacKay, 2012). There are additional factors to consider including the emotional process of the family, generational processes that have unfolded and been reinforced over time, and the relation of these processes to the larger society (Bowen, 1966, 1976). All of these patterns have been established early on and are perpetuated in family systems, so they are not likely recognized as problematic (Kerr & Bowen, 1988).

When considering the application of Bowen's theory to depression, normal family development can unfold when there is successful navigation of family expectations, emotional regulation, handling of distress, and working through the need for approval by others in the system (Kerr & Bowen, 1988; Nichols & Schwartz, 2005). Trangkasombat (2008), when comparing depression and schizophrenia, highlights depression characteristics of depressed mood, affect, and irritability as receiving more negative reactions by family members as an indication that there were far more negative reactions to depressed clients than those with schizophrenia. As a result, this could lead to problems with communication, affective involvement, and responses with others (Trangkasombat, 2008). Bowen Family Systems Theory can be utilized to help conceptualize the emotional process not only in family but across all systems as well (Chambers, MacDonald, & Mikes-Liu, 2013) when approaching a diagnosis such as the depressive disorders. Structural family therapy was developed by Salvador Minuchin, who drew from Bowen Family Systems Theory. Minuchin's approach encourages therapists to enter into a family structure and work to clearly understand the rules that hold it together. A systemic clinician cannot delve into the lives of the family system and shake up the rules without knowing what type of glue holds it together (Minuchin & Lappin, 2011). If a systemic clinician wants to treat a depressed family, he or she must evaluate the family boundaries, establish coalitions between members, and evaluate and reorganize hierarchies so that the rules can change and new adaptive behaviors can begin to form (Minuchin & Lappin, 2011).

RELATIONAL AND CULTURAL FEATURES

According to Hollon and Sexton (2012), "Depression is a major public health problem that clearly runs in families" (p. 199). Depression in the family system is an interaction of the family members' inner experiences and the various outer systems affecting the individuals within the family (Craner et al., 2014). The *DSM-5* (APA, 2013a) has created a symptom, evidence-based system that focuses on the individual. Thus, tension is created by trying to mix oil and water with family therapists focusing on the patterns of thought, emotion, and interaction within the family system. The *DSM-5* has created a more dimensional approach to diagnosis with the family system that is linked to the severity measures, which will help not only with the diagnostic thresholds, but also in determining the level of psychopathology (Kupfer, Kuhl, & Regier, 2013). This reemphasis on clinical judgment in the *DSM-5* is likely to be welcomed by many clinicians, who will have more personal input in defining the content and margins of the diagnostic categories.

Relational Factors

In the area of depression, the systems clinician will have to determine if the depressive response to a significant loss is normal or pathological when the severity, duration, and distress/impairment criteria are completely fulfilled but the family and cultural background provides evidence of a normal response to the loss (Maj, 2013). As a result of this problem of applying clinical judgment, the relationship context of human suffering has become progressively important and applicable to good diagnosis, treatment, and prevention (Beach et al., 2006b). The authors further stated, "In humans, the risk factors associated with depression include a family history of depression, certain genetic polymorphisms, prior personal episodes of depression, a history of anxiety disorders, female gender, and a stressful or an adverse environment" (Beach et al., 2006b, p. 43). When examining relational formulations in diagnosis, especially with depression, it is important to take into account the client's primary social group and the relevance this interaction has upon clinical care. The authors stated, "Areas to be highlighted might include level of family conflict about the disorder, family view of the source and likely course of the illness, family view of the patient and the patient's potential for improvement, family view of treatment and treating agencies, family strengths and sources of support, and family sense of caregiver burden" (Beach et al., 2006a, p. 14). Many times a stressful social or relational factor triggers the depressive episode. Some examples of the events are death of a loved one, divorce, loss of a job, violence in the family, abusive relationships, social failures, moving to another city, serious trauma, and social isolation (Nemade, Reiss, & Dombeck, 2007).

Larner, Strong, and Busch (2013) stated that regardless of the relationship issues involved with family therapy, systems clinicians will have to engage and embrace the *DSM-5*. The authors stated that a possible strategy may be to accept a tenet of hospitality toward an inhospitable language of diagnosis and to actively embrace the manual while challenging, enriching, or even "dancing" with *DSM-5* in a way that is affirming of systemic therapy. Simblett (2013) also uses this dance metaphor as he takes up a fluid positioning in using a narrative style in therapy while he dances with the *DSM-5* as his partner.

Another relational factor in the diagnosis and treatment of depression from a systemic perspective is the relationship between the primary care physician, behavioral health professional, patients, and families. Gask (2013) stated, "During the last 2 decades of the 20th century, there was an increased recognition of the prevalence of major depression in the general population, and the importance of ensuring its recognition and treatment in primary care" (p. 450). The author further adds that psychotherapy and psychoeducation should be considered along with proper administration of medication, and that the relationship between the physician and behavioral health care system is crucial.

Reiss and Wamboldt (2006) discussed the origins, outcomes, and relationships of genetics to individual psychopathology. The authors stated that two major genetic techniques have been used to validate and revise *DSM-5* classifications. These two techniques consist of quantitative behavioral genetics, which uses twin and adoption studies, and polymorphism, which identifies individual differences in biochemical structure. Many years ago Kendler et al. (1993a) studied the persistence or recurrence of MDD in a large sample of female twins and found that genetic factors accounted for the entire covariance of depression scores when analyzed over a 1-year period. Kendler et al. (1993b) also studied MDD and found that the covariance relationship between neuroticism and depression was almost entirely attributed to genetics. Current studies have validated these studies and the genetic influences of the predictability and susceptibility of depression (Bukh, Bock, & Kessing, 2014; Ching-Lopez et al., 2014; Hankin et al., 2014).

Cultural Factors

Alarcon (2009) stated, "Cultural psychiatry deals with the description, definition, assessment, and management of all psychiatric conditions, inasmuch as they reflect and are subjected to the patterning influence of cultural factors" (p. 134). The author added that cultural psychiatry is more than just consideration of ethnic minorities or exotic lands, but of cultural factors in everyday life. In addition, the author discusses five variables that are important in the well-structured clinical interview. These are (a) cultural variables such as gender, sexual orientation, traditions, beliefs, migration history, and level of acculturation; (b) family data, which includes raising modalities, roles, hierarchies, values, eating habits, and social interactions; (c) pathogenic and pathoplastic factors such as sociopolitical structures, rules of public behavior, church affiliation, schedules, rituals, and schooling norms; (d) explanatory models, which discuss the origin of the symptoms, why they occur, and the cultural pathogenesis; and (e) patients' strengths and weaknesses.

The National Institute of Mental Health (2014) found that in 2014, an estimated 10.2 million adults aged 18 or older in the United States had at least one major depressive episode in the past year with severe impairment. Figure 4.1 graphically illustrates the data concerning depression by race.

For the systems clinician, an evaluation of cultural factors including race is important in understanding the many risks factors that are involved with a diagnosis of depression. The recent data does indicate that White adults are reporting a greater number of depressive episodes; however, varying attitudes toward depression among racial groups may stem from beliefs that psychological problems may not require medical care or that mental problems should not be revealed.

Hedaya (2009) discusses the culture of depression and stated that the physical world we created is made of concrete, steel, glass, and asphalt. The author adds that we breathe bad air, eat harmful foods, and drink plasticized bottle water, and that Western civilization has no personal sense of any connection to nature. The author further adds that we live in an imbalanced physical world, which is creating more and more individuals with symptoms of depression. He also stated that hopefully a future look at the incidence and prevalence of depression on the public health scale will not come from antidepressants, individual psychotherapy, or fish oil. Instead, this holistic view will reconnect the individual with the larger whole of the family, the community, culture, and a dialogue with nature and values. Dowrick (2013) adds to the discussion of depression as a culture-bound syndrome. The author stated, "We would benefit from a fundamental shift in perspective,

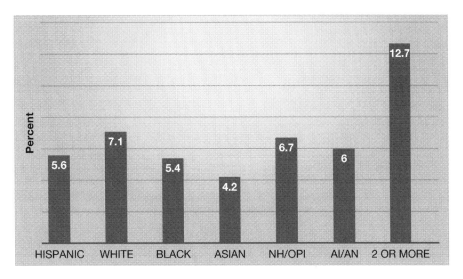

FIGURE 4.1 Twelve-month prevalence of major depressive episode among U.S. adults (2014) by race.

AI/AN, American Indian/Alaskan Native; NH/OPI, Native Hawaiian/Other
Pacific Islander.

Source: National Institute of Mental Health (2014).

understanding distressed patients not as passive victims of circumstance but as individu-als whose capacity to lead purposeful lives has been temporarily disrupted" (p. 230).

FAMILY SYSTEMS ASSESSMENTS

Assessment of family relationships and interactions is an important matter in treatment interventions for couples, families, and children. Ghanbaripanah and Mustaffia (2012) added that assessment information can be used to obtain better understanding of the nature of the problem, the roots of the problem, the individual member's perspective, and the strengths and weaknesses of the family system. Serra, Spoto, Ghisl, and Vidotto (2015) validate this view by stating, "The correct identification of depression during the assessment phase is a critical issue. In general, the quality of the clinical evaluation is always funda-mental for diagnosis and treatment. An incorrect psychological assessment may result in patient's dissatisfaction and suffering" (p. 122). Depression influences family communica-tion, problem resolution, and role functioning, which places a significant strain on all family members (Keitner, Miller, & Ryan, 2005). Zimmerman (2011) stated that depression outcome scales should have two desirable functions: (a) patients should find the scale to be easily understood, brief, relevant to the problem, and easily completed at each follow-up visit to evaluate treatment outcomes; and (b) the instrument should be of practical value provid-ing useful information.

The Interview

The family interview is one of the main modes of assessment for the systems clinician. Indicating current relational status and patterns, family environment, and diversity, this dialogue with family members serves as a powerful source of information. Erford (2013) proposed the following questions as part of the interview process to assess problems in the family:

- What is the problem as the family views it?
- Who has defined the problem?
- Who within the family is more involved in the problem?
- Who within the family is uninvolved and why?
- How do the views of the family members disagree or agree according to the problem?
- What experiences have led the family to view the problem in the way they do?
- What are the unresolved questions?
- What are the expectations for the future?
- Are there any past unresolved mourning or grief questions?

The questions provide information that allows the counselor to have a broader understanding of the problem leading to a correct diagnosis and effective treatment plan. It is through these shared understandings, sentiments, and beliefs that the systems clinician can help create a new narrative for the family. In addition, the interview acts as an inspiration for change and creates shared expectations for healing and well-being. For example, a 16-year-old female is experiencing depression, which is manifesting with mood swings, irritability, and general sadness both at school and home. After a general intake session with the client, the family therapist would schedule a time to meet with the parents, client, and siblings together in a family meeting to conceptualize a systems picture of the problem.

Assessments

There are a variety of assessment measures to be administered at the initial intake session and to monitor treatment and progress. These tools should be used to enhance clinical decision making and to provide valuable data concerning the client. In addition, outcome measures for depression should have a sound basis in psychometrics, provide good reliability and validity, and be sensitive to change (Zimmerman, 2011). For the systems clinician, using formal assessment tools provides a source of validation both for the individual diagnosed with depression and for the comorbidity involved from the family interaction. Some examples of measures for the systems clinician are as follows:

- *DSM-5 Self-Rated Level 1 Cross-Cutting Symptom Measure—Adult*
- *DSM-5 Self-Rated Level 1 Cross-Cutting Symptom Measure—Child Age 11–17*
- *DSM-5 Parent/Guardian-Rated Level 1 Cross-Cutting Symptom Measure—Child 6–17*

The American Psychological Association is offering these assessments online for clinicians to use to enrich the decision-making process, to understand patient status, and to improve patient care. All three measures can be downloaded free of charge and reproduced without permission by researchers and by clinicians for use with their patients (APA, 2013b). The measures can be downloaded from the APA website (www.psychiatry .org/psychiatrists/practice/dsm/dsm-5/online-assessment-measures).

Beck Depression Inventory—Second Edition (BDI-II)

This assessment has a 21-item format with four options under each item. It has been used for 35 years to assess depressive symptoms and has sound psychometric properties. This inventory was developed to highly correlate with the diagnostic criteria for depression and was constructed for use in the general population. Even though it is a measure used for individual evaluation, this assessment provides validation for the client and promotes a comprehensive and collaborative process between the therapist and family members. The general assessment kit is $131.00, which includes the manual and 25 forms (Beck, Steer, & Brown, 1996). For example, in a family-focused grief therapy, the clinician would be able to measure and validate the intensity, severity, and depth of depression in the family system. Also, the ease of administration and scoring provides the systemic therapist with a viable means to provide research-based information concerning the family problem.

Geriatric Depression Scale (GDS)

Consisting of 30 items, this assessment was constructed for rating depression in the elderly and was tested in a population above the age of 65. It has excellent test–retest reliability and is externally valid with other comparison assessments for depression. It is in the public domain and there are iPhone apps that will calculate the results (Heidenblut, 2014; Yesavage et al., 1983). Aging seniors and their families have a complexity of issues concerning depression, and this assessment may serve as a caregiver-based evaluation tool. For example, the entire family would be concerned with the 85-year-old nursing home parent and grandparent who is withdrawn and eating poorly. Assessing for depression with this aging family member would be a vital part of the overall system analysis.

Quick Inventory of Depressive Symptomatology (QIDS)

There are 16 items on the instrument, and these items are similar to the Beck Depression Inventory-II; however, the QIDS is more involved with the severity of the depressive disorder. It is copyrighted by the author but is available for unlimited use and can be downloaded from the IDS/QIDS website (www.ids-qids.org). The total scores range from 0 to 27 with a score of 16 and above being considered severe (Rush et al., 2003). A diagnosis of depression in children and adolescents requires careful examination of symptoms and exclusions that might mimic depression. This assessment allows the systemic clinician to quickly validate the existence of depression and the severity of the disorder.

Child Depression Inventory 2 (CDI2)

This assessment can be used in both clinical and educational settings and provides a comprehensive report of depressive symptoms in children and adolescents ages 7 to 17. The CDI2 qualifies the reports with both parent and teacher surveys. The inventory can be found at MHS Psychological Assessment and Services with a cost of $399.00 for the complete software kit, which includes the manual software instruction and 25 self-report forms for the child. The kit also includes 25 teacher and parent report instruments (Bae, 2012; Kovacs, 2011). Because children may not be able to verbalize depression or sadness, the systems therapist would be able to validate symptoms of depression in children through the use of this assessment.

Clinically Useful Depression Outcome Scale (CUDOS)

This instrument contains 18 items that assess the criteria for MDD. It is a Likert scale and takes less than 2 minutes to complete the instrument. The CUDOS is highly correlated with other self-report measures of depression and has good test–retest reliability and internal consistency. Scores are scaled from 0 to 64, with scores above 21 indicating mild depression. Scores from 31 to 45 indicate moderate depression and 46 to 64 severe depression. The scale can be downloaded from the website for public use at https://outcometracker.org/CUDOS.pdf (Zimmerman, 2011). When a client is depressed, somatic and cognitive changes may occur that significantly affect the individual's capacity to function in the family. Evaluating outcomes by the systemic clinician can be enhanced by using this assessment, which includes a scale for psychosocial impairment and quality of life.

Hamilton Depression Rating Scale

Even though this scale was created in 1960, it is still one of the most used interview scales to measure the severity of depression. The scale takes between 20 and 30 minutes to administer and contains 21 items with scores of 0 to 7 being considered normal and scores above 20 indicating moderate to severe depression. This instrument is to be administered by the clinician and is not constructed to be a self-report measure. The scale is in the public domain and can be downloaded from various websites (Bienenfeld & Stinson, 2016). This assessment is actually administered by the systemic clinician and has the unique ability to be incorporated at any point during family therapy.

One way to acquire a deeper understanding of the client is to obtain generational information that will allow the clinician to see patterns within the family of origin. For example, if you have an adult client with depression and you want to see if depression or other mental health issues run in the family, you might consider using a genogram. A genogram is another type of family assessment, which is a pictorial representative of the psychological and physiological history of the client (Ghanbaripanah & Mustaffia, 2012). The systems clinician is able to construct a historical pattern of the behavioral and emotional interactions of the family. The genogram will show a wealth of information concerning not only the members of the family unit but also diseases, depression, divorce rates, and alcoholism. Using the information from the genogram, the systemic clinician might choose to use role-play as a visual way for family members to understand the concepts of depression within the household unit and to view the dynamics of the family from a new window.

FAMILY SYSTEMS INTERVENTIONS

After the systemic clinician has made sure the diagnosis is accurate and complete, treatment goals should be stated in terms that are observable and measureable (e.g., specific depressive disorder behaviors, scores on assessments, self-reports, mental status exam). According to Leahy, Holland, and McGinn (2012), goals should cover the following areas: (a) conclusion of tasks required as part of treatment, (b) relief of defined symptoms, (c) reduced impairment, and (d) end-state goals. These goals should also include the roles, behaviors, and emotional regulation within the framework of system thinking and the family network. Hill et al. (2014) discussed a domain-based analysis for the family process of treatment. The authors identified five main issues in treatment planning: (a) basing the treatment on standardized assessment, (b) explaining the domain framework to the family, (c) deciding with whom to work in therapy, (d) identifying sequences for review in sessions, and (e) implicating the domain framework for the therapist stance (p. 70). The authors explain the domain process by exploring three domains of family life. These domains are safety, attachment, and discipline/expectation, and these domains are contrasted with exploratory processes in the family such as emotions, roles, and hierarchy. With depression, the client(s) experiencing the emotion would express any areas of risk, and the other family members would take action to lower the risk. The attachment domain would involve expressions of fear, worry, distress, illness, injury, and sadness, which would include any evidence of depression. Finally, the disciple/expectation domain would look at any inappropriate or dangerous behaviors caused by the depression. This type of analysis reveals any hidden misunderstandings, arguments, or distresses and allows family members to reflect on their perspectives of experiences. One advantage of domain family work is that the therapist has the option to work with the client alone or include the entire family.

Medication Treatment

The APA (2010) postulated that antidepressant medications represent one form of treatment for moderate or severe depressive disorders. There are four major classes of antidepressants: (a) monoamine oxidase inhibitors, (b) tricyclic antidepressants, (c) selective serotonin reuptake inhibitors, and (d) new drugs such as Venlafaxine, Duloxetine, and Wellbutrin. Monoamine oxidase inhibitors are the most powerful and most difficult to manage and are usually reserved for cases in which other medications have not been successful. Tricyclic antidepressants are the next most powerful and can cause problematic side effects, and selective serotonin reuptake inhibitors are the most preferred by primary care physicians and have less major side effects. Prescriptions are becoming frequent for new drugs that target multiple neurotransmitter systems; however, these types of drugs are more difficult to manage (Hollon & Sexton, 2012).

Even though a pharmacological approach ought to be used with caution, there should always be a discussion of medication as part of treatment for depressed patients. When another biological member of the patient's family has reacted well to a specific class of medications, then that medication class is more prone to be effective. Experience in the field of mental health has indicated that medications are especially helpful in increasing motivation, energy, appetite, concentration, and the ability to gain distance from negative thoughts—especially with severely depressed patients (Leahy et al., 2012). As stated earlier in the chapter, systems clinicians who have good collegial relationships with a family care physician and/or a psychiatrist are better able to meet the needs of their clients. For example, a 45-year-old man visits his family physician with symptoms of poor appetite, feeling hopeless, suffering from insomnia, and feeling sad. After a routine physical and a referral to the behavior health practitioner in the clinic, the physician would have a treatment planning meeting with the therapists and discuss medication for the patient.

Cognitive Behavioral Therapy (CBT)

Cognitive behavioral interventions are grounded on the idea that it is not the circumstance that happens to individuals that determines how they feel and what behaviors they exhibit, but rather the way they interpret the event (Beck, 2005). Hollon and Sexton (2012) stated that studies with experienced cognitive behavioral therapists found that cognitive behavioral interventions were as efficacious as antidepressants medications and superior to pill placebo. The authors stated, "The implication is that patients treated with CBT learn to deal with their own depressions in a way that medications just cannot match. In a recurrent disorder like depression, an indication of an enduring effect is very welcome indeed" (p. 203).

Leahy et al. (2012) discussed cognitive behavioral therapy for depressive disorders and stated, "Cognitive therapy involves the initial assessment of the patient's depression, with a focus on automatic thoughts, maladaptive assumptions, and core beliefs/schemas" (p. 25). Cognitive behavioral therapy examines the interactional dynamics of the family and how the dynamics are contributing to the problem. The systemic clinician can engage

TABLE 4.1 Cognitive Behavioral Techniques for Depression

Technique	Action Plan
Cognitive restructuring	Working to change thinking patterns and finding new behavioral actions
Focus on specific problems	Problems are acknowledged, ranked, and viewed from a new action plan
Identifying faulty thinking	Train the patient in accepting and understanding the difference
Defining goals	Define goals both short term and long term
Education	Teaching clients to monitor and evaluate negative thoughts and mental images
Active role	Homework assignments to discuss at each session
Socratic questioning	"Why is this so important?" "Why must this happen and what makes this be so important?" "Why is this a problem if it is true?"
Role-playing	Working with clients to actually practice new behaviors, new thoughts, and new statements
Imagery	Working with clients to reconstruct negative images to positive goal-directed mental pictures
Self-statements	Helping the client create caring and accepting supportive statements

the family and analyze the emotions, beliefs, and behaviors of the family system. CBT works well across cultures and is a primary source for uncovering faulty thinking leading to depression. Table 4.1 summarizes possible techniques.

At the family level, cognitive behavioral therapy addresses problematic family interactions by changing behaviors through addressing not only the client's thoughts or perceptions but also the thinking patterns of the family. Changing these cognitive patterns offers strategies to help reframe how problems are viewed and helps the family understand circumstances and consequences of dysfunctional thoughts. Education and training in new interpersonal skills are important elements to enhance social competence and to develop new constructive interactions.

Interpersonal Therapy (IPT)

Interpersonal Therapy is built around the notion that most depressions are associated with problems in relationships. IPT concentrates on four kinds of problem areas, with different tactics recommended for each: interpersonal loss (grief), interpersonal disputes, interpersonal deficits, and role transition, which usually has relational overtones (Hollon & Sexton, 2012). Having considerable relevance to depression, IPT predicates that the disorder is the result of dysfunctions in interpersonal relationships. Swartz, Grote, and Graham (2014) discussed the following overview of a brief IPT treatment plan for depression: (a) During the initial phase, the systemic clinician looks at the important interpersonal relationships and makes a case formulation; (b) continuing to collect information is the focus of the second session and offers the client a revised formulation of the case; (c) using role dispute, role transition, and homework assignments are the contents of the following sessions; and (d) activating behavioral activities such as hobbies, church, and enjoyable interest completes the sessions.

Attachment-Based Family Therapy

Especially designed for depressed and suicidal youth, Attachment-Based Family Therapy is a short-term, research-supported approach to counseling that improves communication, trust, and strength within the family system. The primary goal of treatment is to improve the attachment relationships between the parent and child, so that when adolescents feel loved and supported, they will reach out to others for guidance rather than experiencing depression and distress. There are three types of interventions: relational reframes, a focus on primary emotions, and facilitating corrective attachment relationships (Diamond, 2013). Shpigel, Diamond, and Diamond (2012) added to this discussion of interventions, "To improve intra- and interpersonal skills and work through past trauma and relational ruptures, four therapeutic tasks are implemented in sequence" (p. 272). The four therapeutic tasks are included within the types of interventions and have the goal of strengthening or repairing relationships between the child and parent. The authors stated that the first task involves improving the relationship between the family members, whereas the second and third tasks focus on building alliances within the family. According to the authors, the fourth task of reattachment episode is a culmination of eliciting and validating the child's point of view while being supportive and empathic with the parents. For example, a teen feels withdrawn, impaired, and perceives himself or herself as uncared for, unsafe, and alone. During the family session, these feelings would be explored to see if they are based on real circumstances such as abandonment, rejection, high levels of criticism, or if they are products of the depressive disorder thinking. The family would actually become the medicine by using a combination of increased sustained engagement by the adolescent and sensitive caregiving by the parent. The sessions would focus on healing and strengthening the family relationships so that the teen would feel understood, cared for, and validated.

ETHICAL AND LEGAL IMPLICATIONS

Is it possible to avoid ethical and legal implications of making a *DSM-5* depressive disorder diagnosis? There are ways to ensure at least minimal impact is acquired if one makes sure criteria are met prior to determining a diagnosis. There is a risk of labeling that could influence the current functioning of the family system and other environmental links in regard to employment, insurance coverage, school systems, peer relationships, and overall overwhelming feelings of stigma (Chambers et al., 2013; Denton & Bell, 2013; Nolen-Hoeksema, 2014a; Insel et al., 2010). There are steps that a clinician can take to avoid a misdiagnosis including the use of valid and reliable assessment tools that are both formal and informal, a detailed clinical interview, family relational considerations (Denton & Bell, 2013) and behavioral observation along with the useful decision trees detailed criteria outlined in the *DSM-5* (APA, 2013a; Nolen-Hoeksema, 2014a). With all of these factors being considered, a systemic clinician should always have his or her eyes on the ethical codes and legal obligations that apply to diagnoses of individuals, couples, and families.

There are two major organizations that are working primarily with couples and families, namely the International Association for Marriage and Family Counseling, which is a division of the American Counseling Association (ACA); and the American Association for Marriage and Family Therapy (AAMFT). However, the applicable ethical codes span across marriage and family therapy, mental health, and school counselors who serve families in varied capacities (AAMFT, 2012; ACA, 2014; Hendricks, Bradley, Southern, Oliver, & Birdsall, 2011). There are some specific codes to consider when working with families.

The ACA and AAMFT both have a requirement of mandating report in the event that there is a report of abuse, neglect, or harm to self or someone else (AAMFT, 2015, Standard 2.1; ACA, 2014, Section B.2.a). These are considered legal and ethical limits to confidentiality and all codes are worded differently but are applicable to systemic clinicians based on licensure. Other specific codes that apply are the consideration of the law and ethical requirements when working with minors. All three codes highlight the significance of parents' and legal guardians' roles when a systemic clinician is working with a minor (AAMFT, 2015, Standard 1.1, 1.2; ACA, 2014, Section B.5.a). With the requirement of assessment and diagnosis, one must adhere to the ethical standards regarding the assessment and evaluation of clients using formal and informal assessments, diagnostic tools, and make competent and professional decisions based on those assessments (AAMFT, 2015, Standard III; ACA, 2014, Section E). These specific sections and subcategories of codes need to be closely evaluated along with having clear alignment with one's licensure board ethical standards. It is not uncommon for a minor to attend a session alone and report suicidal ideation with a plan; if one looks closely at the codes presented, this is a limit to confidentiality and would need to be reported but should have been clearly outlined in an informed consent document (AAMFT, 2015, Standard 1.2; ACA, 2014, Section A.2). Considering the codes of ethics when working with a depressed client, there are various scenarios that might unfold leading to the need of an ethical decision. If a parent presents with an MDD, it may be necessary to consider the risk of harm to the children. As indicated by the codes (AAMFT, 2015; ACA, 2014), if there is potential abuse or neglect evident, systemic clinicians are mandated reporters. As a result, this is a limit to confidentiality that should be explored with the parent and family from the beginning of treatment via the informed consent (AAMFT, 2015; ACA, 2014). Knowing there is a likelihood for suicidal ideation with clients suffering from depressive disorders, systemic clinicians should be transparent with their clients regarding the limit of confidentiality and mandated requirement to prevent harm to client (AAMFT, 2015; ACA, 2014). It is important to know not only respective codes of ethics that apply with all clients but also careful consideration of the ethical codes applicable to symptoms or behaviors associated with a diagnosis.

One of the driving forces of all medical and mental health treatment is the Health Insurance Portability and Accountability Act that was put into place in 1996 (U.S. Congress, 1996). This act requires specific standards to be met so that privacy and security standards are in place to protect patients. One specified area to look at closely in regard to working with families is the privacy rule (U.S. Congress, 1996). One cannot use or reveal an entire medical record unless there is an explicit purpose to do so and an authorization needs to be in place (U.S. Congress, 1996). This makes the consideration of a civil commitment challenging in that a mental health professional must take the entire case into consideration before proceeding with releasing the records of family case notes or one client within that family system. Another specified concern is the Health Insurance Portability and Accountability Act privacy rule that was implemented in 2013. This rule is designed to ensure that there are measures in place to protect access to clients' records. This includes indicating the designated individuals within an agency, practice, or hospital who will ensure this security is maintained (Department of Health and Human Services security rule,

2003; U.S. Congress, 1996). These measures are in place to protect the public and medical and mental health professionals who are required to adhere to these laws.

Looking closely at the federal law, one cannot discount the specific state laws and applicable ethical codes to which systemic clinicians must adhere. Although not all laws are applicable to ethical codes, the importance of confidentiality (AAMFT, 2015, Standard 2.2; ACA, 2014, Section B.1.c) and adherence to appropriate documentation (AAMFT, 2015, Standards 2.4–2.5; ACA, 2014, Section A.1.b) and record keeping (AAMFT, 2015, Standard 2.3; ACA, 2014, Section B.6.a) are clearly outlined. Part of legitimizing the work of systemic clinicians is the adherence to a professional code of ethics. These codes provide a standard of care that sets guidelines, reinforces standards, establishes expectations, and provides a framework to guide competent practice. Considering the various diagnostic criteria outlined for depressive disorders, ethical codes need to be considered. The process of ethical decision making starts at the onset of treatment with the implementation of a clear and concise informed consent document and carries over into the sessions to ensure client welfare is maintained. By looking closely and adhering to the codes, clients and the public can be safeguarded and systemic clinicians can do their best to prevent harm and promote the well-being of clients.

CASE CONCEPTUALIZATION

In order to conceptualize the content of this chapter, the authors have provided a case study that presents a family that is experiencing multiple concerns and symptoms related to a depressive disorder. This case will introduce students to how a family might present for treatment outlining the perspective of each member. Readers are provided a brief glimpse into background information, presentation of strengths, ethical implications, diagnostic impression and potential assessment, and treatment options. This case will enable students to consider the systemic perspective to outline an applicable diagnosis and treatment plan.

Presenting Concerns

The Compton family is a Caucasian family consisting of Brent (42), Gloria (41), John (18), and Lisa (12). Both Brent and Gloria work full time outside the home, although Gloria's schedule is more flexible. Gloria has been working as a cosmetologist at a local high-dollar hair salon for 15 years. She is a sought-after cosmetologist who stays up-to-date with the latest hair colors, style, and trends to technique. She has been married for almost 20 years to her high school sweetheart and she reports a happy marriage with some "bumps" in the road. Together, they have an 18-year-old son and a 12-year-old daughter. Gloria has always been a very positive person and a listening ear for her cosmetology clients, friends, and family members. However, over the last 6 months, she is feeling unfulfilled in her work, marriage, and as a mother. Gloria reports this lack of fulfillment with her life after she turned 41. She reports feeling tearful, a low mood, having difficulty sleeping at night causing her to fall asleep late at night and then difficulty rising from sleep to attend to her daughter and morning routine. She reports feeling very tired, but her mind is racing and she is unable to shut it off long enough to fall asleep. This pattern is causing tension between her and her husband and frustration from her children.

Brent works at a local advertising agency on a regular schedule during the week and sometimes works on weekends when there are required promotion obligations. He has noticed over the last 6 months that his wife is not coming to bed at a normal hour and he has difficulty waking her up in the morning. This is a different pattern for Brent as he has been accustomed to his wife being up before him, having coffee ready and cheerful and energetic with him and the kids. Brent is concerned that something has occurred to change Gloria, possibly an affair, due to her total change in personality, being withdrawn, lack of sleep, weight gain, and loss of interest in sex and any other level of intimacy with him.

John attends a local community college and is happy to be out of the house attending classes and spending time with his girlfriend. He notices that his mother has changed quite a bit over the last 6 months, and that his father is more agitated with his mom than usual. He has always felt his parents were happy in their marriage and could weather any obstacles. He gets along well with his 12-year-old sister although he perceives her as quite spoiled and strong willed. John prefers to avoid addressing any issues and keeps his eyes on personal and career goals.

Lisa loves attending school where she is very popular and stays up on the latest fashion trends. She is accustomed to her mom doing everything for her including packing her a lunch, ironing her clothes, and helping with her homework. She is angry that her mom has become "lazy" and is beginning to look frumpy. She is embarrassed by her mother and just wants her to get back to her old self. Lisa confronts her mom telling her that she is ruining her reputation at school by allowing everything to fall apart.

Gloria's clients, friends, and colleagues notice that she is not herself and has become disconnected, quiet, and seems withdrawn. For the past month and a half, Gloria has expressed lack of interest in work, participating in the usual "chit chat," and no longer desires to have sex with her husband, attend her children's activities, or spend time with friends. She reports not having enough energy to muster up the desire to engage with others. With her lack of sleep she finds herself staying up at night and surfing social media, snacking, and gaining weight. With the weight gain, her self-esteem has diminished. At work, she finds herself staring off into space, unable to concentrate on the task at hand, and clients have chosen other cosmetologists to style their hair. All the areas of her life have been impacted and she expresses an interest in merely giving up and going off alone because she is causing problems in her family and work setting, and her life is not headed anywhere.

Brent has attempted to talk with Gloria about her change with no success. He reached out to John and Lisa about their mom, and about them all attending family therapy. There was a clear reluctance from both children. Brent waited one morning, until after both the kids had left for school, and expressed his concerns to Gloria. He indicated a desire to attend family counseling because the whole house is in "disarray." Gloria reluctantly agreed, but felt guilt for making the family go through the stress.

Concurrent Problems

The family has never attended individual, couple, or family counseling before. Brent is concerned about his wife's sleeping and eating patterns and wants answers regarding what is happening to his wife, marriage, and the family. Gloria knows that she is not herself, but feels that neither Brent nor her children should be so dramatic about the changes, but rather leave her alone. Lisa is reluctant to attend counseling because her friends might find out, and John feels he is an adult and should not have to attend when his mom is the problem. Lisa has a good relationship with her school guidance counselor, and John has access to college counseling.

Background History and Stressors

Gloria grew up in a dysfunctional home and was the youngest of three children. There is a history of sexual abuse happening on two separate occasions at the hands of her uncle, but there was no history of intervention of treatment. Gloria's mother was diagnosed with anxiety and depression. Her mother was not consistent with treatment and would take out her frustration, worry, and agitation on Gloria. Brent indicates a very strict family upbringing with defined gender roles and high expectations for success. Both report no history of medical conditions except for Brent having acid reflux disease and Gloria having a thyroid disorder, both of which are both treated with medication.

Strengths

Brent considers himself to be strong willed and does admit to taking life too seriously. When faced with obstacles, he quickly goes into problem-solving mode and seeks out his friends to help bounce off ideas. He feels that he is a family man and loves his wife and children and desires to be a good father and husband. He enjoys exercising and outdoor activities. Gloria is a social butterfly when she is herself and loves spending time with family, friends, and her clients. She sees the good within people, enjoys being on top of the newest trends in cosmetology, and feels her belief in God has helped her through most obstacles. John was the top of his class in school, attends community college on a full scholarship, and enjoys life. He enjoys being around people, being active in college social clubs, and is considering running for student body president. Lisa is popular in her school, has average grades, and is considered trendy, funny, and all around cool to friends. Her social status is important since many girls look up to her and ask her for advice.

DSM-5 Impressions and Implications

Gloria seems to be a primary focus of clinical concern because her symptoms are impacting the entire family system. The initial diagnostic impression for Gloria would be: Major Depressive Disorder, Single Episode, Unspecified, Moderate With Melancholic Features (APA, 2013a).

The following symptoms started 6 months ago and have increased the last month with persistence of the symptoms on a daily basis. Gloria reports depressed mood and tearfulness on and off daily, decreased interest in attending work, sexual intercourse, and intimacy with others. Gloria has reported weight gain due to eating late at night and surfing social media since she is having difficulty sleeping. She reports feeling fatigued and slow at work and with other life activities that are impacting her and her family. When needing to attend to work or other required activities, Gloria has difficulty concentrating on the task at hand and has reported feeling her life is not headed anywhere and has guilt about how her behavior is affecting others. There has never been a diagnosis of another mental health disorder, but there is the human growth and development phase to consider with turning 41 years of age.

Relational Problems

When looking at the family dynamic with Gloria, Brent, John and Lisa, several relational problems should be considered for the family unit. With Gloria undergoing a complete change in her personality from just 6 months prior, it is important that one consider a heightened expressed level of emotion within the family unit due to how the family is coping, relating, and making sense of the changes in the environment due to Gloria's level of distress (APA, 2013a). With Gloria reporting that her symptoms began after turning 41, it is important to highlight a phase of life problem (APA, 2013a). Gloria is in middle adulthood where she is facing different challenges in life from her oldest child going off to college, reflecting on her life choices thus far, and in a stage of life where she is drawn to generating new ideas and possibly life changes or feels very stuck in her current state of being with little hope for perceiving things to be different (Newman & Newman, 2015b).

Assessments

One assessment tool that can be utilized with the whole family is a genogram. The genogram is a visual representation of family structure that identifies demographic information that is gathered from each individual in the family, the type and nature of specific relationships, and the interaction patterns between deceased relatives, family members outside of the family unit, careers, culture, and heritage (McGoldrick et al., 2016). This genogram will help to shed light on the biological links to depression, life stressors, and unfolding of events including types of relationships.

Beck Depression Inventory—Second Edition (APA, 2013b) is another assessment that would be relevant to this family but would be administered only to Gloria. This assessment will evaluate her current level of functioning, symptoms, and provide a tool for pre- and post-treatment evaluation of progress. This 21-item assessment evaluates for depression and is linked to the diagnostic criteria that is outlined in the *DSM-5* for depression (Beck et al., 1996).

Interventions

When a diagnosis of a depressive disorder is made, a systemic clinician must consider the clinical goals, techniques, and interventions that would benefit the family system. The goals for depression can vary. One goal includes improvement in overall mood and maintenance of daily functioning skills.

Another goal is improvement in sleeping up to 8 hours, completion of a daily to-do list for work and home. There should be an increase in effective communication and engagement in pleasurable activities for self, family, and with others. In addition, the therapist should work toward helping the client develop an increased ability to implement strategies concerning negative self-talk, feelings of guilt, and feelings of worthlessness. This can be accomplished via cognitive behavioral therapy with the client and the family by implementing techniques such as goal setting, cognitive restructuring, and use of role-play (Beck, 2005; Leahy et al., 2012).

Family-focused therapy is essential to the overall success of the unit. As part of the family therapy, the family would benefit from education regarding the depression diagnosis, concerning new communication skills, and understanding and applying problem-solving skills (Miklowitz, George, Richards, Simoneau, & Suddath, 2003).

It is critical that psychopharmacology be a consideration for an individual who has been diagnosed with an MDD. Thase and Denko (2008) outlined various medications that would assist individuals with mood disorders, including their various classes, generic names, brand names, and potential side effects. With these treatment options, a psychiatrist would be the prescriber who works directly with the family regarding the needs of Gloria and her family.

Ethical and Legal Implications

Licensed marriage and family therapists, mental health counselors, and other systemic clinicians are required to adhere to their respective state board ethical standards. The

AAMFT has a code of ethics that one is required to understand, adhere to, and agree to comply with when working with individuals, couples, and families (AAMFT, 2011). The first applicable code is informed consent indicating that the identified client and all parties have been provided the opportunity to approve or decline treatment and understand the potential risks and benefits of treatment (AAMFT, 2011; Sommers-Flanagan & Sommers-Flanagan, 2014). There is another consideration associated with confidentiality where information is retained within the context of a session and is not disclosed to outside parties or nontherapy session parties without consent or otherwise indicated within the informed consent document without a signed release of information. There are additional codes pertaining to security of records and appropriate billing procedures (AAMFT, 2015). The ACA (2014) *Code of Ethics* has a very detailed requirement for informed consent that is signed by all parties involved in therapy, including the counselor. This outlines confidentiality adherence and limits, record keeping, and emphasis on assessment based diagnoses. (ACA, 2014, Section E.5.a).

DISCUSSION

As you continue to reflect on the case study and the overall approach, contemplate these questions:

- What additional questions would you ask this family to get a better idea of the family structure, interaction, and coping?

- What specific psychosocial and relational factors would you consider to capture the larger systemic impact?

- Knowing that each of the family members is coping differently with the life stressors and changes within Gloria, how would you approach the Compton family to help them see that "depression" is a systemic problem, not merely an individual problem?

- There are various ways to approach the counseling of a family. How would you engage the family so that they all feel the clinician has provided each member a time to speak, along with reinforcing and understanding, while promoting change as a family unit?

- In what ways would you assess that change has occurred with a reduction in the family "depression" and improve family interaction, communication, and functioning?

SUMMARY

This chapter has provided important considerations in regard to family system counseling and depressive disorders. There are many factors to consider and analyze before assigning the *DSM-5* (APA, 2013a) diagnosis of a depressive disorder. The evaluation of presenting symptoms, diagnosis criteria, assessment considerations, cultural issues, and relational factors are all intertwined. Once a specified depression diagnosis is secured, the systemic clinician must not only consider all ethical and legal implications, but also proper treatment measures, which will have an effective impact on improving the overall health and well-being of the family system.

The process of diagnosis begins as soon as the family comes into session. As a family unfolds its life story through the myriad of varied perspectives, a clinician will begin to formulate the relationships that exist between members and will ask follow-up questions with each system member to gather more information to solidify a diagnosis. Many options may follow such as: (a) a specific diagnosis for a child in the family system of a mood dysregulation disorder, (b) a specified female diagnosis of PDD, or (c) a specific depressive disorder diagnosis such as MDD, Dysthymia, or Depressive Disorder

(APA, 2013a). Regardless of the decision, all family system members should have full knowledge of the diagnosis process and be involved in treatment as well as assessing progress.

Part of this consideration involves taking into account the rich cultural framework of families and considering all the relational interactions as indicated in the case study of Gloria. As part of that cultural framework, clinicians should considered the biological, psychological, and sociocultural factors that influence the makeup of individual members of the family and how they unfold within the system. Individuals relate within the context of relationships, and the family relationship is the primary source of early interactions. Rich information can unfold in the counseling process when the therapist takes the time to assess the family structure.

A specific diagnosis of depression includes the exploration of assessments, which provide a collection of information for going beyond differentiating the clients according to just symptomatology. Assessments provide a formal framework for validating the presence of a depressive disorder and offer a means to verify the established criteria. Correctly identifying a depressive disorder is a critical issue that is fundamental for sound ethical treatment. Assessments may include clinical interviews, psychophysiological measurements, self-report questionnaires, formal surveys, or structured questions. Regardless of the method, assessment tools should be suited to the client, valid, reliable, culturally correct, and age appropriate. In addition, assessments should be time sensitive and should obtain information that builds a solid framework for the diagnosis.

Once a diagnosis is made, there are varied approaches that can be utilized for depression specific to the individuals and specific family members. As has been shown in the chapter information, relational formulations with depression are relevant and important in clinical care. Family therapists will be required to use the *DSM-5* in a way to affirm a systemic approach to counseling and will be involved in allowing the relational factors to highlight twists and turns of depressive disorders. Other relational factors include a common bond between the primary care physician and the behavioral health care system and an understanding of the role of genetic factors within the family. Many cultural factors should be considered when diagnosing depressive disorders such as: (a) gender, (b) sexual orientation, (c) traditions, (d) beliefs, (e) patient strengths and weakness, and (f) family roles. As stated in the chapter, ultimately sound clinical judgment is the key factor in understanding mental illness and engaging in clinical care.

As evident in the case study of Gloria, no diagnosis or treatment should be considered without ethical and legal considerations. Depending on the specific licensure of one's professional identity, there are ethical codes that are uniform across paradigms. There is a need for proper and informed consent, clarity regarding training, confidentiality and the limits to it, sound diagnostic assessment, and competent treatment. Along with ethical adherence is the obligation to ensure that counselors, marriage and family therapists, and other mental help professionals adhere to their respective state legal obligations to protect and ensure the privacy of those seeking treatment. When warmly addressing the family with care, concern, and unconditional positive regard, the family story can unfold and a proper depression diagnosis and course of treatment can be outlined.

REFERENCES

Alarcon, R. D. (2009). Culture, cultural factors and psychiatric diagnosis: Review and projections. *World Psychiatry, 8*(3), 131–139. doi:10/1002/j.2051-5545.2009.tb00233x

American Association for Marriage and Family Therapy. (2012). *AAMFT code of ethics.* Retrieved from http://www.aamft.org/imis15/content/legal_ethics/code_of_ethics.aspx

American Association for Marriage and Family Therapy. (2015, January). *Code of ethics.* Alexandria, VA: Author. Retrieved from www.aamft.org/imis15/Documents/Legal%20Ethics/Board%20Approved%20Code%20for%20Weeb%20Secured.pdf

American Counseling Association. (2014). *ACA code of ethics.* Alexandria, VA: Author. Retrieved from http://www.counseling.org/knowledge-center/ethics

American Psychiatric Association. (1968). *Diagnostic and statistical manual of mental disorders* (2nd ed.). Washington, DC: Author.

American Psychiatric Association. (1994). *Diagnostic and statistical manual of mental disorders* (4th ed.). Washington, DC: Author.

American Psychiatric Association. (2013a). *Diagnostic and statistical manual of mental disorders* (5th ed.). Arlington, VA: American Psychiatric Publishing.

American Psychiatric Association. (2013b). Online assessment measures. Retrieved from https://psychiatry.org/psychiatrists/practice/dsm/dsm-5/online-assessment-measures

American Psychiatric Association. (2016). *Depressive disorders.* Washington, DC: American Psychiatric Association.

Bae, Y. (2012). Test review. *Journal of Psychoeducational Assessment, 30*(3), 304–308. doi:10.1177/0734282911426407

Beach, S. R. H., Kaslow, N., Wambolt, M., Heyman, R., & Reiss, D. (2006a). Describing relationship problems in DSM-V: Toward better guidance for research and clinical practice. *Journal of Family Psychology, 20*(3), 359–368. doi:10.1037/0893-3200.20.3.359

Beach, S. R. H., Wamboldt, M. Z., Kaslow, N. J., Heyman, R. E., First, M. B., Underwood, L., & Reiss, D. (2006b). *Relational processes and DSM-V: Neuroscience, assessment, and intervention.* Washington, DC: American Psychiatric Publishing.

Beck, A. T. (2005). The current state of cognitive therapy: A 40-year retrospective. *Archives of General Psychiatry, 62,* 953–959. doi:10.1001/archpsyc.62.9.953

Beck, A. T., Steer, R. A., & Brown G. K. (1996). *Beck depression inventory manual.* San Antonio, TX: The Psychological Association.

Bhattacharya, R., Chan, S., & Sambamoorthi, U. (2014). Excess risk of chronic physical conditions associated with depression and anxiety. *BMC Psychiatry, 14*(1), 1–19.

Bienenfeld, D., & Stinson, K. N. (2016). Medscape. Screening test for depression. Retrieved from http://emedicine/medscape/com/article/1859030-overview#a2

Blazek, M., Kazmierczak, M., & Besta, T. (2015). Sense of purpose in life and escape from self as the predictors of quality of life in clinical samples. *Journal of Religion and Health, 54*(2), 517–523.

Bowen, M. (1966). The use of family theory in clinical practice. *Comprehensive Psychiatry, 7,* 345–374.

Bowen, M. (1976). Theory in the practice of psychotherapy. In P. J. Gurin (Ed.), *Family therapy: Theory and practice* (pp. 42–90). New York, NY: Gardner Press.

Braverman, P. K. (2007). Premenstrual syndrome and premenstrual dysphoric disorder. *Journal of Pediatric Adolescent Gynecology, 20,* 3–12.

Brown University. (2013). New to DSM: Disruptive mood dysregulation disorder. *Brown University Child and Adolescent Behavior Letter, 29*(4), 3.

Bukh, J. D., Bock, C., & Kessing, L. V. (2014). Association between genetic polymorphisms in the serotonergic system and comorbid personality disorders among patients with first-episode depression. *Journal of Personality Disorders, 28*(3), 365–378.

Chambers, M., MacDonald, C., & Mikes-Liu, K. (2013). Dialogues from the Coalface: DSM-5 and emotional process in a clinical setting. *Australian and New Zealand Journal of Family Therapy, 43,* 129–146. doi:10.1002/anzf.1008

Ching-Lopez, A., Cervilla, J., Rivera, M., Molina, E., McKenney, K., Ruiz-Perezm, I., & Gutierrez, B. (2014). Epidemiological support for genetic variability at hypothalamix—pituitary—adrenal axis and serotonergic system as risk factors for major depression. *Neuropsychiatric Disease and Treatment, 11,* 2743–2754.

Clayton, A. (2008). Symptoms related to the menstrual cycle: Diagnosis, prevalence, and treatment. *Journal of Psychiatric Practice, 14*(1), 13–21.

Craner, J. R., Sigmon, S. T., Martinson, A. A., & McGillicuddy, M. L. (2014). Premenstrual disorders and rumination. *Journal of Clinical Psychology, 70*(1), 32–47. doi:10.1002/jclp.22007

Denton, W., & Bell, C. (2013). DSM-5 and the family therapist: First-order change in the new millennium. *Australian and New Zealand Journal of Family Therapy, 34,* 147–155. doi:10.1002/anzf.1010

Diamond, G. M. (2013). Attachment-based family therapy interventions. *Psychotherapy, 51*(1), 15–19. doi:10.1037/a0032689

Dickstein, D. P., Finger, E. C., Brotman, M. A., Rich, B. A., Pine, D. S., Blair, J. R., & Leibenluft, E. (2010). Impaired probabilistic reversal learning in youths with mood and anxiety disorders. *Psychological Medicine, 40*(7), 1089–1100.

Dowrick, C. (2013). Depression as a culture-bound syndrome: Implications for primary care. *British Journal of General Practice, 63*(610), 229–230. doi:10.3399/bjgp13x665189

Epperson, C. N., Steiner, M., Hartlage, S. A., Eriksson, E., Schmidt, P. J., Jones, I., & Yonkers, K. A. (2012). Premenstrual dysphoric disorder: Evidence for a new category for DSM-5. *American Journal of Psychiatry, 169*, 465–475. Retrieved from https://www.lapresse.ca/html/1716/appiajp201211081302.pdf

Erford, B. T. (2013). *Assessment for counselors.* Belmont, CA: Brooks/Cole.

Gask, L. (2013). Educating family physicians to recognize and manage depression: Where are we now? *Canadian Journal of Psychiatry, 58*(8), 449–455.

Ghanbaripanah, S., & Mustaffia, M. S. (2012). The review of family assessment in counseling. *International Journal of Fundamental Psychology and Social Sciences, 2*(2), 32–35.

Guyer, A. E., McClure, E. B., Adler, A. D., Brotman, M. A., Rich, B. A., Kimes, A. S., . . . Leibenluft, E. (2007). Specificity of facial expression labeling deficits in childhood psychopathology. *Journal of Child Psychology and Psychiatry, 48*(9), 863–871.

Hankin, B. L., Young, J. F., Abel, J. R., Smolen, A., Jenness, J. L., Gulley, L. D., . . . Oppenheimer, C. W. (2014). Depression from childhood into late adolescence: Influence of gender, development, genetic susceptibility, and peer stress. *Journal of Abnormal Psychology, 124*(4), 803–816. doi:10.1037/abn0000089

Hartlage, S. A, Brandenburg, D. L, & Kravitz, H. M. (2004). Premenstrual exacerbation of depressive disorders in a community-based sample in the United States. *Psychosomatic Medicine, 66*(5), 698–706.

Hasin, D., Samet, S., & Nunes, E., (2006). Diagnosis of comorbid psychiatric disorders in substance user assessed with the psychiatric research interview for substance and mental disorders for DSM-IV. *American Journal of Psychiatry, 163*, 689–696.

Hedaya, R. J. (2009, January). The culture of depression: Nature, materialism, and depression. *Psychology Today.* Retrieved from https://www/psychologytoday.com/blog/heath-matters/200901/the-culgture-depression-nature-materialism-and-depression

Heidenblut, S. (2014). Screening for depression with the Depression in Old Age Scale (DIA-S) and the Geriatric Depression Scale (GDS15): Diagnostic accuracy in a geriatric inpatient setting. *The Journal of Gerontopsychology and Geriatrics, 27*(1), 41–49. doi:10.1024/1662-9647/a000101

Hendricks, B. E., Bradley, L. J., Southern, S., Oliver, M., & Birdsall, B. (2011). Ethical code for the International Association of Marriage and Family Counselors. *The Family Journal, 19*, 217–224. doi:10.1177/1066480711400814

Hill, J., Wren, B., Alderton, J., Bruch, C., Kennedy, Eilis, E., Senior, R., Aslam, N., & Broyden, N. (2014). The application of a domains-based analysis to family processes: Implications for assessment and therapy. *Journal of Family Therapy, 36*, 62–80. doi:10.1111/j/1467-6427.2011.00568.x

Hollon, S. D., & Sexton, T. S. (2012). Determining what works in depression treatment: Translating research to relational practice using treatment guidelines. *Couples and Family Psychology, 1*(3), 199–212. doi:10.1037/a0029901

Hyman, S. E. (2010). The diagnosis of mental disorders: The problem of reification. *Clinical Psychology, 6*, 155–179.

Insel, T. R. (2007). Neuroscience: Shining ling on depression. *Science, 317*, 757–758.

Insel, T. R., Cuthbert, B., Garvey, M., Heinssn, R., Pine, D. S., Quinn, K., . . . Wang, P. (2010). Research domain criteria (RDoC): Toward a new classification framework for research on mental disorders. *American Journal of Psychiatry, 167*, 748–751.

Katon, W. J. (2011). Epidemiology and treatment of depression in patients with chronic medical illness. *Dialogues in Clinical Neuroscience, 13*(1), 7–23.

Keitner, G. I., Miller, I. W., & Ryan, C. E. (2005). Family functioning in severe depressive disorders. In L. Grunhaus & J. F. Greden (Eds.), *Severe depressive disorders* (pp. 89–110). Arlington, VA: American Psychiatric Publishing.

Kendler, K. S., Neale, M. C., Kessler, R. C., Heath, A. C., & Eaves, L. J. (1993a). A longitudinal twin study of personality and major depression in women. *Archives of General Psychiatry, 50*, 853–862.

Kendler, K. S., Neale, M. C., Kessler, R. C., Heath, A. C., & Eaves, L. J. (1993b). A longitudinal twin study of 1-year prevalence of major depression in women. *Archives of General Psychiatry, 50*, 843–852.

Kerr, M. E., & Bowen, M. (1988). *Family evaluation.* New York, NY/London, UK: W. W. Norton.

Kovacs, M. (2011). *Children's Depression Inventory 2* (CDI 2; 2nd ed.). North Tonawanda, NY: Multi-Health Systems.

Kupfer, D., Kuhl, E., & Regier, D. (2013). DSM-5: A diagnostic guide relevant to both primary care and psychiatric practice. *American Family Physician, 88*(8). Retrieved from http://www.aaftp.org/afp/2013/1015/od2.html

Larner, G., Strong, T., & Busch, R. (2013). Family therapy and the spectre of DSM-5. *Australian and New Zealand Journal of Family Therapy, 34*(2), 87–89. doi:10.1002/anzf.1013

Leahy, R., Holland, S., & McGinn, L. K. (2012). *Treatment plans and interventions for depression and anxiety disorders* (2nd ed.). New York, NY: Guilford Press.

MacKay, L. (2012). Trauma and Bowen family systems theory: Working with adults who were abused as children. *Australian and New Zealand Journal of Family Therapy, 33*(3), 232–241. doi:10.1017/aft.2012.28

Magidson, J. F., Wang, S., Lejuez, C. W., Iza, M., & Blanco, C. (2013). Prospective study of substance-induced and independent major depressive disorder among individuals with substance use disorders in a nationally representative sample. *Depression and Anxiety (1091–4269), 30*(6), 538–545. doi:10.1002/da.22122

Maj, M. (2013). Clinical judgment and the DSM-5 diagnosis of major depression. *World Psychiatry, 12*(2), 89–91. doi:10.1002/wps.20049

Margulies, D. M., Weintraub, S., Basile, J., Grover, P. J., & Carlson, G. A. (2012). Will disruptive mood dysregulation disorder reduce false diagnosis of bipolar disorder in children? *Bipolar Disorders, 14*(5), 488–496. doi:10.1111/j.1399-5618.2012.01029.x

Matsumoto, T., Asakura, H., & Hayashi, T. (2013). Biopsychosocial aspects of premenstrual syndrome and premenstrual dysphoric disorder. *Gynecological Endocrinology, 29*(1), 67–73. doi:10.3109/09513590.2012.705383

McGoldrick, M., Preto, N., & Carter, B. (2016). The life cycle in its changing context: Individual, family and social perspective. In M. McGoldrick, N. Preto, & B. Carter (Eds.), *The expanding family life cycle* (5th ed., pp. 1–41). Boston, MA: Pearson.

Miklowitz, D. J., George, E. L., Richards, J. A., Simoneau, T. L., & Suddath, R. L. (2003). A randomized study of family-focused psychoeducation and pharmacotherapy in outpatient management of bipolar disorder. *Archives of General Psychology, 60*, 904–912.

Minuchin, S., & Lappin, J. (2012). Instructor's manual for Salvador Minuchin on family therapy [pdf version]. Retrieved from http://www.psychotherapy.net

National Institute of Mental Health. (2014). Major depression among adults. Retrieved from https://www.nimh.nih.gov/health/statistics/prevalence/major-deression-among-adults.shtml

Nemade, R., Reiss, N. S., & Dombeck, M. (September, 2007). *Social and relational factors in major depression.* Retrieved from https://www.mentalhelp.net/articles/social-and-relational-factors-in-major-depression

Newman, B. R., & Newman, P. R. (2015a). Infancy (First 24 months). *Development through life: A psychosocial approach* (12th ed., pp. 137–191). Stamford, CT: Cengage.

Newman, B. R., & Newman, P. R. (2015b). Major theories of understanding human development. In B. Newman & P. Newman (Eds.), *Development through life: A psychosocial approach* (12th ed., pp. 21–60). Stamford, CT: Cengage.

Nichols, M. P., & Schwartz, R. C. (2005). *The essentials of family therapy.* Boston, MA: Allyn & Bacon.

Nolen-Hoeksema, S. (2014a). Assessing and diagnosing abnormality. In S. Nolen-Hoeksema (Ed.), *Abnormal psychology* (6th ed., pp. 58–79). New York, NY: McGraw-Hill.

Nolen-Hoekseman, S. (2014b). Characteristics of depressive disorders. In S. Nolen-Hoeksema (Ed.), *Abnormal psychology* (6th ed., pp. 22–55). New York, NY: McGraw-Hill.

Patten, S., Williams, J., Lavorato, D., Bulloch, A., Currie, G., & Emery, H. (2014). Depression and painful conditions: Patterns of association with health status and health utility ratings in the general population. *Quality of Life Research, 23*(1), 363–371.

Pryor, K. (1999). *Don't shoot the dog: The new art of teaching and training* (2nd ed.). New York, NY: Bantam Books.

Rasmussen, P. R. (2010). *The quest to feel good.* New York, NY: Routledge.

Rasmussen, P. R., & Aleksandrof, D. (2014). Depression and bipolar disorders. In L. Sperry, J. Carlson, J. B. Sauerheber, & J. Sperry (Eds.), *Psychopathology and psychotherapy: DSM-5 diagnosis, case conceptualization, and treatment* (3rd ed., pp. 95–120). Florence, KY: Taylor & Francis.

Reiss, D., & Wamboldt, M. Z. (2006). Genetic strategies for delineating relational taxons. In S. R. Beach, M. Z. Wamboldt, N. J. Kaslow, R. E. Heyman, M. B. First, L. G. Underwood, & D. Reiss (Eds.), *Relational processes and DSM-V: Neuroscience, assessment, prevention, and treatment* (pp. 89–104). Arlington, VA: American Psychiatric Publishing.

Rich, B. A., Grimley, M. E., Schmajuk, M., Blair, R. J., & Leibenluft, E. (2008). Face emotion labeling deficits in children with bipolar disorder and severe mood dysregulation. *Development and Psychopathology, 20*(2), 529–546.

Roy, A., Klein, R., Angelosante, A., Bar-Haim, Y., Leibenluft, E., Hulvershorn, L., . . . Spindel, C. (2013). Clinical features of young children referred for impairing temper outbursts. *Journal of Child and Adolescent Psychopharmacology, 23*(9), 588–596. doi:10.1089/cap.2013.0005

Rush, A. J., Trivedi, M. H., Ibrahim, H. M., Carmody, T. J., Arnow, B., Klein, D. N., . . . Keller, M. B. (2003). The 16-item Quick Inventory of Depressive Symptomatology (QID) Clinical Rating (QIDS-C) and Self-Report (QIDS-SR): A psychometric evaluation in patients with chronic major depression. *Biological Psychiatry, 54*, 573–583.

Serra, F., Spoto, A., Ghisl, M., & Vidotto, G. (2015). Formal psychological assessment in evaluating depression: A new methodology to build exhaustive and irredundant adaptive questionnaires. *PLoS ONE, 10*(4), 122–131. doi:10.1371/journal.pone.0122131

Shpigel, M. S., Diamond, G. M., & Diamond, G. S. (2012). Changes in parenting behaviors, attachment, depressive symptoms, and suicidal ideation in attachment-based family therapy for depressive and suicidal adolescents. *Journal of Marital and Family Therapy, 38*(1), 271–283. doi:10.1111/j.1752-0606.0212 .00295.x

Simblett, G. (2013). Dancing with the DSM: The reflexive positioning of narrative informed practice. *Australian and New Zealand Journal of Family Therapy, 34*(2), 113–127.

Sommers-Flanagan, J., & Sommers-Flanagan, R. (2014). *Clinical interviewing* (5th ed.). Hoboken, NJ: Wiley.

Swartz, H., Grote, N. K., & Graham, P. (2014). Brief interpersonal psychotherapy (IPT-B): Overview and review of evidence. *American Journal of Psychotherapy, 68*(4), 443–462.

Thase, M. E., & Denko, T. (2008). Pharmacotherapy of mood disorders. *Annual Review of Clinical Psychology, 4*, 53–92.

Trangkasombat, U. (2008). Family functioning in mental illness: A study in Thai families with depressive disorders and schizophrenia. *Journal of Family Psychotherapy, 19*(2), 187–201.

U. S. Congress. (1996). Health Insurance Portability and Accountability Act of 1996 (HIPPA). 104th U. S. Congress. H.R. 3103. 104–191 (21 August). H.R. 104–496.

U.S. Department of Health & Human Services. (2003). The Security Rule. Retrieved from https://www .hhs.gov/hipaa/for-professionals/security

Wakefield, J. (2013). DSM-5: An overview of changes and controversies. *Clinical Social Work Journal, 41*, 139–154. doi:10.1007/s10615-013-0445-2

Yesavage, J. A., Brink, T. L., Rose, T. L., Lum, O. Huang, V., Adey, M., & Leirer, V. O. (1983). Development and validation of a geriatric depression screening scale: A preliminary report. *Journal of Psychiatric Research, 17*, 37–49. doi:10.1016/0022-3956(82)90033-4

Zimmerman, M. (2011). Tools for depression: Standardized rating scale. *Medscape Education Psychiatry and Mental Health.* Retrieved from http://www.medscape.org/viewarticle/749921

5

APPLYING SYSTEMS TO ANXIETY DISORDERS

Danielle A. Black

A family systems approach to understanding anxiety within a family or couple is complex. The *Diagnostic and Statistical Manual of Mental Disorders* (5th ed.; *DSM-5*; American Psychiatric Association, 2013) provides a framework for identifying and understanding Anxiety Disorders. It is important as systemic clinicians to understand and use the *DSM-5* for several reasons. These reasons include the following: (a) Most of the empirical research studies investigating Anxiety in children, adults, couples, and families are based on *DSM-5* criteria. Thus, most of the research knowledge base that exists to inform treatment of children, families, and couples is based on *DSM-5* criteria; (b) insurance companies that pay for therapeutic services require a diagnosis from *DSM-5* and now the *International Classification of Diseases, Tenth Revision, Clinical Modification (ICD-10-CM*; National Center for Health Statistics, 2017) in order to provide reimbursement to providers; and (c) many if not most mental health providers use *DSM-5* as a common language to understand and communicate with one another. The purpose of this chapter is to review the *DSM-5* Anxiety Disorders through a systemic perspective.

DSM-5 AND FAMILY SYSTEMS

The *DSM-5* Anxiety Disorders share the key feature of excessive or paralyzing fear and/or intense anxiety with associated disturbances in behavior. Anxiety is a normal human emotion that all persons experience. However, in order to be considered experiencing an anxiety disorder, the individual must experience significant distress or impairment across multiple domains in functioning (e.g., familial, social, academic, or occupational). This section covers the essential aspects of anxiety disorders: diagnostic features and associated features of anxiety disorders.

Diagnostic Features of Anxiety Disorders

Anxiety disorders share the key features of intense fear or anxiety, avoidance of feared stimulus, and physical symptoms common to the experience of anxiety. Although *DSM-5* distinguishes different anxiety disorders, the research literature supports similar factors maintaining each of the anxiety disorders (Wilamowska et al., 2010). Table 5.1 provides an overview of the key features of the anxiety disorders. The distinguishing feature differentiating the *DSM-5* Anxiety Disorders is the focus of each anxiety disorder or the core feared stimuli, and the focus of the fear informing the other individual domains of focus in the *DSM*. These domains include a cognitive response, physical response, and behavioral response. The cognitive response for the anxiety disorders is worry. Individuals with anxiety tend to exhibit two cognitive errors: overestimating the probability of a negative event (i.e., thinking a negative event or outcome is much more likely to happen than objective reality) and catastrophizing (i.e., thinking the worst case scenario will happen). The physical component is the physical response to fear such as muscle tension, difficulty in breathing, dizziness, and other symptoms associated with the activation of the sympathetic nervous system. The behavioral response to anxiety is the active avoidance of the feared stimuli.

In order to meet criteria for an anxiety disorder besides the core features, an individual must experience the disorder for a specified period of time (see Table 5.1).

For example, in Social Anxiety Disorder (SAD; also known as *social phobia*), the core feature is the fear of negative evaluations by others. It follows that across the other individual domains the core feature of fear, anxiety, or both would be consistent. An individual meeting criterion for SAD would fear being evaluated by others (core focus of his or her anxiety). Thus, the individual with SAD would worry about being judged by others and being evaluated negatively. This individual might believe if he or she speaks in class, classmates will judge the performance: "They will think I am stupid" (cognitive component); therefore, the individual may avoid giving speeches or talking in class (behavioral component).

Associated Features of Anxiety Disorders

Anxiety disorders represent one of the highest prevalent disorders within children (Merikangas et al., 2010) and adults (Kessler, Petukhora, Sampson, Zaslavsky, & Wittchen, 2012). Prevalence estimates for the anxiety disorders vary across studies. The most reliable prevalence estimates for anxiety disorders come from the replication of the National Comorbidity Survey (NCS; Kessler et al., 2012). The NCS provides the most reliable prevalence estimates because of the NCS use of a national representative sample. Table 5.2 provides the lifetime prevalence of *DSM-5* Anxiety Disorders. Lifetime prevalence is the percentage of individuals who meet criteria for an anxiety disorder at any point during their lifetimes. In the NCS, Selective Mutism was not studied, and a national representative sample studying the prevalence rates of selective mutism is unavailable. However, studies using community or clinic samples estimate the prevalence rate of selective mutism to range between 0.47% and 0.76% (for a review, see Viana, Beidel, & Rabian, 2009).

Table 5.3 provides the *point prevalence* rates. Point prevalence is the percentage of individuals who meet criteria for an anxiety disorder during a specific period of time (e.g., 6 months or 1 year). Further, anxiety disorders represent a high majority of clients obtaining services in outpatient settings (Kessler et al., 2012). Thus, it is highly likely that most clinicians will have a need to treat anxiety disorders in their practices.

(continued)

TABLE 5.1 Key Individual Features of DSM-5 Anxiety Disorders

	Focus of Anxiety	Symptom Duration	Physical Component	Cognitive Component	Behavioral Component
Separation anxiety disorder	Fear of separation from major attachment figure	Children: 4 weeks or more Adolescents and adults: 6 months or more	Difficulty sleeping, stomach aches, headaches, nausea, vomiting	Worry about losing major attachment figure due to a catastrophic event: car accident, kidnapping, illness, or murder	Avoidance of being separated from major attachment figure; for example: sleeping in bed with parents, refusing to go to sleepovers with friends, refusing to go to sleep away camp
SM	DSM-5 does not include fear as a specific criterion for SM	1 month or more	Not identified in DSM-5 criteria	Not identified in DSM-5 criteria	Avoidance of speaking in specific situations, typically school
Specific phobia	Fear of specific object or situation. Common phobias include animals, needles, heights, storms, etc.	6 months or more	Possible panic symptoms in the presence of the phobic stimulus or fainting or near fainting	Worry about being in the presence of the feared object or situation	Avoidance of any situations or places in which the feared object/situation may be
Social anxiety disorder	Fear of negative evaluation by others	6 months or more	Possible panic symptoms	Worry about the probability of being negatively evaluated or embarrassed by others	Avoidance of social situations and/or development of safety behaviors in order to endure feared social situations

TABLE 5.1 Key Individual Features of DSM-5 Anxiety Disorders (continued)

	Focus of Anxiety	Symptom Duration	Physical Component	Cognitive Component	Behavioral Component
Panic disorder	Fear of having a panic attack after experiencing recurrent panic attacks	1 month or more	Difficulty breathing, accelerated heart rate, chest pain, dizziness, etc.	Fear of having a panic attack or fear that one is going to die or go crazy if one has a panic attack	Avoidance of any activities or situations that may produce panic symptoms
Generalized anxiety disorder	Pervasive, pronounced, and distressing worry about typical everyday things such as money, health of family members, etc.	6 months or more	Muscle tension, restlessness, difficulty sleeping	Excessive worry about everyday things, such as social concerns, physical concerns, and concerns about mental functioning	Avoidance of completing tasks involving worries

DSM-5, *Diagnostic and Statistical Manual of Mental Disorders, Fifth Edition*; SM, selective mutism.

TABLE 5.2 Lifetime Prevalence of DSM-5 Anxiety Disorders in NCS

	Ages 13–17		Ages 18–64	
	Female	Male	Female	Male
Panic disorder	2.5%	2.1%	7%	3.3%
Generalized anxiety disorder	2.8%	1.6%	7.7%	4.6%

DSM-5, *Diagnostic and Statistical Manual of Mental Disorders, Fifth Edition*; NCS, National Comorbidity Survey.
Source: Kessler et al. (2012).

TABLE 5.3 Point Prevalence Rates (12-Month Period) From the NCS

	Ages 13–17	Ages 18–64
Panic disorder	1.9%	3.1%
Generalized anxiety disorder	0.9%	2.9%
Agoraphobia	2.0%	1.7%
Social phobia	7.9%	8.0%
Specific phobia	16.3%	10.1%
Separation anxiety disorder	1.5%	1.0%
Selective mutism	Not available	Not available

NCS, National Comorbidity Survey.
Source: Kessler et al. (2012).

Impact of Anxiety Disorders

Anxiety disorders have a considerable impact on children, adults, families, and society. Anxiety disorders severely impair physical, psychological, social functioning, and quality of life (e.g. Roy-Byrne & Katon, 1997; Wittchen, Carter, Pfister, Montgomery, & Kessler, 2000). Further, the financial cost of anxiety disorders on society is significant. Anxiety disorders have a significant financial impact on the health care system and the work place. The cost to the work environment is in the loss of productivity. Individuals suffering from anxiety disorders are sick more days from work (Stein et al., 2005) and have lower work productivity (Hoffman, Dukes, & Whittchen, 2008). Anxiety disorders are associated with considerable economic costs due to lost work productivity and high use of medical care (Hoffman et al., 2008). Individuals with anxiety disorders are common patrons of primary care settings, specialty clinics, and emergency room services (Fogarty, Sharma, Chetty, & Culpepper, 2008). Further anxiety disorders have been linked to problems within the family. Individuals with anxiety disorders have higher rates of relationship distress and divorce. Thus, anxiety disorders have a negative impact both within the family and the larger systems in our society such as the workplace and medical costs.

Risk Factors for Anxiety Disorders

A *risk factor* is defined as any attribute, characteristic, or experience that increases the likelihood of developing an anxiety disorder. Identifying risk factors for anxiety disorders helps the field develop prevention and interventions to treat anxiety disorders. As a systemic clinician, understanding a client's risk for developing a disorder may aid in developing interventions. However, a risk factor is not the same as causing an anxiety disorder.

Genetics or hereditability increases risk for all of the anxiety disorders. Individuals with first-degree relatives (e.g., parent or sibling) with an anxiety disorder are at an increased risk to develop an anxiety disorder. Research on the genetic contribution to anxiety disorders estimates that 30% to 40% of the variance in the anxiety disorders is due to genetics (for a review, see Norrholm & Ressler, 2009). Thus, other risk factors contribute more than half of the variance to the development of anxiety disorders.

Specific temperaments relate to increased risk for developing an anxiety disorder. *Temperament* is defined as an individual's early innate expression of biological, behavioral, and emotional responses to the environment. Several research studies have found a strong link between the temperament style of behavioral inhibition (BI) and anxiety disorders (Degnan, Almas, & Fox, 2010). BI is a temperament style that is characterized by withdrawal and avoidance of novel situations or interacting socially. Another temperament style related to risk for developing anxiety disorders is emotionality or the tendency to become emotionally aroused (Karevold, Roysamb, Ystrom, & Mathiesen, 2009). Children and adults with a temperament style of emotionality may become upset easily and then have difficulties calming down (e.g., it takes them more time than the average person to regulate their emotions). Most temperaments are inherited, and family members are also likely to have similar temperaments. For example, a parent of a child with an anxiety disorder is likely to also have BI or emotionality. Thus, parents are likely to model and reinforce their child's tendency toward BI or emotionality (for a review, see Rappee, 2012).

Stressful life events and trauma relate to an increased risk of developing an anxiety disorder (McLaughlin & Hatzenbuehler, 2009). Stressful life events such as early parental loss (Blanco et al., 2014), childhood abuse (Blanco et al., 2014; Moffitt et al., 2007), previous trauma (Blanco et al., 2014), peer victimization (Bond, Carlin, Thomas, Rubin, & Patton, 2001) increase the risk for developing an anxiety disorder. For example, a child who experiences a parent with a serious chronic illness, such as cancer, may later develop separation anxiety disorder. The child may witness his or her parent's extensive hospital stay and treatment fearing the loss of the parent. Once the cancer is in remission, the child may still fear losing the parent and develop Separation Anxiety Disorder.

Individual and System Factors Maintaining Anxiety Disorders

There are several individual factors identified as maintaining anxiety disorders. An individual factor is identified as something that is internal or based on the individual as opposed to a family or societal factor that maintains anxiety disorders. Considering that a core concept of family systems theory is that individuals are embedded in larger systems, it is still important to understand the individual and internal factors that may influence anxiety disorders. Further, the individual factors and systemic factors influence one another in a reciprocal manner. The individual factors identified as maintaining anxiety include behavioral and cognitive. Both of these individual factors are greatly influenced by family culture. An individual's behavioral response and cognitions develop within the context of his or her family.

Several behavioral factors have been linked to the maintenance of anxiety disorders. Behavioral avoidance maintains all of the anxiety disorders (Olatunji, Cisler, & Deacon,

2010; Whiteside, Gryczkowski, Brown-Jacobsen, McCarthy, & Denis, 2013). Behavioral avoidance occurs when an individual avoids the stimuli or situations that trigger a fear response. For example, a socially anxious client might avoid meeting new people or speaking in public. A client struggling with panic disorder might avoid any situation in which he or she thought the situation would cause a panic attack. In the short term, behavioral avoidance is a coping strategy that temporarily relieves anxiety; however, long-term behavioral avoidance is a key factor in maintaining all the anxiety disorders.

Many times the larger system, either the family or school, reinforces behavioral avoidance of feared stimuli. For example, a socially anxious child may avoid talking in class or giving speeches. The school and parents may shield the child from giving speeches or talking in class. The parents and school may be well meaning (e.g., Why make the child speak in class when speaking in class will cause the child distress?). However, by allowing the child to avoid giving speeches, the school personnel and parents of the child reinforce the child's anxiety and avoidance.

Cognitive factors that maintain anxiety are the thoughts or thinking styles contributing to maintaining an anxiety disorder. There is clear and consistent evidence that attentional bias for threat maintains anxiety disorders (Bar-Haim, Lamy, Pergamin, Bakermans-Kranenburg, & van IJzendoorn, 2007). Individuals with an anxiety disorder tend to pay more attention to stimuli that appear threatening to them, and they have difficulty noticing anything else other than the perceived threatening stimuli. An abundance of research suggests individuals with anxiety disorders perceive neutral stimuli as dangerous compared to individuals without an anxiety disorder. A second cognitive factor related to the maintenance of anxiety disorders is cognitive avoidance (Arch, Wolitzky-Taylor, Eifert, & Craske, 2012; Beesdo et al., 2012). Cognitive avoidance is when someone avoids any thoughts or images. Cognitive avoidance includes behaviors such as avoiding thinking about the worry and engaging in distraction to avoid thinking about the worry.

Attentional bias and cognitive avoidance are internal processes; however, the family system or larger systems influence the internal process of attentional bias and cognitive avoidance. Many parents model attentional bias for children (for a review, see Rappee, 2012). For example, a parent may constantly be concerned with safety and model vigilance to neutral stimuli. The parent's behavior teaches the child to focus attention (i.e., attentional bias) toward potential threats within the world. Further, parents may model cognitive avoidance teaching their children to respond in the same manner. In adult romantic relationships, a partner may influence the process of cognitive avoidance as well. For example, a partner with Generalized Anxiety Disorder (GAD) may express worry and concern to his or her partner about finances. In an effort to soothe the partner with GAD, the non-anxious partner may help the partner with GAD distract through activities, discussing other topics, or reassure the partner that the worry is unfounded. Reassurance on the surface is a supportive response; however, the research supports reassurance giving (i.e., without challenging some of the worry) maintains worry and anxiety.

RELATIONAL AND CULTURAL FEATURES

The majority of research on the etiology and treatment of anxiety disorders focuses on individual variables or individual therapy. Most likely this is due to the majority of researchers who are focused on the topic have an individual orientation instead of a systemic orientation. However, there are several relational and cultural variables that are related to the anxiety disorders. It is important to understand how these systemic factors may maintain anxiety disorders and aid in the treatment of anxiety disorders.

Relational Factors Associated With Anxiety Disorders

There are many relational factors related to the etiology or maintenance of anxiety disorders. These different factors can be distilled into three different categories: *relationship quality, communication,* and *accommodation.*

Lower relationship quality within the couple or family system relates to anxiety disorders. Relationship quality or the health of a relationship can be defined in many ways. Couple conflict, lower relationship satisfaction, and couple violence all correlate with adult anxiety disorders (Bryne, Carr, & Clark, 2004; McLeod, 1994). Couple distress has been linked to an increased risk in developing an adult anxiety disorder (Whisman, 2007; Whisman, 1999). For example, conflict between parents consistently relates to childhood anxiety disorders (Cummings & Davies, 2010). The research suggests that the relationship between relationship quality and the anxiety disorders is both a risk factor and a sequelae of anxiety disorders. Lower relationship quality increases risk for anxiety disorders, and an individual with an anxiety disorder has lower relationship quality compared to individuals without an anxiety disorder.

Communication is closely linked in the literature to the quality of relationships. Expressed emotion (EE) by family members relates to treatment outcome across a variety of anxiety disorders. EE is conceptualized as three factors: criticism and hostility, emotional overinvolvement, and positivity (Chambless, Steketee, Bryan, Aiken, & Hooley, 1999). EE relates to worse treatment outcome for the anxiety disorders (Chambless & Steketee, 1999; Zinbarg, Lee, & Yoon, 2007). An example of EE is the following exchange:

> *IP:* "I'm really scared to give this speech tomorrow. I'm scared the other kids will laugh at me."
>
> *Parent:* "That's not going to happen. You need to just start practicing right now. If you had practiced this earlier in the week, you wouldn't be in this position." [said with a hostile voice]

However, constructive criticism or nonhostile criticism relates to better treatment outcome (Peter & Hand, 1998; Zinbarg et al., 2007). Thus, providing support and validation while gently trying to support the family member toward approach behaviors produces better treatment outcome. An example of nonhostile criticism is the following:

> *IP:* "I'm really scared to give this speech tomorrow. I'm scared the other kids will laugh at me."
>
> *Parent:* "I know giving speeches is really difficult and scary for you. Let's try to work on the speech together. I will be your audience and you can practice with me. If you practice with me as your audience, you will feel more prepared to give your speech tomorrow."

Thus, two factors, hostility and emotional overinvolvement, maintain anxiety disorders, whereas positivity with gentle pushing toward approach behaviors decreases the identified patient's (IP's) avoidance and anxiety.

Several behaviors of parents and partners have been linked to the maintenance of anxiety disorders. Although the research literature defines these behaviors with different terms, the essence of these behaviors is the definition of *enmeshment.* Enmeshment describes families with diffuse boundaries and an overconcern for other family members leading to the loss of autonomous development (Minuchin, 1974). The two family behaviors found to relate consistently to the anxiety disorders are parent accommodation and overinvolved parenting.

Accommodation is when a parent tries to reduce a child's anxiety by either participating in the anxious symptoms or adjusting the family routine due to the child's anxiety

(Lebowitz et al., 2013). For example, a family with a child with separation anxiety may accommodate the fear of separation by always staying at home with the child, letting the child not go to school, or providing excessive reassurance (e.g., helping the child avoid his or her fears). Another example might include accommodation of the anxiety within a couple in which the wife has agoraphobia. The husband may accommodate the wife's fear of leaving the house by doing all the grocery shopping or other errands needed to run the household, thus allowing the wife to stay within the house and lowering her anxiety. However, accommodation in the long run results in maintaining the anxiety disorder. The child with separation anxiety never resolves his or her fears due to the accommodation, and similarly the wife with agoraphobia continues to have fears of leaving the house.

Overinvolved parenting is when parents become involved to a high degree in their child's life to reduce the child's distress; however, the level of involvement is not developmentally appropriate. Thus, the parents' overinvolvement disrupts healthy child development. Overinvolvement is similar to accommodation; however, overinvolved parenting includes behaviors such as psychological control or overprotection (Barber, 1996). Further, accommodation does not include the psychological control component. Overinvolved parenting results in child behavioral avoidance of feared stimuli, and child behavioral avoidance maintains the child's anxiety disorder (Hudson & Rapee, 2001).

Cultural Features of Anxiety Disorders

As systemic clinicians, it is important to understand an individual within the context in which he or she lives. Traditionally, individual-focused disciplines have either ignored cultural factors or placed less emphasis on their importance. Marsella (2006) defines culture as "shared learned behavior and meanings that are socially transmitted in various life-activity settings for purposes of individual and collective adjustment and adaptation" (Marsella, 2006, p. 353). It is important to always consider an individual's cultural background in order to provide competent assessment and treatment. It is important to understand the prevalence of anxiety disorders across different cultures and understand how to assess and treat anxiety disorders through a multisystemic cultural framework.

Prevalence Across Cultures

DSM-5 provides little information regarding the cultural variables and anxiety disorders. Baxter and colleagues (2013) investigated the largest number of studies investigating culture and anxiety disorders. Non-Western cultures were associated with a reduced risk for anxiety disorders while Western cultures had higher rates of anxiety disorders. Non-Western countries such as China and Indonesia have lower rates of anxiety disorders compared to the United States or European countries. The prevalence rates of anxiety disorders were significantly higher in populations exposed to conflict (e.g., war) compared to non-conflict populations. Finally, countries that were developed had higher rates of anxiety disorders compared to developing countries. For example, countries such as the United States (a developed country) compared to Ethiopia (a nondeveloped country) have higher rates of anxiety disorders.

Cultural Framework for Anxiety Disorders

Culture informs an individual's and family's identity. Thus, it is important to understand our clients' cultural backgrounds and how they may influence treatment. Sue and Sue (2012) outline some core competencies for providing culturally competent treatment for clients. There are three competencies that therapists need in order to provide culturally competent treatment. The first is awareness of one's own assumptions, beliefs, values, and biases. The second competency is an understanding of the worldview of culturally diverse clients. The third competency is developing appropriate interventions or strategies or techniques.

These competencies can be achieved by understanding the influence of society and culture on marginalized populations. A *marginalized population* is a group of people who are not part of the majority group. A marginalized population lacks privilege and as a result is excluded from mainstream social, economic, cultural, or political life. Marginalized populations include individuals belonging to a certain race, religion, political or cultural group, age, gender, sexual orientation, or financial status. Thus, it is important to understand a client's level of marginalization in society as well as the impact of marginalization on the individual's expression of anxiety symptoms and treatment for these symptoms. Further, cultural competency strongly relates to positive treatment outcomes for marginalized populations (Sue, 2010), whereas lack of cultural competency predicts worse treatment outcomes and treatment drop out for marginalized populations (Sue, 2010).

How do we develop cultural competency as clinicians? Hayes (2001) developed a model to help guide clinicians in developing cultural competency with clients. The ADDRESSING acronym represents the nine areas of culture clinicians need to consider when working with marginalized populations. ADDRESSING stands for: age and generational influences; developmental and acquired disabilities; religion and spiritual orientation; ethnicity (and race); socioeconomic status, which includes education; sexual orientation; indigenous heritage; national origin (and generational status); and gender. Clinicians need to consider the possible worldview the client may have based on these areas and validate the client's experience of possible prejudice or microaggressions experienced. This is especially important when working with marginalized populations with anxiety disorders. It is understandable that clients may become anxious or experience worsening of symptoms due to prejudice or microaggressions. Many of the extant empirically validated treatments for anxiety disorders focus on changing cognitions or threat bias (Barlow, 2010; Barlow et al., 2010). However, it may be advantageous in some situations for an anxious client to be anxious. For example, a client who is experiencing racial discrimination may need to be on guard (need his or her anxiety) in order to take action to protect himself or herself. It is important that the clinician is able to validate the client's anxiety and help the client cope with his or her experiences of marginalization (e.g., "It's difficult being a minority in a workplace that does not value diversity. It has to be frustrating and hurtful.").

FAMILY SYSTEMS ASSESSMENTS

In order to develop an effective family intervention for individuals with an anxiety disorder, it is important to complete a thorough assessment. An initial assessment should measure the anxiety symptoms (e.g., social anxiety, GAD), the severity of symptoms, and the factors maintaining the anxiety disorder (s). The initial assessment for anxiety disorders includes three stages: (a) alliance building, (b) assessment of symptoms, and (c) assessment of factors maintaining the symptoms.

The alliance or relationship between the client and the therapist is important to the foundation of any therapy. The alliance is the most important common factor (e.g., the elements of therapy are important across all therapies). The therapeutic alliance is strongly related to positive treatment outcomes. Pinsof et al. (2008) developed the first alliance model for multisystemic therapy. The model consists of two domains: content and interpersonal. The *content domain* includes three dimensions: tasks, goals, and bonds. Tasks and goals refer to the agreement between the client and the therapist regarding the tasks and goals of treatment. In order to develop an alliance with a client, the therapist and client must agree on the goals of therapy and the tasks to reach these goals. The bond refers to the attachment between the client and the therapist (e.g., the client feels attached to the therapist). The second domain of the multisystemic model of alliance is the interpersonal domain. The *interpersonal domain* includes the relationship or alliance between the therapist and each client and the system as a whole (i.e., the therapist's alliance with the entire family). Split alliances, where one family member has a high alliance with the therapist and the other member has low alliance ratings, predict worse treatment outcomes. Thus, it is important at the beginning of treatment to not rush the process of assessment, but to develop the alliance before proceeding to formal self-report measures and assessment.

The second stage of assessment for anxiety disorders is to assess the focus/type and severity of the individual's anxiety. Several self-report measures exist that assess for the type and severity of anxiety disorders for both children and adults. These measures can be completed by the identified patient (IP) in a short period of time and scored easily by the clinician. There are many different measures developed to assess anxiety symptoms. Two measures that are reliable, valid, and clinically useful are the Multidimensional Anxiety Scale for Children-2 (MASC-2; March, 2013) and the Screen for Child Anxiety Related Emotional Disorders (SCARED; Birmaher et al., 1999). The MASC-2 is a 39-item measure that yields scores across four domains: physical symptoms, social anxiety, harm avoidance, and separation/panic. The SCARED is a 38-item self-report measure that assesses symptoms for Separation Anxiety Disorder, GAD, SAD, and School Phobia.

The third stage in the initial assessment is to assess the family factors maintaining the IP's anxiety disorder(s). The family factors identified in the literature as maintaining anxiety disorders include relationship quality (i.e., marital satisfaction), EE (i.e., high levels of criticism and emotional overinvolvement), and accommodation (i.e., reinforcing behavioral avoidance). The two relationship quality variables consistently identified in the literature to relate to anxiety disorders are couple conflict or violence and couple distress (e.g., lower couple satisfaction). The Revised Dyadic Adjustment Scale (Anderson et al., 2014) is a 14-item self-report measure that assesses couple satisfaction. The Revised Conflict Tactics Scale (Straus, Hamby, Boney-McCoy, & Sugarman, 1996) is a self-report measure to assess aggression between two intimate partners.

Communication, specifically EE, between family members and the IP is a key variable in the maintenance of anxiety disorders. The gold standard measure of EE is the Camberwell Family Interview (CFI; Leff & Vaughn, 1985), a semistructured interview of the IP's family members without the IP present. The use of the CFI in clinical practice is not practical. In order to use the CFI a clinician needs extensive training that is difficult to obtain. The CFI is time-consuming to administer and score (4.5 hours). Hooley and Parker (2006) identified alternative clinically useful measures of EE. The Family Attitude Scale (FAS; Kavanagh et al., 1997) is a 30-item questionnaire that assesses EE from family members toward the IP. Each family member completes the FAS separately about the IP. An example item from the FAS is the following: "He/She is really hard to take."

The Family Accommodation Scale—Anxiety (Lebowitz et al., 2013) is a 9-item parent-report questionnaire assessing frequency of parental accommodation over the past month. Closely linked to accommodation is overinvolved parenting and overparenting can be measured using the Overparenting Scale (OS; Segrin, Woszidlo, Givertz, Bauer, & Murphy, 2012). The OS is a 39-item scale completed by parents. Example items include: "I make suggestions to my child to help him or her get things accomplished," and "I do what I can to keep my child out of difficult situations."

These three stages of assessment should be completed early in the treatment process. However, given the importance of the alliance, the clinician should complete these three stages in a time frame that supports the alliance. The first several sessions should focus on developing rapport and identifying goals before proceeding to the assessment phase. The clinician should explain the purpose of the assessment to the family. For example, "I want to understand your family better and the ways in which Sandra's (IP) anxiety interferes with her goals in life. I am going to give you some questionnaires to complete. After you complete the questionnaires, we will have a family feedback session. We will work together to understand the results and develop ways that you can support Sandra." After completing the assessment phase, the clinician can give the IP and family feedback regarding the results of the assessment.

The family assessment feedback session is an opportunity to reflect the strengths and areas of growth for the family. All of the results of the assessments should be framed in a validating manner. For example, "Sandra, the results of the assessment indicate that you really have a lot of anxiety about social situations. So it makes sense that going to parties and meeting new people is really hard for you. I want us to work together to find ways to decrease the amount of social anxiety you experience. As a family, your family experiences a lot of conflict around different topics. I want us to work together to increase the amount of positivity with each other and find ways to support you so you can feel less anxious."

FAMILY SYSTEMS INTERVENTIONS

The research on family therapy for anxiety disorders is limited. The most well-researched Family Therapy Model for anxious adults and children is family cognitive behavioral therapy (FCBT). Brendel and Maynard (2014) completed a statistical review of all the FCBT clinical trials. In this meta-analysis, FCBT performed better than child-only or group CBT. In the adult population, only two randomized clinical trials have been conducted comparing individual CBT treatment of agoraphobia to spouse-assisted FCBT (Arnow, Taylor, Agras, & Telch, 1985; Barlow, O'Brian, & Last, 1984; Emmelkamp et al., 1992). In two studies FCBT performed better than individual CBT; however, one study found individual CBT performed better than FCBT. Overall, FCBT is empirically supported for childhood anxiety disorders. For the adult population, the only empirically supported treatment is FCBT for panic disorder agoraphobia.

FCBT is the most empirically supported family therapy to treat the anxiety disorders. However, the treatment components of FCBT vary greatly across studies. The following treatment components across the different models of FCBT include family psychoeducation, teaching coping skills, communication training, and reduction of accommodation behaviors.

Family Psychoeducation

The first step in a systemic treatment for anxiety disorders needs to include psychoeducation for the family. Many family members are not aware of the individual factors that maintain anxiety disorders. Thus, they can inadvertently worsen the IP's anxiety symptoms by accommodating the IP's avoidance of feared stimuli. These family members have the best of intentions (e.g., "I just don't want my child to suffer."). Conversely, many family members can become invalidating or express negativity toward the IP because they are unaware of the individual factors that maintain the IPs symptoms. Helping the family understand some of the key factors that maintain anxiety disorders will help set the stage for later interventions (e.g., decreasing EE, overinvolved parenting). One of the key factors to help families understand is the relationship between avoidance and anxiety disorders. Avoidance maintains all anxiety disorders. However, it is very important for families to understand to be validating and supportive of the IP's efforts to face his or her fears.

Coping Skills Training

During the Coping Skills Training phase of FCBT, children and parents learn CBT skills. The CBT skills taught to the family include deep breathing exercises, progressive muscle relaxation, and cognitive restructuring. The therapist first teaches the family a deep breathing technique called *paced breathing*. Next, the therapist teaches the family progressive muscle relaxation, a relaxation technique that includes tensing and releasing different muscle groups.

Cognitive restructuring consists of identifying anxious thoughts and replacing these thoughts with more objectively balanced thoughts. The family is taught to be a detective looking for evidence that supports its anxious beliefs and evidence against its anxious beliefs. The family uses a worksheet called a *thought record* to write down the following: situation (the situation that triggered the anxiety), moods (rated on a 0–10 scale), anxious thought (e.g., "I am going to fail the test."), evidence for the thought (e.g., "I received a C on the last test."), evidence against the thought ("I have never failed a math test before."), and identification of a more balanced thought based on the evidence ("Even though I feel unsure about the test, I won't fail because I will study hard."). The therapist guides the family through the worksheet, and the therapist helps the family be objective regarding the evidence for thoughts. The parents complete the thought record based on their own worries. This helps the parents understand the process so they can continue to support the IP outside of session. At the end of every session, the family is assigned homework to continue working on the skills it is taught in session.

Communication Training

Two very important variables maintaining anxiety disorders are relationship quality and EE. Both of these family factors are related to communication. The important target of intervention is decreasing negativity and increasing positivity. The therapist helps the family identify EEs and helps the family change its communication patterns over time. Techniques that help with this process include the speaker–listener technique and problem-solving training (e.g., assigning specific homework that increases positive communication at home).

The speaker–listener technique is a very structured technique to help families communicate more productively. One family member is identified as the speaker, and the other family members are identified as the listeners. Each listener takes a turn responding to the speaker. The therapist explains the rules of the speaker–listener technique. There are three main rules for the speaker: (a) The speaker speaks only about his or her own thoughts and feelings using "I" statements ("I was mad when you said I shouldn't worry about the test."). (b) The speaker says only a couple of statements (e.g., no more than three statements). (c) Once the speaker has finished, he or she cannot speak again until the listener has paraphrased what he or she heard. The listener then responds by paraphrasing the speaker's message ("You felt mad when I said you shouldn't worry."). The speaker is allowed to clarify the message. The therapist acts as a coach and intervenes only if the family does not follow the rules of the speaker–listener technique. The second part of this technique is to have the family engage in practice conversations. The therapist guides the practice conversations in session and intervenes as necessary (e.g., sees the family engage in EE or negativity). The family starts by discussing a positive topic, then progressively discusses more difficult topics. During these discussions, the therapist provides feedback and validates positive behaviors by the family. After each communication training session, the therapist assigns homework to the family to practice the techniques at home. At the next session, the therapist reviews the homework with the family and problem solves any issues that may have occurred while completing homework that week.

The next phase of communication training is problem-solving training. Problem-solving training teaches families concrete techniques for problem solving. The first is that the family must define the problem. Once the family has defined the problem, the family is instructed to brainstorm as many solutions to the problem as possible in a collaborative manner. The family works together to identify a solution to the problem and discusses the pros and cons of each solution. The therapist guides this problem-solving process, and the therapist intervenes if the family members start to express negativity toward one another.

Decrease Accommodation (Increase Approach Behaviors)

Avoidance is one of the main factors maintaining anxiety disorders. Often families unknowingly accommodate avoidance of the IP. The systemic clinician aids the family in understanding the relationship between accommodation and maintenance of the IP's anxiety symptoms. The therapist helps the IP and family identify key situations or stimuli that the IP avoids. Together the family and the IP develop a plan to gradually expose the IP to feared situations and stimuli. The role of the other family members is to help the IP approach feared situations and provide encouragement and praise for completing exposures. The systemic clinician helps monitor the progress of both the IP and the family's progress completing exposures.

ETHICAL AND LEGAL IMPLICATIONS

Ethical and legal implications are always important to consider with any client population. The American Association for Marriage and Family Therapy (AAMFT, 2012) provides a code of ethics for systemic clinicians. The *AAMFT Code of Ethics* delineates eight different principles to guide ethical professional standards. Many of the ethical codes would apply across the treatment of all *DSM-5* disorders. Therefore, this section focuses on the most common ethical and legal issues that pertain to working systemically with individuals diagnosed with anxiety disorders.

Informed Consent (AAMFT Ethics Code, Standard 1.2)

The AAMFT ethics code Principle 1, Responsibility to Clients, provides guidelines for ensuring therapeutic services are used appropriately by clients. Typically, most clinical practices, hospitals, or institutions have a standard form that includes the following: the terms of treatment, the cost of treatment, the potential risks and benefits of treatment, the limits of confidentiality, and any legal issues. It is suggested that clinicians review a written document outlining these points with clients. Once the consent for treatment form is reviewed, clients sign the form, indicating they understand the terms and agreement between them and the therapist. The consent for treatment form should be included in the clinical record of the client.

Many times in family therapy, a minor is involved in treatment. In many states, parents are allowed to sign consent for their children to participate in therapy. Although this satisfies a legal standard, ethically it is important that children understand and consent for treatment. The terms of treatment should be explained in developmentally appropriate language to children and teens. Probably the most salient and important issue working with minors revolves around confidentiality and the limits of confidentiality. It is suggested that all members of a family sign the consent for treatment including minors.

Confidentiality (AAMFT Ethics Code, Standard 2.1)

The AAMFT ethics code states that systemic clinicians must explain the possible limits of confidentiality. The clinician reviews the specific circumstances in which confidential information might need to be shared. It is important to explain the limits of confidentiality regarding safety. Individuals meeting criteria for anxiety disorders may experience comorbid conditions that place them at risk. Individuals with anxiety disorders are at risk for both suicide attempts and nonsuicidal self-injury (e.g., cutting self). A recent study found significant rates of suicide attempts and nonsuicidal self-injury among individuals diagnosed with an anxiety disorder (Chartrand, Sareen, Toews, & Bolton, 2012). Thus, it is important to explain the limits of confidentiality around safety issues.

Another common issue when working within a family system is the potential for sharing secrets with the therapist. It is important to identify and clarify the "client." Many times systemic clinicians need to work with the full family and subsystems within the family. Thus, it is important for the therapist to define "the client" to the family. The clinician also needs to explain the limits of confidentiality within the family. For example, the therapist needs to explain that he or she is not the holder of secrets in the family. When the therapist needs to switch between full family sessions to individual or subsystem work, the clinician needs to remind the individuals that the clinician does not keep secrets.

Professional Competence (AAMFT, Standard 3)

Systemic clinicians need to maintain their professional competency. Clinicians need to maintain their competence in family therapy through education, training, and/or supervision. The research on the treatment of anxiety disorders is constantly changing and new advances are emerging in the field. Thus, systemic clinicians working with anxiety disorders need to be aware of advances in the field. The clinician should take steps to gain training in any new treatments or techniques developed to treat anxiety disorders.

CASE CONCEPTUALIZATION

In order to further understand a systemic case conceptualization of a family impacted by anxiety disorders, a case example is provided. The IP is an emerging adult, Sandra, coping with multiple anxiety disorders. Sandra's parents initiated treatment due to Sandra's difficulties functioning within the family and school.

Presenting Concerns

Sandra is a 17-year-old African American and Latina female who recently dropped out of an Ivy League school on the East Coast. Sandra grew up with her parents, Arthur and Sonia, and her elder sister (Kendra) in an affluent, predominately Caucasian community in a suburb of New York City. Sandra felt "other" in her community growing up. She also never felt that she fit in at her elite private school she attended in New York City. She was often the only person of color in both her community where she lived and her school. Sandra left school due to feeling stressed and feeling home sick. During the first week of school, she had felt anxious about meeting new people and her academic performance. She often worried about what her peers thought of her, and she felt she was different than everyone else. One day on her way to class, she felt an unbelievable tightness in her chest and felt that she could not breathe. Sandra thought she was dying. She returned to her dorm room and did not go to class. Once she was in her dorm room, she started to feel better. Every day since this initial panic attack, Sandra was unable to attend class. She called Sonia everyday crying because she was so fearful to leave her room. Sonia decided her daughter needed to come home and withdraw from school. Currently, Sonia reports Sandra will not leave the house for fear of having a panic attack. She also reports being fearful of leaving her parents because "something bad might happen."

Sonia made the initial phone call for therapy. She described the precipitating events to the therapist before Sandra withdrew from college. Sandra was currently living at home and not engaged in any activities outside the home. Sonia described Sandra's day as mostly watching TV or playing games on her phone. Sonia noticed Sandra did not want to leave the house even with her parents. However, when her parents did leave the house for work, Sandra would call her mom at least 20 times a day to check on her mom. Sonia would become so worried she would often leave work to go home and check on Sandra. Sandra refused to leave the house and Sonia was worried about Sandra's ability to become a functioning adult.

Concurrent Problems

Sandra is experiencing difficulties in multiple domains in her life. She has dropped out of school, and she has limited a social network at home because most of her friends are still away at college. Sandra is living at home, and she spends most of her time alone because both of her parents work. Sonia's (mom) anxiety about Sandra (IP) has increased due to her concern and worry about Sandra's future. Thus, Sonia will nag Sandra to start making plans to re-enroll in a different university. Sonia's nagging produces more anxiety in Sandra, and she often becomes very frustrated and yells at her mother during these interactions. Thus, the general level of conflict in the home has increased overall. The family has never received therapy previously, and Sandra has never been prescribed any medications for her anxiety.

Background History and Stressors

Early in therapy, the therapist gathered some history and background regarding Sandra's presenting problems. Sonia (mom) described Sandra as a difficult baby to soothe (e.g., emotionality temperament style). Sandra was slow to warm to strangers, and she had difficulty separating from her mom and dad early on in childhood (e.g., behavioral inhibited temperament). Sonia described Sandra as being shy all of her childhood, and Sandra always had difficulties with transitions (e.g., going to kindergarten, transitioning from grade school to middle school). Arthur barely spoke during the session, and when the therapist would ask him questions, he would respond with very brief answers. The therapist inquired about other family members and family history of anxiety. Sonia reported her entire family had struggled with anxiety (i.e., a genetic vulnerability). Sonia reported she struggled with GAD, and her sisters all had struggled with various problems with anxiety. Arthur reported that he was very shy, and he felt that he saw a lot of himself in Sandra. The parents described a very conflictual and distant relationship between Sonia and her sister Kendra. The parents described Kendra as being "very different from Sonia. She is outgoing and doesn't understand why Sonia can't handle life."

Another very important factor contributing to Sandra's anxiety was the experience of being a minority person growing up in a Caucasian neighborhood. She was also the only minority person at her private school she attended before going away to college. Over the years, Sandra experienced both overt and subtle forms of racism. She had experienced many different microaggressions while attending high school, and she described feeling "other" and "different" at her Ivy League school. These experiences fueled Sandra's social anxiety, and she often worried others would "see my differences and reject me."

Strengths

Despite many difficulties, the family system is reliant and possesses many strengths. First, the family members have a strong attachment to one another, and they are invested in therapy. Further, the family was willing to be open and nondefensive regarding their inter-actions and the behaviors that may contribute to Sandra's anxiety. Although the family members have a high level of EE, they also express validation often, and they are moti-vated to change their interactions with one another (e.g., they expressed wanting to have more positive interactions with one another).

DSM-5 Impressions and Implications

Sandra presents with several different anxiety symptoms. She has experienced panic attacks, worry about school performance, fear of rejection by peers, and fear of separating from her family. Sandra's symptoms are most consistent with Separation Anxiety Disor-der and SAD. First, Sandra often experiences distress when her parents leave. During her assessment, Sandra explained to the therapist that she worries something "bad will hap-pen" to her parents when they are not with her. Further, she often refuses to leave home because she fears something will happen to her or her parents. Thus, she meets *DSM-5* criteria for Separation Anxiety Disorder.

Sandra also described feeling fearful in social situations, and she fears she will behave in a manner that will result in others judging her. Sandra's parents reported her fear of social situations dates back to childhood. Sandra reported her anxiety regarding social sit-uations upsets her, and her fear prevents her from accomplishing important goals in her life. Thus, Sandra also meets *DSM-5* criteria for SAD.

Finally, Sandra reports experiencing panic attacks. However, she does not meet *DSM-5* criteria for Panic Disorder. In order to meet criteria for Panic Disorder, an individ-ual must experience panic attacks and fear of having another panic attack. The fear of having a panic attack interferes with the individual's functioning. Although Sandra has experienced panic attacks, she does not fear having panic attacks. She reported her panic attacks have been due to specific situations (e.g., eating lunch with peers). Sandra also understands her panic attacks will not harm her. Although she finds her panic attacks uncomfortable, she does not avoid situations for fear of having a panic attack.

Relational Problems

Sandra is experiencing many different relational problems. First, her parents have engaged in accommodation (e.g., reinforcing Sandra's avoidance responses). Further, there is a lot of conflict within the family. Both of these factors influenced the course and prognosis of Sandra's anxiety disorder (Parent–Child Relational Problem). Sandra is also very different from her sister, and the two often argue (Sibling Relational Problem). The family has a high level of EE (High EE Level Within Family).

Sandra's life transition to college contributed to her worsening symptoms (Phase of Life Problem). Sandra dropped out of college to move home (Academic or Educational Problem). Finally, Sandra experienced microaggressions while she was attending her Ivy League school, and she continues to live in a predominately Caucasian community. As a result, Sandra continues to experience discrimination on a daily basis (Z60.5; Target of [per-ceived] discrimination and persecution).

Assessments

The therapist developed rapport and goals for treatment over the course of three sessions. At the fourth session, the therapist explained the purpose of the assessment. Sandra com-pleted the Multidimensional Anxiety Scale for Children-2 (MASC-2; March, 2013) and the

Screen for Child Anxiety Related Emotional Disorders (SCARED; Barmier et al., 1999). Sonia (mom) and Arthur (dad) completed the Revised Dyadic Adjustment Scale (Anderson et al., 2014), the Revised Conflict Tactics Scale, the Family Accommodation Scale—Anxiety (Lebowitz et al., 2013), and the Overparenting Scale (OS; Segrin et al., 2012). The family members each separately completed the Family Attitude Scale (FAS; Kavanagh et al., 1997).

The results of the assessment revealed many strengths as well as areas to improve in therapy. Sandra (IP) scored high on social anxiety scales and separation anxiety scales on both the MASC-2 and the SCARED. Her scores were within the clinical range, indicating that she is experiencing high levels of separation anxiety and social anxiety. The couple, Sonia and Arthur, scored within the healthy range on the Dyadic Adjustment Scale (DAS) (measure of marital quality), and the couple scored low on the Revised Conflict Tactics Scale, indicating they do experience interpersonal physical aggression with each other. Thus, the marital subsystem represents a strength within the family system. However, the parents scored high on the Family Accommodation Scale and the OS. The high scores on these scales indicate both Sonia and Arthur have high levels of accommodation behavior and overparenting with Sandra. Finally, the family members scored moderately high on the Family Attitudes Scale, indicating they have moderate levels of EE within the family.

Interventions

The therapist and family agreed to start family therapy focusing on the goals of decreasing the following: Sandra's anxiety symptoms, family EE, parent accommodation, and overparenting behaviors. The first phase of therapy focused on helping the family understand the targets of therapy and psychoeducation. The therapist explained the relationship between Sandra's anxiety and the family's interaction patterns. The second phase of therapy focused on teaching the family coping skills for anxiety. The therapist taught the family paced breathing, progressive muscle relaxation (PMR), and cognitive restructuring. The third phase of treatment focused on communication training. The therapist taught the family the speaker–listener technique and problem-solving techniques. The therapist also identified specific sequences that occur within the family that increase negativity and Sonia's anxiety.

Ethical and Legal Implications

The therapist obtained informed consent from all family members at the beginning of the first session. The therapist was careful to explain the limits of confidentiality and identified the family as the "client." After the fifth session, Sandra asked to meet with the therapist alone. The therapist agreed to have an individual session with Sandra. At the beginning of the session, the therapist reminded Sandra about the limits of confidentiality and the importance of not holding secrets. Sandra disclosed that she had cut her arm with a razor blade. The therapist completed a risk assessment regarding the cutting and determined the cutting was an emotion regulation strategy. The therapist explained that for Sandra's safety, they would need to tell Sandra's parents to help her manage if she started to have urges to cut in the future. The therapist and Sandra worked collaboratively to discuss the topic with the parents. They decided together, the therapist would tell Sandra's parents without Sandra in session. The decision was made because the therapist believed the parents' initial response might be negative. The therapist then discussed the cutting incident with Sandra's parents. After processing and explaining the behavior to the parents, Sandra returned to session. The family and therapist worked on a specific safety plan to prevent Sandra from engaging in cutting in the future.

There were two ethical issues that needed to be addressed. The first issue was involving confidentiality. Confidentiality was maintained because the client is the family and not Sandra as an individual client. The second ethical issue was safety and the proper level of care. Sandra was not suicidal, and she cut as an emotion regulation strategy. The therapist completed a risk assessment and determined Sandra was not suicidal. Further, Sandra's cut was very shallow and did not require medical attention, and this was her first time using self-injury as an emotion regulation strategy. The therapist developed a safety plan and contract regarding cutting with the family. Further, the therapist increased the number of sessions per week to increase the level of care. Finally, the therapist and the family developed a safety contract, and they agreed collaboratively that if Sandra engaged in cutting again, she would need to be referred to a higher level of care (e.g., an Intensive Outpatient Program). The family agreed to this treatment contract, and Sandra did not engage in self-injury during the remaining treatment.

DISCUSSION

As you continue to reflect on the case study and the overall approach, contemplate these questions:

- What cultural factors may contribute to or exacerbate Sandra's social anxiety and panic disorder?
- What factors do you think might maintain Sandra's accommodation and overparenting?
- How would you motivate Sandra to work on her avoidance given she will not leave her house?
- How would you approach working with the high EE and accommodation in this family?

SUMMARY

The anxiety disorders share the common symptom of fear, worry, and avoidance of specific situations. Each anxiety disorder has a theme or focus (e.g., separation, social situations). Avoidance is one of the key factors that maintain anxiety disorders. Family factors directly influence and contribute to both the maintenance of individual factors maintaining anxiety disorders. There is a bidirectional relationship between family factors and anxiety disorders. The family influences the individual diagnosed with an anxiety disorder, but the symptoms of anxiety also impact the family. The research indicates that families often exacerbate anxiety symptoms through EE, accommodation, and overparenting. Many of the existing empirically validated treatments for the anxiety disorders ignore systemic factors such as family and culture that may influence the presentation and treatment of anxiety disorders. Thus, a systemic approach to the treatment of anxiety disorders provides a rich framework for intervening with anxiety disorders.

REFERENCES

American Association for Marriage and Family Therapy. (2012, July 1). *AAMFT code of ethics.* Retrieved from http://aamft.org
American Psychiatric Association. (2013). *Diagnostic and statistical manual of mental disorders* (5th ed.). Arlington, VA: American Psychiatric Publishing.

Anderson, S. R., Tambling, R. B., Huff, S. C., Heafner, J., Johnson, L. N., & Ketring, S. A. (2014). The development of a reliable change index and cutoff for the Revised Dyadic Adjustment Scale. *Journal of Marital and Family Therapy, 40*, 525–534.

Arch, J. J., Wolitzky-Taylor, K. B., Eifert, G. H., & Craske, M. G. (2012). Longitudinal treatment mediation of traditional cognitive behavioral therapy and acceptance and commitment therapy for anxiety disorders. *Behavior Research and Therapy, 50*(7), 469–478.

Arnow, B. A., Taylor, C. B., Agras, W. S., & Telch, M. J. (1985). Enhancing agoraphobia treatment outcome by changing couple communication patterns. *Behavior Therapy, 16*, 452–467.

Barber, B. K. (1996). Parental psychological control: Revisiting a neglected construct. *Child Development, 67*, 3296–3319.

Bar-Haim, Y., Lamy, D., Pergamin, L., Bakermans-Kranenburg, M., & van IJzendoorn, M. H. (2007). Threat-related attentional bias in anxious and nonanxious individuals: A meta-analytic study. *Psychological Bulletin, 133*, 1–24.

Barlow, D. H. (2010), Conceptual background, development, and preliminary data from the unified protocol for transdiagnostic treatment of emotional disorders. *Depress Anxiety, 27*, 882–890.

Barlow, D. H., Farchione, T. J., Fairholme, C. P., Ellard, K. K., Boisseau, C. L., Allen, L. B., & May, J. T. E. (2010). *Unified protocol for transdiagnostic treatment of emotional disorders: Therapist guide.* New York, NY: Oxford University Press.

Barlow, D. H., O'Brian, G. T., & Last, C. G. (1984). Couples treatment of agoraphobia. *Behavior Therapy, 15*, 41–58.

Baxter, A. J., Scott, K. M., Vos, T., & Whiteford, H. A. (2013). Global prevalence of anxiety disorders: A systematic review and meta-regression. *Psychological Medicine, 43*(5), 897–910.

Beesdo-Baum, K., Jenjahn, E., Höfler, M., Lueken, U., Becker, E. S., & Hoyer, J. (2012). Avoidance, safety behavior, and reassurance seeking in generalized anxiety disorder. *Depression and Anxiety, 29*, 948–957.

Birmaher, B., Brent, D. A., Chiappetta, L., Bridge, J., Monga, S., & Baugher, M. (1999). Psychometric properties of the Screen for Child Anxiety Related Emotional Disorders (SCARED): A replication study. *Journal of the American Academy of Child & Adolescent Psychiatry, 38*(10), 1230–1236.

Blanco, C., Rubio, J., Wall, M., Wang, S., Jiu, C. J., & Kendler, K. S. (2014). Risk factors for anxiety disorders: Common and specific effects in a national sample. *Depression and Anxiety, 31*, 756–764.

Bond, L., Carlin, J. B., Thomas, L., Rubin, K., & Patton, G. (2001). Does bullying cause emotional problems? A prospective study of young teenagers. *British Medicine Journal, 323*, 834–856.

Brendel, K. E., & Maynard, B. R. (2014). Child–parent interventions for childhood anxiety disorders: A systematic review and meta-analysis. *Research on Social Work Practice, 24*(3), 287–295.

Bryne, M., Carr, A., & Clark, M. (2004). The efficacy of couple-based interventions for panic disorder with agoraphobia. *Journal of Family Therapy, 26*, 105–125.

Chambless, D. L., & Steketee, G. (1999). Expressed emotion and behavior therapy outcome: A prospective study with obsessive-compulsive and agoraphobic outpatients. *Journal of Consulting and Clinical Psychology, 67*, 658–665.

Chambless, D. L., Steketee, G., Bryan, A. D., Aiken, L. S., & Hooley, J. M. (1999). The structure of expressed emotion: A three-construct representation. *Psychological Assessment, 11*, 67–76.

Chartrand, H., Sareen, J., Toews, M., & Bolton, J. M. (2012). Suicide attempts versus nonsuicidal self-injury among individuals with anxiety disorders in a nationally representative sample. *Depression and Anxiety, 29*(3), 172–179.

Cummings, E. M., & Davies, P. T. (2010). *Marital conflict and children: An emotional security perspective.* New York, NY: Guilford Press.

Degnan, K. A., Almas, A. N., & Fox, N. A. (2010). Temperament and the environment in the etiology of childhood anxiety. *Journal of Child Psychology and Psychiatry, 51*, 497–517.

Emmelkamp, P., van Dyck, R., Bitter, M., Heins, R., Onstein, E. J., & Eisen, B. (1992). Spouse-aided therapy with agoraphobics. *British Journal of Psychiatry, 160*, 51–56.

Fogarty, C. T., Sharma, S., Chetty, V. K., & Culpepper, L. (2008). Mental health conditions are associated with increased health care utilization among urban family medicine patients. *Journal of the American Board of Family Medicine, 21*, 398–407.

Hays, P. A. (2001). *Addressing cultural complexities in practice: A framework for clinicians and counselors.* Washington, DC: American Psychological Association.

Hoffman, D. L., Dukes, E. M., & Wittchen, H. U. (2008). Human and economic burden of generalized anxiety disorder. *Depression and Anxiety, 25*(1), 72–90.

Hooley, J. M., & Parker, H. A. (2006). Measuring expressed emotion: An evaluation of the shortcuts. *Journal of Family Psychology, 20*, 386–396.

Hudson, J. L., & Rapee, R. M. (2001). Parent–child interactions and anxiety disorders: An observational study. *Behaviour Research and Therapy, 39*, 1411–1427.

Karevold, E., Roysamb, E., Ystrom, E., & Mathiesen, K. S. (2009). Predictors and pathways from infancy to symptoms of anxiety and depression in early adolescence. *Developmental Psychology, 45*, 1051–1060.

Kavanagh, D. J., O'Halloran, P., Manicavasagar, V., Clark, D., Piatkowska, O., Tennant, C., & Rosen, A. (1997). The Family Attitude Scale: Reliability and validity of a new scale for measuring the emotional climate of families. *Psychiatry Research, 70*, 185–195.

Kessler, R. C., Petukhova, M., Sampson, N. A., Zaslavsky, A. M., & Wittchen, H. U. (2012). Twelve-month and lifetime prevalence and lifetime morbid risk of anxiety and mood disorders in the United States. *International Journal of Methods in Psychiatric Research, 21*, 169–184.

Lebowitz, E. R., Woolston, J., Bar-Haim, Y., Calvocoressi, L., Dauser, C., Warnick, E., & Leckman, J. F. (2013). Family accommodation in pediatric anxiety disorders. *Depression and Anxiety, 30*(1), 47–54.

Leff, J. P., & Vaughn, C. E. (1985). *Expressed emotion in families.* New York, NY: Guilford Press.

March, J. S. (2013). *MASC-2: Multidimensional Anxiety Scale for Children* (2nd ed.). Toronto, ON, Canada: Multi-Health Systems.

Marsella, A. J. (2006). Education and training in global psychology: Foundations, issues, and actions. In M. Stevens & U. P. Gielen (Eds.)., *Toward a global psychology: Theory, research, intervention, and pedagogy* (pp. 333–362). Mahway, NJ: Lawrence Erlbaum.

McLaughlin, K. A., & Hatzenbuehler, M. L. (2009). Stressful life events, anxiety sensitivity, and internalizing symptoms in adolescents. *Journal of Abnormal Psychology, 118*, 659–669.

McLeod, J. D. (1994). Anxiety disorders and marital quality. *Journal of Abnormal Psychology, 103*, 767–776.

Merikangas, K. R., He, J. P., Burstein, M., Swanson, S. A., Avenevoli, S., Cui, L., . . . & Swendsen, J. (2010). Lifetime prevalence of mental disorders in US adolescents: Results from the National Comorbidity Survey Replication–Adolescent Supplement (NCS-A). *Journal of the American Academy of Child & Adolescent Psychiatry, 49*(10), 980–989.

Minuchin, S. (1974). *Families and family therapy.* Oxford, UK: Harvard University Press.

Moffitt, T. E., Caspi, A., Harrington, H., Milne, B. J. Melchior, M., Goldberg, D., & Poulton, R. (2007). Generalized anxiety disorder and depression: Childhood risk factors in a birth cohort followed to age 32. *Psychological Medicine, 37*, 441–452.

National Center for Health Statistics. (2017). *International classification of diseases, tenth revision, clinical modification.* Retrieved from https://www.cdc.gov/nchs/icd/icd10cm.htm

Norrholm, S. D., & Ressler, K. J. (2009). Genetics of anxiety and trauma-related disorders. *Neuroscience, 164*, 272–287.

Olatunji, B. O., Cisler, J. M., & Deacon, B. J. (2010). Efficacy of cognitive behavioral therapy for anxiety disorders: A review of meta-analytic findings. *Psychiatric Clinics of North America, 33*, 557–577.

Peter, H., & Hand, I. (1988). Patterns of patient-spouse interaction in agoraphobics: Assessment by Camberwell Family Interview (CFI) and impact on outcome of self-exposure treatment. In *Panic and Phobias 2* (pp. 240–251). Heidelberg, Germany: Springer-Verlag. doi:10.1007/978-3-642-73543-1_23

Pinsof, W. M., Zinbarg, R., & Knobloch-Fedders, L. M. (2008). Factorial and construct validity of the revised short form integrative psychotherapy alliance scales for family, couple, and individual therapy. *Family Process, 47*(3), 281–301.

Rapee, R. M. (2012). Family factors in the development and management of anxiety disorders. *Clinical Child and Family Psychology Review, 15*, 69–80.

Roy-Byrne, P. P., & Katon, W. (1997). Generalized anxiety disorder in primary care: The precursor/modifier pathway to increased health care utilization. *The Journal of Clinical Psychiatry, 58*, 34–40.

Segrin, C., Woszidlo, A., Givertz, M., Bauer, A., & Murphy, M. T. (2012). The association between overparenting, parent–child communication, and entitlement and adaptive traits in adult children. *Family Relations, 61*, 237–252.

Stanton, M. E. (2009). The systemic epistemology of the specialty of family psychology. In M. E. Stanton, (Ed.), *The Wiley-Blackwell Handbook of Family Psychology.* Hoboken, NJ: Blackwell.

Stein, M. B., Roy-Byrne, P. P., Craske, M. G., Bystritsky, A., Sullivan, G., Pyne, J. M., . . . & Sherbourne, C. D. (2005). Functional impact and health utility of anxiety disorders in primary care outpatients. *Medical Care, 43*, 1164–1170.

Straus, M. A., Hamby, S. L., Boney-McCoy, S., & Sugarman, D. B. (1996). The revised conflict tactics scales (CTS2) development and preliminary psychometric data. *Journal of Family Issues, 17*(3), 283–316.

Sue, W. (2010). *Microaggressions and marginality.* Hoboken, NJ: Wiley.

Sue, D. W., & Sue, D. (2012). *Counseling the culturally diverse: Theory and practice.* Hoboken, NJ: Wiley.

Viana, A. G., Beidel, D. C., & Rabian, B. (2009). Selective mutism: A review and integration of the last 15 years. *Clinical Psychology Review, 29,* 57–67.

Whisman, M. A. (1999). Marital dissatisfaction and psychiatric disorders: Results from the national comorbidity survey. *Journal of Abnormal Psychology, 108,* 701–706.

Whisman, M. A. (2007). Marital distress and DSM–IV psychiatric disorders in a population-based national survey. *Journal of Abnormal Psychology, 116,* 638–643.

Whiteside, S. P., Gryczkowski, M., Ale, C. M., Brown-Jacobsen, A. M., & McCarthy, D. M. (2013). Development of child- and parent-report measures of behavioral avoidance related to childhood anxiety disorders. *Behavior Therapy, 44,* 325–337.

Wittchen, H. U., Carter, R. M., Pfister, H., Montgomery, S. A., & Kessler, R. C. (2000). Disabilities and quality of life in pure and comorbid generalized anxiety disorder and major depression in a national survey. *International Clinical Psychopharmacology, 15,* 319–328.

World Health Organization. (1992). *The ICD-10 classification of mental and behavioural disorders: Clinical descriptions and diagnostic guidelines.* Geneva, Switzerland: Author.

Zinbarg, R. E., Lee, J. E., & Yoon, L. (2007). Dyadic predictors of outcome in a cognitive-behavioral program for patients with generalized anxiety disorder in committed relationships: A "spoonful of sugar" and a dose of non-hostile criticism may help. *Behaviour Research and Therapy, 45,* 699–713.

SYSTEMIC FUNCTIONING OF OBSESSIVE-COMPULSIVE AND RELATED DISORDERS

Kelly Dunbar Davison, Joelle P. France, and Candace M. McLain-Tait

While evaluating Obsessive-Compulsive Disorder (OCD), whether using the *Diagnostic and Statistical Manual of Mental Disorders* (5th ed.; *DSM-5*; American Psychiatric Association [APA], 2013a) or the *International Classification of Diseases, Tenth Revision, Clinical Modification (ICD-10-CM*; National Center for Health Statistics, 2017), a systems perspective is necessary. In considering Obsessive-Compulsive and Related Disorders (OCRDs), case conceptualization points toward a systems perspective while considering the biopsychosocial and ecological models at its very foundation.

DSM-5 AND FAMILY SYSTEMS

One significant change from the *Diagnostic and Statistical Manual of Mental Disorders* (4th ed., text rev.; *DSM-IV-TR*; APA, 2000) to the *DSM-5* was the removal of Obsessive-Compulsive Disorder (OCD) from the Anxiety Disorders category, placing it as a stand-alone category: Obsessive-Compulsive and Related Disorders (OCRD). This group of conditions now includes OCD, hoarding disorder, body dysmorphic disorder (BDD), trichotillomania (hair-pulling disorder), excoriation (skin-picking disorder), substance/medication-induced OCRD, OCRD due to another medical condition, other specified OCRD, and unspecified OCRD. Many mental health professionals from a variety of disciplines utilize a family systems approach, which influences conceptualization and treatment protocol to assist clients with a variety of concerns, including OCD and related disorders. According to Kaplan, Tarvydas, and Gladding (2014), the definition of counseling itself was crafted by professionals: Systemic clinicians have "a professional relationship that empowers diverse individuals, families, and groups to accomplish mental health, wellness, education, and career goals" (p. 368). Within the *DSM-5*, there exists a variety of disorders that impact individuals and systems. At a basic level, Bronfenbrenner (1979) believed in human ecology theory, or ecological systems theory, which states that in order to understand human development, one must consider the entire ecological system in which growth occurs (Bronfenbrenner, 1979). Within these layers are included the *microsystem*, the *mesosystem*, the *exosystem*, the *macrosystem*, and the *chronosystem*.

Bronfenbrenner (1979) noted that the microsystem is a pattern of activities, social roles, and interpersonal relations experienced by the developing person in a given face-to-face setting with particular physical, social, and symbolic features that invite, permit, or inhibit engagement in sustained, progressively more complex interaction with, and activity in, the immediate environment (p. 39).

A few examples of this include family, school, peer culture, and work. The mesosystem includes the weaving of two or more setting connections containing the developing person (Bronfenbrenner, 1979). An example of this includes the relationships between work and school. "The Exosystem comprises the linages and processes taking place between two or more settings, at least one of which does not contain the developing person, but in which events occur that indirectly influence processes within the immediate setting in which the developing person lives" (Bronfenbrenner, 1979, p. 40). For example, with a child, the relation between the home and the parent's workplace or supervisor represents an exosystem. "Macrosystems consist of the overarching pattern of micro, meso, and exosystem characteristics of a given culture or subculture with particular reference to the belief systems, bodies of knowledge, material resources, customs, lifestyles, opportunity structure, hazards, and life course options that are embedded in each of these broader systems" (Bronfenbrenner, 1979, p. 40). Finally, the chronosystem extends the environment into a third dimension of change over time, not only of the characteristics of the person, but also the environment in which the person lives. Consider changes over time with socioeconomic status, education, and health. What is apparent in the ecological model is indeed biopsychosocial and even spiritual in its nature, hence reflecting a "Systems" theory approach. In summary, at a core basic level, family systems theory looks at how individuals suffering from OCD or related disorders are impacted by their symptoms and how their experiences and behaviors impact the system within which they live.

OCD and Related Disorders

Obsessive Compulsive Disorder or OCD is a mental health disorder "characterized by recurrent intrusive, anxiety provoking thoughts and or repetitive behaviors that cause marked distress or interferences" (Thompson-Hollands, Edson, Tompson, & Comer, 2014, p. 287). The disorders that are categorized in this chapter of the *DSM-5* have features in common, such as obsessive preoccupation and repetitive behaviors. Oftentimes, there exists a comorbidity of OCD coupled with mood and anxiety disorders as well (Lochner et al., 2014; Saleem & Mahmood, 2009). This understanding of comorbidity is imperative for developing the best case conceptualization process, and hence systems treatment toward efficacy.

Body Dysmorphic Disorder

Body Dysmorphic Disorder (BDD) involves a preoccupation with an imagined defect in appearance; if a slight physical anomaly is present, the person's concern is markedly excessive. In addition, the preoccupation causes clinically significant distress or impairment in social, occupational, or other important areas of functioning, and it cannot be better accounted for by another mental disorder, such as anorexia nervosa. BDD generally presents in adolescence (Brewster, 2011; Grant & Odlaug, 2009) and affects both men and women (Grant & Odlaug, 2009).

Body-Focused Repetitive Behaviors

Body-Focused Repetitive Behaviors "(BFRBs) is a general term that refers to any repetitive self-grooming behavior (e.g., pulling, picking, biting, or scraping of the hair, skin, or nail) that results in damage to the body" (Golomb et al., 2016, p. 4). Other common examples of BFRBs include, but are not limited to, picking of scabs, acne, skin imperfections, or cuticle, nail biting and picking, and lip or cheek biting. Common symptoms may include the person spending time searching for particular imperfections in the body/hair to then pick, pull, scratch, or rub off. Some also examine, roll, or eat the piece of skin or hair afterward (Golomb et al., 2016). These particular disorders often start between the ages of 11 and 15, though they can begin as early as 1 year of age, and wax and wane throughout the lifetime. What is known is that there is a significant genetic component to BFRBs. But also factors such as temperament, environment, age of onset, and family stress are key indicators contributing to BFRBs (Golomb et al., 2016).

Trichotillomania

Trichotillomania is a hair-pulling disorder characterized by compulsions to pull hair somewhere on the body. The disorder causes people to pull out the hair from their scalp, eyelashes, eyebrows, pubic area, underarms, beard, chest, legs, or other parts of the body, resulting in noticeable bald patches on the body. The disorder causes the person distress and can lead to impairment in social, occupational, or other important life areas of functioning. Sometimes individuals will examine the hair, or root bulb, roll it in their mouths, "pop" the root between their teeth, and touch their face with it as well.

Excoriation

Excoriation is a skin-picking disorder characterized as a new classification to the *DSM-5*, which includes constant and recurrent picking at one's skin, resulting in skin lesions. Normally, the person has made repeated attempts to decrease or stop the skin picking, which then causes clinically significant distress or impairment in social, occupational, or other important areas of functioning. Treatment for Excoriation includes cognitive behavioral therapy (CBT), habit reversal training, awareness training, competing response training, social support through family therapy, and comprehensive behavioral treatment.

Hoarding Disorder

Hoarding Disorder is the persistent difficulty of discarding or parting with possessions, regardless of the value others may attribute to these possessions. The behavior usually has harmful effects such as emotional, physical, social, financial, and even legal implications. Symptoms cause clinically significant distress or impairment in social or occupational or other important life areas of functioning. Even if the behavior is not distressing to the person who hoards, it may distress other people such as family or friends. A family systems perspective would facilitate a supportive therapeutic intervention to assist the individual, family, and friends toward health, especially considering the microsystem, mesosystem, ecosystem, macrosystem, and chronosystem mentioned in the ecological stance.

Finally, the disorders in this area include Other Specified and Unspecified Obsessive-Compulsive and Related Disorders. This section may include conditions such as BFRB, obsessional jealousy, or unspecified OCD and related disorder (APA, 2013a; 2013b).

Substance/Medication-Induced Obsessive-Compulsive and Related Disorders

Substance/Medication-Induced Obsessive-Compulsive and Related Disorders include individuals who take a medication, which results in the exhibition of symptoms from one or more of the OCD and related disorders categories. There must be substantiation that the disorder did not exist until the medication, substance, or intoxication was introduced, or withdrawal from the medication was initiated. Some substances that have been known to contribute to OCD symptoms include amphetamines and cocaine (Van Ameringen, Patterson, & Simpson, 2014). These disorders are diagnosed and labeled within the *DSM-5* under the specific substance or medication.

Obsessive-Compulsive and Related Disorder Due to Another Medical Condition

If there is OCD due to another medical condition, it is often evidenced by history of the medical condition and pattern of symptoms directly tied to the medical diagnosis such as Syndeham's Chorea (Van Ameringen et al., 2014). If OCD due to another medical condition is suspected, the systemic clinician should refer the client to a medical practitioner. The systemic clinician can also consult with the medical professional to develop the best course of action for the client.

Etiology for OCD and Related Disorders

Evidence suggests the role of dopaminergic mechanisms in the manifestation of OCD as well as roughly a 40% heritability factor (Lochner et al., 2014; Saleem & Mahmood, 2009). One meta-analysis of 21 studies published reported that the heterogeneity of symptoms was best explained by a structure with four similar factors. The first factor included symmetry obsessions and repeating, ordering, and counting compulsions; the second included symptoms of aggressive, sexual, religious, and somatic obsessions, and checking compulsions; the third included contamination obsessions and cleaning compulsions; and the fourth factor included hoarding obsessions and compulsions (Lochner et al., 2014). It is important to note that skin picking or excoriation did not appear to fit into these categories specifically.

It appears that not only is OCD multidimensional, consisting of four symptom clusters, but that for each symptom cluster, there are variances in the behaviors that are influenced potentially by different genes or neural pathways and responses to the environment (Lochner et al., 2014). Therefore, it is important to consider neurological and genetic aspects of OCD in looking at case conceptualization. In addition to genetic factors, it appears that temperament, environment, family stress, and relational aspects may have an impact on the individual struggling with OCD and related disorders as well (Golomb et al., 2016). In evaluating the biopsychosocial implications within the case conceptualization process of OCD and related disorders, it is apparent that family systems perspective is embedded in the understanding of these diagnoses both from an etiological standpoint and in terms of diagnosis and treatment. In addition to considering the *DSM-5* and *ICD-10*, relational and cultural features specifically stand out within the systems perspective.

RELATIONAL AND CULTURAL FEATURES

When evaluating OCD and related disorders, there is a clear indicator that in addition to genetic influences, the environment and family play a significant role, not only in the etiology but also in the most effective treatment for these disorders. "The expression of human behavior is inextricably linked to social and cultural realities in ways that gives individual differences as well and inter and intra cultural variations" (Saleem & Mahmood, 2009, p. 37). Family and culture as systems continue to be explored in the research in order to understand how to best support those struggling with symptoms of OCD and related disorders. However, it appears to be clear that there is not only a genetic or neurobiological factor influencing the "transmission" of OCD and related disorders, but also a relational environmental component.

In addition, there appear to be demographic associations with OCD and related disorders, such as more males than females struggling with symmetry, sexual obsessions, checking compulsions, and rituals, while dirt and contamination obsessions and hand washing are more common in females (Saleem & Mahmood, 2009). In addition, regarding BDD, there appear to be gender-specific symptoms such as men focusing on thinning hair, genitalia, and body building aspects. In behavioral response, men often use substances and engage in weight lifting, whereas women focus on their breasts, buttocks, excessive hair, nose, skin, stomach, hips, thighs, teeth, and weight in general. Normally, women's behavioral response is one of camouflaging an eating disorder with clothes and makeup (Hunt, Thienhaus, & Ellwood, 2008).

There is ample support that culture influences the content of obsessions and, to some extent, compulsions (Saleem & Mahmood, 2009). In addition to this, while evaluating other cultures and their view of OCD and related symptomatology, it is interesting to note that what appears to be "deviant" in one culture most certainly is not in another. Considering anthropology and the history of grief, loss, mourning, and beauty related to pulling one's hair, care must be taken not to pathologize something that is considered desirable or normal by the person's culture.

As we reflect back on our early coursework, we recall the following criteria must be met to determine whether something is in fact "abnormal." Statistical infrequency, violation of social norms, failure to function adequately, and deviation from the person's ideal mental health must be met, all while considering one's cultural context. We look at Ezra 9:3 "When I heard this, I tore my tunic and cloak, pulled hair from my head and beard and sat down appalled" (Bible Hub, 2015). Ezra, in his sorrow and great grief, pulled his own hair out. Culturally, pulling one's hair was a sign of managing a distressing experience. One important reminder is for systemic clinicians to continue to use a multiculturally competent approach when working with OCD and Related Disorders, considering the diversity of human behavior across cultures. Even the *DSM-5* calls for a cultural formulation requiring a systematic assessment of the cultural identity of the individual, and cultural conceptualization of distress. Additionally, assessment must include psychosocial stressors, cultural features of vulnerability and resilience, cultural features of the relationship between the client and the systemic clinician, and overall cultural assessments, all of which are needed for a diagnosis of OCD and Related Disorders. As we consider environmental or "systemic" aspects of OCD, other risk factors may also include early childhood trauma, abuse, neglect, or experiences of childhood such as stressful events (Lochner et al., 2002). In fact, there is growing evidence to support that individuals with OCD and Related Disorders often report childhood abuse and neglect. "The findings showed a significantly greater severity of childhood trauma in general, and emotional neglect specifically, in the patient groups [of clients diagnosed with OCD and related disorder] compared to the controls" (Lochner et al., 2002, p. 66).

In a study looking at the Japanese culture, it was found that the Japanese displayed very similar OCD symptoms as those in the United States, thus leading researchers such as Pallanti to believe that, despite cultural differences, there exists a core neurobiological underpinning to the diagnosis (Anderson, 2008).

Understanding the biopsychosocial aspects of OCD leads us to evaluate how a systems approach in counseling can assist those struggling with OCD and Related Disorders. According to Seligman (2012), family involvement in treatment improves outcomes for children and adolescents; however, success can be limited when there are higher rates of family dysfunction. It is the hope of mental health professionals that advances in neuroscience, genetics, and treatment outcomes pertaining to OCD and Related Disorders will lead to further understanding of holistic and multidimensional treatment support for individuals and their systems.

Z Codes

In addition to reviewing OCD and Related Disorders, it is important to note other conditions and problems that may have clinical significance, and that impact case conceptualization when working with cultural considerations and families. These conditions were known previously in the *International Classification of Diseases, Ninth Revision, Clinical Modification (ICD-9-CM)* as V codes, and currently as *ICD-10-CM* Z codes. The codes address psychosocial and environmental stressors.

One key factor related to OCD and related disorders involves relational problems. As discussed in family systems theory, any key relationships with the client have a significant impact on the client's health from a biopsychosocial perspective. These relationships can be damaging, healing, or neutral in considering the client's overall case conceptualization, including etiology, diagnosis, and treatment planning. One example of relational aspects may include parent–child relational issues, which pertains to any primary caregiver and is often considered if the relationship itself appears to be affecting the etiology or course of treatment for the client. Additional relational problems relate to client's upbringing, which can impact behavior, cognition, and emotional aspects related to OCD and related disorders. For example, if a child grew up in a home with a parent who demonstrated excessive hand washing, the child in treatment may be impacted by the parent's past and current OCD behavior as well.

Sibling relational problems are included if there is significant impairment and clinical focus on a pattern of relationship impairment with one or more siblings or if the relationship with the sibling affects the course of therapy. For example, a client comes to treatment to work on his or her hoarding symptoms, and it appears there is a sibling living with the client accommodating the behaviors; this will, in turn, impact treatment. In addition, if a client grows up away from his or her parents and it appears to be significant in contributing to impairment and/or clinical focus, this may indicate designation of significance in growing up away from parents.

In addition, the child may be affected by parental relationship distress; this is apparent if the child is experiencing negative effects of parental discord, thus contributing to the OCD or related disorder. Other problems related to primary support group may include relationship distress with a spouse or intimate partner. There is also a category denoted regarding disruption of family by separation or divorce. For example, a client may begin pulling his or her hair as a young child when coping with the reality of his or her parents' discord and divorce. In addition, there may be a high emotional expression level within family, and it is often seen with hostility or an overenmeshment and criticism directed to one person in the family who may be seen as the "identified patient" or as the "black sheep" of the family. These clients may find "coping" in OCD and related disorders to "self soothe" the negative experiences of childhood.

We may also want to consider uncomplicated bereavement in a client with OCD or a related disorder. If there is a death and a normal response to loss, this code can be used. Additionally, a large set of Z code areas include abuse and neglect of a child, which includes maltreatment by a family member or nonrelative as well. Abuse is categorized specifically and can include physical abuse, psychological abuse, abandonment, neglect, and sexual abuse on varying levels. It is important to keep these factors in mind when assessing for personal history of abuse in childhood, as well as when looking closely at OCD and related disorders, even in adults. Interesting to note, there is also a category looking at problems related to current military deployment status, and this is used when clinical attention is directed around a deployment in the family unit. For example, a wife begins to check and recheck the stove, locks, and the house only after her husband has recently been deployed. Furthermore, there also may be clinical attention and problems revolving around a family member's employment or occupational problem, which is impacting treatment or prognosis.

Next to consider are housing and economic problems related to the OCD or related disorder. Some considerations in this area include a client's homelessness, inadequate housing, neighborhood discord, or problems while living in a residential institution. If the living situation itself is contributing to, or directly tied to, the OCD or related disorder, this consideration is often given. Various economic problems that can impact OCD and related disorders as well may include a lack of adequate food or safe water, extreme poverty, or low socioeconomic status. A client experiencing extreme poverty may later develop hoarding of food or trash as a result of going without basic needs being met for so long.

Finally, the Z codes consider other problems related to the social environment. Some of these areas include a potential phase of life problem, problem living alone, acculturation difficulty, social exclusion or rejection, and also the experience of being targeted for discrimination or persecution. There may be problems related to OCD and related disorders when the client has a history of problems related to crime or legal system issues. For example, being a victim of a crime, experiencing a conviction of any kind, jail time, imprisonment, or other legal issues can impact OCD. Problems related to other psychosocial, personal, and environmental issues, such as religious or spiritual problems, can also be related to OCD or related disorders. Issues such as an unwanted pregnancy, communication, or relational problems with social workers, probation officers, attorneys, or other professional staff support are included. Other social problems clients may experience include victimization of terrorism, disaster, or war.

It is important to include any circumstances of personal history that may be related, or of clinical value, or include other personal psychological trauma, personal history of self-harm, history of deployment, and other problems related to lifestyle such as poor sleep. It may be imperative in light of OCD and related disorders to consider problems related to access to medical and other health care. For example, a client who was denied or unable to have health services, and who has experienced an illness, may be seen as "germophobic" by others, behaviorally accommodating his disease prevention with hand washing or excessive cleaning.

Given the myriad of factors that can contribute to OCD and related disorders, systemic clinicians should be aware that symptom presentation can occur in multiple ways, from the person perfectly arranging items to the person such as the character in the television show, *Monk* played by Tony Shalhoub (Breckman, Creator, 2002). Adrian Monk was a police detective who retired after losing his wife as a result of a car bomb. Her traumatic death exacerbated his OCD to the point where he needed to touch items, to have his home in a perfect condition, with exact placement of items on surfaces, in drawers, furniture, and so on. He would become agitated and anxious when things were out of place. If he had to touch anything or shake hands, his trusty aide was available with a wipe for him. However, he was a brilliant detective, and, due to his OCD, would see miniscule bits of evidence that ultimately led to the solution of cases in each episode.

Another fictional character exuding the characteristics of OCD was that played by Jack Nicholson in the movie *As Good As It Gets* (Brooks, Producer/Director, 1998). This character, Melvin Udall, compulsively washed his hands with multiple bars of soap and scalding hot water, was compelled to turn the lock on his front door a specific number of times, could not step on a crack when walking outside, took his own plastic silverware to the same restaurant every day, ordered primarily the same thing every day, and needed to be served by the same waitress. His manners were harsh, potentially in an effort to keep people away from him so he did not have to interact and risk disrupting his own self-imposed schedule and ordered life.

Although these are fictional examples, they do bring to light some of the issues practiced and experienced by real people with OCD. The nature of the disorder creates some unique challenges when assessing and treating families who have member(s) with OCD.

FAMILY SYSTEMS ASSESSMENTS

When using assessments from a family systems perspective, it is important to consider the entire family and not just the individual who may appear to be the identified patient with the presenting problem. Many families with members who are diagnosed with OCD and/or related disorders often display accommodating behaviors that can negatively impact individual treatment interventions (Wu et al., 2016). Therefore, it is important to identify assessments that consider family influence on behavior and treatment.

While there are many evidence-based assessments that explore OCD and related disorders from an individual perspective (Foa et al., 2010; Iniesta-Sepúlveda, Rosa-Alcázar, Rosa-Alcázar, & Storch, 2014; Scahill et al., 1997; Shafran et al., 2003; Storch et al., 2007), there are also assessments available for exploring information from the perspectives of family members and parents. For example, the LEVEL 2, Repetitive Thoughts and Behaviors—Adult (adapted from the Florida Obsessive-Compulsive Inventory Severity Scale [Part B]) and the LEVEL 2, Repetitive Thoughts and Behaviors—Child Age 11 to 17 (adapted from the Children's Florida Obsessive-Compulsive Inventory Severity Scale) contain questions that identify how thoughts or behaviors are interfering with family life and other social functioning (Goodman & Storch, 1994a, 1994b). Furthermore, the LEVEL 2, Repetitive Thoughts and Behaviors—Adult can be completed by family members so the systemic clinician can gain additional information from the family perspective. This increased awareness can assist the systemic clinician in developing strategies that involve the family and possibly improve positive outcomes (Goodman & Storch, 1994a, 1994b). Another commonly used measure of family functioning is the Family Accommodation Scale for Obsessive-Compulsive Disorder, which looks at family-accommodating behaviors and levels of distress (Calvocoressi et al., 1999). In addition, there is the Parental Attitudes and Beliefs Scale, which is a parent report questionnaire used to rate behaviors and beliefs about the OCD indications in children (Peris, Benazon, Langley, Roblek, & Piacentini, 2008). The OCD Family

Functioning Scale has a patient version and a relative version that aims to assess the functional impairment within families (Stewart et al., 2011). It can be used for children and adults and can be a key factor for gaining information when counseling families. Additionally, the Family Accommodation Scale for Obsessive-Compulsive Disorder—Patient Version has shown promise for providing information on the degree of family accommodation; this can be particularly useful to systemic clinicians who do not have the entire family presenting for treatment (Wu et al., 2016). Finally, the Child Obsessive-Compulsive Impact Scale-Revised includes a parent-report and a child-report measure that may be used for assessing child and adolescent OCD symptoms and functioning (Piacentini, Peris, Bergman, Chang, & Jaffer, 2007).

What may be of further benefit are assessments specifically developed or modified for OCD and related disorders with children and adolescents (Iniesta-Sepúlveda et al., 2014). The Children's Yale-Brown Obsessive-Compulsive Scale (Scahill et al., 1997) is a widely used and studied systemic clinician-administered instrument. The Obsessive-Compulsive Inventory—Child Version is a self-report assessment that is used to assess the dimensions and presence of OCD symptoms (Foa et al., 2010). Another self-report assessment used to identify symptoms along with impairment is the Children's Obsessional Compulsive Inventory (Shafran et al., 2003). A less studied yet widely used assessment is the Leyton Obsessional Inventory Child-Version Survey-Form self-report measure focused on the symptoms and their frequency (Berg, Whitaker, Davies, Flament, & Rapoport, 1988; Iniesta-Sepúlveda et al., 2014). The Children's Florida Obsessive-Compulsive Inventory (C-FOCI; Storch et al., 2007, 2009) assesses the severity of OCD symptoms and it has the possibility to be administered over the Internet (Iniesta-Sepúlveda et al., 2014). This can be useful for systemic clinicians who are working with underserved and rural populations.

There are many assessments available for use in assessing OCD from a family systems perspective. These include systemic clinician-administered and self-administered assessments. It would be beneficial for systemic clinicians working from a family systems approach to have access to self-report questionnaires and assessments to gain information from family members who might not be present for therapy sessions. As noted earlier in this chapter, families often display responses that accommodate the OCD behaviors of family members. Therefore, it is important to have tools to assess family members who will aid in the development of systems-based intervention strategies.

FAMILY SYSTEMS INTERVENTIONS

Although assessments are useful in identifying dimensions and frequency of symptoms, it is also important to place focus on the strengths in addition to the challenges that families face when working with OCD and related disorders (Hilton, Turner, Krebs, Volz, & Heyman, 2012). Focusing on strengths and instilling hope can be key stepping stones in treatment. Additionally, research indicates that family members may experience feeling angry or depressed (among other distressing feelings) as a result of the continual family disruptions that can be present with OCD and related disorders (Peris et al., 2008; Thompson-Hollands et al., 2014). Therefore, systemic clinicians need effective treatment strategies to help families develop positive interactions, thus reducing the distressful feelings. According to Thompson-Hollands et al. (2014), there are several treatment models utilized for OCD including the use of psychotropic medications and CBT as leaders in efficacy. In terms of psychotropic medications, serotonin reuptake inhibitors are often the first implemented (Dembo, 2014). Despite the effectiveness of these two lines of treatment, there is evidence that treatment responses vary depending on differences in treatment protocols with children versus adults and other potential confounding variables within the literature (Thompson-Hollands et al., 2014). Within the family system there are several implications in considering the role of OCD and its impact on the system. There is research on accommodation for example, which is the act of family members accommodating or helping assist the person with OCD to check or recheck items in an effort to help the member struggling with OCD. The problem appears to be that it can make OCD symptoms worse for the individual already struggling and can cause depression, anxiety, and relational difficulties for the family members attempting to "help" (Peris et al., 2008). Family accommodation can also hinder CBTs and has been linked to poor results in treatment (Wu et al., 2016).

Cognitive Behavioral Therapy

It is becoming commonplace for systemic clinicians to include family members when using CBTs for OCD due to the increased potential for improved clinical outcomes, maintenance of newly achieved positive behaviors, and an overall increase in family member engagement (Thompson-Hollands et al., 2014). In utilizing a family-centered model, the conceptualization, maintenance, and enrichment are implemented more broadly. Family systems models allow for more integration of resources and seek to understand the broader environment of the family. Family inclusive treatment (FIT) for OCD has been utilized and researched offering an overall association having a large effect on OCD. FIT can include family psychoeducation, family skills training, or individualized family treatment protocols symptoms (Thompson-Hollands et al., 2014).

When searching for family-based intervention strategies to treat OCD and related disorders, it is common to find studies that focus on children and adolescents (Drake & Ginsburg, 2012; Hildebrandt, Bacow, Markella, & Loeb, 2012.) This may be due to parents being the ones most likely to identify OCD or related disorder behaviors and then seek treatment for their child. For example, FIT using CBT has been studied in chronic pediatric headache and anxiety disorders (Drake & Ginsburg, 2012). Drake and Ginsburg (2012) presented a case study of a 10-year-old boy who met criteria for generalized anxiety disorder, separation anxiety disorder, and displayed symptoms of OCD in addition to his chronic headaches. His parents were involved in his treatment that included the Children's Headache and Anxiety Management Program, "which is a family-based intervention grounded in cognitive-behavioral and operant conditioning theories" (Drake & Ginsburg, 2012, p. 581). In a 1-month follow-up to treatment, the child no longer had debilitating headaches and no longer displayed criteria for any anxiety-related diagnosis. Additionally, the accommodating behaviors of his mother were reduced. This particular case study provides an example of the importance of considering mental health factors when treating physical symptoms and diagnosis. Oftentimes, there can be comorbid mental health diagnoses that are related to physical symptoms. There may also be important family systems factors involved as well.

A disorder that can be characterized as related to OCD and with a high comorbidity is anorexia nervosa. Treating anorexia nervosa using FIT has shown promise (Hildebrandt et al., 2012). Systemic clinicians can coach parents on how to interact using CBT strategies including exposure. Parents can be assigned feeding-related tasks that aim to develop new patterns of interaction among family members. When participating in treatment involving exposure, "parents no longer support avoidance strategies such as food refusal, discussion of calories, or refusing to eat in front of others" (Hildebrandt et al., 2012, p. 9). Instead, they can offer food and encourage their child to eat more than they intended. Although it can be challenging, parents can assume the role of being in charge over their child's eating habits which can create an environment for continued exposure to anxiety-provoking foods and an increased opportunity for gaining positive ground.

As we have seen, involving family members in treatment can have significant effects on the outcome. Systemic clinicians can continue to develop strategies for implementing FITs that might accommodate families who may not have access to effective treatment. Video-conferencing is an area of FIT that has also shown promise (Comer et al., 2014). In a provisional study, Comer et al. (2014) implemented CBT via videoconferencing with participants aged 4 to 8 years and their parents while focusing on exposure and response prevention. FIT using videoconferencing can be particularly useful when working with rural or underserved families. It is also important to note that special considerations must be taken when using Internet-based interventions and systemic clinicians should examine the most up-to-date ethical standards for practice using distance-based or technology-assisted methods.

Another method showing potential is incorporating mindfulness into OCD treatment (Fairfax, Easey, Fletcher, & Barfield, 2014). Mindfulness is versatile and can be described as a practice of being in the present moment and focusing on the here and now (Kabat-Zinn, 1994). Fairfax et al. (2014) introduced Mindfulness into a group for clients with OCD. Along with other techniques used in the group, including CBT, Mindfulness was received positively by the group members who reported that the techniques were memorable and could be applied outside of the group environment. "It can be argued that Mindfulness, therefore, may be a form of exposure, and the discipline of returning one's attention away from an obsessive thought back to the current moment as a form of response prevention" (Fairfax et al., 2014, p. 19). Although the focus of this study was on group treatment, it may be of benefit for further study from a family systems perspective given the close relationship of group dynamics and family dynamics in treatment.

Evidence-based approaches including the use of CBT and psychotropic medications are current standards in the treatment of OCD and related disorders (Thompson-Hollands et al., 2014). However, as we have read, there is room for additional treatment modalities that incorporate family members, help to treat underserved populations, and those that can provide techniques that can be easily incorporated at home. Additionally, family members can be a support or a hindrance to treatment and effective psychoeducation may be necessary for positive treatment outcomes (Wu et al., 2016). As previously noted, family members often develop accommodating behaviors that can impede progress in treatment. Conversely, supportive family members can increase the overall maintenance of therapeutic gains.

ETHICAL AND LEGAL IMPLICATIONS

Family systems therapy inherently has ethical and legal risks, especially in the process of identifying who the "client" is, who is being treated, and in managing confidentiality among the individuals within the family (American Association for Marriage and Family Therapy [AAMFT] *Code of Ethics*, 2015, Standard 2.1; American Counseling Association [ACA] *Code of Ethics*, 2014, Section B.4.b). Ethical and legal implications within the family systems therapy theory and families who are also dealing with OCRDs provide additional responsibilities. This section reviews the legal and ethical implications when using family systems therapy with families dealing with OCD, BDD, Hoarding Disorder, Trichotillomania, Excoriation, and Other Related Disorders. Because legal consequences are decided by each state, and each state may have unique laws pertaining to clients with these disorders, legal issues must be researched in the state(s) where the systemic clinician is licensed to operate. However, there are some universal legal issues that apply to every systemic clinician/client situation, such as the prohibition against sexual relations between systemic clinicians and clients and their immediate families. It is incumbent upon each systemic clinician to thoroughly review the statutes in the state that controls their professional practice, and it is strongly recommended that the systemic clinician review those laws regularly, or sign up for automated notices when laws are changed or added to the statutes regarding the field of mental health providers.

Ethical Issues With OCD

When treating families who have one or more members diagnosed with OCD, there are certain ethical issues that come to the forefront for consideration. Initially, the identification of who the client is begins the ethical dilemmas experienced in working with families. Generally, the "client" is the family. This is an important perspective to maintain while working with a family who has a member(s) diagnosed with OCD. Counseling can quickly become focused on the person identified with OCD, and thus sidetrack the systemic clinician from treating the family as the client. When the attention is placed on the identified client, the family may consider themselves "off the hook" as it were. However, using systems theory, it is critical to recognize that the family is the client, and their interaction is both part of the problem and, more importantly, part of the solution.

Ethical Considerations in Systems Theory

Systems of all kinds seek stasis; the system wants and seeks balance. Anything in the system that is out of whack throws the entire system off. Consider Newton's Cradle: When a ball or balls are activated to swing, the energy from that movement is passed through the balls in the middle, and kicks out the ball(s) on the opposite end. This is an illustration of how the identified patient impacts the family; the energy clearly goes through each family member in one way or another, and creates movement on the other side. That process invites stasis; balance within the family system. Furthermore, the balls will continue to stay in action for a long time, usually until stopped by human or feline intervention. The system is self-sustaining. The individual interactions within the system are the target of the treatment (Berg-Cross, 2000).

One of the detrimental family responses to OCD is to accommodate the OCD person's compulsive behavior within the family system. According to multiple researchers, accommodation can increase the OCD behavior of the person (Cooper, 1996; Peris et al., 2012; Stewart et al., 2011; Wu et al., 2016). Similar to the addictions process, the family can become codependent with the OCD family member and not only assist with the OCD behaviors, but potentially inspire an increase of those behaviors. Certainly, the family members are attuned to the stress expressed by the OCD member, and seek to relieve some of that tension and stress. However, like Newton's Cradle, the behavior continues and continues, and the family can become complicit in the continuation of that process. Change will throw the family system out of homeostasis, but as it rearranges itself within the system, stasis will again be reached, hopefully with diminishing OCD behaviors. Therefore, it is up to the systemic clinician to be aware of the dynamics in the system, and specifically with OCD family members, and engage in a therapeutic alliance that will contribute to making the system healthier. There is an ethical obligation when working with families to not pathologize individuals, but to positively impact interactions within the family system (Berg-Cross, 2000).

Ethical Considerations in Confidentiality

Confidentiality is an ethical responsibility for every systemic clinician (AAMFT *Code of Ethics*, 2015, Standard II; ACA *Code of Ethics*, 2014, Section B). The client holds the confidentiality and for it to be broken, the client would have to give his or her signed consent. There are times when confidentiality can be broken because of mandatory reporting requirements, which may vary state to state, but generally include when there is a potential for self-harm or harm to someone else, concerns about child or elder abuse, threats against national security, or by court order (ACA *Code of Ethics*, 2014, Section B.2.a.–e). In each case, the systemic clinician should endeavor to gain a release from the client prior to the disclosure and limit the disclosure to a minimal amount to protect the client and the therapeutic relationship.

When the "client" is the family, confidentiality can become more complicated. For instance, in groups, the systemic clinician cannot guarantee confidentiality (Sperry, 2007). Similarly, the systemic clinician cannot guarantee confidentiality of the family members, only of the systemic clinician. Other family members may share information that violates confidentiality in the family; therefore, it is the systemic clinician's responsibility to review confidentiality restrictions, and review those with the family at various times throughout the counseling relationship.

Another aspect of confidentiality that may be challenging is the confidentiality between and among members of the family. It is common for family members and/or families to maintain family secrets (Berg-Cross, 2000). A challenge to the systemic clinician is when a family member approaches, discloses something, and pleads for you to keep what he or she says confidential for that member of the family. Berg-Cross (2000) identified four types of family secrets, "supportive, protective, manipulative, or avoidant" (p. 155). When a systemic clinician becomes aware of secrets, it is critical for the systemic clinician to seek supervision and consultation to help process through the risks and potential benefits of exposing or discussing any of those secrets. The risks and benefits for the family as a system need to be reviewed and evaluated. In the meantime, Berg-Cross suggests the confidentiality be respected by the systemic clinician.

Ethical Considerations in Informed Consent

In order for consent to be an informed one, the systemic clinician must explain in language clearly understood by the client(s), and be confident that the understanding is clear. Informed consent is also not limited to the first session. The systemic clinician needs to return to the parameters of confidentiality and informed consent throughout the work he or she does with the client(s), particularly when significant events or outcomes may be anticipated. The client(s) must clearly understand what treatment is and give consent for services. Furthermore, if the systemic clinician intends on seeking consultation with other professionals, such as physicians, teachers, school systemic clinicians, other mental health professionals, and so forth, specific consent in the form of a release of information must be obtained before contact is made with other professionals. Clients may limit the scope of the consent, which needs to be clearly explained and put in writing (AAMFT *Code of Ethics*, 2015, Standards 1.2 and 2.1, 2.2, 2.7; ACA *Code of Ethics*, 2014, Sections A.2. and A.3).

Legal Implications With OCD

Ethical violations may certainly lead to legal implications for systemic clinicians. A brief search on one state's licensing database showed 1,302 records found for licensed marriage and family therapists (LMFTs; Department of Regulatory Agencies, 2016); a cursory review of those in the regulatory database found 828 of them were listed as "active," 464 were "expired," and 7 had one or more violations that prompted investigations. One person with three different entries did not respond to inquiries by Department of Regulatory Agencies, so the license was revoked. Another did not respond, and that license was suspended. One person violated professional boundaries, including attendance at birthday parties, weddings, and babysitting for a client, borrowed $5,000 from a client, and failed to maintain records for the client, and so that license was voluntarily surrendered. Three others voluntarily surrendered the license rather than risk being referred to the State Attorney General for potential legal prosecution. Another voluntary surrender of the license was due to a complaint that the LMFT looked up confidential information on a database, and shared that information with her partner, who was the mother of that client. An additional voluntary surrender was an LMFT with four complaints filed against him for having sexual relations with clients, and having disclosed that to a colleague. Finally, one more LMFT voluntarily surrendered the license based on one case that included five allegations of misconduct surrounding practicing outside of scope and related allegations, including failure to disclose limitations.

In every one of these cases, systemic clinicians avoided legal charges by surrendering or not responding to the complaints filed. That does not protect them from civil or criminal actions that could be brought against them for violations. Understanding that there is both a licensing issue and potentially a legal issue is vital for the systemic clinician. This writer knows personally of two very serious cases that went to court. One resulted in the psychologist's license being revoked, and he was convicted, did some jail time, and probation . . . and had to find a whole new career path, as a 50- to 60-year-old. In addition, he will need to register as a sex offender for the rest of his life. The other case involved a trial, but the systemic clinician was found "not guilty" because the sexual and cohabitating relationship he had with a client was mutually consensual, disregarding the point of law that he was prohibited from entering such a relationship. However, he also lost his license and needed to seek a new career path.

Clearly, violations are made by licensed mental health systemic clinicians, and consequences can be life changing, even with the best intentions. In family therapy with an OCD family member, there may be points of disagreement, and the systemic clinician may risk being pulled into the dysfunctional family system, thus risking ethical violations that may become legal charges.

Knowing and conquering the common foundational counseling skills, such as emotional regulation, flexibility, ability to receive and give feedback, professionalism, empathy, active listening, and so forth provide a layer of protection to the serious systemic clinician. Reviewing the codes of ethics regularly will help the systemic clinician stay on track with what is allowed and what is not allowed. In addition, it is critical to have supervision or consultation as well so that objectivity remains at the forefront of the systemic clinician's thinking and actions to avoid violations. The systemic clinician would be wise to seek a peer support group, good supervision with an experienced supervisor, and case consultation. If the situation within the family becomes worsened as the systemic clinician works with family members to stop accommodating the OCD behavior, the risk is heightened for potential complaints and litigation. Working through resistance, continual informed consent, discussions, and planning are all helpful in working with the OCD family. Professional boundaries are essential.

Body Dysmorphic Disorder (BDD)

There may be ethical and legal issues that arise when working with someone who has BDD. The diagnosis includes the *perception* of some sort of abnormality or defect of the body. The individual may wish to have surgery that may be expensive, risky, or even dangerous. Adults have the right to make bad decisions, which we do all of the time; and so the question remains, when is a bad decision dangerous to the point of needing intervention? If the person is at risk of doing something to himself or herself that could lead to infections, disfiguration, and other high-risk consequences, when do systemic clinicians intervene? When is an intervention appropriate of any kind? What can you do? Knowing the ethics codes and the laws in your state is critical to guide you.

One must tread very carefully through this jungle of questions, as both too little and too much involvement may result in harm to the client. The ACA *Code of Ethics* (2014) requires systemic clinicians to foster autonomy (self-determination of the client), nonmaleficence (not causing harm to the client), and beneficence (working for the good of the client/society; ACA *Code of Ethics*, 2014, Preamble). The AAMFT *Code of Ethics* (2015) also supports autonomy (Standard 1.8) and actions that benefit the client (Standard 1.9). There-fore, there is a duty to the client for professional behavior by the systemic clinician, whether the "client" is a person or the family. That is where all decision making should begin in relational systemic work.

The next step after reviewing the codes of ethics applicable to the systemic clinician's practice is to consult with supervisors, professional peers, and experts in the field. It is also advisable to find and use a good decision-making model from which to operate. There are many available through ACA, the Internet, and texts on ethics. One example is by Forester-Miller and Davis (1996) who presented a seven-step model to follow, which is based on previous models developed by Kitchener (1984), Van Hoose and Paradise (1979), Stadler (1986), Haas and Malouf (1989), Forester-Miller and Rubenstein (1992), and Sileo and Kopala (1993), as cited in Forester-Miller & Davis (1996, p. 2). Every situation is unique, and having a model that helps the systemic clinician work through the possibilities is critical to help the systemic clinician process the issues involved. In the ethical world, everything is gray . . . there is no black and white, except for sexual contact.

Hoarding Disorder

There may be not only health and safety issues when working with a hoarding disorder, but there can also be community issues that bring attention to the family hoarding, or the person who is hoarding. There may be code violations in the community if the hoard-ing results in pests, rodents, feral animals, or if the hoarder is hoarding live animals, such as cats or dogs. There are laws, regulations, and codes involved, which may bring unex-pected consequences to the hoarder(s). Issues arise when the family will no longer reside in the hoarder's home due to the risks and discomfort in the home. There may be a risk of a social services intervention, condemnation of the home, injury due to an unsafe environ-ment, and intervention through animal control.

Trichotillomania (Hair-Pulling Disorder) and Excoriation (Skin-Picking Disorder)

Pulling one's hair out can result in many issues with the family and in various settings in society, such as workplace, school, and so on. Excoriation can do the same thing. When the person is doing either of these in areas that are easily seen in street clothes, the person may suffer abuse and condemnation by others, including his or her own family. When is it self-abuse? When does the person need medical attention? When should Social Ser-vices get involved? What are medical implications? Again, these questions need to be processed through with a good decision-making model, supervision by experts in these areas, and consultation. There may be instances when there may be medical complications requiring surgery or other medical interventions to eliminate infections and/or potential internal physical blockages as a result of deep infection, deep digging, or ingested hair. A discussion with the family and the member(s) who is(are) identified as having these disor-ders that specifies circumstances of outside involvement, and gains releases of information from the family and the identified patient for physicians and other health professionals, who may be involved in treatment. Confidentiality and informed consent must be a continu-ous conversation with families who run the risk of having medical consequences connected to the behavior being exhibited.

Substance/Medication-Induced Obsessive-Compulsive and Related Disorder and Obsessive-Compulsive and Related Disorder Due to Another Medical Condition

Substance- or medication-induced OCD may have a swift onset for a client who otherwise did not display OCD and Related disorders, as may another medical condition; careful conversation about introducing new medications, herbs, home remedies, and so on should be explored. A release of information to consult with the treating medical physician may assist in determining effects that are beyond the scope of the systemic clinician, such as the interaction with OCD and other medical conditions. The systemic clinician may not have the expertise to determine the effects, so releases of information for physicians, pharmacists, or other health providers may be necessary to help determine this diagnosis. A caution is not to practice medicine without being licensed as a physician, so medical issues require licensed medical input.

Other Specified Obsessive-Compulsive and Related Disorders and Unspecified Obsessive-Compulsive and Related Disorders

Consultation in the *DSM-5* is required for these diagnoses as the client may not fully meet the criteria for the actual disorders, or may have a cultural component to his or her behavior that is not necessarily diagnosable with the disorders previously mentioned. This section reminds us how crucial it is to seek multicultural competence, consult sources and others with expertise for any specific culture, before we diagnose any disorder. This is an ethical requirement in ACA and AAMFT, as well as just about any code of ethics used in the field of mental health. We are strongly cautioned about pathologizing cultural practices. Gain awareness and competence in whichever cultures are associated with the family with whom you are working. The *DSM-5* has some excellent resources in the appendices that may help in gathering more information. Furthermore, seek information in the additional sections regarding other conditions that may influence the client in the Z code section of the *DSM-5*.

CASE CONCEPTUALIZATION

Case conceptualization is a critical component of ethical and successful clinical interventions. It has implications for the treatment plan, the focus and direction of counseling, and ultimately, the outcome of the counseling. Missing the mark here may result in a client not returning to counseling or stopping prematurely. Therefore, from the beginning session, the clinician must conceptualize the client correctly.

Presenting Concerns

To assist the reader in conceptualizing how a systemic clinician might respond to a family impacted by OCD and related disorders, a case study is provided. The authors have included a background of the client including a history of behaviors as well as personal strengths. In reviewing this case study, the authors encourage the reader to evaluate the systemic impact on the selection of assessments and strategies for interventions.

Presenting problems: The client's family has come to counseling and includes "Cassie," her husband "Jack," and 3-year-old daughter, "Zoe." Their chief complaint was offered by Cassie, who reported that she does not feel "normal" in her relationship with her husband and in her role as a mother due to her many "fears" that seem to be getting in the way. The client stated that she believes she has married the "love of her life" but for the last 3 years, she has felt out of sorts in her role as wife and mother. She reported she is fearful that she will "lose" her husband and damage her daughter if she cannot "get it together" soon. Her husband, Jack, stated he loves his wife and child very much. Jack continued, and stated that Cassie was always anxious and "different" since they met in college, but now she seems to be struggling to function at a minimal level. He appeared to be very supportive of the family receiving counseling, but admitted he has recently been fearful for his wife and daughter's well-being, given the escalated time consumed in the negative thinking and behaviors his wife has exhibited. Cassie reported some prior fragmented relationships with her mother, father, and half-brother since childhood, stating, "I cannot rely on them or go to them for any amount of emotional support; never have been able to." Cassie is a 24-year-old Caucasian woman, married, mother of one child (a daughter aged 3). In addition, Cassie holds a bachelor's degree in nursing. She reported that she is also currently debating whether or not to go back to school to further her nursing education or change to a more manageable career in order to be a mother and wife. Cassie's husband, Jack, is 26 years old, Caucasian, married, and father to their 3-year-old daughter, Zoe. Jack reportedly has a secure job as a project manager, secure family health care, and enjoys providing for Cassie and their daughter. They currently live in a middle-class neighborhood in a suburban area outside of Chicago, Illinois. Zoe is a Caucasian female who appears to be happy, bright, and engaged in playing with toys during the initial session. She attends part-time day care at a local school and currently no concerns are reported about her.

Cassie stated that in addition to her relationship issues revolving around various "fears," she also fears that she may lose her part-time job due to more recent episodes of being late to work; her tardy arrival at work is due to her needing to attend to personal hygiene issues, such as washing her hands and feet, and plucking the hair on her legs to ensure they are smooth. Cassie reported that she spends substantial time prior to work frantically worrying whether she has packed her child's day care bag adequately with all the needed essentials. When asked further about her most pressing presenting "issue," she reported that she has always been an "anxious" person who was "superstitious" in nature. However, it was not until she entered college that she began to notice her fears escalate. She stated she feared she would fail out of school, be on the streets, and have no one around her while she was dying of some terrible disease. In turn, she began creating lists to ensure she remembered all of her assignments and responsibilities in classes. She stated she did well in school, but she had few friends, so often stayed at home cleaning, or doing extra research. She began to "push herself" to make friends in her college program prior to graduating since many lived in the local city and she, too, wanted to try to obtain a job there. After college, Cassie stated she had two solid friends, including Jack, but noticed after she was hired as a part-time certified nursing assistant, she began to feel anxious and a desire to isolate again. She began having thoughts that she would accidently insert a needle into a patient incorrectly, viciously harming them. She had never had a negative aggressive experience in her life and yet she reportedly began having these fearful thoughts. She often would attempt to get "rid" of the thought by reciting a calming poem, or washing her hands, or drinking water. In addition, when asked if she had ever previously experienced any type of anxiety such as this, she appeared perplexed, paused, and then reflected, "Well yes, actually when I was 11, and my parents separated. I began picking my eyelashes and eyebrows out." When asked if this was something she still did today, Cassie relayed that she actually has not plucked her facial hair out, but does tend to spend about 1 hour a day using tweezers to pull hairs on her legs. She replied that she does this after an especially stressful long day at work, and when she does it, she often loses track of time, and misses important responsibilities she knows she "should be tending to instead." When asked what the main issue she would like to see resolved was, she replied, "I have these bad thoughts sometimes even about my husband or my lack of parenting that I will accidently neglect my daughter, then I sometimes do neglect her in all my worry. I worry I will somehow harm someone in some way, and I get so anxious and upset I sometimes just isolate or I have been known to run out of a restaurant, etc. to avoid the possibility that the thoughts would come to pass. Then, I do a ritual where I have to cleanse myself of the horrific thoughts because I feel so evil." She reported she has never had a plan to harm anyone, and does not wish to hurt anyone, but cannot get the "thoughts" out of her head. She also reported sometimes she has thoughts and fears that she will accidently leave her daughter at home and get to the day care without her in the car, or somehow will be unable to care for her daughter and her daughter will get hurt. When asking her husband his response to this, he reported that he feels terrible that she struggles like this, because often he is at work during the day unable to "help her." He has been left baffled and confused when she gets up and disappears during dinner or events. He has offered Cassie support, talking, and even stress reducing activities the family could do together but they do not seem to help. Jack mentioned the concern he has for their daughter in "potentially picking up these behaviors" and has hopes they can get some support to help the behaviors be reduced. In summary, Cassie loves her husband and daughter, she knows there is something "wrong," and she wants support to be able to have a successful relationship with Jack, parent Zoe in a healthy way, and maintain her job serving patients in her field.

Concurrent Problems

The client reported that when she was 11, her parents separated and later divorced; they went to a family therapist briefly to discuss the divorce and new parenting dynamics. In addition, she reported they also went to "hypnotherapy" to try to stop the hair pulling. At age 18, she went to individual counseling and learned CBT, which reportedly helped her switch from pulling the hair from her eyebrows and eyelashes to pulling them from her legs, spending far less time and helping her feel better about her self-appearance.

Background History and Stressors

Cassie stated she grew up fairly poor in a family in rural Indiana with her biological mom, dad, and a half-brother, who was 8 years older than she, in the house. She stated that for as long as she remembered, her mom and dad worked long hours and she was left alone much of the time on the farm. She spent long periods of time with her pet farm animals. At around age 7, she stated her father began aggressively punishing her brother and would often drink at home in excessive amounts. He often got angry and violent, and took it out on Cassie's mother and her brother; however, she was left to watch and often felt powerless and guilty for not doing "more" to help. Cassie's mother had been in two previous marriages in which she was abused by those spouses as well. Cassie recalls feeling so anxious that one day, she saw her aunt using tweezers to pluck her eyebrows into a pretty shape. Cassie went home and decided to try this out, only to keep pulling. As she did it, she found comfort in pulling the hair, examining it, and placing it on a white wall. She stated she became so enraptured while doing this that one night she simply started pulling her hairs, examining them, and next thing she knew, they were all gone. Cassie stated this caused her "shame and further fear beyond description". It was not until 4 days later that anyone noticed, and it was her mom who did. Cassie's mother yelled at her, asking her "What is wrong with you Cassie?" Cassie said she really did not understand any of it, and felt very helpless to answer her mother. It was decided at that point that the family would see a systemic clinician; however, the focus was not on Cassie, but on the divorce and violence in the home. Soon after, Cassie reported that her brother was removed from the home and placed in foster care due to the father's violence, and she was left to the "wayside" to figure things out for herself. Cassie stated that while in seventh grade, she began forcing herself to stop plucking since there was a boy she liked, and she was made fun of for her missing eyebrows, tormented almost daily. She was called all kinds of names including "cancer patient" and "baldy," which reinforced her sense of low self-worth. Cassie excelled in school performance, sports, art, and music despite the ridicule. Things did eventually seem to level out for her, until high school. Here, she reportedly began dating a senior who gradually became abusive to her, and ended up date-raping her when she was 14.

Cassie stated she was living with her dad at the time because her mom had left when they divorced. She had nowhere to turn and took all the shame, guilt, and pain inward; she began cutting her arm superficially to "feel better." In addition, she reportedly still felt anxious, but continued to heal through support from her church youth group, friends, and grandmother, who took care of her. She stated she had always struggled with "bad thoughts," including others, or herself, but attempted to manage these thoughts through various behaviors such as cleaning, organizing, and washing herself. Upon entering college, she reported that "it was perfect to be so busy, consumed, and organized with school so as to try to avoid the bad thoughts"; however, they have begun to bombard her more recently, even more than before.

Strengths

Cassie appears to be a very intelligent, articulate, and likeable young woman. She has many strengths such as endurance, perseverance, and a strong will to overcome. She has completed a bachelor's degree and is working in a professional occupation. Cassie has a loving husband who appears supportive of the family receiving treatment, and Cassie has successfully parented her 3-year-old daughter to this point, without major concerns. She has a strong desire for personal growth, and motivators for her appear to be her family and her career.

DSM-5 Impressions and Implications OCD With Trichotillomania

Cassie demonstrated multiple issues that would need to be reviewed and considered prior to making a diagnosis. She stated she has repetitive behaviors, such as cleansing, hand washing, and intrusive thoughts. She stated she has anxiety that has been long-standing, has childhood traumatic experiences including domestic violence, neglect, date rape, and abandonment. Cassie also has intrusive thoughts of harming self or others. She has developed coping skills, such as pulling her hair out with tweezers and rather ritualistically examining them and putting them on her wall; she has plucked her eyebrows and eyelashes completely off at times, and found a more socially acceptable location to pluck hair by doing so on her legs. She has participated in nonsuicidal self injurious (NSSI) behavior by cutting following her sexual assault.

Relational Problems

Cassie appears to be struggling with several relational areas that are to be considered conditions that are of clinical concern, especially when implementing a family systems perspective. For example, Cassie appears to have struggled herself as a child with parent–child relational issues going back to her early childhood. She reported that she was often alone, and her physical, emotional, and psychological needs were not attended to, which falls under parental neglect. In addition, parental relationship distress likely may be applicable given her report of her parents not only not being attentive to her needs, but also their discord, fighting, and violence in the home to which she was a witness. This has appeared to now begin to cause parent–child relational struggles for Cassie in her own relationship with her daughter, Zoe, as Cassie fears she is unable to adequately parent. It would be beneficial to also examine if her lower socioeconomic status has impacted her level of functioning, as she reported coming from "poverty," which also impacts social factors. In addition, Cassie was a victim of an unreported crime of "date rape," which needs further exploration, specifically as it relates to her current relational experiences. Finally, Cassie reported a long-standing history of other problems related to the social environment, including social rejection.

Currently, Cassie is struggling with her self-efficacy in light of the disturbing thoughts she has about harming others or neglecting to parent her child. She appears to spend long amounts of time obsessively thinking about these fears, which then cause her to behaviorally isolate, pick her hair, self-loathe, or check and recheck her circumstances. These behaviors then cause a fragmentation within her family and occupational roles, as she reported being late to work, not being present for her daughter, and isolating from her husband. Cassie appears to have a long-standing discord with her parents and immediate family as she repeatedly mentions that they are not supportive of her, and have not been since she can remember. Cassie's husband has appeared to understand her past struggles with these thoughts and behaviors and is very supportive of the family receiving help. He recognizes "it has gotten worse recently" and his concern is for her well-being and his daughter's and their family happiness. It is of clinical concern as well that Cassie does not mention having any other outside friends or family relationships that may contribute to her isolation.

In conclusion, the main concern that has brought Cassie and her family to counseling is her fear of not being a good wife and mother due to OCD thoughts and behaviors that she believes are damaging the relationship at worst, and hindering healthy growth at best. Underlying this appears to be a fear of being alone, and thus her motivation for family counseling is presented. An accurate assessment and stance looking at both Cassie's and Jack's prior family histories in light of their family system today would be most beneficial to help them focus relationally on their future as a family together.

Assessments

In order to assess for the degree of functional impairment with this family, the OCD Family Functioning Scale can be used (Stewart et al., 2011). Both the patient version and a relative version will be given to gather information about the impact of Cassie's diagnosis on their family life, social life, and work- or school-related activities. Additionally, it may be beneficial to assess for accommodating behaviors in Cassie's family. The Family Accommodation Scale for Obsessive-Compulsive Disorder, which looks at family accommodating behaviors and levels of distress, can be used (Calvocoressi et al., 1999). This information can be particularly beneficial as the presence of accommodating behaviors may lead to negative implications or outcomes in treatment.

Interventions

Cognitive behavioral interventions that include the family can be beneficial. Since Zoe is only 3, the systemic clinician will focus on Cassie and Jack in session. However, the systemic clinician should monitor Zoe's interactions with mom and dad individually and together to check for any OCD symptoms that may be manifesting. It may also benefit Zoe to see a play therapist while Cassie and Jack are in session. Psychoeducation can be helpful to inform the family of aspects of OCD, accommodation, and the impact of this behavior. Additionally, the systemic clinician can use exposure interventions in session and can coach Cassie and Jack on how to conduct exposure exercises between sessions, which can positively impact the overall treatment outcomes. Practicing the techniques learned in session can help family members to reduce accommodating behaviors in day-to-day life. Finally, it is recommended that Cassie be referred to a physician or psychiatrist for a medication evaluation.

Ethical and Legal Implications

First and foremost, it is always recommended that a systemic clinician utilize an established professional ethical decision-making model and consult with his or her supervisor or peers. Cassie's family of origin has a long history of dysfunctional behavior. There may or may not be any reportable behavior based on the events Cassie remembers, depending on the state laws and the statute of limitations in Indiana. The systemic clinician should consider whether there are any mandatory reporting requirements based in his or her license and state of practice.

A preliminary discussion with this client may include whether or not her intrusive thoughts and fears are affecting her job as a certified nursing assistant. In her work, she is responsible for caring for and providing care to those who are not necessarily capable of caring for themselves. Her confidence in being able to do so professionally, causing no harm to her patients, may be an important discussion to have. Certainly, that discussion would have to be very supportive to Cassie, not accusatory, but exploratory.

Should she be a danger to herself or others, the systemic clinician will likely be a mandated reporter in most states. Specifically, there are states that require reporting of threats toward a specific person, building, or area, a threat to national security, or if the threat is for the person's own welfare, such as in suicidal plans. Risk assessments for danger to self and for danger to others may be recommended for this client, even though she denied having any suicidal thoughts. Asking a scaling question for a baseline could be quite beneficial as the systemic clinician continues to assess any risk while working with this family.

Being very clear about the exceptions to confidentiality is always critical to do; in this case, although Cassie denies ever having taken any action on the "bad thoughts" she has had, due to Zoe's young age, and Jack's work schedule, it would be important to check in with the family to ensure that Zoe's needs are being met, and that she is safe in her environment. There may be some contracting that could be done with Cassie and Jack to contact the systemic clinician or another mental health professional, such as a hotline, and contact information provided to them.

All of the legal and ethical issues should be documented in the case and discussed openly and from a supportive position. Consultation with supervisors and professional peers is highly recommended as family therapy can result in the systemic clinician being pulled into the family system without realizing it. Therefore, supervision and consultation may prevent or minimize any transference/countertransference issues.

DISCUSSION

As you continue to reflect on the case study and the overall approach, contemplate these questions:

- What are your initial thoughts about applying a family systems approach to this case? Which potential biases or triggers might you have after reviewing this case?

- What would your diagnosis for each family member be and why? Be sure to include Z codes in your discussion.

- Are there any foreseeable ethical or legal concerns? What ethical decision-making model might you employ?

- What is your biopsychosocial spiritual approach in case conceptualization for this family?

- What are your thoughts on specific techniques and interventions that may prove helpful for this family and why?

SUMMARY

The *DSM-5* placed Obsessive-Compulsive and Related Disorders (OCRDs) as a stand-alone category. This group of conditions now includes OCD, Hoarding Disorder, BDD, Trichotillomania (hair-pulling disorder), Excoriation (skin-picking disorder), Substance/Medication-Induced OCRD, OCRD Due to Another Medical Condition, Other Specified OCRD, and Unspecified OCRD. It is important to note other conditions and problems that may be of clinical significance that can impact case conceptualization when working with cultural considerations and families. These conditions were known previously in the *ICD-9-CM* as *DSM V* codes, and currently as *ICD-10-CM* Z codes.

Since biologically predisposed factors, environment, and culture can play a role in the development and treatment of OCD and related disorders, it stands to reason that these conditions can and should be assessed, diagnosed, and treated from a family systems perspective. There are many assessments for OCD and related disorders that consider the impact of family and explore information from the perspectives of family members and parents (Calvocoressi et al., 1999; Peris et al., 2008; Piacentini et al., 2007; Stewart et al., 2011; Wu et al., 2016).

In addition to assessments, treatment from a family systems perspective can be effective with OCD and related disorders. When family members are a part of the therapy, there can be an integration of resources that can broaden the perspective of the family environment and overall impact on relationships. Research indicates that family members can play a significant role in the overall outcomes of treatment for OCD and related disorders based on the degree of accommodation of behaviors such as hand washing or excessive cleaning. Current standards in the treatment of OCD and related disorders include the use of CBT while integrating the family system and psychotropic medications (Thompson-Hollands et al., 2014).

When incorporating family into the treatment of OCD and related disorders, there are many ethical and legal considerations at hand. Confidentiality and informed consent are two ethical domains that can be complex when working with families. Therefore, it is critical for the systemic clinician to have a professional ethical decision-making plan in order to follow the most up-to-date standards set forth by his or her professional specialization area's ethical codes as well as current state laws, regulations, and/or mandates for working under various professional mental health licensures.

REFERENCES

American Association for Marriage and Family Therapy. (2015, January 1). *AAMFT code of ethics.* Retrieved from http://www.aamft.org/iMIS15/AAMFT/Content/Legal_Ethics/Code_of_Ethics.aspx

American Counseling Association (2014). *ACA code of ethics.* Alexandria, VA: Author.

American Psychiatric Association. (2000). *Diagnostic and statistical manual of mental disorders* (4th ed., text rev.). Washington, DC: Author.

American Psychiatric Association. (2013a). *Diagnostic and statistical manual of mental disorders* (5th ed.). Arlington, VA: American Psychiatric Publishing.

American Psychiatric Association. (2013b). *Obsessive-compulsive and related disorders* [Fact Sheet]. Retrieved from http://www.dsm5.org/Documents/Obsessive%20Compulsive%20Disorders%20Fact%20Sheet.pdf

Anderson, P. (2008). *Obsessive-compulsive disorder: Not just a North American phenomenon.* Retrieved from http://www.medscape.com/viewarticle/570221

Berg, C. Z., Whitaker, A., Davies, M., Flament, M. F., & Rapoport, J. L. (1988). The survey form of the Leyton Obsessional Inventory-Child Version: Norms from an epidemiological study. *Journal of American Academy of Child and Adolescent Psychiatry, 27,* 759–763.

Berg-Cross, L. (2000). *Basic concepts in family therapy: An introductory text* (2nd ed.). New York, NY: The Haworth Press.

Bible Hub. (2015). *Ezra 9:3*. Retrieved from http://biblehub.com/ezra/9-3.htm

Breckman, A. (Creator), & Mandeville Films, & Touchstone Television (Producers). (2002–2009). *Monk* [Television show]. United States of America: Universal Studios.

Brewster, K. (2011). Body dysmorphic disorder in adolescence: Imagined ugliness. *The School Psychologist*. Retrieved from http://www.apadivisions.org/division16/publications/newsletters/school-psychologist/2011/07/adolescent-dysmorphic-disorder.aspx

Bronfenbrenner, U. (1979). *The ecology of human development*. Cambridge, MA: Harvard University Press.

Brooks, J. L. (Producer), & Brooks, J. (Director). (1998). *As good as it gets* [Motion picture]. United States of America: Sony Pictures Entertainment.

Calvocoressi, L., Mazure, C. M., Kasl, S. V., Skolnick, J., Fisk, D., Vegso, S. J., . . . Price, L. H. (1999). Family accommodation of obsessive compulsive symptoms: Instrument development and assessment of family behavior. *Journal of Nervous and Mental Disease, 187*, 636–642. doi:10.1097/00005053-199910000-00008

Colorado Department of Regulatory Agencies. (2016). Division of professions and occupations: Marriage and family clinicians. Retrieved from https://www.colorado.gov/dora/licensing/Lookup/DownloadRoster.aspx

Comer, J. S, Furr, J. M., Cooper-Vince, C. E., Kerns, C. E., Chan, P. T., Edson, A. L., . . . Freeman, J. B. (2014). Internet-delivered, family-based treatment for early-onset OCD: A preliminary case series. *Journal of Clinical Child & Adolescent Psychology, 43*(1), 74–87. doi:10.1080/15374416.2013.855127

Cooper, M. (1996). Obsessive-compulsive disorder: Effects on family members. *American Journal of Orthopsychiatry, 66*(2), 296–304.

Dembo, J. S. (2014). "The ickiness factor:" Case study of an unconventional psychotherapeutic approach to pediatric OCD. *American Journal of Psychotherapy, 68*(1), 57–79.

Drake, K. L., & Ginsburg, G. S. (2012). Family-based cognitive behavioral treatment of chronic pediatric headache and anxiety disorders: A case study. *Child Youth Care Forum, 41*, 579–598. doi:10.1007/s10566-012-9174-x

Fairfax, H., Easey, K., Fletcher, S., & Barfield, J., (2014). Does mindfulness help in the treatment of obsessive compulsive disorder (OCD)? An audit of client experience of an OCD group. *Counselling Psychology Review, 29*(3), 17–27.

Foa, E. B., Coles, M. E., Huppert, J. D., Pasupuleti, R., Franklin, M. E., & March, J. S. (2010). Development and validation of a child version of the Obsessive Compulsive Inventory. *Behavior Therapy, 41*, 121–132.

Forester-Miller, H., & Davis, T. (1996). *A practitioner's guide to ethical decision making*. Alexandria, VA: American Counseling Association.

Golomb, R., Franklin, M., Grant, J. E., Keuthen, N. J., Mansueto, C. S., Mouton-Odum, S., . . . Woods, D. (2016). *Expert consensus treatment guidelines: Body-focused repetitive behaviors: Hair pulling, skin picking, and related disorders*. Retrieved from http://www.bfrb.org/storage/documents/Expert_Consensus_Treatment_Guidelines_2016w.pdf

Goodman, W. K., & Storch, E. (1994a). LEVEL 2—Repetitive Thoughts and Behaviors—Adult (Adapted from the Florida Obsessive-Compulsive Inventory [FOCI] Severity Scale [Part B]) [Measurement instrument]. Retrieved from http://www.psychiatry.org/practice/dsm/dsm5/online-assessment-measures

Goodman, W. K., & Storch, E. (1994b). LEVEL 2—Repetitive Thoughts and Behaviors—Child Age 11–17 (Adapted from the Children's Florida Obsessive-Compulsive Inventory [C-FOCI] Severity Scale) [Measurement instrument]. Retrieved from http://www.psychiatry.org/practice/dsm/dsm5/online-assessment-measures

Grant, J. E., & Odlaug, B. L. (2009). Obsessive-compulsive spectrum and disorders of the skin. *Expert Review of Dermatology, 4*(5), 523–532. doi:10.1586/edm.09.40

Hildebrandt, T., Bacow, T., Markella, M., & Loeb, K. L. (2012), Anxiety in anorexia nervosa and its management using family-based treatment. *European Eating Disorders Review, 20*, 1–16. doi:10.1002/erv.1071

Hilton, K., Turner, C., Krebs, G., Volz, C., & Heyman, I. (2012). Parent experiences of attending a specialist clinic for assessment of their child's obsessive-compulsive disorder. *Child and Adolescent Mental Health, 17*(1), 31–36, doi:10.1111/j.1475-3588.2011.00607.x

Hunt, T. J., Thienhaus, O., & Ellwood, A. (2008). The mirror lies: Body dysmorphic disorder. *American Family Physician, 78*(2), 217–222.

Iniesta-Sepúlveda, M., Rosa-Alcázar, A. I., Rosa-Alcázar, A., & Storch, E. A. (2014). Evidence-based assessment in children and adolescents with obsessive-compulsive disorder. *Journal of Child and Family Studies, 23*, 1455–1470. doi:10.1007/s10826-013-9801-7

Kabat-Zinn, J. (1994). *Wherever you go, there you are: Mindfulness meditation in everyday life.* New York, NY: Hyperion.

Kaplan, D. M., Tarvydas, V. M., & Gladding, S. T. (2014). 20/20: A vision for the future of counseling: The new consensus definition of counseling. *Journal of Counseling and Development, 92,* 366–372. doi:10.1002/j.1556-6676.2014.00164.x

Lochner, C., du Toit, P. L., Zungu-Dirwayi, N., Marais, A., van Kradenburg, J., Seedat, S., Niehaus, D. J. H., & Stein, D. (2002). Childhood trauma in obsessive-compulsive disorder, trichotillomania, and controls. *Depresssion and Anxiety, 15,* 66–68.

Lochner, C., Fineberg, N. A., Zohar, J., van Amerigan, M., Juven-Wetzler, A., Altamura, A. C., & Stein, D. (2014). Comorbidity in obsessive-compulsive disorder (OCD): A report from the International College of Obsessive-Compulsive Spectrum Disorders (ICOCS). *Comprehensive Psychiatry, 55*(7), 1513–1519. doi:10.1016/j.comppsych.2014.05.020

National Center for Health Statistics. (2017). *International classification of diseases, tenth revision, clinical modification.* Retrieved from https://www.cdc.gov/nchs/icd/icd10cm.htm

Peris, T. S., Benazon, N., Langley, A., Roblek, T., & Piacentini, J. (2008). Parental attitudes, beliefs, and responses to childhood obsessive compulsive disorder: The Parental Attitudes and Behaviors Scale. *Child and Family Behavior Therapy, 30,* 199–214.

Peris, T. S., Sugar, C. A., Bergman, R. L., Chang, S., Langley, A., & Piacentini, J. (2012). Family factors predict treatment outcome for pediatric obsessive-compulsive disorder. *Journal of Consulting and Clinical Psychology, 80*(2), 255–263.

Piacentini, J., Peris, T. S., Bergman, R. L., Chang, S., & Jaffer, M. (2007). Functional impairment in childhood OCD: Development and psychometrics properties of the Child Obsessive–Compulsive Impact Scale-Revised (COIS-R). *Journal of Clinical Child and Adolescent Psychology, 36,* 645–653.

Saleem, S. S., & Mahmood, Z. A. (2009). OCD in a cultural context: A phenomenological approach. *Pakistan Journal of Psychological Research, 24*(1–2), 27–42.

Scahill, L., Riddle, M. A., McSwiggin-Hardin, M., Ort, S. I., King, R. A., Goodman, W. K., . . . Leckman, J. F. (1997). Children's Yale-Brown Obsessive–Compulsive Scale: Reliability and validity. *Journal of the American Academy of Child and Adolescent Psychiatry, 36,* 844–852.

Seligman, L. (2012). *Diagnosis and treatment planning in counseling.* New York, NY: Springer.

Shafran, R., Frampton, I., Heyman, I., Reynolds, M., Teachman, B., & Rachman, S. (2003). The preliminary development of a new self-report measure for OCD in young people. *Journal of Adolescence, 26,* 137–142.

Sperry, L. (2007). *The ethical and professional practice of counseling and psychotherapy.* New York, NY: Pearson.

Stewart, S. E., Hu, Y. P., Hezel, D. M., Proujansky, R., Lamstein, A., Walsh, C., . . . Pauls, D. L. (2011). Development and psychometric properties of the OCD Family Functioning (OFF) Scale. *Journal of Family Psychology, 25*(3), 434–443.

Storch, E. A., Kaufman, D. A., Bagner, D., Merlo, L. J., Shapira, N. A., Geffken, G. R., . . . Goodman, W. K. (2007). Florida Obsessive–Compulsive Inventory: Development, reliability, and validity. *Journal of Clinical Psychology, 63,* 851–859.

Storch, E. A., Lehmkuhl, H., Pence, S. L., Jr, Geffken, G. R., Ricketts, E., Storch, J. F., & Murphy, T. K. (2009). Parental experiences of having a child with obsessive compulsive disorder: Associations with clinical characteristics and caregiver adjustment. *Journal of Child and Family Studies, 18,* 249–258.

Thompson-Hollands, J., Edson, A., Tompson, M. C., & Comer, J. S. (2014). Family involvement in the psychological treatment of obsessive-compulsive disorder: A meta-analysis. *Journal of Family Psychology, 28*(3), 287–298. doi:10.1037/a0036709

Van Ameringen, M., Patterson, B., & Simpson, W. (2014). DSM-5 obsessive-compulsive and related disorders: Clinical implications of new criteria. *Depression and Anxiety, 31*(6), 487–493. doi:10.1002/da.22259

Wu, M. S., Pinto, A., Horng, B., Phares, V., McGuire, J. F., Dedrick, R. F., . . . Storch, E. A. (2016). Psychometric properties of the family accommodation scale for obsessive-compulsive disorder—Patient version. *Psychological Assessment, 28*(3), 251–262. doi:10.1037/pas0000165

TRAUMA- AND STRESSOR-RELATED DISORDERS: SYSTEMIC PROCESSES

Christie Jenkins, Annabelle Shestak, John Laux, and Jennifer Jancsin

As a diagnostic category, Trauma- and Stress or-Related Disorders represent a new grouping in the *Diagnostic and Statistical Manual of Mental Disorders* (5th ed.; *DSM-5*; American Psychiatric Association [APA], 2013). After all, the immediately preceding version of the *DSM* (*Diagnostic and Statistical Manual of Mental Disorders*—4th ed., text rev.; *DSM-IV-TR*; APA, 2000) conceptualized Posttraumatic Stress Disorder (PTSD) among Anxiety disorders. Some would argue that this change reflected a true evolution of research and understanding about trauma and its consequences for individuals, families, and communities. Others have argued that this change reflects only the APA's refusal to recognize the full implications of trauma research (Van der Kolk, 2005).

In one of the most extensive research projects from the Center for Disease Control and Prevention, referred to as the Adverse Childhood Experiences survey, exposure to childhood adversity was identified as a primary contributing factor to a still-growing list of physiological and emotional impairments (Anda et al., 2006; Felitti et al., 1998). Advances in the study of intergenerational transmission of trauma (Yehuda & Bierer, 2009), as well as research into consequences of maltreatment in early childhood (Teicher et al., 2003), suggest that consequences of traumatic exposure can be experienced and passed on from one generation to the next. Simply put, traumatic exposure does not mark merely the individual who has experienced and remembered a traumatic incident, but also the individual's children, family, and health.

DSM-5 AND FAMILY SYSTEMS

Traumatic stress, perhaps as much as or more than any other diagnostic presentation, closely aligns with the family systems philosophical underpinnings. Trauma takes root in and impacts an individual's limbic and endocrine systems (Miller, Chen, & Zhou, 2007). But, in order for the individual to develop a stress reaction, some sort of exogenous traumatic event must occur. That exogenous event originates in the individual's system, or environment. In this respect, traumatic stress is not a consequence of irrational thinking, an imbalance in neurotransmitters, or endocrine malfunctions, but rather a likely cause for all of these and other problems (Anda et al., 2006).

In addition to having origins outside of the individual, traumatic stress disrupts the affected individual's larger systems. In fact, the traumatized individual's reaction to stress is best understood in the context of his or her experiences as a member of the family system. The traumatized individual's reaction to the trauma(s) radiates beyond the epicenter and effects the way the whole family functions. Homeostasis keeps the trauma from resolution and makes it increasingly intractable. The National Child Traumatic Stress Network (2011) noted that trauma affects family and family members in the following six ways:

1. The stress resulting from trauma can negatively affect adult intimate relationships when one or both partners experience disruptions in the ability to communicate, manage their emotions, and engage in intimate relations.
2. A parent or parents who are struggling to respond to personal trauma may end up with compromised abilities to help their children grow and develop.
3. Compromised parental availability can allow for the development or exacerbation of children's issues.
4 Sibling relationships can be compromised when trauma has significantly impacted one of the members of the relationship.
5. Traumatic events can impair the family's ability to support and nurture one another.
6. Traumatic events can require families to expend time, energy, effort, and money in ways previously not required. This change in the way that family resources are allocated can result in a decreased availability to meet previously important family commitments, such as support, safety, food, health, and affection (National Child Traumatic Stress Network, 2011).

In some families, the trauma survivor may become the "scapegoat" in the family. The survivor becomes a safe person for blame as he or she has complex symptomatology and behaviors that may be problematic in the family unit. This can lead to some family members taking sides for or against the survivor. Although families may feel bad for the survivor, the resentment of preferential treatment and the guilt for having these negative feelings is often directly below the surface.

One common response to trauma and stress is PTSD. Although originally referred to as "shell shock" and contextualized in relation to combat-related events, PTSD is a serious condition that impacts not only military veterans but also many survivors of domestic violence, sexual abuse, and other relationship-based violations. Although some of the PTSD symptoms may seem similar to those of other disorders, there are some marked and important differences. For example, PTSD symptoms may cause many individuals to present with the sadness and hopelessness characteristic of a Depressive Disorder, others to exhibit the intense worry that is a common marker of Anxiety and Obsessive-Compulsive disorders, and even others with the disruption in reality testing typical to Dissociative or Psychotic disorders. However, despite a superficial similarity in presentation, PTSD typically causes only symptoms that are logical and easily understood within the context of the individual's traumatic exposure. In contrast to the irrational fears in anxiety disorders, or the odd persecutory beliefs in psychosis, PTSD causes fears and beliefs that are based in real terrifying past experiences, or the intrusive, inescapable recollection of these experiences. In children, PTSD is most frequently expressed in reenactment and play, which mimic the content of trauma exposure. Unlike the repetitive, sometimes bizarre play of autistic children, trauma-affected children often act out traumatic scenes from their lives with remarkable precision and authenticity.

Acute Stress Disorder and PTSD are very similar. As a differential diagnostic rule, acute stress disorder occurs after 3 days of exposure to the trauma source and no longer than 1 month. If acute stress disorder symptoms last longer than 1 month and other symptoms relevant to PTSD emerge, a person's diagnosis may be changed from acute stress disorder to PTSD. However, an acute stress disorder diagnosis is not sufficient, even in the absence of intervention, to predict development of PTSD (Bryant, 2010). With appropriate and timely intervention, acute stress symptoms are less likely to endure and become sufficiently severe to justify a PTSD diagnosis (Bryant et al., 2008).

PTSD symptoms, at a minimal level, can also look like an adjustment disorder because they each harbor emotional distress and behavioral dysfunction that can form after exposure to stress. With PTSD, this stressor is exposure to a life-threatening, traumatic experience. With an adjustment disorder, the stressor is situational or developmental and is not typically sufficiently severe to be considered traumatic. Typically, adjustment disorders are best thought of as stress reactions of unusual intensity to normal life circumstances. Similar to acute stress disorder, adjustment disorders are time-limited conditions, which are expected to occur within 3 months of the onset of the stressor, and resolve within 6 months of the stressor's resolution.

Particularly relevant to systemic clinicians are the diagnoses of Reactive Detachment Disorder and Disinhibited Social Engagement Disorder. These conditions, or their symptoms, are common in young children who have experienced severe relational traumas, such as disrupted caregiving and parental neglect. In fact, such early experiences are a core requirement for both diagnoses. In reactive attachment, disruption in the relational processes that foster the supportive bond between a child and his or her caregiver causes the child to display affective dysregulation, behavioral dyscontrol, and a lack of engagement in the parent–child dyad. Children diagnosed with reactive attachment typically do not show age-appropriate ability to regulate their emotions, and do not seek or respond to adult support when upset. In the most extreme cases, these children appear to have given up on expressing and experiencing love and support. However, reactive attachment is much more than a relational disorder. Children diagnosed with reactive attachment often also experience neurodevelopmental difficulties, speech delays, and attention problems (Tirella, Chan, & Miller, 2006).

In contrast, children diagnosed with Disinhibited Social Engagement Disorder are those who are very much interested in engaging and connecting with adults. Many of these children seem to be continuously searching for a caregiver; they have no age-appropriate fear of strangers, very loose physical boundaries, and an indiscriminate willingness to follow any adult who pays them attention (Lawler, Hostinar, Mliner, & Gunnar, 2014). Interestingly, these children are equally likely to struggle with very similar developmental and physiological problems to those diagnosed with reactive attachment. In both disorders, the impact on children's safety and family well-being is tremendous.

RELATIONAL AND CULTURAL FEATURES

The importance of culturally competent trauma work is paramount. By providing appropriate services based on the individual's and the family's needs, a counselor can provide the best avenue for healing. Information gathering may determine that the client identifies with his or her culture and ethnicity of origin, or something altogether different. The passage of behavioral, emotional, and physiological manifestations of traumatic stress from one generation to the next, known as *intergenerational transmission of trauma*, must also be considered in treatment. For instance, children of female Holocaust survivors are far more likely to have lower levels of the "stress hormone," cortisol, which is responsible for regulating the fight-or-flight response (Yehuda et al., 2007). Lower than average cortisol levels are predictive of development of PTSD (Yehuda et al., 2007). Some cultures have had nonstop exposure to trauma, across multiple generations. How treatment is approached with these families must be carefully considered, as they may not experience trauma in the same capacity as others.

It is necessary to comprehend how the client's culture and ethnicity have determined the meaning that he or she has attached to the trauma. It is also important that the counselor assess the family's impression of the trauma. A counselor may need to help the client and his or her family members comprehend how the client may be experiencing the trauma based on his or her heritage. For example, a family whose cultural heritage includes patriarchic behavior toward women may include older generations who do not understand the negative effects of domestic violence on a child. The impressions of these elders may cause the child's parent to hesitate to address the trauma in treatment, and extensive education may be required for treatment to occur. The *DSM-5* glossary of the cultural concepts of distress, and sections describing other conditions that may be the focus of clinical attention, may provide more adequate descriptions for some families' experiences of traumatic stress. These should be considered when evaluating the appropriateness of a *DSM-5* diagnosis.

Clients should be encouraged to process their trauma in their native language, with their own cultural tools, and with the methods ascribed by their heritage. This will empower the client to utilize a familiar and enduring skill set to navigate the healing process. This allows the counselor additional tools that are meaningful to the client to facilitate growth. Keeping in mind that each client is an individual and may or may not experience trauma in the same manner as someone else from his or her culture, a counselor should check in with the client to see if his or her assumptions are correct.

Hays (2008) developed the acronym, ADDRESSING, to look at a systemic approach to treatment for age, developmental and acquired disabilities, religion, ethnicity, social class, sexual orientation, indigenous heritage, national origin, and gender/sex. This list is not exhaustive, but is meant to be the foundation for cultural competence in the therapeutic relationship. For better understanding, it is important to look at each piece of the ADDRESSING model to see how it interacts with trauma work.

Age

Age can be thought of in multiple capacities. Age can be seen as the developmental level of a person. A counselor can gain insight from an individual's age cohort and the norms surrounding his or her life experience. Age can also have an impact on how a person responds to trauma and subsequently how it impacts further development and additional propensity for trauma. The age at the time of the initial trauma can teach clients inappropriate boundaries, which can put them at risk for trauma throughout their life cycles (Hays, 2008).

Developmental and Acquired Disabilities

A disability can be seen as a challenge to normative functioning. With this being said, many people may not consider themselves disabled, because they do not necessarily see the deficits determined by society at large. These shortages can become more pronounced when barriers present themselves in society. Counselors should not assume that having a disability in and of itself is an additional trauma. However, it can be a risk factor for specific types of trauma such as abuse and neglect (Hays, 2008).

Religion and Spirituality

Counselors should gather information regarding religion and spirituality before and after the trauma. Many trauma survivors may question God as to why they were forsaken, at least initially. Others find strength in their faith and they are able to heal through their religious practices. Counselors should follow the client's lead and be supportive and knowledgeable regarding his or her particular needs (Hays, 2008).

Ethnicity and Culture

When ethnicity or culture is considered in treatment, a counselor may default to automatically consider persons of color and trauma associated with racism and disenfranchisement. Consequently, many Caucasian individuals may not assume that they have a cultural identity or may have distanced themselves from their cultural heritage as they may have immigrated from poverty, war, or oppression. This trauma can be buried and it may be necessary for a counselor to look at tools such as genograms to truly assess the level of impact on the individual and the family (Hays, 2008).

Socioeconomic Status

Socioeconomic status can be an invisible barrier for clients. Social class does not necessarily mean income level. Some individuals may have a higher level of social class based on their education and the education of their families. However, when social class is mixed with other factors such as age or disability, it is easy to see the income disparity. Trauma survivors may not have the resources to access services due to having no health care coverage, family support, or transportation to obtain treatment (Hays, 2008).

Sexual Orientation

Sexual orientation can be seen as the deeply personal expression toward sex and romantic relationships. Everyone has a sexual orientation that may be fixed or fluid throughout his or her lifetime. People who are from the lesbian, gay, bisexual, transgender, questioning, and intersex (LGBTQI) community are often targeted with heterosexism and homophobia. Most LGBTQI persons have experienced trauma on some level based on their sexual orientation or gender identity. Families can be very harsh and even disown family members when they disagree with a member's LGBTQI status. Counselors need to ensure that they are not experiencing countertransference, whereby they experience feelings toward a client that are rooted in their personal beliefs regarding, or experiences with, sexual orientation or gender identity. For instance, a male counselor whose client is transitioning from a female to a male gender identity may discover that he feels dismissive of his client's masculine identity, due to his own upbringing, in which his own masculinity was ridiculed because of his emotional sensitivity (Hays, 2008).

Indigenous Heritage and Colonization

Indigenous people share the human experience of being invaded, enslaved, and persecuted. A prime example in the United States would be Native Americans. Native Americans have a shared trauma experience that transcends their cultural heritage and is still very much present today. Native American families may not seek treatment outside of the family and/or tribe, even though they may be subjected to horrific trauma by these same people (Hays, 2008).

National Origin, Immigration, and Refugee Status

Immigration and migration may be voluntary or forced. A person may interpret his or her experience based on either of those factors. Within family units, persons may have a very different experience based on things such as age or economic status at the time of the transition. Counselors should be mindful especially of families who are undocumented and how a traumatic experience may not be reported due to fear of being deported (Hays, 2008).

Gender and Sex

Gender and sex are two very different things. Sex refers to the biological makeup, whereas gender is socially constructed. Counselors need to be aware of their own gender rules and how they may transfer those prescribed notions to others. When clients do not conform to a particular mainstream gender expression, it can lead them to increased risk for trauma. As discussed in the sexual orientation section, families may not understand gender nonconformity and add negative layers to any traumatic experience (Hays, 2008).

FAMILY SYSTEMS ASSESSMENTS

According to Harris and Topham (2004), the family system mediates how traumatic events affect individual family members and the family system's response to the trauma. As such, systems-oriented counselors assess the impact of the trauma on the individual as well as the impact of the traumatic event on the entire family system. Individual trauma assessments help to understand the degree to which the directly affected family member responds to the traumatic event. And, individual trauma assessments help to identify the level of trauma that will be brought into the family system. A solid clinical understanding of the severity of the trauma is necessary to help families live with and recover from traumatic events (Connors & Smith Stover, 2011). The goal of a family trauma assessment is to identify the family's presenting issues, determine a path for treatment, and use the treatment plan to provide clinical services. The family therapist assesses the family system's emotional response and collective experience of the trauma (Harris & Topham, 2004). To accomplish this task, the family assessment's goals are to collect information about each family member's personal history, his or her present functioning and his or her presenting symptoms, each family member's role in the system, and the way the members and the system communicate and interact with one another. Of particular importance is a focus on assessing the family's differentiation and anxiety.

In the simplest terms, *differentiation* is a term used to represent the degree to which a family member makes decisions based on feelings versus the degree to which the family member uses intellect to drive decision making (Harris & Topham, 2004). Highly differentiated family members respond to trauma objectively and thoughtfully. Less well-differentiated individuals respond to trauma emotionally. Poorly differentiated persons either set aside their own emotional needs to care for other's needs, to their own detriment, or they take little to no responsibility for other's emotional reactions to the trauma, thus locking themselves into a definition of their own reactions in the context of others. Differentiation can be further broken down into functional differentiation and basic differentiation. Functional differentiation depends on the family system's adaptability to anxiety, the level of trauma in the system, the individual's support system, and the role the individual plays in the family system. Due to variances in the system's level of anxiety, trauma, and support, one's functional differentiation is state specific. Conversely, basic differentiation is a trait that is stable and relatively inflexible. Basic differentiation is a consequence of one's emotional separation from one's family. Basic differentiation delimits one's ability to adapt to trauma and it is for this reason that systems counselors place greater focus on assessing and understanding basic and not functional differentiation (Harris & Topham, 2004). The second variable, anxiety, while generally understood by mental health practitioners, is here placed into one of two subcategories: chronic and acute anxiety (Harris & Topham, 2004). Although chronic anxiety is that emotional state of fear and worry about that which *may* occur, acute anxiety is produced by realized stressors such as trauma. Differentiation and anxiety intersect such that persons who have low levels of differentiation (i.e., they are emotionally enmeshed or emotionally distant from family members) are prone to higher levels of chronic anxiety. By way of example, an individual who is chronically worried about catching a communicable disease might become emotionally enmeshed with a family member who is viewed to be emotionally supportive. To an objective viewer outside of that system, the chronic worry may be seen as a mechanism to elicit emotional soothing and caretaking and the caretaker's nurturance may serve to meet the caretaker's own needs to be wanted and needed. Conversely, a highly differentiated family member is less likely to be seduced into an emotionally needy system and thus will experience lower levels of chronic anxiety. It follows that highly differentiated persons are better able to respond in a healthy manner to acute traumas. As such, a goal for the family systems therapist working with a family affected by trauma is to foster increases in the family members' levels of differentiation (Harris & Topham, 2004).

A long list of standardized instruments is available to help quantify the presence and nature of family members' exposure to trauma. Based on the influence that military experiences have had on the development of combat-related PTSD, it is not surprising that many of the available trauma-screening instruments were either developed for measuring combat-related PTSD or involved military veterans as normative sample populations.

Elhai, Gray, Kashdan, and Franklin (2005) compiled a list and review of those instruments that traumatic stress professionals most frequently employ to assess clients' exposure to and response to traumatic events. Additionally, the U.S. Department of Veteran Affairs website provides a list of trauma-screening instruments that can help the clinician determine if an individual family member is experiencing traumatic stress and, if so, the degree to which the traumatic stress is present (www.ptsd.va.gov/professional/assessment/overview/index.asp).

The following section presents a review of the available trauma assessments. The reader is encouraged to consider each assessment in the context of the following case example. Which instrument(s) might be useful for the case and for what reasons?

Jeff and Thomas are both middle-aged men of mixed race. They have been in a long-term committed relationship for 20 years. Jeff's parents and siblings are supportive of his relationship with Thomas but live 1,000 miles away. Thomas's parents, siblings, and extended family do not approve of his relationship with Jeff. Despite the fact that Jeff and Thomas live in the same midsized city as do Thomas's family, there has been no communication between Thomas and his family for two decades. Jeff and Thomas adopted two children, Robert and Martha, 15 years ago. Robert is now 19 and Martha is 15. The family approached a counselor for help after Robert was assaulted at a party while away at his first semester of college. Robert casually mentioned that he missed his dads. This comment was overheard by another person who convinced two of his friends to "teach Robert a lesson" about "what a real family is." Robert suffered contusions about his body, lacerations on his face, and lost consciousness. He was taken to the hospital and diagnosed with a severe concussion. Robert is having trouble sleeping and is jumpy. He fears going back to that college and also feels badly because he did not stand up for and defend his fathers' honors. In all cases, the goal for the family therapist would be to select an instrument that is best suited for the person who was physically traumatized (Robert) in order to ascertain the degree of impact the assault had upon him and to work with Robert, Martha, Jeff, and

Thomas to ascertain the way the whole family responds to this external source of stress and trauma on each family member and their entire unit.

Brief Trauma Questionnaire (BTQ)

The Brief Trauma Questionnaire was published by Schnurr, Spiro, Vielhauer, Findler, and Hamblen (2002). This 10-item self-report questionnaire addresses the *DSM-5* (APA, 2013) Criterion A, which focuses on "exposure to actual or threatened death, serious injury, or sexual violation" (p. 280). The instrument is designed for use as a screen to determine which respondents should receive further in-depth PTSD screening and which respondents shouldn't. Respondents are presented with a list of 10 questions and asked to identify whether or not each event has happened to them. For those items answered "yes," respondents are further asked to identify if they felt their life was in danger or that they might be seriously injured and if they actually were seriously injured.

The BTQ is a relatively new PTSD measure, but it has gained a foothold in disparate clinical settings. For example, a study of 3,000 women (Koenen et al., 2009) found that there was an excellent agreement between the BTQ results and *Diagnostic and Statistical Manual of Mental Disorders* (4th ed.; *DSM-IV*; APA, 1994) criteria. Kubzansky et al. (2014) used the BTQ in a study intended to determine if weight gain was associated with PTSD symptoms in a sample of adult women. The BTQ was used to investigate the underlying PTSD factor structure among college students (Lancaster, Melka, & Rodriguez, 2009). Interested readers can find the BTQ online at this website: www.ptsd.va.gov/professional/pages/assessments/assessment-pdf/brief_trauma_questionnaire.pdf.

Clinician-Administered PTSD Scale for *DSM-5* (CAPS-5)

Initially published in 1995 (Blake et al., 1995), the current 30-item structured interview is the measure against which other PTSD screens and interviews are compared (Weathers et al., 2013). It is useful for determining three temporal ranges of symptoms: past week, past month, and lifetime. Clinicians use CAPS-5 to ask about each of the *DSM-5* 20 PTSD symptoms. Additionally, follow-up questions regarding endorsed items target the beginning and length of reported symptoms, the impact of symptoms on one's social and occupational functioning, and the severity of the client's PTSD diagnosis: absent, mild/subthreshold, moderate/threshold, severe/markedly elevated, and extreme/incapacitating. A child/adolescent version (Clinician-Administered PTSD Scale for *DSM-5*—Child/Adolescent Version [CAPS-CA-5]) is available (Nader, 2004; Ohan, Myers, & Collett, 2002; Pynoos et al., 2015). The CAPS-5 is available from the U.S. Department of Veterans Affairs's National Center for PTSD. Interested readers can access the instrument by complying an online request at this website (www.ptsd.va.gov/professional/assessment/ncptsd-instrument-request-form.asp). In addition to the English language version, the CAPS-5 has been translated and validated for use with additional populations such as Cambodian refugees (Hinton et al., 2006), Dutch-speaking children (Diehle, de Roos, Boer, & Lindauer,2013), German speakers (Schnyder & Moergeli, 2002), Spanish speakers (Benuto, Olmo-Terrasa, & Reyes-Rabanillo, 2011), and Swedish speakers (Paunovic & Ost, 2005).

Combat Exposure Scale (CES)

As the name implies, this screen was designed for use with persons who were combatants (Keane, Fairbank, Caddell, Zimering, Taylor, & Mora, 1989). This instrument's seven items ask respondents to indicate the number of times they engaged in combat-related activities (e.g., combat patrols, receiving fire, firing a weapon in battle, and being in danger of being injured/killed). Response items range from 1 (no/never) to 5 (varying amounts of incidents across items). Item scores are totaled and interpreted along a classification range from light to heavy combat exposure. This screen was employed with former prisoners of war veterans from World War II, the Korean Conflict, and the Vietnam War (Blake et al., 1990). The Combat Exposure Scale (CES) can be accessed at the following website: www.ptsd.va.gov/professional/pages/assessments/assessment-pdf/CES.pdf. The CES scoring and interpretation guide is located at this website: www.ptsd.va.gov/professional/assessment/documents/CES_Scoring_information.pdf.

Evaluation of Lifetime Stressors (ELS)

The Evaluation of Lifetime Stressors (Krinsley, 1996) is a combined self-report and structured interview tool used to assess for the presence of trauma across the life span. The self-report questionnaire has 56 items and the structured interview has 53 items. The interview portion takes 10 to 20 minutes to complete (Krinsley, Gallagher, Weathers, Kutter, & Kaloupek, 2003). The questionnaire asks persons to endorse one of four response options ("No, this did not happen," "No, but this happened to someone I knew," "I'm not sure if this happened," and "Yes, this happened to me") to questions about a range of traumatic events (e.g., combat, violence, accidents, illnesses, and disasters). The interview questions are designed to prompt the clinician to further investigate traumatic events experienced by the client. Specifically, interviewers ask about the trauma's instigator, the frequency and duration of the trauma, and the individual's response to the trauma. The ELS can be used for adolescents and adult populations. Interested clinicians can obtain this instrument from Karen E. Krinsley (krinsley.karen@boston.va.gov).

Life Events Checklist for *DSM-5* (LEC-5)

The Life Events Checklist presents respondents with 16 events associated with trauma (e.g., natural disaster, fire/explosion, physical assault, combat, captivity) and an open-ended question to ascertain if the client has experienced a traumatic event not covered among the 16 presented. Respondents identify if, at any point in their lives, the event happened to them, was witnessed, was learned about, was part of their job, or they aren't sure, or does not apply. This screen is useful for assessing traumatic experiences across the life span, and not just in adulthood. There are three versions of this screen. The first helps the clinician determine if a traumatic event occurred. The second version is available for use if more than one traumatic event occurred in the respondent's life. The first two versions are self-report instruments. The third version is a structured interview to help determine whether or not the respondent meets *DSM* PTSD Criterion A. For those persons whose trauma history warrants the structured interview, the clinician is instructed to also administer the CAPS-5 (Blake, Weathers, et al., 1990). The LEC's psychometric properties were investigated in a sample of college students and a sample of combat veterans (Gray, Litz, Hsu, & Lombardo, 2004). The results of these investigations indicated that the LEC's 1-week test–retest stability was adequate, the LEC produced similar results as did the Traumatic Life Events Questionnaire (Kubany et al. 2000), and was positively correlated with psychological distress and PTSD symptoms. The Standard Self-Report can be downloaded from the following website: www.ptsd.va.gov/professional/pages/assessments/assessment-pdf/LEC-5_Standard_Self-report.pdf. The Extended Self-Report version for those who experience more than one traumatic event is available from the following website: www.ptsd.va.gov/professional/pages/

assessments/assessment-pdf/LEC-5_Extended_Self-report.pdf. And, the structured inter-view format guide is available online at this website: www.ptsd.va.gov/professional/pages/assessments/assessment-pdf/LEC-5_Interview.pdf.

Life Stressor Checklist—Revised (LSC-R)

The Life Stressor Checklist—Revised (Wolfe et al., 1996) asks about 30 life events associated with stressors and traumas. For each endorsed incident, respondents are asked to identify the age at which the event occurred; to indicate whether or not they believed they or someone else could have been seriously harmed or killed by the event; whether or not the event provoked feelings of intense helplessness, horror, or fear; and to estimate the degree to which, if any, the event affected their lives in the past year (Norris & Hamblen, 2004). One of this screen's strengths is that it includes items that are largely (e.g., prolonged and unwanted separation from children) or solely (e.g., miscarriage) related to women's lives (McHugo et al., 2005; Wolfe et al., 1996). This instrument has been translated into use for Colombian Spanish-speaking women (Humphreys et al., 2011). Interested readers can access the LSC-R at the following website: www.ptsd.va.gov/professional/pages/assessments/assessment-pdf/LSC-R.pdf. The LSC-R scoring rubric is accessible at this website: www.ptsd.va.gov/professional/pages/assessments/assessment-pdf/LSC-R-Scoring.pdf.

Mississippi Scale for Combat-Related PTSD (M-PTSD)

This 35-item instrument was designed for use with veterans who experienced combat. It operationalizes DSM-III PTSD symptoms as well as comorbid pathology (Keane, Caddell, & Taylor, 1988). The Mississippi Scale for Combat-Related PTSD (M-PTSD) has been modified for use with other populations. Two versions of the M-PTSD are available for civilian use. A 24-item version (C-Mississippi) was published in 1997 (Kulka et al., 1990). One study of the C-Mississippi provides evidence of acceptable internal consistency, split-half reliability, and the ability to discriminate between traumatized and nontraumatized persons (Lauterbach, Vrana, King, & King, 1997). A revision of the 1997 version is available for English and Spanish speakers (Norris & Perilla, 1996). A brief, 10-item version demonstrated acceptable test–retest reliability estimates in a sample of Vietnam veterans and measured two factors: guilt and numbing/anger (Hyer, Davis, Boudewyns, & Woods, 1991). A sample of 30 U.S. Marines with 3 months of active duty services during Operation Desert Storm completed a revised version of the M-PTSD and self-reported PTSD symptoms (Sloan, Arsenault, Hilsenroth, & Harvill, 1995). The revised instrument, the M-PTSD-DS, was modified to assess the unique experiences associated with Operation Desert Storm (ODS) and included items to reflect women veterans' experiences. These Marines' M-PTSD score experiences were significantly correlated with self-reported trauma. Finally, a partner-focused instrument is accessible in case the clinician wants corroborating evidence about the veterans PTSD (Taft, King, King, Leskin, & Riggs, 1999).

Primary Care PTSD Screen (PC-PTSD)

The Primary Care PTSD Screen was designed to be used in medical settings (Prins et al., 2003). Its brevity means that it can be easily memorized and administered without use of paper and pencil. The PC-PTSD has four items. It begins by asking the respondent: if he or she has ever had any experience that was so upsetting that, in the past month, the person has had nightmares or had intrusive thoughts about the event; if the person tried not to think about it or avoided stimuli that reminded the person of the event; if the person is hypervigilant; and if the person experiences depersonalization. If any three of these four items are answered affirmatively, the screen's results are positive for trauma. Any person who is screened positively on the PC-PTSD should receive an in-depth trauma assessment. The PC-PTSD demonstrated acceptable psychometric properties among samples of U.S. veterans who served in the military after September 11, 2001; however, the screen produced greater than expected false-positives (Calhoun et al., 2010). Furthermore, the PC-PTSD outperformed a competing instrument in predicting PTSD diagnoses among Veterans Affairs patients (Ouimette, Wade, Prins, & Schohn, 2008). This instrument has proved to be effective for identifying women who have experienced military combat (Dutra et al., 2011). Finally, after a review of primary care setting articles ($n = 15$) involving 14,707 participants, the PC-PTSD was identified as one of the two best-performing PTSD screening instruments (Spoont et al., 2015).

Short Screening Scale for PTSD (SSS-PTSD)

The Short Screening Scale for PTSD contains five yes/no items about avoidance behavior and two yes/no items about hyperarousal (Breslau, Peterson, Kessler, & Schultz, 1999). Any respondent who provides four or more yes responses should receive a full-blown PTSD assessment. Data collected from a large, national sample provided evidence of this instrument's sensitivity, specificity, and positive and negative predictive validity (Bohnert and Breslau, 2011). Male and female patients at a Veterans Affairs clinic were recruited to test the SSS-PTSD's agreement with a longer, clinician-administered PTSD-structured interview (Kimerling et al. 2006). The SSS-PTSD proved to have good 1-month temporal stability and correctly identified 85% of patients diagnosed with PTSD. Interested readers can access the scale's seven items in Bohnert and Breslau's article.

Stressful Life Events Screening Questionnaire (SLESQ)

The Stressful Life Events Screening Questionnaire (SLESQ) was developed using a large sample of nontreatment-seeking college students. Its 13 items inquire about one's lifetime exposure to inter- and impersonal traumatic experiences (Goodman, Corcoran, Turner, Yuan, & Green, 1998). Respondents are asked to answer yes or no to 11 specific and two general categories of potentially traumatic events. The respondent is asked to identify an age range, the frequency and duration, and the impact of any event for which the individual endorsed as having experienced. The SLESQ's utility has been investigated in a sample of persons with serious psychiatric disorders (Allen, Madan, & Fowler, 2015). The results showed that the SLESQ had good reliability in this population and that the SLESQ differentiated between sexual, physical, and emotional trauma. This instrument has demonstrated validity for use among low-income African American women (Green, Chung, Daroowalla, Kaltman, & DeBenedictis, 2006) and Cambodians who experienced the Khmer Rouges' state-sponsored terrorism (Perry, Oum, & Gray, 2007). The SLESQ is available in English and Spanish.

Trauma History Questionnaire (THQ)

The Trauma History Questionnaire inquires about 24 life-events that are linked with the development of trauma (Green, 1996). Hooper, Stockton, Krupnick, and Green (2011) reviewed 14 years' worth of the literature in which the THQ was used or investigated. It is completed in self-report fashion. If a traumatic life event is endorsed, the client is further asked to identify the age at which the event took place, and the frequency with which the event was experienced. The THQ takes 10 to 20 minutes to administer. The 24 items cluster into three types of traumatic events: crime-related, disaster and general trauma, and sexual and physical. Studies have produced acceptable reliability (test–retest and interrater) date. The THQ compares favorably with other established measures of trauma (Hooper et al., 2011). The THQ is available in Spanish and English. The entire instrument is available in Hooper et al.'s (2011) review article.

Trauma History Screen (THS)

Counselors interested in a brief, self-report trauma history may wish to consider the Trauma History Screen (Carlson et al., 2011). This instrument presents 14 yes/no items that inquire about the respondent's life history of exposure to traumatic events. Additionally, respondents are asked to identify the degree to which any endorsed event caused distress and how significant the distress felt. The THS was standardized using individuals from the following groups: homeless veterans, persons who received hospital treatment for injuries at a university trauma center, female college students, and adults and young adults from community samples. The THS can be downloaded from this website: www.ptsd.va.gov/professional/assessment/documents/THS.pdf.

Traumatic Stress Schedule (TSS)

The Traumatic Stress Schedule measures 10 traumatic events and allows for one unspecified event. Examples of traumatic events include automobile accidents, combat, and being mugged. Any positive indicator for trauma is followed up with questions about how the individual was affected by the trauma, including threats to the person's life, physical injury, and the manner in which the person's life was impacted. There is a Spanish version of the TSS. The full version of the instrument is available in the original article (Norris, 1990). The TSS was used in a study of trauma among international samples including New Zealanders (Fleet, Kazantzis, Long, MacDonald, & Millar, 2002; Kazantzis et al., 2010) and South Africans (Hoffmann, 2002) as well as with pregnant women who abuse substances (Thompson, 1998).

Trauma Screening Questionnaire (TSQ)

The Trauma Screening Questionnaire (Brewin et al. 2002) contains 10 items designed to assess trauma among persons who have experienced a wide range of experiences. Persons experiencing any six of these events at least twice in the past week are determined to warrant a full PTSD diagnostic assessment. The TSQ demonstrated acceptable sensitivity, specificity, and negative and positive predictive values among persons seeking emergency treatment following physical assault (Walters, Bisson, & Shepherd, 2007). The CTSQ, the child version of TSQ, combined with measurements of heart rate, was accurate predictor of children's PTSD symptoms at both 1 and 6 months following injury (Olsson, Kenardy, De Young, & Spence, 2008). Evidence suggests that as the length of time passes from the traumatic incident, the TSQ's screening results become more accurate (Brewin, Fuchkan, Huntley, & Scragg, 2010). Finally, this instrument has been translated and validated for use with Malay-speaking individuals, which suggests that it may have additional crosscultural utility (Jaapar, Abidin, & Othman, 2014).

FAMILY SYSTEMS INTERVENTIONS

Despite the deleterious impact of traumatic stress on family systems, most evidence-supported treatments for traumatic stress disorders have been developed for and used with individuals. In fact, research on the effectiveness of many systemic trauma treatment adaptations is only in its infancy (Dekel & Monson, 2010; Galovski & Lyons, 2004; Wieling & Turner, 2003). Furthermore, the majority of available intervention options do not fit neatly with available diagnoses, primarily because of the multilayered, ongoing nature of traumatic experience, which is not well captured by any single diagnostic category (Stolbach et al., 2013). Nonetheless, these interventions can be broadly grouped into three main types: attachment and relationship-based interventions, cognitive behavioral interventions adapted for family systems, and multimodal, social justice-focused interventions. The vast majority of interventions require significant training and/or certification beyond what is required for professional counseling licensure.

Relationship-Based Interventions

These interventions focus on addressing relational disruptions that precipitate and follow traumatic experiences within families. Many relational interventions are based broadly on attachment theory (Ainsworth & Bell, 1970; Bowlby, 1977), which is one of the most research-supported theories of human development and family functioning. The majority of these approaches are more psychoanalytic in nature, and require a longer time commitment for treatment success. Attachment-based interventions have been developed for, and are appropriate in situations where there are clear indicators of problematic familial interactions, or where the nature of the trauma itself is primarily relational. Examples of suitable applications include foster families of children with histories of caregiver abuse or neglect, or in families who have experienced chronic domestic violence. The following represent examples of the most promising relational interventions models.

Attachment, Self-Regulation, and Competency (ARC)

Developed by Blaustein and Kinniburgh (2010), the ARC offers an organized, multilevel treatment model for complex relational trauma. It is appropriate primarily in situations where the child (or children, ages 2–21) in the family has experienced repeated and prolonged exposure to traumatic events, and who is living in a safe situation at the time of treatment (Arvidson et al., 2011). The ARC framework follows three main levels of intervention: (a) strategies that help family members build healthy attachments, (b) tools that aid children in developing effective self-regulation skills, and (c) competency-building activities that enable positive self-esteem and increased resilience. The model requires substantial work with nonoffending caregivers, assisting them in applying the various tools, as well as recognizing and managing their own emotional responses to their children's behaviors. Proficiency in the ARC intervention model typically requires substantial training, and the use of the model's manual (Blaustein & Kinniburgh, 2010). Additional information about ARC can be located at these websites: www.traumacenter.org/research/ascot.php; www.youtube.com/watch?v=eFwNWi9F6tA.

Child–Parent Psychotherapy (CPP)

Inspired by an integrative, attachment-based treatment approach, Lieberman and Van Horn (2005) created a manualized treatment for traumatized families. Child–Parent

Psychotherapy has been validated by several studies as effective in improving behavioral and trauma symptom issues with families who have experienced domestic violence, and in which children (ages 0–6) have witnessed or experienced abuse (Lieberman, Ippen, & Van Horn, 2006). CPP is particularly noteworthy for its suitability for families with preschool children. The model requires ongoing nonoffending parent participation. CPP requires specialized training, along with booster sessions, and supervision, along with the use of the treatment manual (Lieberman & Van Horn, 2005).

Additional information about CPP can be located at these websites: www.cebc4cw.org/program/child-parent-psychotherapy/detailed; www.youtube.com/watch?v=zdSRzNEjBFg.

Strengthening Family Coping Resources (SFCR)

Within traumatic stress intervention models, Strengthening Family Coping Resources is unique in that it is a multifamily group model, designed for addressing complex trauma and chronic stress in family systems (Kiser, Backer, Winkles, & Medoff, 2015). SFCR groups are composed of five to seven families with children aged 6 to 17. Like many other traumatic stress models, SFCR is a manualized, skill-building intervention, designed to address behavioral symptoms in children and reduce caregiver stress (Kiser, 2008). Developed by Laurel Kiser at the University of Maryland, the treatment offers two tracks: a 15-week trauma treatment group and a 10-week high-risk group (Kiser, 2008). The model requires specialized training.

Additional information about SFCR can be located at these websites: www.nctsn.org/sites/default/files/assets/pdfs/sfcr_general.pdf; sfcr.umaryland.edu/SignIn/tabid/291/Default.aspx?returnurl=%2fdefault.aspx.

Circle of Security (COS)

Circle of Security is a 20-week group intervention designed to address problematic attachment patterns in at-risk parent–child dyads (Marvin, Cooper, Hoffman, & Powell, 2002). This intervention, based on the principles of attachment theory, is a multiphase protocol with a pre- and post assessment to evaluate change in attachment patterns (Marvin et al., 2002). One of the unique features of this intervention is its suitability for very young children, ages 1 to 4 (Marvin et al., 2002). The intervention utilizes individualized vignettes and video recordings of parents' interactions with their children to help correct attachment behaviors (Marvin et al., 2002). Implementing COS requires completion of a specialized 10-day training with the intervention's creators (Marvin et al., 2002).

Additional information about COS can be located at these websites: circleofsecurity.net; www.youtube.com/watch?v=1wpz8m0BFM8.

Internal Family Systems (IFS)

Developed by Schwartz (1994), Internal Family Systems is an ego-state therapy approach to processing trauma, founded in a family systems approach. In IFS, each individual is thought to have many parts, each of which may be different in a cardinal way, and important for a specific purpose. Because of this basic premise, IFS is uniquely suited to working with dissociative individuals (Pais, 2009), and has been used successfully in a variety of complex trauma cases. In recent years, the use of IFS has been extended with particular effectiveness to couples and families in distress (Wark, Thomas, & Peterson, 2001; Wilkins, 2007). Effective use of IFS requires completion of one of the most intensive training programs, inclusive of 108 program hours for the basic, first level certification.

Additional information about IFS can be located at these websites: www.selfleadership.org/about-internal-family-systems.html; www.selfleadership.org/outline-of-the-Internal-family-systems-model.html.

Cognitive Behavioral Interventions

These interventions are founded upon cognitive behavioral therapy (CBT) strategies and are geared toward symptom reduction in traumatized children and families. Many of these rely on behavioral strategies and cognitive restructuring techniques common in traditional CBT (Beck, 2011). In managed care settings, these treatments are often favored due to shortened treatment duration. Many of these interventions are also easier to evaluate, thereby creating a stronger evidence base for their use. However, these interventions are sometimes contraindicated in the presence of severely self-harming or suicidal behavior, and may be very challenging to implement with family members experiencing dissociative symptoms (Cohen, Mannarino, & Deblinger, 2006).

Parent–Child Interaction Therapy (PCIT)

Parent–Child Interaction Therapy is one of the best-supported parent–child relationship intervention models. PCIT was originally developed by Eyberg, in the 1980s, to address a variety of behavior problems in children (ages 2–12). The treatment was originally based on Baumrind's (1971) research on parenting styles. According to Eisenstadt, Eyberg, McNeil, Newcomb, and Funderburk (1993), PCIT draws from both play therapy and behavioral therapy approaches, and includes a live-coaching component to help parents in implementing the model's strategies. One of the most interesting aspects of PCIT is its suitability for, and effectiveness in, addressing caregiver maltreatment with offending parents and their children, and thus preventing further abuse (Chaffin et al., 2004; Timmer, Urquiza, Zebell, & McGrath, 2005). PCIT is a manualized approach, requiring extensive initial certification training and ongoing training to support high fidelity (Eyberg & Funderburk, 2011).

Additional information about PCIT can be located at these websites: www.pcit.org; www.childwelfare.gov/pubPDFs/f_interactbulletin.pdf.

Trauma-Focused Cognitive Behavioral Therapy (TF-CBT)

As the name suggests, Trauma-Focused Cognitive Behavioral Therapy is a modification of cognitive behavioral interventions. TF-CBT was originally designed to address traumatic symptoms in sexually abused children. Currently, the model is considered to be a best-practice approach for a variety of traumatic stress problems in children. TF-CBT focuses on improving traumatic stress symptoms in traumatized children (ages 3–18), and requires significant nonoffending caregiver involvement, which is instrumental to treatment success (Malloy & Lyon, 2006). Caregiver participation also helps address any traumatic stress symptoms the caregiver may be experiencing. One of the benefits of TF-CBT is that treatment typically consists of 12 to 16 sessions, a comparatively shorter duration of treatment (Cohen et al., 2006). Effective application of TF-CBT typically requires the counselor to complete a certification course, as well as engage in ongoing consultation in order to maintain fidelity to the treatment protocols (Cohen et al., 2006).

Additional information about TF-CBT can be located at these websites: www.nctsnet.org/nctsn_assets/pdfs/TF-CBT_Implementation_Manual.pdf; www. tfcbt.org.

Risk Reduction Through Family Therapy (RRFT)

Risk Reduction Through Family Therapy is a unique intervention in that it combines cognitive behavioral strategies with an ecological systems perspective, to address serious risk behaviors and trauma symptoms in teens (ages 13–18) who have experienced a variety of traumas, including sexual abuse (Danielson, 2007). The model uses family therapy as a risk reduction strategy, and has been shown effective in minimizing risk of substance abuse and other risk behaviors in affected teens (Danielson et al., 2012). RRFT requires training and ongoing consultation for effective implementation (Danielson, 2007).

Additional information about RRFT can be located at these websites: www.nctsn.org/sites/default/files/assets/pdfs/rrft_072015.pdf; http://academicdepartments.musc.edu/psychiatry/research/labs/invictus_lab/Research%20Home#RRFT.

Real Life Heroes (RLH)

According to Kagan, Douglas, Hornik, and Kratz (2008), Real Life Heroes utilizes an activity-based workbook and manualized, CBT-based protocols to intervene with traumatized children who may not have a nonoffending parent. One of the features of this intervention is the built-in ability to seek out and develop attachments to healthy, lifelong adult supports, which begins with the "pledge," the very first chapter of the workbook, and is made stronger with each chapter (Kagan et al., 2008). Another exciting feature of this approach is its multitude of nonverbal, expressive arts components, which can meet the needs of children for whom talk therapy may not be appropriate (Kagan et al., 2008). The creators of the model recommend completing 3-day training, as well as a monthly small group reflective supervision for effective application.

Additional information about RLH can be located at these websites: www.nctsn.org/nctsn_assets/pdfs/SpeakerSeries_Kagan; www.nctsnet.org/nctsn_assets/pdfs/promising_practices/RLH_General.pdf.

Multimodal/Social Justice-Focused Interventions

In recent years, recognition of the challenges in addressing trauma symptoms in the highest need areas has brought about the development of several social justice-focused interventions. These interventions are typically designed to address barriers to care, and intervene with populations that have been unable to benefit from other types of treatment. For instance, many of these include an integration of case management and clinical services, community- or home-based service delivery, and services that are language or culture neutral. These intervention models are often particularly useful for the most complex families, which have been deemed noncompliant with, or inappropriate for, more traditional models of treatment.

Trauma-Adapted Family Connections (TA-FC)

Trauma-Adapted Family Connections (TA-FC) is a multiphase preventative intervention that reduces risk factors for child abuse and neglect within the most at-risk family systems (Collins et al., 2011). Collins et al. (2011) reported the TA-FC to include comprehensive family assessment, emergency assistance, a service plan, advocacy, and coordinated referrals, along with three treatment phases, each lasting approximately 2 months. One of the unique elements of TA-FC is the inclusion of home-based service delivery and emergency intervention, which are appropriate for families that are in very early phases of trauma recovery (Collins et al., 2011). Because of its intensive nature, TA-FC also addresses secondary traumatic stress in the provider (Collins et al., 2011). TA-FC is a manualized treatment, and requires an organization-wide implementation, with 2-day supervisory trainings and a 5-day staff training, as well as monthly coaching.

Additional information about TA-FC can be located at these websites: www.family
.umaryland.edu/fc-trauma; static1.squarespace.com/static/525fe472e4b09f9731f69c36/t/5372
4ef0e4b09a4c091fcfd9/1400000240350/tafc_general.pdf.

Multisystemic Therapy (MST)

Originally developed to intervene with substance-abusing juvenile offenders, Multisystemic Therapy is an intensive, in-home family treatment that has been successfully applied
to intervening within traumatized families. Swenson, Schaeffer, Henggeler, Faldowski,
and Mayhew (2010) reported that MST was particularly effective in simultaneously
addressing youths' (ages 10–17) mental health needs as well as parents' abusive behaviors in families referred for physical abuse. One of the most interesting elements of MST is
its appropriateness for families with active substance-abusing behaviors as well as forensic involvement (Swenson et al., 2010). MST is an evidence-based intervention, and
requires a 5-day orientation training, as well as 4 hours of weekly group supervision for
treatment fidelity (Swenson et al., 2010).

Additional information about MST can be located at these websites: www.mstservices
.com/files/msttreatmentmodel.pdf; www.cebc4cw.org/program/multisystemic-therapy/
detailed.

The Neuro-Sequential Model for Trauma (NMT)

Unlike many other approaches to treatment, the Neuro-Sequential Model for Trauma
(NMT) is an intervention model that sprang from recent research evidence on the neurological, physiological, and emotional impact of developmental traumatic stress (B. D. Perry,
2009). The model offers a developmentally informed, multidisciplinary treatment approach
for treating youths and families with complex trauma histories, many of whom have significant physical, neurocognitive, and behavioral issues (B. D. Perry, 2009). The approach
brings together trained professionals from multiple disciplines to sequentially address the
needs of children and their caregivers (B. D. Perry, 2009). According to B. D. Perry (2009),
NMT includes a substantial assessment portion (referred to as *brain mapping*), to identify
specific needs and their neurological origins. However, it is one of the few approaches that
strive to respond specifically to developmentally delayed and cognitively atypical children
(B. D. Perry, 2009). NMT certification requires extensive training, and is ideal for implementation within a team of multidisciplinary professionals.

Additional information about NMT can be located at these websites: www.childtrauma
.org/nmt-model; www.childtrauma.org/wp-content/uploads/2013/06/NMT_Description_
Overview_6_22_12x.pdf.

Thought Field Therapy for the Posttraumatic Stress Disorder

Based on the Thought Field Therapy (TFT) program developed by Callahan (1995), TFT for
PTSD is a self-tapping algorithm, which utilizes acupuncture points to provide relief to
traumatized individuals and groups. This curious intervention was, for a long time, considered to be unproven and ineffective. However, today TFT for PTSD has been shown effective in increasing resilience and self-regulation and decreasing traumatic stress symptoms
(see Connolly, Sakai, & Oas, 2010), and is listed in the registry of evidence-based practices
and interventions. TFT for PTSD is unique in that it does not require significant language
capacity, and can be applied with a large number of people simultaneously, making it ideal
for use with entire families who have experienced a trauma. The intervention is also appropriate for situations when a limited number of sessions are available, since results can be

seen in as little as a single session (Connolly et al., 2010). Effective use of TFT techniques requires completion of a 2-day training seminar, with additional training days designated for specializes skills.

Additional information about TFT for PTSD can be located at this website: www .mercola.com/article/mind_body/thought_field_therapy/overview.htm.

The Eye Movement Desensitization and Reprocessing (EMDR) Integrative Group Treatment Protocol (IGTP)

Similarly to TFT, EMDR is another treatment that was once considered questionable, and has since gained widespread support. Developed by Francine Shapiro, EMDR is an eye movement protocol that enables individuals to rapidly process painful trauma memories. EMDR has been applied and studied in a variety of settings, resulting in a substantial number of evidence-supported protocols. The group protocol is of specific interest here, since it enables a mixed group of adults and children to process memories of a traumatic incident (see Jarero, Artigas, & Hartung, 2006). Like TFT, EMDR Integrative Group Treatment Protocol (IGTP) participants have shown positive results in as little as a single session. EMDR can be used effectively in situations where the family requires an interpreter for treatment, or where language is a barrier to treatment. Use of EMDR procedures requires substantial training, including 6 training days and 10 hours of consultation for certification. The group protocol requires additional training beyond the requirements of certification.

Additional information about IGTP can be located at these websites: www.emdrresearch foundation.org/toolkit/igtp-children.pdf; www.powershow.com/view/9ea8-NWRkZ/ Integrated_Treatment_for_Trauma_and_Addiction_Seeking_Safety_powerpoint_ppt_ presentation.

Contextual Issues Affecting Intervention Selection

1. Current Level of Safety
   Intervention selection must always be preceded by a thorough assessment of the family's safety. In the absence of safety from further harm or danger, it would be very difficult for family members to establish trust and begin the healing process. The most appropriate interventions for families that have not reestablished safety are therefore those that focus on crisis stabilization, and may include:
   a. Directive interventions designed to build coping skills and manage in-the-moment emotions
   b. Psychoeducation and/or motivational interviewing to develop and sustain motivation to seek safety
   c. Referral for relevant supports (e.g., a domestic violence shelter), family case management, and/or wraparound services
   d. Harm reduction strategies to improve family outcomes when establishing safety is not feasible
2. Complexity of Exposure
   Generally, the complexity of the family's exposure to traumatic events is correlated to the complexity of their needs and their collective degree of distress. Factors that affect the complexity of exposure include age and developmental maturity at onset, severity, duration, and repetition of the traumatic event(s), as well as the amount of lapsed time between the trauma and the delivery of any intervention to address family members' distress.
   a. Treatment of problems resulting from prolonged, repeated exposure to severe trauma, which started early in development, and has been unaddressed for an extended

period of time, will often necessitate a substantially more complex intervention plan. Attachment-based, relational interventions can be particularly appropriate for such families, since traumatic stress has likely resulted in disruptions in family dynamics.

    b. Historically, clinicians believed that children who had not yet acquired language and episodic memory would not be affected by exposure to adversity. Research has proved this belief to be erroneous (Schore, 2001). Children who have experienced adversity very early in their development tend to present with the most complex trauma symptoms, which are sometimes mislabeled as biologically based developmental, physiological, neurological, or cognitive deficits. Complicating matters further, these children are often unable to recall, describe, or verbally explain their trauma, thus rendering futile any treatments that rely on verbal reprocessing of trauma memories. Treatment approaches such as NMT (previously mentioned) can be particularly appropriate in these cases.

3. Collective Versus Individual Experience

It may seem counterintuitive, but families tend to fare better and require less intensive intervention when the same adverse event is experienced by all family members (e.g., surviving a natural disaster). In contrast, families in which one member survived a traumatic event often experience secondary traumatization as well as relationship discord and functional changes.

    a. Group interventions, such as group-based EMDR protocols and family support groups can be helpful to families who have experienced a collective traumatic event.

    b. Families in which one member experienced a traumatic event can benefit from interventions that include caregiver psychoeducation, high-fidelity multisystemic therapy, and TF-CBT components.

4. Offending and Dismissive Family Members

The experience of victimization takes on an added degree of complexity when it is one family member who victimizes another. This is particularly true in regard to parents who offend against their children. Even when the offending caregiver is removed from the family, multiple types of intervention will likely be required for the family's recovery. However, it is important to note that oftentimes caregivers who have been abusive will not be excluded from the family system. For instance, families might seek treatment in the reunification process after removal by child protective services, or after a formerly abusive substance-abusing parent achieves sobriety. Other times, clinicians may be faced with nonoffending but dismissive caregivers, who may deny the traumatic event ever took place and whose attitudes may cause additional discord and distress.

    a. Realities of child protection and abuse reporting have supported the development of several intervention models that specifically include offending caregivers. For instance, Mohl (2009) offered an intervention model for incestuous families that did not require the removal of the offending caregiver. Chaffin and colleagues (2004) found PCIT to be effective with physically abusive caregivers and their children.

    b. Since caregiver support is a primary indicator for long-term recovery in abused children, specific interventions should be offered to increase caregiver support (Malloy & Lyon, 2006). These interventions should include psychoeducation and specific instructions to caregivers regarding supportive reactions.

ETHICAL AND LEGAL IMPLICATIONS

Legal and ethical issues relevant to working with children and family systems can offer both rewards and challenges. Systemic clinicians who provide this type of service should be well versed in the legal and ethical components necessary to avoid pitfalls and liabilities especially in high-conflict cases or where trauma issues are present.

Professional codes of ethics outline standards for conduct, and administrative and revised codes define specific laws. However, neither of these resources is comprehensive enough to provide direction to the clinician in every possible situation. This leaves room for what is often termed "the gray area" of clinical practice. What is the clinician to do when law and ethical codes conflict? Unfortunately, there is no universal road map that provides clear-cut answers to the ethical dilemmas that systemic clinicians often face.

Legal and ethical issues pertaining to family systems are numerous. This section attempts to address those most relevant especially in working with high-conflict family systems and cases involving trauma. These issues are grouped into three categories: getting started with family systems work, complexities of family systems work, and resolving ethical dilemmas. Each section concludes with learning objectives for the clinician.

Getting Started With Family Systems Work

This section addresses the most pressing legal and ethical issues relevant to engaging in family systems therapy. There are four primary areas of high importance, namely identifying the client, consent versus assent, confidentiality, and mandated reporting. Each area is defined and explained in the following sections.

Identifying the Client

When a systemic clinician provides services to a child or family system, it is important to define who will be the client. The American Counseling Association's (ACA) *Code of Ethics* (2014) reads that when providing services to more than one person, the clinician should "clarify at the outset which person or persons are clients and the nature of the relationships the counselor will have with each involved person" (ACA, 2014, p. 6). The clinician is advised to be clear about who the legal guardian is and/or in the case of family therapy, how many members constitute the family unit (ACA, 2014). Every child younger than 18 has a legal guardian. Guardians can range from one parent to a set of parents or grandparent(s) to the custody of the state or a state agency. The initial step of identifying the client is important because it sets the foundation for the clinical work ahead and has ramifications that can tie into consent for treatment, confidentiality, and issues with noncustodial parents that will be addressed in subsequent sections. It can be difficult to navigate an appropriate balance in serving all individuals in a family system. For this reason, the ACA *Code of Ethics* further advises that if the clinician is asked to perform conflicting roles, the clinician will "clarify, adjust, or withdraw from roles appropriately" (ACA, 2014, Section A.8).

Consent Versus Assent

Informed consent is an essential part of the therapeutic process. It is the second standard listed in the American Association for Marriage and Family Therapy's (AAMFT) *Code of Ethics* (2015) after nondiscrimination, and is second only to discussion of client welfare in the ACA *Code of Ethics* (ACA, 2014). Informed consent refers to the process by which the systemic clinician provides the client with information regarding the treatment process as well as the boundaries of the professional relationship (ACA, 2014). With this information, an individual or family system can choose whether or not to partake in treatment.

There are five components to informed consent as specified by the AAMFT. They are:

[the client's] capacity to consent, [the client] has been adequately informed of significant information concerning treatment processes and procedures, [the client] has been adequately informed of potential risks and benefits of treatments for which generally recognized standards do not yet exist, [the client] has freely and without undue influence expressed consent, and [the client] has provided consent that is appropriately documented. (AAMFT, 2015, p. 1)

Special consideration should be given to these components when providing services to children and adolescents. The clinician should ask and answer several important questions. Has the information been presented in an age-appropriate manner? Can the clinician determine the child's level of understanding? Because of the ambiguity in these areas of informed consent, parents or guardians are the ones who legally give consent for children to receive mental health services (ACA, 2014). Even when a child is identified as the client, it is the adult guardian who holds the authority and rights to accessing records or information regarding treatment. The child or adolescent younger than 18 is thought to give "assent" through which the minor acknowledges involvement in the decision-making process for treatment. Inherent to the concept of assent is the implication that the child client may not be competent in all areas of informed consent (ACA, 2014).

Defining goals is an important component of the treatment process. When working with children, the parent or guardian also has input into the goal-setting process. Conflict may arise if the child is not fully in agreement with what the parent hopes can be accomplished through the course of therapy. In that situation, the systemic clinician must facilitate communication and compromise between the parent and the child as a key part of the development of the therapeutic alliance (ACA, 2014). This is also an important time to clarify which types of information the parent deems necessary to receive and with which areas the parent is comfortable giving the child the space and privacy to share with just the clinician. Children's confidentiality should also be upheld within the parameters of a therapeutic relationship when that information is not deemed to present harm or risk to the child (ACA, 2014). This of course requires the professional evaluation of the systemic clinician.

Informed consent should not be a single event. Rather it should be an ongoing dialogue throughout the therapeutic process where all parties are reminded of the limits of confidentiality and provided with the ongoing choice to engage in or discontinue therapy (ACA, 2014).

Confidentiality

Confidentiality is an integral part of the therapeutic process. In working with children and family systems, however, there are important nuances to this issue. Ethical codes stipulate that the clinician reviews at the onset of treatment the nature of confidentiality as well as its possible limitations (AAMFT, 2015; ACA, 2014).

Those servicing child clients are in a unique and precarious position to enlist trust while being held to legal and ethical obligations to share some of the information obtained during a session. Because of children's innate vulnerabilities, the clinician must be especially careful not to take this balance for granted and to remember that he or she has a duty to advocate on the behalf of his or her client even while respecting that the parent or guardian ultimately has access to the therapeutic process (ACA, 2014). The systemic clinician is advised to

inform parents and legal guardians about the role of the counselors and the confidential nature of the counseling relationship, consistent with current legal and custodial arrangements. Counselors are sensitive to the cultural diversity of families and respect the inherent rights and responsibilities of parents/guardians regarding the welfare of their children/charges according to law. Counselors work to establish, as appropriate, collaborative relationships with parents/guardians to best serve clients. (ACA, 2014, p. 7)

Systemic clinicians seek written authorization to release client information unless otherwise required to do so as in the case of serious foreseeable harm and the duty to warn/protect (ACA, 2014). Clinicians will provide a client reasonable access to his or her records, which includes the legal guardian of a child client. In the case of family therapy, written authorization from each participating member should be obtained prior to the release of the record to any individual party (AAMFT, 2015). The systemic clinician, however, cannot be solely responsible for maintaining confidentiality of the information shared in the session as any of the family members could initiate a breach.

Confidentiality is not a right. It is a privilege upheld in most cases under the premise of mental health services. States' laws vary in the degree to which they determine limitations. Therefore, it is essential that systemic clinicians review their states' laws and understand when information may be disclosed and when it must be disclosed. Occasionally, a judge may issue a court order requiring a release of confidential information. In such a situation, the clinician should first attempt to seek permission from the client and, if not able to obtain written permission, should explore whether or not the court will accept a written summary of treatment in lieu of the full record (ACA, 2014). Systemic clinicians must straddle the responsibility of upholding the law while adhering to ethical codes of practice (AAMFT, 2015; ACA, 2014). This is especially the case when foreseeable harm may come to the client upon the release of his or her confidential information. Systemic clinicians should be advised that subpoenas are different from a court order. Subpoenas require the identified individual to be summoned to court while the confidentiality of the clinical record remains intact. If subpoenaed, the clinician may request that the judge discuss the case in camera, which is Latin for "in chambers" (www.legal-dictionary.the-freedictionary.com/In+camera+(legal). The clinician may then express concerns regarding disclosure of the client's confidential information, which the judge may take into consideration.

In working with children, ethical guidelines suggest that there are times when the systemic clinician may share information provided by the child in session with another responsible party such as the parent or guardian. This would be the case when it is not in the child's best interest to maintain his or her confidence due to foreseeable harm or risk of harm. If a child is sharing information regarding being abused or neglected, engaging in unsafe behaviors, or planning to hurt someone else, the clinician must break confidentiality and connect with other responsible parties to intervene for the child's safety or the safety of an identified other. Reviewing the limits of confidentiality with child and adolescent clients is important not only at the start but throughout the course of therapy so they can maintain an understanding of the nature and boundaries of the therapeutic relationship (AAMFT, 2015; ACA, 2014). If faced with a situation where the child's information needs to be shared, it is recommend that the clinician consult with other licensed mental health professionals or seek counsel from a professional association's ethics committee. Systemic clinicians attempt to maintain a child client's confidentiality by encouraging the child to take the lead in sharing information with his or her parents/guardians to facilitate healthy communication and maturing relationships.

Mandated Reporting

Mandated reporting refers to specific times and situations when a systemic clinician is permitted to breach a client's confidentiality for the purposes of safety of that client or identified others. This is even more salient in cases where there has been abuse or trauma. All states legally require the reporting of child abuse and neglect to the appropriate authorities.

In addition to incidents of child abuse and neglect, systemic clinicians often receive information regarding suicidal or homicidal ideation, plan, or intent. In these situations, the clinician should perform a risk assessment to determine the level of severity, which would dictate a possible breach of confidentiality to facilitate additional intervention for safety. Many states have adopted a mandatory duty to warn in their statues or common law. Systemic clinicians are again advised to check the laws for the state in which they practice. Case law such as *Tarasoff v. Regents of the University of California* (1976) supports systemic clinicians in breaching confidentiality in such cases and provides protection against legal action by the client or client's family members. The ACA *Code of Ethics* (2014) specifically reads, "The general requirement that counselors keep information confidential does not apply when disclosure is required to protect clients or identified others from serious and foreseeable harm or when legal requirements demand that confidential information must be revealed" (ACA, 2014, p. 7).

Complexities of Family Systems Work

Systemic clinicians providing therapy to children and/or families should be clear about the legal and ethical issues unique to this population and how they differ from work with individual adult clients. The following three areas will be discussed in detail: competence of the therapist, dual relationships, and issues related to noncustodial parents.

Competence of the Therapist

The AAMFT *Codes of Ethics* (2015) and the ACA *Codes of Ethics* (2014) advise systemic clinicians to provide services only in their areas of professional competence. The notion of professional competence also includes knowledge of professional ethics and standards as well as the laws that govern their state (AAMFT, 2015; ACA, 2014). These guidelines are rather vague, however, and do not specifically address the issues of working with children or families and whether or not this is a specialty area or what specific level of competency is required. The code simply reads, "Counselors practice in specialty areas new to them only after appropriate education, training, and supervised experience. While developing skills in new specialty areas, counselors take steps to ensure the competence of their work and protect others from possible harm" (ACA, 2014, p. 8). Clinicians who intend to work with children and families should at the very least be knowledgeable about children's developmental issues, and child-specific pathology. Knowledge and training can become outdated, however; thus, the AAMFT *Code of Ethics* suggests, "Marriage and family therapists pursue knowledge of new developments and maintain their competence in marriage and family therapy through education, training, and/or supervised experience" (AAMFT, 2015, p. 2). The ACA *Code of Ethics* (2014) also recommends continuing education in order for the clinician to be knowledgeable regarding changes or advancements in the field as well as potential new interventions. When working with children and families who have experienced trauma, the systemic clinician is advised to utilize trauma-focused assessments and trauma-based treatment interventions.

Dual Relationships

Systemic clinicians are expected by their code of ethics to maintain professional boundaries in their working relationships with clients. This is even more essential when working with children, as they are oftentimes more vulnerable to exploitation than adult clients. Engaging in a dual relationship, anything other than the working relationship, could lead to impaired judgment of the clinician and certainly confuses the boundaries of the therapeutic relations from both the client's and clinician's perspectives (AAMFT, 2015). Providing treatment to friends or their children or one's own family members is prohibited (AAMFT, 2015; ACA, 2014). In the event where a dual relationship cannot be avoided, the clinician will document this condition, and the rationale for continuing to provide treatment. In such cases supervision and/or consultation with other systemic clinicians is advised (ACA, 2014).

When working with children, it is important for the systemic clinician to explore any issues of countertransference. It is not unusual for the clinician to have an urge to be a rescuer or an ideal parent. Especially in cases where the child client has experienced a trauma, there can be issues of countertransference and even transference from the child client. Clinicians are encouraged to seek consultation and supervision in such cases to avoid harm to clients and protect against professional impairment. ACA *Code of Ethics* (2014) advises clinicians to "monitor themselves for signs of impairment from their own physical, mental, or emotional problems and refrain from offering or providing professional services when such impairment is likely to harm a client or others" (ACA, 2014, p.13).

Issues With NonCustodial Parents

In family systems work, it is important to have an understanding of who constitutes the family unit. In families where the parents may be separated or divorced, the family system may include stepparent(s) or significant others. Anyone not part of the immediate family unit with the child may be considered a collateral family member.

Systemic clinicians are advised to request a copy of the custody orders to clarify and officially document the legal mandate. This provides direction for the clinician to be legally compliant with state-specific laws regarding custody and rights of noncustodial parents. In many states, both parents are required to give consent for their child to receive mental health services. An objection from either custodial parent can result in a mandatory termination of services. Laws regarding rights of the noncustodial parent differ from state to state as well. Systemic clinicians should be aware that some states allow even the noncustodial parent legal access to the child's record including all information given to that child's systemic clinician. This may also include access to any information documented in the client record regarding the noncustodial parent. At this time, there is limited support for the protection of the confidentiality of collateral family members (Ellis, 2012).

Family systems separated by conflict and divorce may have different agendas regarding what is in the child's best interest. Systemic clinicians may be enlisted to assist families during these times of struggle. Ellis (2012) recommended that the clinician identify high-conflict cases at the start of treatment and then engage in a thorough informed consent process. Further recommendations for working with high-conflict family systems include limiting meetings with individual family members and making each member aware that information shared during individual sessions will be part of the clinical record (Ellis, 2012). The systemic clinician is also advised to determine his or her role or clinical purpose for working with the family at the onset of treatment. This is discussed in more detail in the following section on scope of practice.

Resolving Ethical Dilemmas

Ethical decision making is the hallmark of sound clinical practice. As previously discussed, however, there are times at which the ethical choice is not easily identified. This section explores two important areas that set the stage for ethical decision making, scope of practice, and recording keeping. This section then concludes by introducing the use of a decision-making model to assist the systemic clinician when faced with an issue that falls into the clinical "gray area."

Scope of Practice

Systemic clinicians are advised to work only within their scope of practice (AAMFT, 2015; ACA, 2014). In addition to that:

> Counselors know and understand the ACA *Code of Ethics* and other applicable ethics codes from professional organizations or certification and licensure bodies of which they are members. Lack of knowledge or misunderstanding of an ethical responsibility is not a defense against a charge of unethical conduct. (ACA, 2014, p. 19)

In addition to standards for ethical conduct, how does one determine one's scope of practice? After an evaluation of proper credentialing, training, and knowledge, the systemic clinician would be wise to additionally clarify his or her role with the child and family system.

Custody issues typically arise when parents divorce. Deciding what is in the child's best interest is a highly subjective decision. The systemic clinician will typically have one of two roles: that of an evaluator or that of a mediator in the family system. If the role is of an evaluator, then it is the clinician's job to gather information on the strengths and weaknesses of both parents and present that information to the court. In this role, the clinician must avoid engaging in therapeutic work with the family, as it would be outside the scope of this role and would compromise the clinician's objectivity. Conversely, in the role of a mediator, the clinician works to help the family agree on custody issues and communicate with one another during this time of change. In the role of mediator, it is not the clinician's responsibility to provide information to the court or to influence the custody decision one way or the other. Systemic clinicians would be wise to remember to clarify their role with the client and especially with any attorneys involved in a high-conflict case or those involving trauma. Clarifying this at the beginning of the therapeutic relationship helps to decrease any confusion or misguided expectations regarding what the clinician will be able to provide. This reinforces the importance of informed consent and collaborative goal setting at the start of the therapeutic relationship so that all parties involved have a clear understanding of their roles.

Record Keeping

Providing clinical services includes documentation of those services in what is referred to as the *clinical record*. The format for this documentation may vary. Furthermore, ethical guidelines describing what should or should not be included in clinical documentation are absent from the ACA *Code of Ethics* (2014) as well as the AAMFT *Code of Ethics* (2015). This leaves significant leeway for the systemic clinician when documenting services rendered and the resulting clinical response. Ethical codes do, however, indicate that clients have a right to access what the clinician has chosen to document. Systemic clinicians are advised to provide reasonable access to their clients of the clinical record when requested (AAMFT, 2015; ACA, 2014). AAMFT (2015) further specifies that for family therapy services, the clinician will request written permission from all family members prior to releasing the record to any one member of the family. Only when there is "compelling evidence to suggest access would cause harm" do clinicians limit a client's access to his or her record (AAMFT, 2015, p. 2; ACA, 2014, p. 8). Clinicians are also required to maintain safe storage of the clinical record to protect the confidentiality of their clients (AAMFT, 2015; ACA, 2014).

Systemic clinicians are advised to be mindful of all the topics that have been discussed thus far when engaging in documentation. The clinical record has the potential to provide protection and create vulnerabilities for both the clinician and the client. In working with children and high-conflict family systems, the clinician is encouraged to be thorough and contentious with documentation practices as well as to provide informed consent to all parties being served the ways in which the clinical record could be requested and utilized within a court of law.

Decision-Making Models

Clinicians are expected to adhere to both laws and ethics governing their state and their practice. Assuming that both law and ethics agree, the clinician is also asked to adhere to the most stringent expectations. But what if there is ambiguity between what laws and ethics dictate? Worse yet, what if law and ethics contradict one another? In these situations, the systemic clinician enters the "gray area" of clinical practice.

Despite a review of pertinent legal and ethical considerations, today's systemic clinician will inevitably be faced with an ethical dilemma for which the appropriate solution may not be immediately clear.

> If ethical responsibilities conflict with the law, regulations, and/or other governing legal authority, counselors make known their commitment to the ACA *Code of Ethics* (2014) and take steps to resolve the conflict. If the conflict cannot be resolved using this approach, counselors, acting in the best interest of the client, may adhere to the requirements of the law, regulations, and/or other governing legal authority. (ACA, 2014, p. 19)

In these situations, it is recommended that a decision-making model be used to assist the systemic clinician with a thorough evaluation of all pertinent materials through a comprehensive stepwise process. Specifically, ACA *Code of Ethics* (2014) reads:

> When counselors are faced with an ethical dilemma, they use and document, as appropriate, an ethical decision-making model that may include, but is not limited to, consultation; consideration of relevant ethical standards, principles, and laws; generation of potential courses of action; deliberation of risks and benefits; and selection of an objective decision based on the circumstances and welfare of all involved. (ACA, 2014, p. 19)

Following is an example of one such decision-making model from Barnett & Johnson (2008). There are many decision-making models available, though most contain similar steps.

1. Define the situation clearly.
2. Determine who will be affected.
3. Refer to both underlying ethical principles and the standards of the ACA *Code of Ethics*.
4. Refer to relevant laws/regulations and professional guidelines.
5. Reflect honestly on professional feelings and competence.
6. Consult with trusted colleagues.
7. Formulate alternative courses of action.
8. Consider possible outcomes for all parties involved.
9. Make a decision and monitor the outcome.

The following list of additional resources has been included to further assist those in need of additional information regarding legal and ethical issues of clinical practice. Membership in the following associations increases access to available resources, which often includes free legal and ethical consultation services.

• American Counseling Association—www.counseling.org
• National Association of Social Workers—www.socialworkers.org
• American Association for Marriage and Family Therapy—www.aamft.org

- American Psychological Association—www.apa.org
- Counselor, Social Worker, Marriage and Family Therapist Board (state specific)—look for tab for laws and rules
- State-Specific Revised Code

CASE CONCEPTUALIZATION

A large subset of the families who come in for treatment of traumatic stress issues have complex histories, difficult relationship dynamics, and a variety of problems secondary to, or co-occurring with, traumatic exposure. In community-based managed care settings, clients are also likely to experience additional, ongoing stressors such as poverty and disenfranchisement, as well as previous treatment failures and mistrust of the care system. As a result, developing an accurate and organized case conceptualization is often a challenging task for systemic clinicians treating traumatic stress issues. Although there is no such thing as a "typical" trauma case, the following conceptualization may serve as a simplified example of one way to organize and approach such a case.

Presenting Concerns

Ben Matthews is a 10-year-old Caucasian male. He is very slender and appears to be suspicious and angry. He has recently been adopted after spending many years in foster care. Ben has a flat affect and appears to be sad, dejected, hypervigilant, and, at times, "lost in space." Ben has a history of losing caregivers. He was removed from his biological parents due to the horrendous abuse and neglect that he suffered at the hands of his biological family. He was placed in five foster homes for 5 years before being adopted. Ben completely avoids talking about pieces of the trauma, especially related to his biological family. When asked about his biological family, he stares off into space and cannot recall necessary information. Ben reports little interest in normal pleasurable activities and reports being "different" from others. Ben is very intelligent, yet he struggles in school and is failing most classes.

Concurrent Problems

Ben has previously received Play Therapy while he was living with his last foster family whom he reports as also abusive. Because of his disinterest in food, Ben has been seen by a medical doctor to ascertain if there is a medical reason driving his low body mass index. He was diagnosed with Failure to Thrive in Childhood, and prescribed nutritional shakes in an effort to help him gain weight. He has also had extensive testing to see if he has a learning disability inhibiting his progress in school. School testing showed elevated scores in inattention and depression, along with above-average IQ and below grade-level performance in mathematics and language. He recently started taking medication to fall and stay asleep due to recurrent nightmares.

Background History and Stressors

Ben's adoptive parents blame his issues on his disorderly upbringing. They report that his biological parents have a history of drug abuse and often left Ben and his brother in the care of his "schizophrenic grandmother." They report that the grandmother locked the boys in a room and would give the boys only small amounts of bread and water. They would soil themselves or use the closet of the locked room as a bathroom. The boys' Child Protective Services records indicate that despite his young age, Ben often attempted to clean and feed his younger brother. These records indicate that during their first three foster placements, Ben would become extremely distraught when his brother cried, and would often attempt to force feed him. Although Ben no longer does this, he continues to react disproportionately (by yelling and trying to block his ears with his hands) to his brother's occasional cries. Ben's adoptive parents report that they believe that Ben has been sexually abused in a past placement. However, Ben refuses to talk about this foster placement.

Ben is emotionally withdrawn. He angers easily, is fearful and often sad, even when the situation does not warrant such emotions. He is generally mistrustful of others and hypervigilant, especially with those who appear to care for him. At times, Ben appears to be lost in his thoughts and appears not to hear his name called. He cannot recount events surrounding his biological family. Ben is incredibly slender, which led his medical provider to call Children's Services to ensure that he is being fed. It is believed that he cannot eat appropriately due to the recurrent memories of food being withheld from him. Ben finds little pleasure in life and has few, if any, meaningful relationships. He struggles to get to sleep and stay asleep due to nightmares surrounding his abuse and neglect.

Strengths

Although Ben has been through some extensive abuse and neglect, Ben is now in a safe place with an adoptive family who loves and cares for him. Ben has always found comfort in his stuffed animals. Ben is able to talk about his anger surrounding some pieces of his past.

DSM-5 Impressions and Implications

Ben is entering counseling at the prompting of his adoptive parents. Based on his presentation and history, Ben's symptoms best align with criteria for a diagnosis of Posttraumatic Stress Disorder, with dissociative symptoms (depersonalization). He has directly experienced multiple traumatic events, and has subsequently struggled with intrusive recurrent nightmares and dissociative symptoms. He has also avoided reminders of past distressing events, and refused to speak of the trauma he has experienced. Ben has also reported memory loss, and has exhibited depression, angry mood, irritability, and angry outbursts. Although the duration of these symptoms remains unknown, they have persisted for more than 12 months, and are unlikely to be attributable to the effects of any substance or medical condition. These symptoms have caused Ben significant distress and impairment in social, academic, and family life domains. Based on Ben's history, the following are additional appropriate elements of a dimensional diagnosis: Child Neglect, Confirmed, initial encounter, Child Psychological Abuse, Confirmed, initial encounter, and Failure to Thrive in Childhood.

Ben was administered the CAPS-CA-5 (Pyrnoos et al. 2015). Ben's results placed him in the moderate range of symptom severity. Specifically, Ben's results indicated that he experienced severity of emotional reactivity and a highly negative emotional state, as well as moderate severity of self-blame and irritability. Ben also reported moderate flashbacks and hypervigilance.

Based on his parents' report of dissociative symptoms, as well as significant inattention measure scores, Ben was also administered the Brief Dissociative Experiences Scale, which indicated dissociative symptoms of moderate severity, with an average total score of 2 out of 4 (Bernstein & Putnam, 1986). He reported primarily depersonalization symptoms, with several symptoms occurring more than once per day.

Relational Problems

Ben has one biological brother who lives with him and one biological sister whom he has not seen in years. His relationship is strained with his biological brother, because everyone dotes on his sibling. Ben is emotionally withdrawn from his adoptive parents and will only on rare occasions seek comfort from his adoptive mother. He intentionally distances himself from anyone who shows him kindness. Ben's adoptive parents report that they feel ill-prepared to meet Ben's needs, and have been arguing about how to best help him in recent months. Ben's adoptive father also expresses some ambivalence regarding having to hear more about Ben's trauma, and shares he is unsure he can handle hearing about sexual abuse that might have occurred.

Assessments

At intake, Ben's parents completed the *DSM-5* Parent/Guardian-Rated Level 1 Cross-Cutting Symptom Measure. They indicated observing severe sleep problems (prior to Ben's start on the sleep medication), depression, and anger, as well as moderate irritability, somatic symptoms, and inattention issues. As a result, they were provided with several Level 2 measures to complete at home, assessing for anger, somatic symptoms, depression, inattention, and irritability. The Level 2 measure for sleep problems was not provided to the family, since it had not been validated for use with children, and may not be useful considering Ben's new medication for sleep. When the family returned for their second appointment, Ben's mother reported she was unable to complete the depression questionnaire, since Ben did not disclose any emotions to her, which limited her ability to report on this. The Level 2 measure for anger was completed, and Ben's parents reported elevated scores in all five items, with a T-Score of 63.5, indicating moderate anger. They also provided the completed measures for the Patient Health Questionnaire 15 (PHQ15), Swanson, Nolan and Pelham Questionnaire IV, Affective Reactivity Index (ARI).

Ben was subsequently individually assessed through administration of the CTSQ combined with measuring his heart rate to determine his PTSD symptoms. This assessment produced high scores for reexperiencing and hyperarousal symptoms. To measure the severity of his symptoms, he was administered the Severity of Posttraumatic Stress Symptoms Level 2 *DSM-5* measure, as well as the Severity of Dissociative Symptoms Scale. Results of these assessments indicated moderate PTSD and dissociation symptoms.

Interventions

Ben and his parents were offered 12 sessions of TF-CBT, with specific focus on teaching Ben new skills to address his traumatic stress symptoms. TF-CBT would allow Ben to develop new self-care strategies, and reduce self-blame and hypervigilance. The trauma narrative portion of the TF-CBT model would enable Ben to talk about the abuse he experienced. Based on this, Ben's parents would complete four psychoeducational sessions to help them understand and support Ben's needs. During these sessions, they would also receive coaching in responding empathically and supportively to Ben's narrative disclosure. They would also be provided with coping skills training to manage their own reactions to Ben's narrative, particularly considering his father's expressed concerns. The family, as a whole, will be invited to partake in a 12-week trauma-sensitive yoga class, to aid in relieving stress that may stem from their daily worries as well as to ease the treatment process. This adjunct intervention can be particularly appropriate given Ben's high level of somatic and dissociative symptoms.

Legal Implications

Counselors need to respect Ben's confidentiality while still allowing the adoptive parents access to vital information and involvement in the counseling process. Counselors should also be mindful of their role as mandated reporters. Ben may disclose past or current abuse. Some of his previous foster families still have children in their homes. A counselor has a legal and ethical obligation to protect this child and other children from possible harm. In contrast, many new adoptive parents report fears regarding their ability to support the children they have adopted, particularly when these children are more complex than originally expected. Clinicians working with adoptive families need not perceive parents' concerns as intention to disrupt an adoption or refusal to meet their child's needs. These parents' fears are, in most cases, not a cause for mandated reporting, but rather a worthy area of clinical focus.

DISCUSSION

As you continue to reflect on the case study and the overall approach, contemplate these questions:

- What other diagnoses might be applicable to this case?
- Is anyone truly able to fully heal from such an abusive past?
- What other treatment options would you use with this family?
- How might the children's status as adoptees impact this family's needs and treatment?
- Assuming their initial TF-CBT treatment is successful, what needs might you address next?
- What could be appropriate long-term treatment goals for this family?

SUMMARY

This chapter has paid close attention to the issues related to trauma and stress within the family dynamic. Trauma does not affect just the individual, but spills out into the family unit and can disrupt even the most stable environments. With this being said, trauma and stress should not be looked at as a death sentence. Survivors of trauma can be fiercely resilient and able to build fulfilling relationships with others even after the most horrific trauma.

When survivors of trauma have been able to heal effectively, it can intensify their relationships with their loved ones. A survivor can have a new sense of self and appropriate human connection. Intense pain and sadness can lead survivors to value each new day as a way to embark on a new positive path.

Through the use of assessment and intervention mentioned in this chapter, a survivor of trauma can improve his or her level of functioning; families can be allowed to support and embrace changes; and family units can end up stronger. When this happens, family can have better relationships due to increased communication, a new sense of values, and the ability to decide together personal boundaries within the family unit.

With this being said, trauma is not simply trauma and should always be considered in the context of the individual and cultural competency. Identity, heritage, and culture not only affect the individual, but also the response to the individual experiencing the trauma. It is a counselor's ethical responsibility to treat trauma through a cultural lens. This will provide the best understanding and ability to heal for the entire family unit.

REFERENCES

Ainsworth, M. D., & Bell, S. M. (1970). Attachment, exploration, and separation: Illustrated by the behavior of one-year-olds in a strange situation. *Child Development, 41*(1), 49–67.

Allen, J. G., Madan, A., & Fowler, J. C. (2015). Reliability and validity of the Stressful Life Events Screening Questionnaire among inpatients with severe neuropsychiatric illness. *Bulletin of the Menninger Clinic, 79*, 187–202. doi:10.1521/bumc.2015.79.3.187

American Association for Marriage and Family Therapy. (2015). *AAMFT code of ethics.* Retrieved from http://www.aamft.org/iMIS15/AAMFT/Content/Legal_Ethics/Code_of_Ethics.aspx

American Counseling Association. (2014). *ACA code of ethics.* Alexandria, VA: Author.

American Psychiatric Association. (1994). *Diagnostic and statistical manual of mental disorders* (4th ed.). Washington, DC: Author.

American Psychiatric Association. (2000). *Diagnostic and statistical manual of mental disorders* (4th ed., text rev.). Washington, DC: Author.

American Psychiatric Association. (2013). *Diagnostic and statistical manual of mental disorders* (5th ed.). Arlington, VA: American Psychiatric Publishing.

Anda, R. F., Felitti, V. J., Bremner, J. D., Walker, J. D., Whitfield, C. H., Perry, B. D., . . . & Giles, W. H. (2006). The enduring effects of abuse and related adverse experiences in childhood. *European Archives of Psychiatry and Clinical Neuroscience, 256*(3), 174–186.

Arvidson, J., Kinniburgh, K., Howard, K., Spinazzola, J., Strothers, H., Evans, M., & Blaustein, M. E. (2011). Treatment of complex trauma in young children: Developmental and cultural considerations in application of the ARC intervention model. *Journal of Child and Adolescent Trauma, 4*(1), 34–51.

Barnett, J. E., & Johnson, W. B. (2008). *Ethics desk reference for psychologists.* Washington, DC: American Psychological Association.

Baumrind, D. (1971). Current patterns of parental authority. *Developmental Psychology, 4*(1p2), 1.

Beck, J. S. (2011). *Cognitive behavior therapy: Basics and beyond.* Guilford Press.

Benuto, L. T., Olmo-Terrasa, A. M., & Reyes-Rabanillo, M. L. (2011). Exploring the factor structure and psychometric properties of a Spanish translation of the Clinician-Administered PTSD Scale. *Journal of Educational and Psychological Assessment, 9*, 14–26.

Bernstein, E. M., & Putnam, F. W. (1986). Development, reliabilty, and validity of a dissociation scale. *Journal of Nervous and Mental Disorders, 174*, 727–735.

Blake, D. D., Keane, T. M., Wine, P. R., Mora, C., Taylor, K. L., & Lyons, J. A. (1990). Prevalence of PTSD symptoms in combat veterans seeking medical treatment. *Journal of Traumatic Stress, 3*, 15–27. doi:10.1002/jts.2490030103

Blake, D. D., Weathers, F., Nagy, L. M., Kaloupek, D. G., Gusman, F. D., Charney, D. S., & Keane, T. M. (1995). The development of a clinician-administered PTSD scale. *Journal of Traumatic Stress, 8*, 75–90. doi:10.1002/jts.2490080106

Blake, D. D., Weathers, F. W., Nagy, L. M., Kaloupek, D. G., Klauminzer, G., Charney, D. S., Keane, T. M. (1990). A clinician rating scale for assessing current and lifetime PTSD: The CAPS-1. *The Behavior Therapist, 18*, 187–188.

Blake, D. D., Weathers, F., Nagy, L. M., Kaloupek, D. G., Klauminzer, G., Charney, D. S., & Keane, T. M. (1990). A clinician rating scale for assessing current and lifetime PTSD: The CAPS-1. *The Behavior Therapist, 13*, 187–188.

Blaustein, M. E., & Kinniburgh, K. M. (2010). *Treating traumatic stress in children and adolescents: How to foster resilience through attachment, self-regulation, and competency.* New York, NY: Guilford Press.

Bohnert, K. M. & Breslau, N. (2011). Assessing the performance of the short screening scale for post-traumatic stress disorder in a large nationally-representative survey. *International Journal of Methods in Psychiatric Research, 20*(1), e1–e5. doi:10.1002/mpr.331

Bowlby, J. (1977). The making and breaking of affectional bonds. I. Aetiology and psychopathology in the light of attachment theory: An expanded version of the Fiftieth Maudsley Lecture, delivered before the Royal College of Psychiatrists, 19 November 1976. *British Journal of Psychiatry, 130*(3), 201–210.

Breslau, N., Peterson, E. L., Kessler, R. C., & Schultz, L. R. (1999). Short screening scale for DSM-IV post-traumatic stress disorder. *American Journal of Psychiatry, 156*, 908–911. doi:10.1176/ajp.156.6.908

Brewin, C. R., Fuchkan, N., Huntley, Z., & Scragg, P. (2010). Diagnostic accuracy of the Trauma Screening Questionnaire after the 2005 London bombings. *Journal of Traumatic Stress, 23*, 393–398. doi:10.1002/jts.20529

Brewin, C. R., Rose, S., Andrews, B., Green, J., Tata, P., McEvedy, C., & Foa, E. B. (2002). Brief screening instrument for post-traumatic stress disorder. *British Journal of Psychiatry, 181*, 158–162.

Bryant, R. A. (2010). Acute stress disorder as a predictor of posttraumatic stress disorder: A systematic review. *The Journal of Clinical Psychiatry, 72*(2), 233–239.

Bryant, R. A., Mastrodomenico, J., Felmingham, K. L., Hopwood, S., Kenny, L., Kandris, E., . . . & Creamer, M. (2008). Treatment of acute stress disorder: A randomized controlled trial. *Archives of General Psychiatry, 65*(6), 659–667.

Calhoun, P. S., McDonald, S. D., Guerra, V. S., Eggleston, A. M., Beckham, J. C., & Straits-Troster, K. (2010). Clinical utility of the Primary Care-PTSD Screen among U.S. veterans who served since September 11, 2001. *Psychiatry Research, 178*, 330–335. doi:10.1016/j.psychres.2009.11.009

Callahan, R. J. (1995). A Thought Field Therapy (TFT) algorithm for trauma. *Traumatology, 1*(1), 2.

Carlson, E. B., Smith, S. R., Palmieri, P. A., Dalenberg, C. J., Ruzek, J. I., Kimerling, R., & Spain, D. A. (2011). Development and validation of a brief self-report measurement of trauma exposure: The Trauma History Screen. *Psychological Assessment, 23*, 463–477. doi:10.1037/a0022294

Chaffin, M., Silovsky, J. F., Funderburk, B., Valle, L. A., Brestan, E. V., Balachova, T., & Bonner, B. L. (2004). Parent-child interaction therapy with physically abusive parents: Efficacy for reducing future abuse reports. *Journal of Consulting and Clinical Psychology, 72*(3), 500.

Cohen, J. A., Mannarino, A. P., & Deblinger, E. (2006). *Treating trauma and traumatic grief in children and adolescents.* New York, NY: Guilford Press.

Collins, K. S., Strieder, F. H., DePanfilis, D., Tabor, M., Clarkson Freeman, P. A., Linde, L., & Greenberg, P. (2011). Trauma Adapted Family Connections (TA-FC): Reducing developmental and complex trauma symptomatology to prevent child abuse and neglect. *Child Welfare, 90*(6), 29–47.

Connolly, S. M., Sakai, C. E., & Oas, P. (2010). Treatment of PTSD in Rwandan child genocide survivors using thought field therapy. *International Journal of Emergency Mental Health, 12*(1), 41–50.

Connors, K., & Smith Stover, C. (2011, August 26). *Evaluating Families Impacted by Trauma.* The national child traumatic stress network. Retrieved from http://works.bepress.com/carla_stover/29/

Dalenberg, C. & Carlson, E. (2010). Severity of Dissociative Symptoms - Child Age 11–17 (Brief Dissociative Experiences Scale [DES-B]—Modified) [Measurement instrument]. Retrieved from http://www.psychiatry.org/practice/dsm/dsm5/online-assessment-measures

Danielson, C. K. (2007). *Risk reduction through family therapy (RRFT): Treatment manual.* National Crime Victims Research & Treatment Center, Medical University of South Carolina, Charleston.

Danielson, C. K., McCart, M., Walsh, K., de Arellano, M. A., White, D., & Resnick, H. S. (2012). Reducing substance use risk and mental health problems among sexually assaulted adolescents: A pilot randomized controlled trial. *Journal of Family Psychology, 26*, 628–635.

Dekel, R., & Monson, C. M. (2010). Military-related post-traumatic stress disorder and family relations: Current knowledge and future directions. *Aggression and Violent Behavior, 15*(4), 303–309.

Diehle, J., de Roos, C., Boer, F., & Lindauer, R. J. L. (2013). A cross-validation of the Clinician-Administered PTSD Scale for children and adolescents in a Dutch population. *European Journal of Psychotraumatology, 4*, 1–9. doi:10.3402/ejpt.v4i0.19896

Dutra, L., Grubbs, K., Greene, C., Trego, L. L., McCartin, T., & Kloezeman, K. (2011). Women at war: Implications for mental health. *Journal of Trauma and Dissociation, 12*, 24–37.

Eisenstadt, T. H., Eyberg, S., McNeil, C. B., Newcomb, K., & Funderburk, B. (1993). Parent-child interaction therapy with behavior problem children: Relative effectiveness of two stages and overall treatment outcome. *Journal of Clinical Child Psychology, 22*(1), 42–51.

Elhai, J. D., Gray, M. J., Kashdan, T. B., & Franklin, C. L. (2005). Which instruments are most commonly used to assess traumatic event exposure and posttraumatic effects? A survey of traumatic stress professionals. *Journal of Traumatic Stress, 18*, 541–545. doi:10.1002/jts.20062

Ellis, E. M. (2012). What are the confidentiality rights of collaterals in family therapy? *American Journal of Family Therapy, 40*, 369–384.

Eyberg, S. M. (1980). Eyberg child behavior inventory. *Journal of Clinical Child Psychology, 9*, 27.

Eyberg, S. M., & Funderburk, B. (2011). *Parent–child interaction therapy protocol*. Gainesville, FL: PCIT International.

Felitti, V. J., Anda, R. F., Nordenberg, D., Williamson, D. F., Spitz, A. M., Edwards, V., . . . & Marks, J. S. (1998). Relationship of childhood abuse and household dysfunction to many of the leading causes of death in adults: The Adverse Childhood Experiences (ACE) Study. *American Journal of Preventive Medicine, 14*(4), 245–258.

Fleet, R. A., Kazantzis, N., Long, N. R., MacDonald, C., & Millar, M. (2002). Traumatic events and physical health in a New Zealand Community Sample. *Journal of Traumatic Stress, 15*, 303–312. doi:10.1023/A:1016251828407

Galovski, T., & Lyons, J. A. (2004). Psychological sequelae of combat violence: A review of the impact of PTSD on the veteran's family and possible interventions. *Aggression and Violent Behavior, 9*(5), 477–501.

Goodman, L., Corcoran, C., Turner, K., Yuan, N., & Green, B. (1998). Assessing traumatic event exposure: General issues and preliminary findings for the Stressful Life Events Screening Questionnaire. *Journal of Traumatic Stress, 11*, 521–542. doi:10.1023/A:1024456713321

Gray, M., Litz, B., Hsu, J., & Lombardo, T. (2004). Psychometric properties of the Life Events Checklist. *(PDF) Assessment, 11*, 330–341. doi:10.1177/1073191104269954

Green, B. L. (1996). Trauma History Questionnaire. In B. H. Stamm (Ed.), *Measurement of stress, trauma, and adaptation* (pp. 366–369). Lutherville, MD: Sidran Press.

Green, B. L., Chung, J. Y, Daroowalla, A., Kaltman, S., & DeBenedictis, C. (2006). Evaluating the cultural validity of the Stressful Life Events Screening Questionnaire. *Violence Against Women, 12*, 1191–1213. doi:10.1177/1077801206294534

Han, C., Pae, C.-U., Patkar, A. A., Masand, P. S., Kim, K. W., Joe, S.-H., & Jung, I.-K. (2009). Psychometric properties of the patient health questionnaire-15 (PHQ-15) for measuring the somatic symptoms of psychiatric outpatients. *Psychosomatics, 50*, 580–585.

Harris, S. M., & Topham, G. (2004). Assessment and treatment of trauma from a Bowen family systems theory perspective. In D. R. Catherall (Ed.), *Handbook of stress, trauma, and the family*. New York, NY: Bruner-Routledge.

Hays, P. A. (2008). *Addressing cultural complexities in practice: Assessment, diagnosis, and therapy* (2nd ed.). Washington, DC: American Psychological Association.

Hinton, D. E., Chhean, D., Pich, V., Pollack, M. H., Orr, S. P., & Pitman, R. K. (2006). Assessment of post-traumatic stress disorder in Cambodian refugees using the Clinician Administered PTSD Scale: Psychometric properties and symptom severity. *Journal of Traumatic Stress, 19*, 405–409. doi:10.1002/jts.20115

Hoffmann, W. A. (2002). The incidence of traumatic events and trauma-associated symptoms/experiences amongst tertiary students. *South African Journal of Psychology, 32*, 48–53.

Hooper, L. Stockton, P., Krupnick, & Green, B. (2011). Development, use, and psychometric properties of the Trauma History Questionnaire. *Journal of Loss and Trauma, 16*, 258–283. doi:10.1080/15325024.2011.572035

Humphreys, J. C., De Pheils, P. B., Slaughter, R. E., Uribe, T., Jaramillo, D., Tiwari, A., . . . Belknap, R. A. (2011). Translation and adaptation of the Life Stressor Checklist-Revised with Colombian women. *Health Care for Women International, 32*, 599–612. doi:10.1080/07399332.2010.528850

Hyer, L., Davis, H., Boudewns, P., & Woods, M. G., (1991). A short form of the Mississippi Scale for Combat-Related PTSD. *Journal of Clinical Psychology, 47*, 510–518.

Jaapar, S. Z. S., Abidin, Z. Z., & Othman, Z. (2014). Validation of Malay Trauma Screening Questionnaire. *International Medical Journal, 21*, 536–538.

Jarero, I., Artigas, L., & Hartung, J. (2006). EMDR Integrative Group Treatment Protocol: A postdisaster trauma intervention for children and adults. *Traumatology, 12*(2), 121.

Kagan, R., Douglas, A. N., Hornik, J., & Kratz, S. L. (2008). Real Life Heroes pilot study: Evaluation of a treatment model for children with traumatic stress. *Journal of Child and Adolescent Trauma, 1*(1), 5–22.

Kazantzis, N., Fleet, R. A., Long, N. R., MacDonald, C., Millar, M., & Clark, B. (2010). Traumatic events and mental health in the community: A New Zealand study. *International Journal of Social Psychiatry, 56*, 35–49. doi:10.1177/0020764008095929

Keane, T. M., Caddell, J. M., & Taylor, K. L. (1988). Mississippi Scale for Combat-Related Posttraumatic Stress Disorder: Three studies in reliability and validity. *Journal of Consulting and Clinical Psychology, 56*, 85–90. doi:10.1037/0022-006X.56.1.85

Keane, T. M., Fairbank, J. A., Caddell, J. M., Zimering, R. T., Taylor, K. L., & Mora, C. A. (1989). Clinical evaluation of a measure to assess combat exposure. *Psychological Assessment: A Journal of Consulting and Clinical Psychology, 1*, 53–55. doi:10.1037/1040-3590.1.1.53

Kilpatrick, D. G., Resnick, H. S., & Friedman, M. J. (2013). Severity of posttraumatic stress symptoms—child age 11–17 (National Stressful Events Survey PTSD Short Scale [NSESSS]) [Measurement instrument]. Retrieved from http://www.psychiatry.org/practice/dsm/dsm5/online-assessment-measures

Kimerling, R., Ouimette, P., Prins, A., Nisco, P., Lawler, C., Cronkite, & Moos, R. H. (2006). Brief report: Utility of a Short Screening Scale for DSM-IV PTSD in primary care. *Journal of General Internal Medicine, 21*, 65–67. doi:10.1111/j.1525-1497.2005.00292.x

Kiser, L. J. (2008). *Strengthening family coping resources: Multi-family group for families impacted by trauma* (Unpublished manual).

Kiser, L. J., Backer, P. M., Winkles, J., & Medoff, D. (2015). Strengthening Family Coping Resources (SFCR): Practice-based evidence for a promising trauma intervention. *Couple and Family Psychology: Research and Practice, 4*(1), 49.

Koenen, K., C., DeVivo, I., Rich-Edwards, J., Smoller, J. W., Wright, R. J., & Purcell, S. M. (2009). Protocol for investigating genetic determinants of posttraumatic stress disorder in women from the Nurses' Health Study II. *BMC Psychiatry, 9*(29), 1–20. doi:10.1186/1471-244x-9-29

Krinsley, K. E. (1996). Psychometric review of the Evaluation of Lifetime Stressors Questionnaire & Interview. In B. H. Stamm (Ed.), *Measurement of stress, trauma, and adaptation* (pp. 160–162). Lutherville, MD: Sidran Press.

Krinsley, K. E., Gallagher, J. G., Weathers, F. W., Kutter, C. J., & Kaloupek, D. G. (2003). Consistency of retrospective reporting about exposure to traumatic events. *Journal of Traumatic Stress, 16*, 399–409. doi:10.1023/A:1024474204233

Kubany, E. S., Haynes, S. N., Leisen, M. B., Owens, J. A., Kaplan, A. S., Watson, S. B., & Burns, K. (2000). Development and preliminary validation of a brief broad-spectrum measure of trauma exposure: The Traumatic Life Events Questionnaire. *Psychological Assessment, 12*, 210–224. doi:10.1037/1040-3590.12.2.210

Kubzansky, L. D., Bordelois, P., Jun, H. J., Roberts, A. L., Cerda, M., Bluestone, N., & Koenen, K. C. (2014). The weight of traumatic stress: A prospective study of posttraumatic stress disorder symptoms and weight status in women. *JAMA Psychiatry, 71*, 44–51. doi:10.1001/jamapsychiatry.2013.2798

Kulka, R. A., Schlenger, W. E., Fairbank, J. A., Hough, R. L., Jordan, B. K., Marmar, C. R., & Weiss, D. S. (1990). *Trauma and the Vietnam War generation: Report of findings from the National Vietnam Veterans Readjustment Study*. New York, NY: Brunnel/Mazel.

Lancaster, S. L., Melka, S. E., & Rodriguez, B. F. (2009). A factor analytic comparison of five models of PTSD symptoms. *Journal of Anxiety Disorders, 23*, 269–274. doi:10.1016/j.janxdis.2008.08.001

Lawler, J. M., Hostinar, C. E., Mliner, S. B., & Gunnar, M. R. (2014). Disinhibited social engagement in postinstitutionalized children: Differentiating normal from atypical behavior. *Development and Psychopathology, 26*(02), 451–464.

Lauterbach, D., Vrana, S., King, D. W., & King, L. A. (1997). Psychometric properties of the civilian version of the Mississippi PTSD Scale. *Journal of Traumatic Stress, 10*, 499–513.

Lieberman, A. F., Ippen, C. G., & Van Horn, P. (2006). Child-parent psychotherapy: 6-month follow-up of a randomized controlled trial. *Journal of the American Academy of Child and Adolescent Psychiatry, 45*(8), 913–918.

Lieberman, A. F., & Van Horn, P. (2005). *Don't hit my mommy! A manual for child-parent psychotherapy with young witnesses of family violence*. Washington, DC: Zero to Three Press.

Malloy, L. C., & Lyon, T. D. (2006). Caregiver support and child sexual abuse: Why does it matter? *Journal of Child Sexual Abuse, 15*(4), 97–103.

Marvin, R., Cooper, G., Hoffman, K., & Powell, B. (2002). The circle of security project: Attachment-based intervention with caregiver-pre-school child dyads. *Attachment and Human Development, 4*(1), 107–124.

McHugo, G. J., Caspi, Y., Kammerer, N., Mazelis, R., Jackson, E. W., Russell, L., . . . Kimerling, R. (2005). The assessment of trauma history in women with co-occurring substance abuse and mental disorders and a history of interpersonal violence. *Journal of Behavioral Health Services and Research, 32*, 113–127. doi:10.1007/BF02287261

Miller, G. E., Chen, E., & Zhou, E. S. (2007). If it goes up, must it come down? Chronic stress and the hypothalamic-pituitary-adrenocortical axis in humans. *Psychological Bulletin, 133*(1), 25.

Mohl, A. (2009). Sexual abuse of the child: A treatment model for the incestuous family. *The Journal of Psychohistory, 38*(2), 168–181.

Nader, K. O. (2004). Assessing traumatic experiences in children and adolescents: Self-reports of DSM PTSD Criteria B–D symptoms. In J. Wilson & T. Keane (Eds.), *Assessing psychological trauma and PTSD* (2nd ed., pp. 513–537). New York, NY: Guilford Press.

National Child Traumatic Stress Network. (2011). Trauma and families: Fact sheet for providers. Retrieved from http://www.nctsn.org/resources/topics/families-and-trauma

Norris, F. H. (1990). Screening for traumatic stress: A scale of use in the general population. *Journal of Applied Social Psychology, 20*, 1704–1718. doi:10.1111/j.1559-1816.1990.tb01505.x

Norris, F. H., & Hamblen, J. L. (2004). Standardized self-report measures of civilian trauma and PTSD. In J. P. Wilson, T. M. Keane, & T. Martin (Eds.), *Assessing psychological trauma and PTSD* (2nd ed., pp. 63–102). New York, NY: Guilford Press.

Norris, F. H., & Perilla, J. L. (1996). The Revised Civilian Mississippi Scale for PTSD: Reliability, validity, and cross-language stability. *Journal of Traumatic Stress, 9*, 285–298. doi:10.1002/jts.2490090210

Ohan, J. L., Myers, K., & Collett, B. R. (2002). Ten-year review of rating scales. IV: Scales assessing trauma and its effects. *Journal of the American Academy of Child and Adolescent Psychiatry, 41*, 1401–1422. doi:10.1097/00004583-200212000-00012

Olsson, K. A., Kenardy, J. A., De Young, A. C., & Spence, S. H. (2008). Predicting children's post-traumatic stress symptoms following hospitalization for accidental injury: Combining the Child Trauma Screening Questionnaire and heart rate. *Journal of Anxiety Disorder, 22*, 1447–1453. doi:10.1016/j.janxdis.2008.02.007

Ouimette, P., Wade, M., Prins, A., & Schohn, M. (2008). Identifying PTSD in primary care: Comparison of the Primary Care-PTSD Screen (PC-PTSD) and the General Health Questionniare-12 (GHQ). *Anxiety Disorders, 22*, 337–343. doi:10.1016/j.janxdis.2007.02.010

Pais, S. (2009). A systematic approach to the treatment of dissociative identity disorder. *Journal of Family Psychotherapy, 20*(1), 72–88.

Paunovic, N., & Ost, L. G. (2005). Psychometric properties of a Swedish translation of the Clinician-Administered PTSD Scale-Diagnostic Version. *Journal of Traumatic Stress, 18*, 161–164. doi:10.1002/jts.20013

Perry, B. D. (2009). Examining child maltreatment through a neurodevelopmental lens: Clinical applications of the neurosequential model of therapeutics. *Journal of Loss and Trauma, 14*(4), 240–255.

Perry, C. T., Oum, P., & Gray, S. H. (2007). The body remembers: Somatic symptoms in traumatized Khmer. *Journal of the American Academy of Psychoanalysis and Dynamic Psychiatry, 35*, 77–84. doi:10.1521/jaap.2007.35.1.77

Prins, A., Ouimette, P., Kimerling, R., Cameron, R. P., Hugelshofer, D. S., Shaw-Hegwer, J., & Sheikh, J. I. (2003). The Primary Care PTSD Screen (PC-PTSD-5): Development and operating characteristics (PDF). *Primary Care Psychiatry, 9*, 9–14. doi:10.1185/135525703125002360

Pynoos, R. S., Weathers, F. W., Steinberg, A. M., Marx, B. P., Layne, C. M., Kaloupek, D. G., & Kriegler, J. A. (2015). Clinician-Administered PTSD Scale for DSM-5: Child/Adolescent Version. Retrieved from http://www.ptsd.va.gov

Schnurr, P. P., Spiro, A., Vielhauer, M. J., Findler, M. N., & Hamblen, J. L (2002). Trauma in the lives of older men: Findings from the normative aging study. *Journal of Clinical Geropsychology, 8*, 175–187. doi:10.1023/A:1015992110544

Schnyder, U., & Moergeli, H. (2002). German version of Clinician-Administered PTSD Scale. *Journal of Traumatic Stress, 15*, 487–492. doi:10.1023/A:1020922023090

Schore, A. N. (2001). The effects of early relational trauma on right brain development, affect regulation, and infant mental health. *Infant Mental Health Journal, 22*(1–2), 201–269.

Schwartz, R. (1994). *The internal family systems model.* New York, NY: Guilford Press.

Sloan, P., Arsenault, L., Hilsenroth, M., & Harvill, L. (1995). Use of the Mississippi scale for combat-related PTSD in detecting war-related non-combat stress symptomatology. *Journal of Clinical Psychology, 51*, 799–801. doi:10.1002/1097-4679(199511)51:6<799::AID-JCLP2270510611>3.0.CO;2-C.

Spoont, M. R., Williams, J. W., Kehle-Forbes, S., Nieuwsma, J. A., Mann-Wrobel, M. C., & Gross, R. (2015). Does this patient have posttraumatic stress disorder? Rational clinical examination systematic review. *Journal of the American Medical Association, 214*, 501–510. doi:10.1001/jama.2015.7877

Stolbach, B. C., Minshew, R., Rompala, V., Dominguez, R. Z., Gazibara, T., & Finke, R. (2013). Complex trauma exposure and symptoms in urban traumatized children: A preliminary test of proposed criteria for developmental trauma disorder. *Journal of Traumatic Stress, 26*(4), 483–491.

Stringaris, A., Goodman, R., Ferdinando, S., Razdan, V., Muhrer, E., Leibenluft, E., & Brotman, M. A. (2012). The Affective Reactivity Index: A concise irritability scale for clinical and research settings. *Journal of Child Psychology and Psychiatry, 53*, 1109–1117. doi:10.1111/j.1469-7610.2012.02561.x

Swanson, J. M. (2011). LEVEL 2—Inattention—Parent/Guardian of Child Age 6–17 (Swanson, Nolan, and Pelham, version IV [SNAP-IV]) [Measurement instrument]. Retrieved from http://www.psychiatry.org/practice/dsm/dsm5/online-assessment-measures

Swenson, C. C., Schaeffer, C. M., Henggeler, S. W., Faldowski, R., & Mayhew, A. M. (2010). Multisystemic therapy for child abuse and neglect: A randomized effectiveness trial. *Journal of Family Psychology, 24*(4), 497.

Taft, C. T., King, L. A., King, D. W., Leskin, G. A., & Riggs, D. S. (1999). Partners' ratings of combat veterans' PTSD symptomatology. *Journal of Traumatic Stress, 12*, 327–334.

Tarasoff v. Regents of the University of California, 17 Cal. 3d 425, 551 P.2d 334, 131 Cal. Rptr. 14 (Cal. 1976).

Teicher, M. H., Andersen, S. L., Polcari, A., Anderson, C. M., Navalta, C. P., & Kim, D. M. (2003). The neurobiological consequences of early stress and childhood maltreatment. *Neuroscience and Biobehavioral Reviews, 27*(1), 33–44.

Thompson, M. P. (1998). The frequency and impact of violent trauma among pregnant substance abusers. *Addictive Behaviors, 23*, 257–262. doi:10.1016/S0306-4603(97)00032-4

Timmer, S. G., Urquiza, A. J., Zebell, N. M., & McGrath, J. M. (2005). Parent-child interaction therapy: Application to maltreating parent-child dyads. *Child Abuse and Neglect, 29*(7), 825–842.

Tirella, L. G., Chan, W., & Miller, L. C. (2006). Educational outcomes of children adopted from Eastern Europe, now ages 8–12. *Journal of Research in Childhood Education, 20*(4), 245–254.

Van der Kolk, B. A. (2005). Developmental trauma disorder. *Psychiatric Annals, 35*(5), 401–408.

Walters, J. T. R., Bisson, J. I., & Shepherd, J. P. (2007). Predicting post-traumatic stress disorder: Validation of the Trauma Screening Questionnaire in victims of assault. *Psychological Medicine, 37*, 143–150. doi:10.1017/S0033291706008658

Wark, L., Thomas, M., & Peterson, S. (2001). Internal family systems therapy for children in family therapy. *Journal of Marital and Family Therapy, 27*(2), 189–200.

Weathers, F. W., Blake, D. D., Schnurr, P. P., Kaloupek, D. G., Marx, B. P., & Keane, T. M. (2013). The Clinician-Administered PTSD Scale for DSM-5 (CAPS-5). Retrieved from http://www.ptsd.va.gov

Wieling, E., & Turner, W. (2003). Healing loss, ambiguity, and trauma: A community-based intervention with families of union workers missing after the 9/11 attack in New York City. *Journal of Marital and Family Therapy, 29*(4), 455–467.

Wilkins, E. J. (2007). Using an IFS-informed intervention to treat African American families surviving sexual abuse: One family's story. *Journal of Feminist Family Therapy: An International Forum, 19*(3), 37–53.

Wolfe, J., Kimerling, R., Brown, P. J., Chrestman, K. R., & Levin, K. (1996). Psychometric review of the Life Stressor Checklist-Revised. In B. H. Stamm (Ed.), *Measurement of stress, trauma, and adaptation* (pp. 198–201). Lutherville, MD: Sidran Press.

Yehuda, R., & Bierer, L. M. (2009). The relevance of epigenetics to PTSD: Implications for the DSM-V. *Journal of Traumatic Stress, 22*(5), 427–434.

Yehuda, R., Teicher, M. H., Seckl, J. R., Grossman, R. A., Morris, A., & Bierer, L. M. (2007). Parental posttraumatic stress disorder as a vulnerability factor for low cortisol trait in offspring of Holocaust survivors. *Archives of General Psychiatry, 64*(9), 1040–1048.

SYSTEMS APPLIED TO DISSOCIATIVE DISORDERS

Kristen Eldredge and LoriAnn Stretch

*I*n this chapter, the experience of dissociation and the Dissociative Disorders from the *Diagnostic and Statistical Manual of Mental Disorders* (5th ed.; *DSM-5*; American Psychiatric Association [APA], 2013a) is explored, specifically illuminating the unique impact of dissociation on couple and/or family systems and, in return, the impact of couple and/or family systems on the individual with a dissociative disorder. Because dissociation is often experienced as an internal, isolating experience, one may not immediately think of the impact on current partners or families when providing treatment to a client with a dissociative disorder. However, this impact is profound and treatment can be enhanced when considering these factors. Mental health professionals need to consider how a client's partner or family system, past or present, may impact the client, whether helpfully, harmfully, or otherwise.

DSM-5 AND FAMILY SYSTEMS

From a systemic perspective, a diagnosis of dissociative disorders may be met by a number of different reactions from a client's family system. Reactions may range from dismissal and disbelief to relief that there is a framework for understanding the family member (i.e., the client). Disbelief and dismissal may result for myriad reasons. For example, clients with dissociative disorders tend to feel shame and have learned how to conceal dissociative symptoms to manage this shame (Brand et al., 2016). Thus, partners and family members can experience surprise when a diagnosis of dissociative disorders is given when they have not previously noticed overt or florid symptomatology.

Alternatively, prior to diagnosis, partners and family members may have been confused by many of the client's dissociative symptoms. For example, a client with dissociative

---

Opening image artwork created by Jesse D. Stretch

disorders can present at some times like an innocent, sweet child intent on pleasing the other person, and then without clear explanation to an outsider may switch into an abrasive, unfriendly presentation. This can cause confusion, frustration, and helplessness in a client's partner or family member. Thus, learning that there is an established diagnosis in the *DSM-5* that explains what seemed unexplainable can offer hope to those in the client's life.

Overview of Dissociation

Dissociation, a term initially put forth by Janet in his treatment of patients diagnosed with hysteria (1887, as cited in Dell & O'Neil, 2009), is a disintegration of psychological functions, such as attention, consciousness, and memory. Symptoms may be categorized as positive symptoms because they intrude into thoughts or behaviors, or negative symptoms because they result in a loss of, or inaccessibility of, functioning that was normally present. Examples of positive symptoms include identity fragmentation, depersonalization, or derealization, which include a discontinuity of one's subjective experience. Examples of negative symptoms, such as amnesia, demonstrate an interruption in functions and processes that are normally integrated (APA, 2013a). There are five major areas of dissociative symptoms: amnesia, depersonalization, derealization, identity confusion, and identity alteration (Gingrich, 2013). *Amnesia* is an inability to recall identity or events, especially autobiographical events (personal life experiences) beyond what would be considered common forgetfulness. Clients often describe amnesia as "losing time." In many cases, clients may be unaware that there are gaps in their memory. *Depersonalization* (an internalized reaction) is the experience that one is disconnected from one's body or that one's body (parts or all) is not real. Similarly, *derealization* (an externalizing reaction) consists of a disconnection with the outside world or a sense of unreality (APA, 2013a). *Identity fragmentation* is a direct result of the lack of integration between an individual's memory and sense of self. When each part functions autonomously (fully or partially), the individual experiences difficulty understanding who he or she is collectively. *Identity alteration* occurs when distinct personality states develop (typically in response to multiple trauma events) having dissimilar roles and functions, thus causing the individual to experience marked discontinuity in sense of self and sense of agency, The individual experiencing this form of dissociation receives feedback from others that he or she has done things differently or the individual may have some awareness of different roles and functions but without any clear understanding of why and when he or she functions in those roles.

Dissociation exists as a continuum, ranging from normal, everyday "zoning out" to the clinical expression of Dissociative Identity Disorder (DID; Gingrich, 2013; Putnam, 1989; Spiegel, 2010). On the "normal" end of this continuum are experiences such as the typical "highway hypnosis," a common experience that occurs when one is performing a mundane, yet regular task such as driving and cannot recall the details of the drive. Simply put, one cannot always be completely aware of all experiences at all times; this is normal. The lack of integrating the memory of such mundane tasks is a basic demonstration of failure to integrate the information or dissociation (Gingrich, 2013). In the mid-range of the continuum are the common responses of posttraumatic stress disorder (PTSD) including flashbacks, numbing, and amnesia. Notably, in the most recent diagnostic classification for PTSD (*DSM-5*; APA, 2013a), there is an option to specify a dissociative subtype that consists of symptoms including depersonalization and/or derealization (APA, 2013a). On the most clinical or pathological end of the spectrum exist dissociative disorders, including experiences that impede personal functioning in multiple life areas and are thus considered pathological (Gingrich, 2013).

Dissociative Disorders in the *DSM-5*

In the *DSM-5* (APA, 2013a), the dissociative disorders include Dissociative Identity Disorder (DID), Dissociative Amnesia, Depersonalization/Derealization Disorder, Other Specified Dissociative Disorder, and Unspecified Dissociative Disorder.

Dissociative Identity Disorder

DID typically consists of all of the common dissociative symptoms (i.e., amnesia, depersonalization, derealization, identity confusion, and identity alteration), but the primary feature of this disorder is the alteration of sense of self and sense of agency resulting in two or more distinct personality states. In the *DSM-5*, Criterion A clarifies that these alterations are characterized by shifts in consciousness, perception, memory, behavior, emotion, thoughts, and sensory-motor functioning (APA, 2013a). In some cultures, these experiences may be described as episodes of possession in which individuals report that a supernatural being or an outside person has taken control of their beliefs, feelings, actions, and so forth. The individual with DID experiences multiple discrete self-states which are relatively distinct from one another. In fact, these self-states may exert autonomy over the other subjective states, including the individual who presents as the client or host identity (International Society for the Study of Trauma and Dissociation [ISSTD], 2011). Criterion B outlines the occurrence of amnesic episodes, namely the inability to recall information that is not explained by normal forgetting, including daily events, personal data, and previous traumatic events. Amnesia in the context of DID typically includes memory gaps for skills that are well learned such as driving, job-specific skills, and events that occur from day to day. Individuals may not be aware of the gaps in memory until others make it known or evidence is discovered of actions they do not recall (APA, 2013a). The identity confusion, alteration, and amnesia cause significant distress and are unwanted and occur involuntarily (Criterion C). Cultural considerations must be explored to determine if the identity disturbances are explainable as a component of a widely understood religious or cultural practice (Criterion D). Finally, physiological causes of the symptoms, including substance use or medical conditions, must be considered as well (Criterion E; APA, 2013a). Ultimately, to establish a diagnosis of DID, a systemic clinician must (a) observe discontinuity in agency, (b) identify an autonomous self-state, (c) document an enduring "disconnectedness from their surroundings," (d) establish that the client is missing various memory constructs, (e) complete a comprehensive supporting history, and (f) identify if the client is responsive to treatment specific to DID (Peterson, 2010).

Dissociative Amnesia

The primary feature of Dissociative Amnesia is the incapacity to retrieve autobiographical information that should be held in one's memory and in usual circumstances would be easy to remember (Criterion A; APA, 2013a). There are various expressions of dissociative amnesia including localized, selective, generalized, systematized, and continuous amnesia, all of which must cause distress or impairment for a diagnosis to be made (Criterion B). Localized amnesia is characterized by an inability to recall events that are specific to a certain period of time; whereas selective amnesia is the lack of memory recall for certain, though not all, aspects of events during a period of time. Generalized amnesia, on the other hand, is a loss of one's memory in a global sense including identity, autobiographical history, and knowledge about the world. This form of dissociative amnesia is less common and typically has an acute onset. Systematized amnesia involves loss of memory for full categories of information, such as childhood abuse or a particular person; continuous amnesia involves forgetting newly occurring events (APA, 2013a). When assessing and diagnosing Dissociative Amnesia, one must rule out the possibility that the memory deficit is due to substance use, medical conditions, or head injuries (Criterion C; APA, 2013a) and is also not better understood as a component of other related disorders, including DID, PTSD, Acute Stress Disorder, and Borderline Personality Disorder. An expansion to this disorder in the *DSM-5* involved collapsing *Diagnostic and Statistical Manual of Mental Disorders* (4th ed.; *DSM-IV*; APA, 1994) Dissociative Fugue disorder into a specifier designation that indicates travel, either intentional or wandering, that is related to the individual's amnesia (APA, 2013a).

For partners and family members of a client with Dissociative Amnesia, common reaction may be grief, sadness, confusion, and fear. When a client loses memory of either his or her identity or the identity of that of a partner/family member, it inevitably interferes with the relationship, sometimes even leading to the end of the relationship. In one instance of Dissociative Amnesia with Fugue, the client who was previously a husband and father left his family as he had no memory of the relationships, understandably causing heartache for those left behind. Depending on the type of dissociative amnesia (e.g., localized, generalized), partners and family members may benefit from their own psychoeducation, therapy, and support.

Depersonalization/Derealization Disorder

In this classification, an individual experiences repeated episodes of depersonalization or derealization and in some cases, both. Duration of episodes can range from days to weeks and in some cases, even longer. As described previously, depersonalization consists of a sense of being detached from, outside of, or disconnected from one's whole self or from aspects of the self. This may include one's body, sensations, thoughts, feelings, or connection with time. Examples include out-of-body experiences, watching oneself as if one is an observer (Criterion A; APA, 2013a). Criterion A, derealization, is characterized by a sense that the world around one is unreal. This is often described by clients as the environment feeling "foggy or fuzzy" or otherwise distorted. Although an individual experiences such episodes of depersonalization/derealization, his or her reality testing (attachment from, or familiarity with, the world) is otherwise unimpaired (Criterion B), and the episode causes the individual significant distress or impairment (Criterion C; APA, 2013a). Understandably, individuals often experience fear, anxiety, depression, disorientation (especially related to the passing of time), and somatic symptoms. Although some degree of depersonalization/derealization is common for all, meeting the full diagnostic criteria for this disorder occurs for about 2% of the population (APA, 2013a). Onset typically occurs in childhood or adolescence with the average age of onset of 16 years old and is significantly less common for onset to occur after the mid-20s (APA, 2013a).

Systemically, Depersonalization/Derealization can be quite challenging. Similar to DID, clients with depersonalization/derealization may be quite skilled at disguising their symptoms. However, the fact that symptoms may not be obvious to an outsider does not mean that he or she does not cause difficulties for the client or the family system. One example of this occurred for a client of the first author. This client relayed a recent, upsetting conflict with his partner; the conflict occurred when he was feeling depersonalized, more specifically feeling disconnected from his body, feeling as if he was "in a fog," and feeling younger than his chronological age. During this time, his partner, unaware of the depersonalized state, attempted to engage in romantic, intimate interactions, which sadly resulted in severe distress for the client, and a deep sense of rejection, confusion, and frustration in the partner. The partner expressed sadness that she had inadvertently caused such distress for her partner but also frustration that she was unaware of the state of her partner and that her partner had not in some way disclosed his current state of depersonalization. In cases such as this, both individual and couple counseling from a trauma-informed perspective can be quite effective. Suggested treatment models are presented later in this chapter.

Other Specified Dissociative Disorder

When dissociative symptoms cause marked distress and impairment but do not meet the frequency, duration, and/or intensity diagnostic criteria of the dissociative disorders discussed so far, Other Specified Dissociative Disorder is an appropriate diagnosis (APA, 2013a). For example, a clinician may provide this diagnosis when an individual has been exposed to "intense coercive persuasion" (APA, 2013a, p. 306) as in the case of political prisoners or cult survivors where indoctrination, brainwashing, and/or torture may have occurred.

Unspecified Dissociative Disorder

The diagnosis of Unspecified Dissociative Disorder is applied when dissociative symptoms are present and cause distress and/or impairment; however, the symptoms do not meet the full criteria of any of the other dissociative disorders. In this case, the clinician applying the diagnosis does not provide the reason that the full criteria for another dissociative disorder are not met. This may be the case when the client is presenting for care in a hospital emergency room (APA, 2013a).

Clearly, dissociative disorders are complex and can be challenging for diagnosticians, mental health providers, and clients. It is also critical that we consider how these disorders can impact a client's family system, including his or her partners. The following sections of this chapter provide discussion on how a systems perspective should be considered in etiology, assessment, and treatment.

Etiology of Dissociative Disorders

In her seminal work, Herman (1992b) described how traumatic events, especially those for which "resistance or escape is not possible," lead to the development of situationally adaptive responses, including dissociation (p. 35). Herman concurred with Janet in explaining that these traumatic events sever normally integrated functions from one another (1992). Through this severance, the trauma is kept separate from the normal body of autobiographical memories and sense of self (Van der Kolk, 2014). Experiences resulting in such responses include repeated and severe interpersonal abuse and/or violence, such as sexual or physical abuse, that occur early in life (Spiegel, 2010). In fact, 90% of individuals diagnosed with DID in North America and Europe have reportedly experienced childhood abuse and/or neglect (APA, 2013a). This data supports the foundational work of Putnam (1989), one of the pioneers in the dissociative disorders field. He described DID (at the time known as multiple personality disorder) as a "psychobiological response" to traumatic experiences occurring during childhood. Children who have been severely and chronically traumatized will likely be unable to develop an integrated sense of self, instead developing the disconnected states which serve to keep the trauma-related material (e.g., memories, sensations, behaviors, affect) away from the child's awareness (ISSTD, 2011). These dissociative responses interfere with the integration of functions that in normal development would be achieved, including behavior, awareness, identity, affect regulation, and memory (DePrince & Freyd, 2014; Herman, 1992b). Herman's statement "traumatized people feel and act as though their nervous systems have been disconnected from the present" demonstrated the early understanding that these responses are natural, psychobiological adaptations (1992b, p. 35). Initially, the severance or dissociative response is adaptive and protects the individual from integrating the trauma and having internal systems become completely overwhelmed. The dissociative response may become maladaptive when the response continues well beyond the trauma or any threat of trauma and prevents integration and ultimately healing (Herman, 1992b).

RELATIONAL AND CULTURAL FEATURES

To fully understand the complexity of dissociation and dissociative disorders, mental health professionals must be mindful of how a client's cultural identity, cultural experiences, and relational interactions throughout the life span shape his or her experience with dissociation and the family system's experience with dissociation. The *DSM-5* also acknowledges the importance of considering these factors when assessing, diagnosing, and treating clinical disorders. Clinicians should thoroughly explore the *DSM-5* section "Other conditions that may be a focus of clinical attention" (APA, 2013, p. 715), which presents Z codes (formerly V codes). For the dissociative disorders, there are numerous V codes that should be considered and are presented here in the exploration of cultural and relational considerations.

Cultural Considerations

Symptoms and indicators relevant to diagnostic assessment must be viewed through the social, familial, and cultural contexts for ethical and culturally appropriate diagnosis to occur. What one individual considers healthy in one culture or community may in fact be viewed as symptoms of distress and illness in another (APA, 2013a; Rhoades, 2006a, 2006b). For example, a woman may have difficulty learning to read. In the United States, women are expected to learn to read, and not being able to learn how to read would be considered a learning disability. However, in some countries, women are forbidden or discouraged from learning to read. In a country where women are not expected to learn to read, the symptom of having difficulty learning to read would not be considered distressful or abnormal and would not warrant the diagnosis of a learning disability.

There are numerous ways in which one's culture can influence presentation of a mental disorder or psychiatric symptom such as dissociation. For example, the interpretations or judgments placed on particular symptoms may influence the client's experience of distress when experiencing such a symptom. In the previous example, a woman in a country where there is no societal expectation for women to read may not even have an opportunity to know that she has a potential learning issue, much less experience that learning issue as a disability. These differing judgments about symptoms influence the behaviors or actions one may take when such symptoms present. If the symptom is viewed as nonproblematic, support may not be sought for relieving the symptom. For example, if a dissociative state is interpreted as possession by a divine spirit or saint, the individual may be revered as spiritual healer and this experience would not be seen as pathological (Gingrich, 2006). On the other hand, if dissociative symptoms are experienced and interpreted to be the possession of an evil spirit or demon, the individual may be viewed to be in the crux of spiritual warfare and in need of deliverance, exorcism, or prayer from his or her religious community (Gingrich, 2006). The same symptoms that are associated with fear and shame in one culture may be the source of reverence or simply normalcy in another.

If support in the form of mental health treatment is sought, one's culture will play a significant role in the perceived stigma of mental illness as well as the acceptance or rejection of diagnosis and treatment (APA, 2013a). One client from Thailand described that in his culture it was not acceptable to show negative or painful emotions in front of others. Crying, in particular, was shunned for both men and women from his small community as it was a sign of weakness of spirit. The societal expectation to keep emotions inside, even in the face of devastation, trauma, and loss, made it very difficult for the client to agree to seek mental health counseling many years later in the United States. Even in counseling sessions, the client took pride in holding back tears and displaying how strong and brave he was for not acknowledging his more vulnerable feelings. In the case of dissociation, if one's culture views the experience as spiritual possession, mental health treatment may be rejected and mental health counselors making a diagnosis of a dissociative disorder may be perceived with mistrust, especially if the counselor is from outside of the client's cultural or religious community. Finally, a client's cultural practices, meanings, and traditions may be protective or lead the client to be more vulnerable and at risk of mental distress and disorder.

Dissociation in Other Cultures

When assessing and diagnosing dissociative symptoms and disorders, professionals must do a thorough differential diagnosis assessment. Several disorders with the *DSM-5* may include dissociative symptoms including Borderline Personality Disorder, PTSD, and Conversion Disorder (APA, 2013a); and systemic clinicians need to understand how reality testing and perceptual alterations differ between dissociative disorders and psychotic disorders. However, when working with a client from a different cultural background, mental health professionals must also consider cultural syndromes, cultural idioms of distress, and cultural explanations. These three constructs were previously referred to as Culture-Bound Syndromes (CBS) in the *DSM IV-TR* (APA, 2000). Several examples include *Ataque de Nervios, Susto, and Latah.*

Ataque de Nervios

This cultural syndrome is common in Latin, Caribbean, and Hispanic cultures. The syndrome is characterized by emotional distress, including anger, rage, grief, fear of being alone, and anxiety. Behaviorally, it may manifest through crying attacks, trembling in the body, fainting, suicidal gestures, uncontrollable screaming or shouting, and physical aggression. In some cases, dissociation in the form of depersonalization, derealization, and amnesia may occur. Etiology of this syndrome is due to problems in key familiar relationships, death of a loved one, intergenerational conflict, or abuse (APA, 2000; Rhoades, 2006a, 2006b). In some cases, the syndrome is found to have no single triggering event but to be due to the accumulation of suffering over time (APA, 2013a).

Susto

Susto, or "fright," is common to Latinos in the United States, Mexico, Central and South American countries. This syndrome is perceived as a direct result of exposure to a frightening event that causes the soul to leave the body, resulting in unhappiness, illness, and difficulty functioning in important social roles. Common symptoms include changes in appetite, too much or too little sleep, sleep disturbances, sadness, feelings of worthlessness, sensitivity in relationships, and low motivation. Somatically, one may experience body pain including muscle, head, and stomach aches, as well as coldness of the extremities. Important to note is that symptoms may appear within days of the precipitating frightening event, but sometimes years may pass between the event and the onset of the symptoms (APA, 2013a; Rhoades, 2006a, 2006b).

Latah

In Malaysia and Indonesia, Latah describes individuals who have a hypersensitivity to being startled and have an exaggerated response to being startled. Simons (1985) noted that similar disorders have been reported in Burma (Yaun), Thailand (Bah-tsche), and the

Philippines (Mali-Mali). These individuals are noted to have (a) an exaggerated response to being startled, (b) a trance-like state after being startled (dissociative state), (c) coprolalia (shouting or saying a string of obscene or forbidden words), and (d) obeying commands of others, even if the command is socially unacceptable (Hegelman, 2016).

Other Cultural Syndromes Related to Dissociation
Although not listed in the *DSM-5*, counselors should also be aware of the following syndromes that include various forms of dissociative expression. These syndromes were included in the previous version of the *DSM* (*Diagnostic and Statistical Manual of Mental Disorders*—4th ed., text rev.; *DSM-IV-TR*; APA, 2000) and may still be relevant for various cultural communities. *Zar*, found in Egypt, Iran, Ethiopia, Somalia, Sudan, North America, and other Middle Eastern countries, is characterized by spirit possession and dissociative episodes. Shouting, laughing, head banging, weeping, and social withdrawal are common. *Shin-Byung*, found in Korea, consists of anxiety, somatic complaints, dissociation, and spirit possession; and is known as the "god illness" or "divine illness" (APA, 2000; Rhoades, 2006a, p. 27). *Pibloktoq*, primarily found in Artic Eskimo communities, includes a sudden dissociative episode that includes extreme excitement and is frequently followed by a seizure and short-term coma (up to 12 hours). During the episodes, extreme and sometimes aggressive or irrational outbursts may occur. Days following the episode, individuals report withdrawal, irritation, even amnesia for the episode (APA, 2000; Rhoades, 2006a, 2006b).

Impact of Culture on the Development and Treatment of Dissociation
In addition to understanding how different cultures conceptualize symptoms, syndromes, and expression of dissociation, mental health professionals must also consider the impact of a client's culture when exploring the etiology of dissociative symptoms or disorders. Recall that dissociation is most commonly a result of exposure to complex trauma experiences (ISSTD, 2011) and/or as a response to particular attachment-based experiences with primary caregivers (Korol, 2008). Certain cultural groups may have a higher exposure to overt traumatic experiences, such as violence, discrimination experiences, or an abusive and/or neglectful home life. Some religious practices may make people more vulnerable to abuse or neglect (Goldsmith, Martin, & Smith, 2014). Additionally, racial and ethnic minorities experience a disparity of resources and access to care, which likely contributes to disproportionate rates of physical and mental illness (Shavers et al., 2012). Cultural and systemic factors that prevent access to services or simply fail to acknowledge that trauma exposures perpetuate an environment for cumulative trauma exposure without support or intervention (Goldsmith et al., 2014) are a feature common in the development of dissociative responses. Smith and Freyd (2014) explore how exposure to mistreatment, chronic stress, and fear from one's own environment (e.g., community, cultural group, and workplace) may compound the impact of trauma exposure, a construct identified as institutional betrayal (p. 577). Institutional betrayal examines how both action and inaction by the system within the culture in which one lives can be experienced as forms of betrayal. When betrayal is a component of a traumatic experience, research has shown that an individual is at greater risk of developing trauma-related symptoms, including dissociation, PTSD, depression, and anxiety (Freyd & Birrel, 2013).

Relevant DSM-5 Z Code Categories
DSM-5 Z code categories that should be considered in relation to these cultural factors include, but are not limited to, (a) Housing Problems (e.g., Homelessness, Inadequate Housing); (b) Economic Problems (e.g., Lack of Adequate Food or Safe Drinking Water,

Extreme Poverty); (c) Other Problems Related to the Social Environment (e.g., Acculturation Difficulty, Target of (Perceived) Adverse Discrimination or Persecution); (d) Problems Related to Crime or Interactions With the Legal System (e.g., Victim of Crime); and (e) Problems Related to Other Psychosocial, Personal, and Environmental Circumstances (e.g., Victims of Terrorism or Torture; Exposure to Disaster, War, or Other Hostilities; APA, 2013a, pp. 723–725).

Although cultural factors can put a person at greater exposure to experiences that might lead to trauma and dissociation, cultural factors may alternatively serve a protective role. For example, although certain religious practices may put one at greater risk of abuse, other religious practices may provide community support, meaning making, and additional restorative practices (Goldsmith et al., 2014). For example, if an individual is in a religious community that utilizes rituals that harm and abuse young, new, and/or weaker members, then the religious community may be a contributing factor to the development of dissociative symptoms. Whereas, a religious community that provides protection or at the very least a reprieve from abuse may serve as a protective factor.

A counselor was working with a female client from a conservative, charismatic Christian faith who presented with symptoms of DID. The counselor, not of the same faith tradition as the client, diagnosed the client with DID and began treatment in an individual, outpatient setting. As treatment progressed, the client wanted to share her experiences with her family, including the increased awareness of her multifaceted identity as well as her distress during challenging times. Naturally, the client's family was one of her primary resources and it was understandable that the client wanted them to be involved. Yet, when the client shared her internal experiences and relayed the nature and course of her treatment (including DID diagnosis), the family system was shaken. The family's conceptualization of her symptoms and experiences were viewed in the context of demon possession, to which their expected treatment was religious deliverance or exorcism. Further complicating the situation was the fact that the counselor was not of the same faith tradition, which resulted in mistrust from the family. As the family saw it, how could a counselor who did not understand or adhere to their belief system thoroughly consider the potential causes of the symptoms, including spiritual causes? As the counselor experienced it, the family's denial of the diagnosis increased the client's distress and interfered with what had been a positive progression in treatment. What proved to be effective in this case was the utilization of a second mental health therapist, with whom this counselor received consultation, who was both expertly skilled in dissociative disorders and was a member of the family's religion. Bringing in this third party served to bridge the gap between the counselor and the client's family, while assuring the family that the counselor was giving consideration and respect to the client's culture, in this case, her religion.

Relational Considerations

As dissociation is experienced primarily as an individual, internal process, one might mistakenly overlook the influence of and impact on relational systems in a client's world. Relational systems play a critical role in the susceptibility to, or the protection against, dissociative symptomatology.

Family of Origin
Risk Factors
Several risk factors for developing dissociative disorders are related to a client's family of origin, including early attachment experiences and abusive experiences. For the purpose of this chapter, family of origin is the family in which a person is born or adopted.

Typically, a family of origin has primary influence over a person's development and early-life experiences.

Early attachment experiences and family environment   More and more research is supporting the notion that disorganized and/or insecure attachment is a risk factor in the development of dissociative disorders, such as DID (Korol, 2008), thus making the consideration of a client's early interactions with significant people (e.g., parent, caregiver) important for counselors to explore. Specifically, experiences that interfere with the child's ability to develop the capacity for secure attachment are related to the development of dissociative reactions (Gold & Seibel, 2009). These experiences often include insufficient levels of consistency, predictability, and affection or high levels of chaos and conflict. Although these dynamics do not illustrate sadistic interactions of overt abuse, the critical component of these interpersonal features is that they often result in the child craving interpersonal relationships that offer attention, even if this attention is unhealthy, violates boundaries, and puts the child at risk for victimization (Gold, 2008).

Main, Hesse, and Seigel (2016) discussed the interactions between frightened or frightening behavior in a parent and the development of disorganized infant behavior. They described the state of a child in this circumstance as fright without a solution. The behaviors of the parent did not have to reach the level of explicit abuse; examples included the parent going into a trance-like state (e.g., a dissociative state), inexplicable signs of fear in the parent (for which the child may learn to see himself or herself as the source of the fear), play that is missing the meta signals of play (pretending to be a stalking animal), and the making of strange or scary sounds (using a "Dracula" voice). The child has to find a way in which to preserve an attachment with his or her primary caregiver, even when the caregiver presents as inconsistent, helpless, frightened, or frightening. The child has to reject the concept that something is wrong with the parent so that faith in the parent (and thus in the child's ability to survive with the parent) is upheld. Rejecting this most obvious conclusion means that the child has to go to various lengths to psychologically defend against the actions, inactions, and interactions with the parent including separating conscious awareness, disconnecting from memories, and minimizing, excusing, and rationalizing what is happening (Herman, 1992b). This might manifest in the child taking all of the blame and responsibility ("I am bad"; "I am scary"; "I am unlovable"), altering the reality of the situation (derealization), and/or escaping the situation in his or her mind (dissociation). Essentially, the child uses dissociative responses to "keep the secret" (Herman, 1992b).

Ford (2009) argues that disorganized attachment actually alters the working and autobiographical memory, manifesting as structural dissociation. The disorganized attachment of experiencing the parent, caregiver, and potentially others as always changing and unpredictable causes relationships to be a source of distress instead of a source of comfort as in secure attachment. Without a stable base with others, the child may not have an external system for regulating affect (e.g., crying in mother's arms) and instead will turn to internal, dissociative survival defenses (Ford & Courtois, 2013; Ford, 2009). Main and Hesse (1990, as cited in Bradfield, 2013) argue that disorganized attachment could be viewed as a generational transmission of effect of unresolved trauma and loss. If the parent was unable to resolve his or her own traumatic experiences, he or she will be unable to respond in the attuned and stable manner characteristic of a secure attachment. Instead, the parent will be erratic, lack empathy, and be unpredictable, leading to the disorganized responses in the infant.

Trauma can impact a family system at numerous levels and in a variety of ways. Trauma may occur at the hands of a parent, as a result of neglect, oversight, or lack of protection. Traumatic experiences may result in negative responses such as silencing, denial, lack of support, shaming, guilt, or further victimization of family members (not just for the family member who directly experienced the trauma/abuse; Ford & Saltzman, 2009). Parents who have experienced their own traumatic experiences may be significantly impaired when it is their turn to protect, support, and respond to their own children. When a traumatic experience happens to their child, parental responses may range from being hostile or anxious to withdrawal, dissociation, or shutdown (Ford & Saltzman, 2009). It is not difficult to see how these traumatic experiences and reactions may lead to the perpetuation of intergenerational trauma responses.

Traumatic experiences   Experiences of oppression involve subjugation of an individual or group by individuals, groups, or systems who hold more power and include depreciation, domination, and violation of rights (Prilleltensky, 2003). Within the dynamic of oppression is a fundamental violation of boundaries, a sense of helplessness, rejection, and inferiority (Naidoo & Rajab, 2005). Although oppression may automatically bring up thoughts of actions (or inactions) perpetuated by organized social systems such as governments or other institutions of a totalitarian nature, the most common oppressive system is the family (Sar, Middleton, & Dohary, 2013). In fact, dissociative disorders could rightly be viewed as "chronic human rights abuse syndrome of childhood" (Sar et al., 2013, p. 124), describing the child's experience in an abusive family as one in which basic rights and needs are rejected, neglected, and invalidated.

Dissociative experts agree that the most common experiences that lead to pathological or clinical degrees of dissociation include severe and ongoing childhood trauma, most notably sexual and physical abuse (Gentile, Dillon, & Gillig, 2013). One of the foremost researchers of dissociation and DID, Putnam (1997, as cited in DePrince & Freyd, 2014) described the development of dissociation as linked to early childhood abuse. The dissociative responses allow the child to survive, mentally escape, and continuously adapt to the abusive situations (Gentile et al., 2013). Situations require such creative separation of consciousness and memory when the same person who is providing safety and protection is the primary source of the danger (Herman, 1992b).

Protective Factors
Counselors treating a client with dissociative disorders will want to avoid jumping to the conclusion that the client's family system is abusive or responsible for the development and maintenance of dissociative symptoms. In fact, family members can play a critical role in protecting against the development or exacerbation of dissociative symptoms, and similarly may be an important participant in treatment. For example, a counselor treated a woman who came from a family of origin whose culture included pervasive sexual abuse, manipulation, and isolation. However, the client's primary advocate and protector was her maternal grandmother. The grandmother recognized the limits of her protection within the family's culture and taught her granddaughter everything she could about how to minimize the effects of the abuse, including how to dissociate. Although the tools her grandmother imparted allowed the client to survive her childhood, those tools would become problematic and harmful when the client was no longer in constant danger. So for some, even in the face of traumatizing experience, there may be one or more family members, friends, or others who offer support and protection. The presence of these individuals and community systems can have an immensely healing effect on a survivor (Herman, 1992a) and build resilience.

Family of Choice
Many individuals who have experienced chronic trauma in their families of origin will choose families of choice later in life. These families of choice may replicate the patterns of the families of origin or model new ways of functioning. The blueprints of early relational interactions set the stage for relationship experiences later in life. Negative relational patterns that receive no intervention, change, or resolution persist over time and are

likely to show up in family of choice relationships, such as intimate relationships with a partner or spouse (Johnson & Courtois, 2009). Despite the persistence of these relational models, for a survivor in relationships later in life, the presence of respect and autonomy in these relationships can restore self-worth and self-esteem that was unable to effectively develop in early childhood (Herman, 1992a). Relational features that may develop in family of choice relationships later in life may include communication, bonding and attachment, and intimacy (both emotional and sexual; Johnson & Courtois, 2009). Because the early models of relational and familial interactions learned from the family of origin show up in the dynamics in the family of choice, and conversely because the interactions and dynamics within the family of choice can either reinforce or serve a healing role for a survivor of traumatic family of origin environments, counselors must consider the incredible value of systemic treatment interventions when treating clients who presented with dissociative symptoms. Addressing the dysfunctional relational models the client learned early, seen now in the context in which he or she is presently functioning (family of choice), will allow for direct and immediate application of new strategies (Johnson & Courtois, 2009). Various systemic treatment models and interventions are presented later in this chapter.

Relevant DSM-5 Z Code Categories

DSM-5 Z code categories that should be examined as they relate to relational factors in dissociative disorders include, but are not limited to, (a) Problems Related to Family Upbringing (e.g., Parent–Child Relational Problem; Upbringing Away From Parents); (b) Child Maltreatment and Neglect Problems (e.g., Child Physical Abuse; Child Sexual Abuse; Child Neglect; Child Psychological Abuse); and (c) Adult Maltreatment and Neglect Problems (e.g., Spouse or Partner Violence, Physical; Spouse or Partner Violence, Sexual; Spouse or Partner Neglect; Spouse or Partner Abuse, Psychological). It should be noted that clinicians can specify if abuse or neglect is suspected or confirmed, as well as if the incident is an initial encounter or a subsequent encounter (APA, 2013a, pp. 715–722).

FAMILY SYSTEMS ASSESSMENTS

First (2014) noted that a clinician must have basic attending skills, the ability to identify and contextualize symptoms, and knowledge of the *DSM-5* to accurately differentiate disorders and diagnose appropriately. The assessment of dissociative disorders is a vital component of accurate diagnosis, treatment planning, and competent practice. Given the fact that there are those who argue that dissociative disorders are iatrogenic or created by therapists, a counselor must be able to clearly and thoroughly document the comprehensive assessment of an individual prior to providing a diagnosis of a dissociative disorder and providing treatment to that effect. Often with dissociative disorders, the client will have sketchy details to offer and initially, the client may not even be fully aware of his or her behaviors and characteristics. This lack of awareness makes a systemic approach to assessment essential. Although the focus of this text is family systems, the authors would be remiss to not include standard assessments for dissociative disorders, especially in light of the obvious gap in the literature in regard to validated and reliable systemic assessments for dissociative disorders.

The ISSTD (2004) provides a comprehensive outline for what should be included in the assessment of dissociative disorders. A comprehensive assessment will include (a) screening tests, clinical interviews with the client, and collateral supports; (b) structured clinical interviews specific to trauma and dissociation; (c) psychological testing; (d) screening for differential and comorbid conditions; (e) a full medical evaluation; and (f) a pharmacological review. The final stage of the ISSTD's (2004) protocol is critically important and that is ongoing assessment throughout treatment. As the client becomes more aware and trauma is recovered, assessment will need to occur to reevaluate the treatment plan and progress. Throughout the process, the counselors need to be attuned to internal and external safety considerations and maintain a nonjudgmental, safe way for the client to examine his or her own self.

Table 8.1 provides a list of common assessments for dissociative disorders. There are three major formats of assessments used for the dissociative disorders, and best practices recommend the use of at least one of each type of assessment for a comprehensive assessment. The three formats are structured interview, clinician-administered and other-administered interview, and self-report rating scales.

TABLE 8.1 Common Assessments for Dissociative Disorders

Measures	Authors	Current Version	What Is Assessed	Age Range
Clinician Administered				
Clinician-Administered Dissociative States Scale (CADSS)	Bremner et al. (1998)	CADSS	Amnesia, depersonalization, derealization	Adults
Clinician-Rated Severity of Nonsuicidal Self-Injury	APA (2013b)	Clinician-Rated Severity of Nonsuicidal Self-Injury	Level/severity of nonsuicidal self-injurious behavior	Not specified
Dissociative Disorders Interview Schedule (DDIS)	Ross and Browning (2016)	DDIS	Positive symptoms of schizophrenia, secondary features of DID, extrasensory experiences, substance abuse, major depression, trauma	Adults
Structured Clinical Interview for *DSM-IV* Dissociative Disorders (SCID-D-R)	Steinberg (1994)	SCID-D-R	Amnesia, depersonalization, derealization, identity confusion, identity alteration	Adults
Other-Administered Rating Scales				
Child Dissociative Checklist	Putnam (1990)	CDC—version 3	Dissociation	Ages 5–12 years

(continued)

TABLE 8.1 Common Assessments for Dissociative Disorders (continued)

Measures	Authors	Current Version	What Is Assessed	Age Range
Self-Report Rating Scales				
Adolescent Dissociative Experience Scale (ADES)	Armstrong, Putnam, and Carlson (1996)	ADES	Dissociative amnesia, absorption and imaginative involvement, depersonalization and derealization, passive influence, total	Ages 11–17 years
Children's Dissociative Experiences Scale & Posttraumatic Symptom Inventory	Stolbach (1997)	CDES-PSI	Differentiating traumatized children from nontraumatized children	7–12 years old
Children's Perceptual Alteration Scale	Evers-Szostak and Sanders (1992)	CPAS	Dissociation	8–12 years old
Dissociation Questionnaire (DIS-Q)	Vanderlinden, Van Dyck, Vandereycken, Vertommen, and Jan Verkes (1993)	DIS-Q	Identity confusion, loss of control over behavior, thoughts and emotions, amnesia, absorption	Adult
Dissociative Experiences Scale (DES-R)	Dalenberg and Carlson (2010a)	DES-II	Amnesia, depersonalization, derealization, absorption	Adult
Multidimensional Inventory of Dissociation (MID)	Dell (2006)	MID v6.0	Dissociative disorder, dissociative disorder NOS, PTSD, borderline personality disorder	Adult
Multiscale Dissociation Inventory (MDI)	Briere (2002)	MDI	Disengagement, depersonalization, derealization, emotional constriction, memory disturbance, identity dissociation	Ages 18 years and older

(continued)

TABLE 8.1 Common Assessments for Dissociative Disorders (continued)

Measures	Authors	Current Version	What Is Assessed	Age Range
Questionnaire of Experiences of Dissociation (QED)	Riley (1988)	QED	Dissociation	Adult
Severity of Dissociative Symptoms—Adult (Brief Dissociation Experiences Scale [DES-B]-Modified)	Dalenberg and Carlson (2010c)	DES-B	Dissociation	Ages 18 years and older
Severity of Dissociative Symptoms—Child Age 11–17 (Brief Dissociation Experiences Scale [DES-B]-Modified)	Dalenberg and Carlson (2010b)	DES-B	Dissociation	Ages 11–17 years
Somatoform Dissociation Questionnaire (SDQ)	Nijenhuis, Spinhoven, Van Dyck, Van Der Hart, and Vanderlinden (1996)	SDQ-20, SDQ-5	Dissociative disorder, dissociative disorder NOS, somatoform disorders	Adult
State Scale of Dissociation (SSD)	Krüger and Mace (2002)	SSD	Severity of dissociative symptoms	Adult

DID, dissociative identity disorder; NOS, not otherwise specified; PTSD, posttraumatic stress disorder.

Structured Interview

An interview with the client and other significant people in the client's life is an important component of assessment for dissociative disorders. Two of the most used structured interviews are the Dissociative Disorders Interview Schedule (DDIS; Ross & Browning, 2016) and the Structured Clinical Interview for *DSM-IV*® Dissociative Disorders (SCID-D-R; Steinberg, 1994).

Dissociative Disorders Interview Schedule (DDIS; Ross & Browning, 2016)

The DDIS (Ross, 1989; 1997; Ross & Ellason, 2005; Ross & Joshi, 1992; Ross et al., 1990) is a structured interview that assesses dissociative disorders, somatic symptom disorder, borderline personality disorder, major depressive episode, childhood physical and sexual abuse,

Schneiderian symptoms, conversion symptoms, suicide attempts, and ESP/paranormal experiences. The DDIS helps clinicians calculate a trauma score using the following factors: "the age at onset for sexual abuse . . . , the number of perpetrators of sexual abuse, the number of different acts of sexual abuse, the number of incidents of sexual abuse, the age at onset for physical abuse . . . , and the number of perpetrators of physical abuse reported" (Ross & Browning, 2016, pp. 4–5). The DDIS is a clinician-administered, structured interview that usually takes 30 to 40 minutes to complete (Ross & Browning, 2016). Ross and his associates have established reliability and concurrent validity for the DDIS and most recently updated the structured interview for the *DSM-5* (Ross & Browning, 2016). The DDIS is helpful to the clinician's understanding of the internal and external factors impacting dissociative symptomatology and the potential risks for continued harm within an individual's family system via abuse.

Structured Clinical Interview for DSM-IV® Dissociative Disorders (SCID-D-R; Steinberg, 1994)

The SCID-D-R is a semistructured interview that seeks client descriptions of experiences related to five core symptoms (amnesia, depersonalization, derealization, identity confusion, and identity disturbance). The SCID-D-R attempts to elicit a spontaneous history of trauma. A key component of this assessment is the intentional structure of the interview to avoid the use of intrusive or leading questions. In addition, the SCID-D-R provides nine sets of optional follow-up questions that allow a clinician to develop an interview that is responsive to the information the client is sharing. The SCID-D-R is time- and cost-effective. There are clear guidelines for the administration, scoring, and interpretation of the instrument. The SCID-D-R results in a *DSM-IV* diagnosis of dissociative amnesia, depersonalization disorder, dissociative disorder not otherwise specified, acute stress disorder, and dissociative trance disorder. The SCID-D-R has yet to be updated to align with the *DSM-5*; however, the criteria between versions of the *DSM*s vary only slightly; therefore, this instrument is still a valid tool for assisting with diagnosis. The SCID-D-R can be used to compare and contrast the experiences of an individual with dissociative symptoms with the experiences others in the family system have of the individual. Often, clinicians will need multiple report sources to gain a comprehensive view of the individual with dissociative symptomatology.

Other-Administered Reports

Collaborating with others involved with the client who is dissociating is critically important since the client may have limited awareness of his or her full self. When possible, counselors should seek assessment input from others who have daily contact with the client. For minors, counselors will want to consider collecting assessment data from parents, caregivers, teachers, and others. For adults, gathering assessment data from partners, close friends, siblings, and even parents may be helpful. The counselor will need to partner with the client to determine the best sources of information and will also need to ascertain client safety and reliability of the information provided by the sources.

Due to the limited availability of tools for use with collateral supports, many clinicians utilize the self-report tools that were designed for client report. For example, a counselor may ask a client's partner to complete the Multidimensional Inventory of Dissociation (MID; Dell, 2006) and compare the results between the client and the partner. Shaffer's Early Development and Home Background (EDHB) Form—Clinician (2013a) and EDHB Parent/Guardian (2013b) can also be a useful tool in assessing the early development and early and current home experiences of a child or adolescent.

Self-Report Rating Scales

Many of the scales available to assist in identifying dissociative disorders are self-report rating scales. Three of the most often used self-report tools include the Dissociative Experiences Scale-Revised (DES-R; Dalenberg & Carlson, 2010a) and the MID (Dell, 2006).

Dissociative Experiences Scale-Revised (DES-R; Dalenberg & Carlson, 2010a)

Based on the original version created by Bernstein and Putnam (1986), this self-report inventory measures a client's experiences across 28 dissociative experiences using a Likert scale from "never" to "at least once per week." The DES was modified for use in the *DSM-5*. The adult version is called the Severity of Dissociative Symptoms—Adult (Brief Dissociative Experiences Scale [DES-B]—Modified; Dalenberg & Carlson, 2010b) and child version is called the Severity of Dissociative Symptoms—Child Age 11–17 (Brief Dissociative Experiences Scale [DES-B]—Modified; Dalenberg & Carlson, 2010c). These tools provide insight into the individual's self-score; however, the clinician may need to also use the assessment informally with others in the individual's family system to ascertain how accurately the individual with dissociative symptomatology is assessing his or her own symptoms.

The Multidimensional Inventory of Dissociation (MID; Dell, 2006)

The MID is a self-report inventory that includes validity scales and produces a comprehensive profile of a client's dissociative experiences and symptoms (Brand, Lanius, Vermetten, Loewenstein, & Spiegel, 2012). The assessment is considered a diagnostic tool as the 218 items cross multiple scales measuring 14 facets of dissociation. The results provide 23 diagnostic scales of symptoms and subjective experiences (Frankel, 2009). This assessment also has an adolescent version (A-MID). Silberg and Dallon (2009) found that the dissociative symptoms in adolescents mirror those found in adults. Much like the other assessments, there may be value in utilizing this assessment with others in the individual's family system to determine the accuracy of symptom awareness and the overall occurrence of experiences and symptoms.

Other Assessments Important to Consider

Cultural Assessment

The Cultural Formulation Interview (CFI; APA 2013c) assists mental health professionals in collecting and organizing culturally relevant information from his or her clients. The cultural interview has client and informant versions. In addition, there are 12 supplementary modules, which comprise the Supplementary Modules to the Core Cultural Formulation Interview (CFI; APA, 2013d). The goal of the supplements is to help clinicians conduct more comprehensive cultural assessment. The first eight modules are similar to the CFI and just explore the content a bit deeper. The next three supplements focus on the unique needs of specific populations, such as children, adolescents, immigrants, older adults, and so forth. The final supplemental module focuses on caregivers and the impact of the nature and cultural context of caregiving. Finally, there is a section of the interview for collecting collateral information from caregivers or family members.

Early Development and Home Background (EDHB) Form

The EDHB Form is an assessment of the early development and past and current home background experiences of a child. There are two versions of this assessment: the EDHB

Form—Parent/Guardian (Shaffer, 2013b) and the EDHB Form—Clinician (Shaffer, 2013a). A parent or guardian completes the first assessment by responding to 19 items either before or during a session. The clinician then completes eight items after reviewing the parent/guardian responses, clarifying any information, and reviewing additional information, if any is available.

Suicide Assessment

Individuals with dissociative disorders have higher rates of both suicidality and self-harming behaviors than do individuals with other mental health disorders (Foote, Smolin, Neft, & Lipschitz, 2008, as cited in Brand et al., 2012), and thus it is of utmost importance for counselors to conduct thorough and frequent suicide and self-harm assessments (Gentile et al., 2013). In fact, the APA (2013c) reports that 70% of clients diagnosed with DID have attempted suicide and multiple suicide attempts are common. An important consideration, especially in the earlier stages of therapy, with suicide and harm assessments, is that each personality must be assessed independently since there may be limited awareness and integration between the different parts. In addition, individuals with dissociative disorders engage in nonsuicidal self-injurious behaviors as well. Clinicians will want to utilize the Clinician-Rated Severity of Nonsuicidal Self-Injury (APA, 2013b) to assess the level/severity of the nonsuicidal behaviors. Clinicians will need to educate family and other healthy support members about the differences between suicidal and nonsuicidal self-injurious behavior and provide tools for supporting the whole family system.

FAMILY SYSTEMS INTERVENTIONS

Family systems approaches differ based on the specific systemic theoretical perspective (e.g., structural, strategic, and narrative). However, in general, family systems therapies with survivors of complex trauma (arguably applicable to clients with dissociative disorders, as well) focus on several core areas including roles (i.e., scapegoat, rescuer), rules (i.e., don't break the silence, don't feel), myths and secrets (i.e., core "truths" about the family, hiding the truth from other family members or society), hierarchies and boundaries (i.e., parentified children, enmeshment), and communication and problem-solving styles (i.e., rigid, controlling communication and coping; Ford & Saltzman, 2009). Integrating exploration of these themes in family therapy with clients who dissociate may provide illumination and a chance for resolution and education around facets of family dynamics that are clearly impacted by traumatic experiences and environments.

Treatment of Dissociative Disorders

A primary focus of treatment of these dissociative disorders is integration. Treatment occurs in a series of stages working toward integration or associating those elements of functioning that have been disconnected (APA, 2013a; Van der Kolk, 2014).

When treating clients who dissociate, the therapist can apply a family systems approach both internally (within the client who dissociates) and externally (within the client's family/social system). There is an abundance of focus on individual treatment models, for which some experts argue comes at the expense of systemic models, such as couple and family therapy (Johnson & Courtois, 2009). Despite the predominant focus on individual therapy, couple and family therapy, especially if done concurrently and in alignment with the sequence of individual therapy, can illuminate and resolve the traumatic responses that likely originated in a relational system (Johnson & Courtois, 2009). When applying any model of treatment, individual or systemic, the client's current family environment is vital to the treatment prognosis (Peterson, 2010). Due to the systemic nature of dissociative disorders as a coping strategy, the clinician will also want to screen other family members for dissociative symptoms as well (Peterson, 2010). The goal is to establish a stable environment for ego strengthening (Peterson, 2010).

Prior to exploring specific systems interventions, counselors must have a solid foundation for the recommended treatment stages of dissociative disorders. Regardless of the specific therapeutic model that is applied, there is consensus among experts in this field that using a phase-oriented treatment approach, also known as a tripartite or triphasic approach, is important (Gingrich, 2013; Herman, 1992a; ISSTD, 2011; Ross & Halpern, 2009). These stages include (a) safety, stabilization, and symptom management/reduction; (b) processing of traumatic material/memories; and (c) integration, resolution, and rehabilitation (ISSTD, 2011). In Stage 1, attention and energy are devoted to building the therapeutic alliance, educating the client about treatment, assessing and educating about the symptoms and diagnosis, establishing safety, and managing symptoms. Discussion of coping skills, especially as they relate to client safety, is paramount; counseling will prioritize building the client's ability to establish safety from unsafe or risky urges and behaviors before treatment can fully progress. For clients with DID, this stage also involves identification of alternate self-states and works toward awareness and collaboration (e.g., "coconsciousness") between these states. Paramount to building this cooperation among self-states is helping the client (and parts of the client) consider that all parts are adaptive and have contributed to the client's survival and general functioning. Through these introductions, treatment is focused on building constructive and adaptive coping skills and behaviors among all parts. This may involve negotiation with self-states that act in unsafe or aggressive ways, reducing maladaptive coping behaviors such as substance abuse and/or eating disorders, and addressing abusive relationships the client may currently be in (ISSTD, 2011).

Only after the client has developed a significant amount of coconsciousness and internal collaboration does treatment progress into the second stage of treatment. The systemic clinician will need to not only utilize the therapeutic alliance that has been built but also continue to model consistency, acceptance, and trustworthiness. At this stage, the goal of the counselor is to be oddly reliable and consistent in role and boundaries as most clients with DID have a history of unstable, abusive, and even exploitive relationships and may test and/or question why the counselor is being supportive and nurturing. As Gingrich (2013) states, counselors need to not only become a safe person to the client, but must *remain* a safe person as well. Clients with histories of childhood and/or interpersonal traumas will have had plenty of experiences with betrayal, mistrust, and disappointment in others, and these features often appear in the context of the therapeutic relationship. Systemic clinicians must be aware of this likelihood and manage the traumatic transference and countertransference that can be evoked so that these responses do not sabotage or damage the treatment process (ISSTD, 2011).

Stage 2 focuses on working through the client's trauma memories. The purpose is not simply for the client to recall the events but to process, tolerate, and integrate the aspects of these memories. Understandably, the processing of traumatic memories that have been contained, dissociated, and unintegrated for likely years can be an immensely intense and dysregulating process. Systemic clinicians must help the client be intentional about the processing, including planning what will be processed, how it will be processed, what self-states will be active in the processing, and how safety and containment will be utilized. Careful pacing, or titration, of these sessions is critical (ISSTD, 2011).

Stage 3 focuses on supporting the client as he or she continues toward internal cohesion and integration, which typically results in an improvement of overall functioning. The focus and energy of therapy shift from processing events of the past to working on managing present-day challenges. Additionally, the client may feel able to look to the future for the first time, identifying goals, desires, and hopes for how the client wants to live life now

(ISSTD, 2011). In this stage, the client may also experience a fair degree of loss as he or she learns to cope with life without the long-time practice of dissociating or having another part of self to take over. This can be quite challenging when faced with new issues or obstacles. With integration, the client may feel as if the previously distinct parts of self are gone; in reality, all parts of self remain, but are experienced as one "self" that has access to all thoughts, emotions, memories, and so on. This shift can bring about feelings of loneliness as the client starts to go through life without internal "others" with whom to interact (Gingrich, 2013). Clients may also report fatigue and being overwhelmed by having to manage life alone.

The ISSTD (2011) acknowledges that the primary modality for the treatment of DID is typically long-term individual, outpatient therapy with varying degrees of frequency and duration. During Stage 2, some clients may require intensive, short-term inpatient support to recover and stabilize during trauma processing.

Types of treatment orientations and interventions vary. The psychodynamic orientation is the most commonly recommended approach, but integration from other orientations and interventions is quite common. For example, cognitive behavioral therapy and hypnosis are frequently used for skill building, relaxation, calming, and containment. Specialized interventions can be effective in supplementing this work, including Eye Movement Desensitization and Reprocessing (EMDR; ISSTD, 2011; Paulsen, 2009; Shapiro, 1989); Dialectical Behavior Therapy (DBT; ISSTD, 2011; Linehan, 1983), sensorimotor therapy (ISSTD, 2011; Ogden & Fisher, 2015), and couple and family therapies (ISSTD, 2011; MacIntosh, 2013; Sweezy & Ziskind, 2013). The remainder of this section is devoted to exploring systemic therapeutic model approaches, such as inclusion of family in therapy, Internal Family Systems (IFS; Schwartz, 1995), Contextual Therapy, and Developmental Couple Counseling.

In the various family systems interventions presented in this section, readers should keep in mind the phase-oriented foundation of therapy and apply specific interventions within this framework. Although some models may propose additional stages beyond the core three identified by ISSTD (2011), the concept of working from one stage to the next only when ready, and returning to previous stages as necessary, is core to the treatment of dissociative disorders.

Inclusion of Family in Therapy

Careful consideration must be practiced when utilizing family systems therapy for a client with DID or other dissociative disorders. As the research has shown, a very high percentage of individuals with DID have experienced childhood trauma such as physical or sexual abuse (Gentile et al., 2013). Additionally, there is a growing body of research that demonstrates that ongoing incest, even into and throughout adulthood, is more common than many could have suspected (Middleton, 2013). Thus, even if the counselor is treating an adult individual with DID, the counselor cannot assume that the client is out of the abusive system. Likewise, because certain patterns of abuse may occur in the family of choice as well, the counselor must carefully assess including this family into the process. In some cases, bringing in, or even suggesting to bring in, family members to treatment may at the least be unproductive and at the worst be traumatizing (Pais, 2009).

Before engaging in any family therapy, the counselor must be able to confirm thorough assessment of and discussion with the client that the family therapy could be conducted with safe, nonabusive family members. The counselor will need to examine how the client will cope with the session and what factors might potentially be retraumatizing (Pais, 2009). The therapeutic relationship, and usually by association, the physical space of the therapy office are seen by the client as a safe space. Discussion between the counselor and the client should include how to best maintain the safety and security of the relationship and space when family members join. Well-defined boundaries between all participants are critical and can allow for a more productive session for all (Pais, 2009). For example, a counselor worked with an adult female with DID who was experiencing conflict with a few members of her family of choice. A family member requested that they be allowed to come into a session to share the recent challenges with the systemic clinician and the client agreed to this request. For weeks prior to this session taking place, sessions focused on helping the client feel in control; reviewing coping strategies that could be used before, during, and after session; and what topics would be helpful or concerning for the client. In addition, the systemic clinician discussed where the client wanted people to sit in the office. This seemingly minor factor gave the client a sense of consistency and reliability. No matter what was going to occur, the client could have a reasonable expectation that the counselor (and the office) would remain the same. In another case, the counselor made arrangements to meet with the family in a colleague's office to "protect" the safe space of the counselor's office. The systemic clinician and client met in the colleague's office a couple of times prior to the family session to prepare for the family session.

If the systemic clinician determines that the client is and will remain safe, conducting family therapy sessions can be quite helpful. Family members may be able to offer observations about the client's symptoms, challenges, behaviors, and therapeutic progress in a way that the client alone cannot. Family members can assist in mapping the internal system; family members may interact with parts of self while the client remains unaware. Bringing this information into awareness may feel safer and easier to regulate in the safety of the therapy office instead of at home (Pais, 2009).

If the family members are unaware or not educated about dissociation and the client's dissociative disorder, the therapist may be able to be an educator and advocate on the client's behalf. Not only will the counselor be able to provide current, objective information about dissociative disorders, he or she will also be able to offer suggestions on how family members can support and empower themselves along with the client (Pais, 2009). Useful topics to discuss include recognizing dissociation and dissociative shifts in the client, understanding triggers for dissociation to occur, recognizing and practicing helpful communication and interaction patterns (especially in conflict and high stress), knowing how to participate in the client's affect regulation, and valuing the use of boundaries for the client and all family members. Additionally, the involvement of family members in the client's treatment, even if not in the therapy office, can be extremely beneficial to the client and the counselor. Family members can participate in safety plans, being the immediate source of support and intervention if the client becomes suicidal, has urges to self-harm, or engages in destructive behaviors (e.g., substance abuse, promiscuity, spending sprees). The counselor can provide education and resources to support the family members in being on the "frontline."

Critical to family therapy is acknowledging that the material explored may evoke negative reactions and traumatic memories in family members, not just in the client. Memories or material that the client is working through may be difficult for family members to process or acknowledge. Some family members may have their own amnesia related to events. If the strengths, coping skills, and positive interactions of the family can be highlighted, these sessions may prove to be quite useful. However, if proper assessment of such strengths and coping skills is not completed by the systemic clinician prior to processing the material, the session may become counterproductive for all (Pais, 2009).

When a family is sufficiently stable and operates in a secure familial environment (physical, emotional, and psychological), family members might be immensely effective in helping the client address traumatic material while gently confronting the client's distorted beliefs and feelings of shame (Pais, 2009). Since families in which trauma and abuse occur often experience system-wide negative effects of trauma, finding stability and security may be difficult to achieve and family systems therapy interventions can help (Ford & Saltzman, 2009). Again, however, family therapy with an abusive family system may perpetuate continued distorted, shaming messages, even if these are not seen in session by the clinician.

Therefore, with sufficient assessment of safety and healthy relationships, family therapy can be a valuable approach for a client with a dissociative disorder, such as DID. This systems-focused approach can communicate to the client that although he or she likely once felt alone, unlovable and isolated, there is an opportunity for different interpersonal and relational experiences now. In fact, after a session with a client's partner, the client returned and, with an amazed expression on her face, exclaimed that even after she had worked through a conflict with her partner, he was still committed to the relationship. The client was able to engage in and tolerate a new experience of voicing her feelings, working through the conflict with someone she cared about deeply, and seeing the relationship continue in a consistent and healthy manner. This type of restorative healing could not have been done as effectively simply in conversation between the client and the counselor alone.

Internal Family Systems

Originally developed by Schwartz (1995), the IFS model sought to combine existing models of systems theory with multiplicity of the mind (Schwartz, 1995). Systemic features of this theory originate from family therapies, such as the structural, strategic, Bowenian, and narrative models (Pais, 2009). From the multiplicity of the mind paradigm, Schwartz argued that the mind is made up of "parts" instead of existing as one single entity. Each part is not simply a fragmented emotional state, but a distinct part of the mind that has a unique role, set of beliefs, mode of interacting, and characteristic moods. Furthermore, Schwartz argued that this multiplicity is normal, as demonstrated in common language such as "a part of me feels pulled to do this but another part is really hesitant" (Engler, 2013). Under healthy developmental conditions, these parts develop and engage in an interactional system. However, under highly stressful experiences such as abuse or trauma, the parts may divert from their productive roles into extreme or rigid roles (Pais, 2009). When safety and stability are regained, parts return to the original valuable roles (Pais, 2009). However, in cases of ongoing childhood abuse or other chronic traumatic experiences, the return to safety and valuable roles may not be experienced and internal roles may remain rigid and polarized. The IFS model considers the fact that external family and cultural interactions can influence internal polarizations, whereas the internal family dynamics conversely impact other relationships in the person's life (Pais, 2009).

IFS organizes parts of self into three categories with respective functions: the managers, the exiles, and the firefighters. The managers are protective and focus on task completion, managing everyday situations, and mitigating trouble before it occurs (Pais, 2009). The managers are oriented to external conditions and may get caught up in perfectionism, obsessive worry, and excessive caretaking (Engler, 2013). The goal of these parts is to avoid feelings of hurt and rejection (Pais, 2009), yet in the course of this pursuit they ultimately exile parts that hold pain, injury, and vulnerability. Thus, the second group of parts are known as the *exiles*. These parts are young parts who have and are the parts that have experienced trauma, abuse, and chaos. As the title implies, these exile parts are isolated from the rest of the internal systems. Congruent with the concept of protection, this isolation of the *exiles* keeps the pain and fear held by these parts out of the awareness of the self and the other parts (Engler, 2013; Pais, 2009). When the exiles become activated, resulting in emotional "takeover" of the individual, the third group, the *firefighters* responds (Engler, 2013). The firefighters' primary goal is to, by whatever means possible, put an end to this emotional response. In a contradictory manner, however, these parts put out the emotional fire but start distracting "fires" in the form of impulsive actions (Pais, 2009), such as substance abuse, eating disorders, sexual promiscuity, self-harm, and suicidal behaviors (Engler, 2013). The stimulation from these impulsive behaviors distracts, or separates, parts and the self from vulnerable feelings brought out by the exiles (Pais, 2009).

Beyond these three core parts, IFS argues that there is a core "self," which has qualities of leadership, confidence, compassion, and calmness (Engler, 2013; Pais, 2009). The managers, exiles, and firefighters all work to protect the self from the dangers of trauma. The self is understood as one's "natural state of wholeness and completeness" (Engler, 2013, p. xx). The three core parts of IFS frequently blend with the self. When the self is secure (Pais, 2009), rarely is complete differentiation ever achieved (Engler, 2013). When parts are working collaboratively, the self is involved.

When applying IFS to clients with dissociative disorder, namely DID, the counselor may notice that the internal family members are more separated and often even inaccessible to one another than when using the IFS model with nonclients who dissociate (Twombly, 2013). Compared to a nondissociative internal family, the client who dissociates will have a family characterized by isolation, disconnection, and polarization. There are greater protective efforts exerted. Although the counselor knows that integration, or at least internal collaboration, is the goal of treatment, the client may view this goal initially as threatening since the dissociative system is what the client knows for survival (Pais, 2009).

Similarly, to the standard triphasic model of trauma treatment, the goal of IFS is to facilitate cohesiveness and positive cooperation between the client and all parts of the client's internal system (Haddock, 2001, as cited in Pais, 2009). IFS is organized in four distinct steps that are included in the three treatment phases. These steps include (a) negotiating with manager parts to gain access to the self or self-energy (Phase 1); (b) witnessing the experiences of the exile part(s) (Phase 2); (c) unburdening the exile part(s) from the painful, extreme emotions (Phase 2); and (d) developing positive qualities to replace the previous burdens (Phase 3). Within each step of IFS, the clinician works to access the internal parts of self (Twombly, 2013). This "access" to the internal family system can be achieved through "insight" or "direct access" (Pais, 2009, p. 80). Access through insight invites the client to identify and describe his or her experience of the internal self-states and world, reporting this back to the counselor (Pais, 2009). This may sound like the client stating "There is a part over to the side that is swearing at you (counselor) and glaring." This report is actually quite common in the beginning of therapy as protector parts may view the systemic clinician as trying to upset the system that has aided in survival for so long (Pais, 2009). Access through insight can be quite helpful to the client in between sessions as he or she can work with internal parts simply through thinking, observing, and inner dialogue. When utilizing direct access, the counselor speaks directly to the internal self-states and/or listens as self-states talk openly to one another (Pais, 2009). This type of access also allows for internal states to develop relationships with the clinician, which Schwarz (1995) argues may allow parts to express themselves thoroughly to the counselor, provide a better view of the internal system, and allow the counselor to intervene more directly with internal states. In a session, this might sound like the counselor saying "I'd like to ask to speak to the part or parts of you that could share more about the . . ." In many cases, both types of access are utilized (Pais, 2009) often throughout the same session. For example, if the systemic clinician hears an insight or observation directly from one part, he or she may then ask if that part would be willing to share that insight internally with other parts, either during the session or throughout the week. This combination encourages collaboration between internal parts and the systemic clinician, and even more importantly increased communication and ultimately compassion and productive interaction within the internal family system.

The first step in IFS is to access and negotiate with manager parts (Twombly, 2013). As noted previously, these parts may view the counselor as an adversary since the counselor is apparently trying to disrupt the rigidity of the functioning of the various parts. Showing respect to the managers can go a long way in working toward getting all parts to work together. Failure to do so may initiate a chain reaction in which the exile part(s) are activated, subsequently evoking the reactions of the firefighters, which perpetuates further disconnections (Pais, 2009). In this first step, parts are encouraged to develop and show compassion for each other; the goal is not to process any trauma materials, which is in alignment with the ISSTD (2011) guidelines (Twombly, 2013). Specific interventions utilized in this stage include Safe Space Imagery and Containers. Using these imagery techniques, these interventions focus on building the coping skills that will prepare the parts and self for the next step in treatment, processing the dissociated material. Providing education to the client, in the language of IFS, can help the client conceptualize and map the internal system in a nonjudgmental way, which reduces the resistance and denial that may occur (Pais, 2009).

The second step in the IFS model mirrors the second stage of the ISSTD (2011) guidelines, and includes working through the traumatic material. The coping skills from the first stage are enacted and the client participates in selecting a memory (partial or full) to have parts witness. This witnessing is done by parts who were not directly involved in the event itself or who have the capacity to handle the burden of the event. This witnessing unburdens the exile part(s) and the traumatic memory is shared within the system. Starting with very small amounts of a particular event (e.g., 2 seconds of the material) can empower the client, including parts of the client, to feel stability and control (Twombly, 2013). A clinician working with a client may want to use the analogy of a film and encourage the client to review the memory in brief clips.

In the third stage of IFS with a client who dissociates, the traumatic material has been processed and the client's parts are unburdened from the traumatic material. Integration of the parts may occur and the client may experience more access and awareness of self-leadership. Focus often shifts to other areas of life, such as work or relationship performance and satisfaction. To navigate this shift, the client may benefit from engaging in supplemental couple or group therapy (Twombly, 2013).

Contextual Treatment

Contextual treatment is based on the clinical and empirical findings that treatment of clients with prolonged childhood abuse, including a client who dissociates, needs to not simply focus on processing the traumatic memories and experiences but also must address the myriad contextual factors present in the family environment of trauma survivors (Gold, 2009). Although this is a model of individual therapy, the therapy prioritizes the impact of the individual's early systemic environment, such as family and society. This model is based on the notion that resolving the traumatic memories with trauma-informed interventions simply will not be enough to address the developmental and relational deficits born out of the deficient family of origin system. Contextual treatment considers the impact of a traumatic experience for a client who dissociates and focuses on the impact of the environment of the family of origin, influences of society, and other developmental factors on the client's adaptive responses (or lack thereof) to traumatic experiences (Gold, 2008). This model believes that the traumatic incident(s) alone is not all that disrupts an individual's ability to adapt and function; in fact, the client's family environment may be the critical contributing factor to the occurrence of abusive or traumatic experiences in the first place (Gold, 2008).

Treatment based on this contextual model views the deficits suffered by the client as an absence of skills and attainments themselves (e.g., affect regulation, secure attachment) and not simply the failure to perform or utilize these skills. Thus, although the traditional three-stage model historically views Stages 1 and 3 as components of treatment in which the client strengthens or reestablishes critical capacities injured in the traumatic exposure, contextual therapy argues that clients of prolonged childhood abuse, such as a client who dissociates, never develop these capacities in the first place (Gold, 2009). Thus, treatment must acknowledge the "developmental gaps" and address these gaps as a central part of treatment (Gold, 2008).

Contextual treatment is focused on three main areas including interpersonal, practical, and conceptual areas (Gold, 2009). In the interpersonal area, counselors must remain aware that the client has most likely not experienced an early secure attachment that would provide the capacity for forming healthy, productive relationships with others, including the clinician. These clients have experienced relationships with others that have been inconsistent, chaotic, and unpredictable at the least, and harmful, exploitative, and sadistic at the worst. The systemic clinician must help the client learn, maybe for the first time, how to relate interpersonally with others and how to regulate "attachment-related behaviors" that play out within the therapeutic relationship (Gold, 2009, p. 233).

In the practical area of contextual therapy, the systemic clinician assesses the wide array of skills and/or capacities that may be lacking or insufficiently developed and prioritizes these as treatment goals (Gold, 2009). One of the most important goals is to help the client build an ability to self-soothe, which the client can use to relieve the perpetual state of arousal he or she will likely experience. Learning adaptive ways to self-soothe provides effective alternatives to the common impulsive, short-term strategies for relief that are commonly used, such as substance abuse, self-harm, and other compulsive behaviors. If the client can learn and utilize effective self-soothing strategies as early in treatment as possible (Stage 1), he or she will likely not need to turn to the harmful strategies as often and may also decrease other symptoms, such as flashbacks, depression, and so forth (Gold, 2009).

The practical area of contextual treatment also addresses the client's dissociation, understanding that although the dissociative response may have been initially adaptive, the response may now interfere with the client's ability to fully benefit from treatment (Gold, 2009). The client's ability to remain attentive to the present moment is most often achieved only after the client has learned the self-soothing, regulation skills as dissociation understandably occurs as a response to elevated levels of distress. After these two areas are addressed (i.e., self-soothing and dissociation), attention is shifted to the client's cognitive skills. Therapy focuses on teaching the client how to use evidence-based reasoning, judgment, and decision making. When the client has sufficiently learned how to self-soothe, stay grounded in the present, and utilize cognitive processing skills, therapy proceeds to processing traumatic memories and experiences (Gold, 2009). Although the client will be more successful with trauma resolution with the foundational cognitive skills, he or she will likely face continued struggles in building a healthy adult life, posttrauma. These challenges are based on the combination of a lack of skills as well as the pervasive, internalized messages from life experiences that the client does not deserve a rewarding existence. Thus, the practical area of treatment continues to build the skills and apply the cognitive processes that may help the client surmount these challenges (Gold, 2009).

Finally, during the conceptual area of contextual treatment, the counselor helps the client utilize the skills from the previous treatment areas to explore the process of working through something to a conclusion, based on the client's thinking, not the counselor's (Gold, 2009). Using a Socratic method, the counselor guides (not leads) the client through his or her own cognitive processing about a matter so that the client can identify and understand his or her own interpretations. Examples of topics may be the motives behind specific behaviors or the client's beliefs. In this stage of treatment, the counselor must differentiate what types of scenarios the client can be encouraged to conceptualize on his or her own (e.g., feelings, values, beliefs) and what scenarios may require explicit tutorials because the client has never had previous exposure (e.g., how to create a time management system for his or her work; Gold, 2009).

Couples Therapy

The literature on couples therapy related to dissociative disorders is rare. Historically, therapy for a couple in which at least one partner is dissociative has been viewed as secondary to the individual treatment of the partner who dissociates. The issues and needs of the couple as a system have been neglected, resulting in a scarcity of literature on this topic (MacIntosh, 2013). Unfortunately, the lack of research on couples therapy for couples in which at least one partner dissociates does not accurately mirror the lack of challenges for these couples or the desire that the partners have to participate in a loving and intimate relationship. Furthermore, the experience of a supportive, close relationship could be significantly healing for the trauma survivor (MacIntosh & Johnson, 2008). One of the earliest experts on dissociation, Putnam (1989), identified that individuals with DID frequently found romantic partners who also experienced mental illness. Even if the partner does not come into the relationship with his or her own psychopathology, being in a relationship with a survivor of trauma, such as in DID, often results in elements of vicarious trauma as the partner is exposed to the horrors of the partner's traumatic past (and sometimes present). The impact of vicarious trauma for these partners manifests through a shift in beliefs about safety, trust, existential beliefs, and experiences of intimacy (MacIntosh, 2013). Features such as isolation, anger, communication issues, and dissatisfaction are common in partners of childhood sexual abuse survivors (Reid, Wampler, & Taylor, 1996, as cited in MacIntosh, 2013).

Developmental Couples Therapy for Complex Trauma

Only recently have couples therapy models been modified to fit the needs of couples with childhood trauma histories (Johnson & Courtois, 2009; MacIntosh & Johnson, 2008) with adaptation for dissociative couples even more in its infancy (MacIntosh, 2013). These studies have found that couple counseling models, such as Emotion-Focused Therapy, require modifications in order to be effective with couples with a partner(s) with complex trauma and/or dissociative responses (Johnson & Courtois, 2009). These modifications are necessary to manage affect dysregulation, difficulties in the ability to engage in perspective taking, and engaging fully in other therapeutic tasks (MacIntosh, 2016; MacIntosh, & Johnson, 2008). Themes proposed for consideration with these couples include communication skills, resisting sabotage of the treatment, maintaining a here-and-now focus, conflict management, mitigating conflicting needs, providing trauma-focused education, addressing the needs of child self-states, managing impatience with the therapy, working with integration, dealing with sexual intimacy, and maintaining a shared focus on both partners, not just the partner with DID (MacIntosh, 2013).

Developmental Couples Therapy for Complex Trauma is one such model that has integrated modifications of empirically established couples therapy models, such as Emotion-Focused Therapy, into treatment for couples who have a partner or partners with a history of complex trauma and dissociation (MacIntosh, 2016). This model prioritizes developing capacities within each member of the couple and healing the trauma within the relational context. The therapy proposes four stages. The first stage of the model, establishing context, focuses on building safety and alliance within the therapeutic relationship and providing psychoeducation about trauma, attachment, and how these are reenacted in current relationships. The second stage of the model, capacity building in the attachment context, focuses on building mentalization and emotional regulation skills. Stage 3, attachment-focused dyadic processing, includes an exploration of the impact of past relationships on current interpersonal dynamics. During this stage, partners disclose and process their traumatic experiences within the context of the couple counseling. Finally, Stage 4 of the developmental couples therapy for complex trauma is consolidation, which focuses on mutual regulation and integrating the newly built capacities for emotion regulation, bonding, and mentalizing. Macintosh (2016) proposed that as a result of working through these four stages of a modified couples therapy model, the couple will be able to participate effectively in other models of couples therapy.

Internal Family Systems Couples Therapy

Just as Schwartz's IFS model can be applied to individual therapy, it can also be applied in the context of couple counseling (Herbine-Blank, 2013). However, although Herbine-Blank

(2013) has presented this model for couples who are not identified as including a partner or partner with a dissociative disorder, the IFS couple model may prove to be an effective option and warrants continued exploration. In IFS Couples Therapy, each partner is educated about the IFS principles of the multiplicity of the mind, the notion that all individuals have parts of the mind that serve to manage, protect, and hold vulnerable emotions. Clients are invited to pause their focus on their outward experiences with their partner and first turn inward to better understand, differentiate from, and convey compassion to the parts of himself or herself that may be influencing emotional and relational reactions (Herbine-Blank, 2013). Differentiation is viewed to be one of the primary goals of therapy in this model, arguing if one can find internal differentiation between self and parts, one will be more able to find differentiation (as opposed to avoidance or enmeshment) with one's partner (Herbine-Blank, 2013). Thus, in seeking to achieve the goal of improving healthy dynamics within the "external" couple, the IFS Couples Therapy model prioritizes exploration of the internal family first. The work with internal parts focuses on the same external systemic facets addressed in therapy, such as attachment, roles, and developing relationships among members (Herbine-Blank, 2013). In addition, internal work seeks to access vulnerable parts of each client to unburden the pain from traumas that the parts carry. The internal work seeks to improve affect regulation, communication, management and resolution of shame, and addressing needs, all of which are then paralleled in the external relationship. IFS Couples Therapy navigates a delicate balance between guiding each client in the partnership with individual, internal work while then returning to the external dynamics in the couple's relationship with one another. This often occurs by asking one partner to "look/check/ask inside," while the counselor helps the other client stay connected to the here and now. Through this vacillation, clients learn to interact with and relate to his or her partner in new patterns (Herbine-Blank, 2013). In a couple with a partner who dissociates, this perspective of parts of self may feel quite familiar as the individual who dissociates and operates on a daily basis from this type of experience. Normalizing this experience of parts of self for both partners may offer a bridge or a shared framework for accepting, valuing, and attending to each partner's internal world and working to understand how internal parts may impact and even strengthen the relationship.

ETHICAL AND LEGAL IMPLICATIONS

Working with clients who have dissociative disorders presents some unique and challenging ethical considerations for clinicians. First and foremost, clinicians must "facilitate growth and development . . . that fosters the interest and welfare of the clients and promote formation of healthy relationships" (American Counseling Association [ACA], 2014, Introduction). This may mean the clinician must slow down the process of treatment until the client is fully ready or in a safe situation to begin trauma processing. As Peterson (2010) noted, there is no reason to pull trauma memories to the surface; these memories will surface when the client is ready to become aware of the traumatic experiences. Forcing a memory to the surface can cause significant harm through retraumatization and potential self-harm behaviors. The systemic clinician is ultimately responsible for assessing the safety of the client and the client's parts.

A systemic clinician working with a client who dissociates is a lot like conducting group or family counseling with an individual, at least in the initial stages of treatment. As such, the systemic clinician must review informed consent with each part (American Association for Marriage and Family Therapy [AAMFT], 2015, Standard 1.2; ACA, 2014, Section A.2.a), define the counseling relationship and identify who the client is (ACA, 2014, Section A.8), engage in relationships beneficial to the client (AAMFT, 2015, Standard 1.9), and be respective of the varying developmental and cultural needs of each part (ACA, 2014, Section A.2.c). Much like AAMFT's requirement that clients be informed of the treatment process (2015, Standard 1.2), ACA (2014, Section A.2.b) notes that clinicians will need to educate the client about the therapeutic process, including the "purposes, goals, techniques, procedures, limitations, potential risks, and benefits" (p. 4). When working with individuals who dissociate, systemic clinicians will want to explain the goal of integration and the lasting impact awareness can have on the individual and the family systems within which the client functions. When developing the treatment plan, counselors must consider the client's age, cognitive ability, as well as social and sexual maturity as these developmental areas tend to be significantly impacted by trauma (ACA, 2014, Section A.1.c., Peterson, 2010). Ultimately, systemic clinicians need to avoid harming the client, which may occur with premature disclosure of other parts or traumatic memories (AAMFT, 2015, Standard 9.7; ACA, 2014, Section A.4). Maybe more than with any other diagnosis, systemic clinicians must follow the client's lead and pace the process accordingly.

The client's culture also plays a significant role in treatment; thus, systemic clinicians must be culturally sensitive and multiculturally competent (AAMFT, 2015, Aspirational Core Values 1 and 4, 1.1; ACA, 2014; Association for Multicultural Counseling and Development [AMCD], 2015). Multicultural competency requires that a clinician have awareness, knowledge, and skills specific to incorporating the client's cultural identity into the crosscultural therapeutic relationship (ACA, 2014; AMCD, 2015). Systemic clinicians need to be skillful in how to raise the topic of race, ethnicity, and cultural differences within the counseling relationship. Systemic clinicians need to be aware that each part of the client may have differing values and cultural beliefs; therefore, as each part emerges in the therapeutic relations, the counselor must take time to understand the culture of each part.

Clinicians must consider the laws within the jurisdiction in which the counselor practices (AAMFT, 2015, Standard 3.2; ACA, 2014, Section C.1). For example, clients who dissociate typically come from and may still be in abusive and exploitative situations. Systemic clinicians need to clearly understand the duty to protect in his or her state. This is even more important in the case of minors or adults who are in protected classes (disability, age, immigrant, and so forth).

Working with clients who dissociate requires a significant amount of training and supervision. Clinicians must practice within the boundaries of their competence (AAMFT, 2015, Standard 3.10; ACA, 2014, Section C.2.a) and should work only in this specialty area after completing training and receiving supervision (AAMFT, 2015; ACA, 2014, Section C.2.b). In addition, counselors must seek ongoing training to stay current and knowledgeable of evidence-based practices specific to working with this population (AAMFT, 2015, Standard 3.1; ACA, 2014, Section C.2.f).

One area that is important in all therapeutic relationships, but for which there is extreme importance when working with clients who dissociate, is boundaries (AAMFT, 2015, Standard 1.3; ACA, 2014, Section A.6). Clients who dissociate have typically experienced insecure attachments and have little to no emotional regulation or interpersonal effectiveness. Systemic clinicians working with this population must have a clear set of treatment guidelines that are reviewed throughout the counseling relationship. Although clients and the parts of the client may resist the clear boundaries initially, ultimately the safety within these boundaries will create the safe space necessary for healing to occur.

CASE CONCEPTUALIZATION

In this section, readers are offered a clinical snapshot of a client with a dissociative disorder. The case conceptualization of "Sandy" describes how a client with a dissociative disorder may present in treatment and how a mental health professional can effectively apply a systemic approach to assessment, diagnosis, and treatment.

Presenting Concerns

Sandy is a 43-year-old, Caucasian female. She has a bachelor's degree in human services and is currently employed at a local rehabilitation center that specializes in stroke and heart cases. She served 8 years in the military and utilized her educational benefits to earn a degree while serving. Sandy comes to counseling to figure out what is "wrong" with her. During her first session, she appears casually dressed and has a personable presentation. She engages the counselor easily and responds to the prompts with very factual information. Sandy reports that Ron, her husband, "has had it with her." According to Sandy, Ron has threatened to take their two children, Candice who is 14 years old and Thomas who is 8 years old, and live with his parents who live out of state. Sandy reports that Ron is frustrated because Sandy loses things and is moody. She notes that at times Ron is very nice to her and then minutes later he is upset with her and she has no idea why.

One concern Sandy notes in the intake is that she is worried about losing her job. She feels like she can never perform at the level expected by her boss. Sandy reports feeling as if she is an imposter and that "it is just a matter of time before" she is found out. However, she notes that when she is at work she feels like someone else is in control of her. She describes observing herself at work and being amazed at how well she can respond to situations that arise. Sandy notes "it's almost as if I am watching myself work and it's not really me." She credits this ability to look like she knows what she is doing to her training from the military.

In the second session, Sandy brings Ron to session. Sandy seems small in session and presents a bit disheveled and scattered in her thoughts. Ron presents as supportive and concerned. He is frustrated with his wife's absentmindedness. He shares how she will go to the store and get lost and come home hours later with no idea where she has been. Ron does not understand how Sandy can be so organized and efficient at work and so disorganized in her personal life. He reports she often loses things like her keys and forgets to go to appointments for herself and the children. Ron clearly loves his wife and is at a loss for how to best support her. He depends on her to "run their home and manage the children." He regrets that she has to work to help support the family. Sandy says little in the session and appears to be distracted and not present through most of the session.

In her third session, the counselor meets with Sandy alone and notices that Sandy comes in dressed very professionally and sits with a near-perfect posture. Sandy explains that she does not believe counseling is necessary; however, "Sandy's husband is making us come." When asked about the use of the world "us," Sandy appears confused and asks how long she has been in session. She clearly looks disoriented but quickly recovers and asks the counselor to repeat the question again please. The counselor recaps what has occurred in the session without clinical terms and simply reflects in descriptive language what has been observed. Sandy admits she often loses time and relies on Ron and her children to "fill in the blanks." The counselor reflects that Sandy depends on her family system and recommends that, at least initially, having Ron participate in sessions may be beneficial to Sandy's progress and in helping Sandy better understand what she is experiencing.

Ron attends the next three sessions with Sandy. During Sandy's sixth session, Sandy discussed her feelings of guilt for her recent marital discord and knows she is responsible for keeping her marriage together. She grew up in a fundamental Christian church and although she no longer attends, she sees herself as a sinner for her lack of attendance and for not bringing her children to church as well. At this point, Ron steps out of session to use the restroom. As Sandy discusses her guilt, the counselor notices a switch and Sandy becomes playful and starts to ask the counselor questions about what the counselor likes and what the items around the office are. The counselor engages this playful side and notices that Sandy's language has become almost childlike. As the counselor engages the playful Sandy, Sandy shares that her name is Missy and "Mommy will get mad that I am here." At this point, Ron reenters the room, and Sandy looks confused and says, "I'm sorry, what were we talking about?"

Concurrent Problems

Her most recent counseling ended abruptly when her counselor became ill and had to take an extended leave of absence. Sandy reports feeling abandoned and notes that they were doing good work. She then reports in a very matter-of-fact manner that she had recalled being sexually abused by several male cousins during her childhood and as an adolescent she tried to disclose the abuse to her mother who told her the abuse was in her head and had not happened. Sandy reported feeling very confused by what her mother said and has only brief glimpses of what she thought had happened when she was around her male cousins. She shares that there were times when she felt like she was in a fog and just going through the motions as a child and adolescent. She has no consistent memories until she joined the military, where she reported feeling safe because she knew what to expect. The last vague memory she has was just a few years ago at a wedding and all she remembers is one of her male cousins insisted she follow him to the back of the church and then her memory goes blank. She remembers nothing until Ron found her later and was angry with her for being gone so long from the reception.

Background History and Stressors

In the initial intake, Sandy notes an intermittent history of counseling since she was an adolescent. She reports that she has a history of cutting as an adolescent and had a counselor she really liked but her mom "got jealous" of the counselor and made her stop going.

Sandy's parents were married for 40 years prior to her father's sudden death of a heart attack 5 years ago. She has had no contact since her father's death with her family of origin, which includes two older brothers and one younger sister, as well as a large extended family. Sandy is unable to explain the lack of contact with her family of origin and shuts down when asked about this. Ron indicates that Sandy's personality and behaviors change significantly around her family of origin. He describes her as "almost childlike."

Strengths

Sandy is proud of her education. In fact, she was the first in her family to finish a college degree. She hopes to pursue a graduate degree in counseling as soon as she can afford the tuition. She also appears to have a supportive husband who wants to learn more and know how to better help her. Sandy wants to learn more about herself and why she "frustrates Ron so." By the seventh session, she seems invested in learning more about herself and is starting to realize there may be more to her history and current self than she fully understands. Sandy indicates she wants to pick up where she left off with her last counselor and really "get to the bottom of this."

DSM-5 Impressions and Implications

The counselor reviews the *DSM-5* (APA, 2013a) and notes that across six sessions she has observed Sandy switch to a potentially alternate part at least three times (identity alteration) and has observed a manager part and an exile part. Sandy has reported several losses of time (amnesia), functioning in a fog (derealization), and observing herself as if she was apart from herself (depersonalization). Ron has reported times that may be reflective of amnesia, depersonalization, derealization, identity confusion, and identity alteration as well, though he is not aware of the specific terms yet. The primary symptom that stands out to the counselor is Criterion A (APA, 2103a), which describes the presence of two or more specific personality states. Sandy has demonstrated having multiple discrete self-states which are relatively distinct from one another or at least very unaware of one another. She and her husband have reported incidents of amnesia that appear to exceed normal forgetting. Although her symptoms are not causing significant distress at the moment (or at least Sandy is not aware of significant distress), the symptoms are unwanted and occur involuntarily (APA, 2013a, Criterion C). Finally, Sandy's symptoms are not better explained as a component of a widely understood religious or cultural practice (APA, 2013a, Criterion D) or physiological causes of the symptoms, related to substance use/abuse or medical conditions (Criterion E).

Assessments

At the next session, the counselor explains to Sandy that she has two assessments she would like to do with Sandy to better inform their work together. Sandy agrees to the assessments, the first of which is readily accessible and available for the counselor to use from the APA assessment website. The first is the Severity of Dissociative Symptoms—Adult (Brief Dissociative Experiences Scale [DES-B]—Modified), which asks Sandy to rate her dissociative experiences across the last 7 days. Sandy rates four items as 4, one item as 3, two items as 2, and one item as 1. Sandy's average total score was 3.125, which falls in the severe range.

Next, the counselor conducted the Structured Clinical Interview for *DSM-IV*® Dissociative Disorders (SCID-D-R; Steinberg, 1994). (The counselor attended a training through the ISSTD several months prior during which the counselor was trained in the administration and interpretation of the SCID-D-R.) To begin the interview, the counselor explained the underlying concepts and the format of the interview. Sandy was able to explore and discuss her dissociative experiences during the interview in a nonjudgmental, safe way. Her ratings for all five core symptoms were severe. She reported significant periods of amnesia, having internal battles for control, forgetting significant events with loved ones, and feeling as if she was not real. Sandy also described times where she was unable to control what she said or did, but she was able to observe herself. Although the SCID-D-R was developed to be used with the *DSM-IV-TR* (APA, 2000), the interview still provides excellent insight into the client's dissociative experiences and allows a counselor to evaluate using the *DSM-5* (APA, 2013a).

Interventions

Ultimately, Sandy's treatment will need to have three components: (a) safety/stabilization, (b) processing traumatic experiences, and (c) integration (ISSTD, 2011; Peterson, 2010). Sandy appears to have a supportive and potentially safe family of choice; therefore, utilizing a combination of the IFS (Schwartz, 1995) model for individual and couples therapy will most likely be the best course of treatment. The counselor and Sandy will have to work closely and carefully to determine the reasons for Sandy's disconnection from her family of origin. This is an area where Ron may be very helpful and may be able to provide at least some initial rationale for the separation, though he may not be fully aware of all the reasons Sandy has separated from her family of origin.

Initially, the focus of therapy will be on helping Sandy develop the coping skills necessary to prepare for the trauma recovery and stabilization during the second stage of her treatment. Sandy will learn about DID, identify her positive and negative coping strategies, and increase awareness and acceptance of her diagnosis. The counselor will set clear guidelines and boundaries and will invest months in establishing a therapeutic relationship with Sandy and her parts.

During the second stage of the treatment, the counselor will help pace but not lead Sandy through her trauma recovery and stabilization. During this stage, Ron's involvement and support could be extremely helpful. Blending individual and couples therapy may help the couple work through Sandy's trauma more efficiently and safely than if she were to do this work in isolation.

Ultimately, the goal of treatment would be to have Sandy's part integrate and learn how to function in the present with a responsive approach to life versus a reactive approach. The counselor will want to remain available even after termination as new developmental stages may elicit new memories or awareness. The counselor will want to offer "booster" sessions to assist Sandy through these times. A large part of the work in these follow-up sessions is reminding Sandy of the cognitive and affective skills she acquired during the initial counseling.

Ethical and Legal Implications

The key considerations in Sandy's case include meeting Sandy where Sandy is developmentally. This requires that the clinician be respective of the varying developmental and cultural needs of each part (AAMFT, 2015, Aspirational Core Values 1 and 4, 1.1; ACA, 2014; AMCD, 2015). In addition, the clinician needs to recognize that Sandy's parts have been functioning autonomously, and the clinician must first join with the parts and this includes providing informed consent to each part (AAMFT, 2015, Standard 1.2; ACA, 2014, Section A.2.a) and engaging in a beneficial relationship with each part (AAMFT, 2015, Standard 1.9) by clearly defining the counseling relationship and identifying Sandy as the primary client (ACA, 2014, Section A.8). Identifying Sandy as the client will also be important in the adjunct couples therapy. Providing a clear boundary of the intent of the couples therapy will be important. Although the clinician can certainly be supportive of Ron, the ultimate goal of couples therapy is to provide the couple with the skills necessary to function and grow as a couple as Sandy gains new awareness of self and her past.

DISCUSSION

As you continue to reflect on the case study and the overall approach, contemplate these questions:

- Identify three questions a counselor could ask Sandy that would help Sandy gain more awareness of her dissociative experiences (be sure to avoid leading questions). What questions could the counselor ask Ron to enhance the systemic view of Sandy's case?

- What other assessments might the counselor consider administering to Sandy as well? What if any assessments should Ron complete as part of Sandy's system?

- What other ethical and cultural considerations need to be examined in this case?

- How might the counselor need to approach each part of Sandy differently from a systemic, developmental perspective?

- What impact would the developmental differences of Sandy's parts have on the systemic interventions used during treatment?

SUMMARY

Dissociative disorders are a complex and varied set of disorders. Familial, cultural, and societal factors play a part in the etiology of dissociative disorders. Systemic clinicians must conceptualize, assess, and treat clients from these respective systemic frameworks. Systemic clinicians need to assess the individual as well as the family of origin and the family of choice to determine if including these families will be helpful or harmful to the client. Although much of the literature to date has focused on individual therapy for clients with dissociative disorders, recent research has begun to modify traditional systemic models. Clinicians should remain alert for these updated models to be presented and validated by both clinical and empirical reports.

REFERENCES

American Association for Marriage and Family Therapy. (2015). *AAMFT code of ethics.* Alexandria, VA: Author. Retrieved from http://www.aamft.org/iMIS15/AAMFT/Content/Legal_Ethics/Code_of_Ethics.aspx

American Counseling Association. (2014). *ACA code of ethics.* Alexandria, VA: Author.

American Psychiatric Association. (1994). *Diagnostic and statistical manual of mental disorders* (4th ed.). Washington, DC: Author.

American Psychiatric Association. (2000). *Diagnostic and statistical manual of mental disorders* (4th ed., text rev.). Washington, DC: Author.

American Psychiatric Association. (2013a). *Diagnostic and statistical manual of mental disorders* (5th ed.). Arlington, VA: American Psychiatric Publishing.

American Psychiatric Association. (2013b). Clinician-rated nonsuicidal self-injury. Retrieved from https://www.psychiatry.org/psychiatrists.practice/dsm/dsm-5/online-assessment-measures

American Psychiatric Association. (2013c). Cultural Formulation Interview. Retrieved from https://www.psychiatry.org/File%20Library/Psychiatrists/Practice/DSM/APA_DSM5_Cultural-Formulation-Interview.pdf

American Psychiatric Association. (2013d). Supplementary Modules to the Core Cultural Formulation Interview (CFI). Retrieved from https://www.psychiatry.org/File%20Library/Psychiatrists/Practice/DSM/APA_DSM5_Cultural-Formulation-Interview-Supplementary-Modules.pdf

Armstrong, J., Putnam, F., & Carlson, E. (1996). Adolescent dissociative experiences scale. Retrieved from http://www.aspen-therapy.com/pdfs/Aspen%20-%20Adolescent%20Dissociative%20Scale.pdf

Association for Multicultural Counseling and Development. (2015). *Multicultural and social justice counseling competencies.* Alexandria, VA: Author.

Bernstein, E. M., & Putnam, F. W. (1986). Development, reliability, and validity of a dissociation scale. *Journal of Nervous and Mental Disease, 174*(12), 727–735.

Bradfield, B. C. (2013). The intergenerational transmission of trauma as a disruption of the dialogical self. *Journal of Trauma and Dissociation, 14*(4), 390–403, doi:10.1080/15299732.2012.74280

Brand, B. L., Lanius, R., Vermetten, E., Loewenstein, R. J., & Spiegel, D. (2012). Where are we going? An update on assessment, treatment, and neurobiological research in dissociative disorders as we move towards the DSM-5. *Journal of Trauma and Dissociation, 13*(1), 9–31. doi:10.1080/15299732.2011.620687

Brand, B. L., Sar, V., Stavropoulos, P., Kruger, C., Korzekwa, M., Martinez-Taboas, A., & Middleton, W. (2016). Separating fact from fiction: An empirical examination of six myths about dissociative identity disorder. *Harvard Review of Psychiatry*, 24(4), 257–270. doi:10.1097/HRP.0000000000000100

Bremner, J. D., Krystal, J. H., Putnam, F. W., Southwick, S. M., Marmar, C., Charney, D. S., & Mazure, C. M. (1998). Measurement of dissociative states with the Clinician-Administered Dissociative States Scale (CADSS). *Journal of Traumatic Stress*, 11(1), 125–136.

Briere, J. (2002). *Multiscale dissociation inventory*. Lutz, FL: Psychological Assessment Resources.

Courtois, C. A., & Ford, J. D. (Eds.). (2013). *Treating complex traumatic stress disorders in children and adolescents: Scientific foundations and therapeutic models*. New York, NY: Guilford Press.

Dalenberg, C., & Carlson, E. (2010a, November). New versions of the Dissociative Experiences Scale: The DES-R (revised) and the DES-B (brief). In Annual meeting of the International Society for Traumatic Stress Studies, Montreal, Quebec.

Dalenberg, C., & Carlson, E. (2010b). Severity of dissociative symptoms—child age 11–17 (Brief Dissociation Experiences Scale [DES-B]-Modified). Retrieved from https://www.psychiatry.org/File%20Library/Psychiatrists/Practice/DSM/APA_DSM5_Severity-of-Dissociative-Symptoms-Child-Age-11-to-17.pdf

Dalenberg, C., & Carlson, E. (2010c). Severity of dissociative symptoms—adult (Brief Dissociation Experiences Scale [DES-B]-Modified). Retrieved from https://www.psychiatry.org/File%20Library/Psychiatrists/Practice/DSM/APA_DSM5_Severity-of-Dissociative-Symptoms-Adult.pdf

Dell, P. F. (2006). The Multidimensional Inventory of Dissociation (MID): A comprehensive measure of pathological dissociation. *Journal of Trauma and Dissociation*, 7(2), 77–106.

Dell, P. F., & O'Neil, J. A. (Eds.). (2010). *Dissociation and the dissociative disorders: DSM-V and beyond*. New York, NY: Routledge.

DePrince, A. P., & Freyd, J. J. (2014). Trauma-induced dissociation. In M. J. Friedman, T. M. Keane, & P. A. Resick (Eds.), *Handbook of PTSD: Science and practice* (2nd ed., pp. 219–233). New York, NY: Guilford Press.

Engler, J. (2013). An introduction to IFS. In M. Sweezy & E. L. Ziskind (Eds.), *Internal family systems therapy: New dimensions* (pp. xvii–xxvi). New York, NY: Routledge.

Evers-Szostak, M., & Sanders, S. (1992). The Children's Perceptual Alteration Scale (CPAS): A measure of children's dissociation. *Dissociation*, 5(2), 91–92.

First, M. B. (2014). *DSM-5 handbook of differential diagnosis*. Washington, DC: American Psychiatric Association Publishing.

Ford, J. (2009). Dissociation in complex traumatic stress disorder or disorders of extreme stress not otherwise specified (DESNOS). In P. F. Dell & J. A. O'Neill (Eds.), *Dissociation and the dissociative disorders: DSM-V and beyond* (pp. 471–483). New York, NY: Routledge.

Ford, J. D., & Saltzman, W. (2009). Family systems therapy. In C. A. Courtois & J. D. Ford (Eds.), *Treating complex traumatic stress disorders: An evidence-based guide* (pp. 391–414). New York, NY: Guilford Press.

Frankel, S. A. (2009). Dissociation and dissociative disorders: Clinical and forensic assessment with adults. In P. F. Dell & J. A. O'Neill (Eds.), *Dissociation and the dissociative disorders: DSM-V and beyond* (pp. 571–584). New York, NY: Routledge.

Freyd, J., & Birrell, P. (2013). *Blind to betrayal: Why we fool ourselves we aren't being fooled*. Hoboken, NJ: Wiley.

Gentile, J. P., Dillon, K. S., & Gillig, P. M. (2013). Psychotherapy and pharmacotherapy for patients with dissociative identity disorder. *Innovative Clinical Neuroscience*, 10 (2), 22–29.

Gingrich, H. J. D. (2006). Trauma and dissociation in the Philippines. *Journal of Trauma Practice*, 4(3–4), 245–269.

Gold, S. N. (2008). Benefits of a contextual approach to understanding and treating complex trauma. *Journal of Trauma and Dissociation*, 9(2), 269–292. doi:10.1080/15299730802048819

Gold, S. N. (2009). Contextual therapy. In C. A. Courtois & J. D. Ford (Eds.), *Treating complex traumatic stress disorders* (pp. 227–242). New York, NY: Guilford Press.

Gold, S. N., & Seibel, S. L. (2009). *Treating dissociation: A contextual approach*. In P. F. Dell & J. A. O'Neil (Eds.), *Dissociation and the dissociative disorders: DSM-V and beyond* (pp. 625–636). New York, NY: Taylor & Francis.

Goldsmith, R. E., Martin, C. G., & Smith, C. P. (2014). Systemic trauma. *Journal of Trauma and Dissociation*, 15(2), 117–132.

Hegelman, E. (2016). Latah, an ethnic syndrome with dissociative features: A sadomasochistic pattern? In E. Howell & S. Itzkowitz (Eds.), *The dissociative mind of psychoanalysis* (pp. 138–145). New York, NY: Routledge.

Herbine-Blank, T. (2013). Self in relationship: An introduction to IFS couple therapy. In M. Sweezy & E. L. Ziskind (Eds.), *Internal family systems therapy: New dimensions* (pp. 55–71). New York, NY: Routledge.

Herman, J. L. (1992a). Complex PTSD: A syndrome in survivors of prolonged and repeated trauma. *Journal of Traumatic Stress, 5*(3), 377–391.

Herman, J. L. (1992b). *Trauma and recovery: The aftermath of violence—from domestic abuse to political terror.* New York, NY: Basic Books.

International Society for the Study of Trauma and Dissociation. (2004). Guidelines for the evaluation and treatment of dissociative symptoms in children and adolescents. *Journal of Trauma and Dissociation, 5*(3), 119–150.

International Society for the Study of Trauma and Dissociation. (2011). Guidelines for treating dissociative identity disorder in adults, third revision: Summary version. *Journal of Trauma and Dissociation, 12*(2), 188–212. doi:10.1080/15299732.2011.537248

Johnson, S. M., & Courtois, C. A. (2009). Couple therapy. In C. A. Courtois & J. D. Ford (Eds.), *Treating complex traumatic stress disorders: An evidence-based guide* (pp. 371–390). New York, NY: Guilford Press.

Korol, S. (2008). Familial and social support as protective factors against the development of dissociative identity disorder. *Journal of Trauma and Dissociation, 9*(2), 249–267. doi:10.1080/15299730802048744

Krüger, C., & Mace, C. J. (2002). Psychometric validation of the State Scale of Dissociation (SSD). *Psychology and Psychotherapy: Theory, Research and Practice, 75*(1), 33–51.

Linehan, M. (1993). *Cognitive-behavioral treatment of borderline personality disorder.* New York, NY: Guilford Press.

MacIntosh, H. B. (2013). Dissociative identity disorder and the process of couple therapy. *Journal of Trauma and Dissociation, 14*(1), 84–96. doi:10.1080/15299732.2012.710185

MacIntosh, H. B. (2016, April). Developmental couples' therapy for complex trauma: An empirically based approach to couples' therapy with childhood trauma survivors. Workshop presented at the meeting of the International Society for the Study of Trauma and Dissociation, San Francisco, CA.

MacIntosh, H. B., & Johnson, S. (2008). Emotionally focused therapy for couples and childhood sexual abuse survivors. *Journal of Marital and Family Therapy, 34*(3), 298–315. doi:10.1111.j.1752-0606.2008.00074.x

Main, M., Hesse, E., & Seigel, D. (2016, April). Disorganized attachment, the mind and psychotherapy. Plenary workshop presented at the meeting of the International Society for the Study of Trauma and Dissociation, San Francisco, CA.

Middleton, W. (2013). Ongoing incestuous abuse during adulthood. *Journal of Trauma and Dissociation, 14*(3), 251–272. doi:10.1080/15299732.2012.736932.

Naidoo, J. C., & Rajab, D. M. (2005). The dynamics of oppression: A psycho-political analysis of the traumatic experiences of minority Asian Indians in apartheid South Africa. *Psychology and Developing Societies, 17*(2), 139–159.

Nijenhuis, E. R., Spinhoven, P., Van Dyck, R., Van Der Hart, O., & Vanderlinden, J. (1996). The development and psychometric characteristics of the Somatoform Dissociation Questionnaire (SDQ-20). *Journal of Nervous and Mental Disease, 184*(11), 688–694.

Ogden, P., & Fisher, J. (2015). *Sensorimotor psychotherapy: Interventions for trauma and attachment.* New York, NY: W. W. Norton.

Pais, S. (2009). A systemic approach to the treatment of dissociative identity disorder. *Journal of Family Psychotherapy, 20*, 72–88.

Paulsen, S. (2009). *Looking through the eye of trauma and dissociation.* Charleston, SC: Booksurge.

Peterson, G. (2010, November). *Assessment and treatment tools for dissociative disorders.* Presented as part of the Clinical Lecture Series, UNC-CH School of Social Work, Chapel Hill, NC. Retrieved from http://ssw.unc.edu/files/web/pdf/CLS_Slides-Peterson.pdf

Prilleltensky, I. (2003). Understanding, resisting, and overcoming oppression: Toward psychopolitical validity. *American Journal of Community Psychology, 31*(1–2), 195–201. doi:10.1023/A:1023043108210

Putnam, F. W. (1989). Pierre Janet and modern views of dissociation. *Journal of Traumatic Stress, 2*(4), 413–429.

Putnam, F. W. (1990). *Child dissociative checklist (v3.0).* Washington, DC: NIMH.

Rhoades, G. F. (2006a). Cross-cultural aspects of trauma and dissociation. *Journal of Trauma Practice, 4*, 21–33. doi:10.1300/J189v04n01_03

Rhoades, G. F. (2006b). Trauma and dissociation in paradise (Hawaii). *Journal of Trauma Practice, 4*(1–2), 133–145. doi:10.1300/J189v04n01_09

Riley, K. C. (1988). Measurement of dissociation. *Journal of Nervous and Mental Disease, 176*, 449–450.

Ross, C. A. (1989). *Multiple personality disorder: Diagnosis, clinical features, and treatment.* New York, NY: Wiley.

Ross, C. A. (1997). *Dissociative identity disorder: Diagnosis, clinical features, and treatment of multiple personality* (2nd ed.). New York, NY: Wiley.

Ross, C. A., & Browning, E. (2016) The Self-Report Dissociative Disorders Interview Schedule: A preliminary report. *Journal of Trauma and Dissociation*. doi:10.1080/15299732.2016.1172538

Ross, C. A., & Ellason, J. W. (2005). Discriminating among diagnostic categories using the Dissociative Disorders Interview Schedule 1, 2. *Psychological Reports*, 96(2), 445–453.

Ross, C. A., & Halpern, N. (2009). *Trauma model therapy: A treatment approach for trauma, dissociation and complex comorbidity*. Richardson, TX: Manitou Communications.

Ross, C. A., & Joshi, S. (1992). Paranormal experiences in the general population. *Journal of Nervous and Mental Disease, 180*(6), 357–361.

Ross, C. A., Miller, S. D., Reagor, P., Bjornson, L., Fraser, G. A., & Anderson, G. (1990). Structured interview data on 102 cases of multiple personality disorder from four centers. *American Journal of Psychiatry, 147*, 596–601.

Sar, V., Middleton, W., & Dohary, M. (2013). Individual and societal oppression: Global perspectives on dissociative disorders. *Journal of Trauma and Dissociation, 14*(2), 121–126. doi:10.1080/15299732.2013.761032

Schwartz, R. (1995). *Internal family systems therapy*. New York, NY: Guilford Press.

Shaffer, D. (2013a). *Early Development and Home Background (EDHB) Form—Clinician*. Washington, DC: American Psychiatric Association Publishing.

Shaffer, D. (2013b). *Early Development and Home Background (EDHB) Form—Parent/Guardian*. Washington, DC: American Psychiatric Association Publishing.

Shapiro, F. (1989). Efficacy of the eye movement desensitization procedure in the treatment of traumatic memories. *Journal of Traumatic Stress, 2*(2), 199–223.

Shavers, V. L., Fagan, P., Jones, D., Klein, W. M., Boyington, J., Moten, C., & Rorie, E. (2012). The state of research on racial/ethnic discrimination in the receipt of health care. *American Journal of Public Health, 102*(5), 953–966.

Silberg, J. L., & Dallon, S. (2009). Dissociation in children and adolescents: At the crossroads. In P. F. Dell & J. A. O'Neill (Eds.), *Dissociation and the dissociative disorders: DSM-V and beyond* (pp. 67–82). New York, NY: Routledge.

Simons, R. C. (1985). The resolution of the *Latah* paradox. In R. C. Simons & C. C. Hughes (Eds.), *The culture-bound syndromes* (Vol. 7, pp. 43–62). doi:10.1007/978-94-009-5251-5_4

Smith, C. P., & Freyd, J. J. (2014). Institutional betrayal. *American Psychologist, 69*(6), 575–587.

Spiegel, D. (2010). Dissociation in the DSM-5. *Journal of Trauma and Dissociation, 11*(3), 261–264. doi:10.1080/15299731003780788

Steinberg, M. (1994). Structured Clinical Interview for DSM-IV® Dissociative Disorders (SCID-D-R). Washington, DC: American Psychiatric Association Publishing.

Stolbach, B. C. (1997). *The Children's Dissociative Experiences Scale and Posttraumatic Symptom Inventory: Rationale, development, and validation of a self-report measure* (Unpublished doctoral dissertation). Boulder, CO: University of Colorado.

Sweezy, M., & Ziskind, E. L. (2013). *Internal family systems therapy: New dimensions*. New York, NY: Routledge.

Twombly, J. H. (2013). Integrating IFS with phase-oriented treatment of clients with dissociative disorders. In M. Sweezy & E. L. Ziskind (Eds.), *Internal family systems therapy: New dimensions* (pp. 72–89). New York, NY: Routledge.

Van der Kolk, B. A. (2014). *The body keeps the score: Brain, mind and body in the healing of trauma*. New York, NY: Penguin Group.

Vanderlinden, J., Van Dyck, R., Vandereycken, W., Vertommen, H., & Jan Verkes, R. (1993). The Dissociation Questionnaire (DIS-Q): Development and characteristics of a new self-report questionnaire. *Clinical Psychology and Psychotherapy, 1*(1), 21–27.

9

SYSTEMIC ECOLOGY IN UNDERSTANDING SOMATIC SYMPTOM AND RELATED DISORDERS

Torey Portrie-Bethke, Brooks Bastian Hanks, Nicole R. Hill, Holly H. Wagner, and Carrie Alexander-Albritton

Somatic symptomatology is a pervasive experience for much of the population with more than 80% of individuals describing somatic symptoms within the last 7 days (Hiller, Rief, & Brahler, 2006). Additionally, about 20% of individuals report experiencing serious or debilitating somatic symptoms. All of the related somatic disorders and symptoms have a common characteristic and distinction of significant impairment, distress, and the way these individuals interpret the atypical thoughts, feelings, emotions, and actions in connection with the symptoms (American Psychiatric Association [APA], 2013). Experiencing debilitating somatic symptoms impacts functioning and life events and can create hopelessness, helplessness, profound suffering, and fear. Approximately 75% of debilitating somatic symptoms are considered medically unexplainable with doctors not being able to diagnose an explanatory medical or health condition (Korber, Frieser, Steinbrecher, & Hiller, 2011). In the *Diagnostic and Statistical Manual of Mental Disorders* (5th ed.; *DSM-5*; APA, 2013), Somatic Symptom Disorder (SSD) is defined as a body-focused concern that is psychologically distressing or negatively impacting an individual's daily life. Individuals with medically unexplainable symptoms or symptoms that are creating disproportionally significant disruption to daily functioning are the focus of SSD and the related disorders.

Within pediatric populations, a significant percentage of youth presenting at hospitals exhibit symptoms that cannot be medically explained (Dale et al., 2010). Somatic symptoms that are medically unexplained can generate significant familial and relational consequences due to cultural beliefs about illness and distress (Kirmayer & Sartorius, 2007). Individuals suffering with symptoms that are not confirmed by a diagnosable condition may experience a lack of trust in self and others, including the family counselor (Stone, 2014). Many clients with unexplained symptoms do not feel validated by the medical profession and transfer this frustration of not being understood to the counseling process. As noted in the previous diagnosis for somatic disorder, a strong connection of unexplained medical factors was associated with this diagnosis. Currently, the professionals generating the research in the *DSM-5* purport that providing a mental disorder diagnosis when a medical condition cannot be determined is inappropriate (APA, 2013).

Given the pervasiveness of distressing somatic symptoms, many families are impacted by somatic issues that intersect the medical and counseling professions. Because of the high level of interaction with the health care system that may be disempowering and stigmatizing, many families express feeling isolated, fearful, and distrustful. Fortunately, systemic clinicians engage the family to explore strengths, wellness, and expand the client's systemic epistemology. Rather than helping the client maintain the view of the symptoms as the problem and counseling as a means to find solutions, the systemic clinician joins with the family and focuses on relational dynamics. Effective clinicians do not insist that the client stop having the symptoms, but rather they encourage the client and family to change the context, thereby leading to changes in meaning and behaviors within the family dynamics. The family therapy process counsels the family as a system, which means that the client is not viewed as the identified patient but rather as the entire family and the interpersonal dynamics are explored as a whole unit. The systems perspective understands the development and maintenance of somatic symptoms as a process beginning with family's functioning and the unresolved family conflicts (Thoburn, Hoffman-Robinson, Shelly, & Sayre, 2009).

In the most recent revision of the *DSM*, the APA (2013) made significant changes to the somatoform disorder section. The SSD in *DSM-5* no longer requires the individual to have a medically unexplained physical issue and now focuses on the presence of distressing physical symptoms that generate considerable impairment in daily life (APA, 2013). Shifting from a reliance on medically unexplainable symptoms fosters the development of a therapeutic alliance that is not built on an assessment that the client's issues are fictitious (Klaus et al., 2015). When an individual is experiencing debilitating somatic symptoms, it can generate significant anxiety within the family system. This chapter explores the family system and the somatic ecology, the case of Miguel, ethical and legal considerations, cultural factors, assessments, and interventions to assist the family in engaging together to gain more effective intrapersonal and interpersonal communication and family relationships.

DSM-5 AND FAMILY SYSTEMS

A systems framework situates the somatic symptoms in the context of family functioning. The family dynamics contribute to the development and sustainability of somatic symptoms. Such symptoms are seen as manifestations of unresolved family conflict or indirect emotional expression (Minuchin, 1974). Family systems theory developed by Dr. Murray Bowen (1978) explores the emotional connectedness within the family unit. The theory's lens captures all family members interwoven with each other and not viewed as separate individuals. To capture the complexity and interdependence of such relationships, consider the image of the family knot in which each individual is connected to multiple family members and the interrelational dynamics are complicated and difficult, at times, to unravel. The images of each family member holding on to another family member in a disorganized pattern creating challenge and difficulty when attempting to unravel provide a visual representation of the interrelatedness of the individuals within a family.

Through the lens of systems theory, all family members compose "the client." Family counseling is helpful in assisting the family to explore the emotional system that connects the family members and the roles that family members enact and ultimately perpetuate homeostasis (Thoburn et al., 2009). Homeostasis is the outcome of having one of the family members experiencing somatic symptoms because the expression of somatic complaints is a more acceptable and congruent way to manifest emotional distress in some families (Minuchin, 1974). Unhealthy or rigid communication patterns contribute to somatic symptoms being the most effective way to symbolically communicate within a family (Thoburn et al., 2009). Relational dynamics unfold as family members develop their own patterns, through avoidance, support, or power, in response to the somatization of a family member. Thus, the family counselor's role within the family system is to develop comfortable and healthy communication and interaction that reduces family stress and increases perceived comfort and safety for an effective homeostasis.

Integrating the Diagnostic Impressions for the Case of Miguel

When considering the case of Miguel, family dynamics are an important conceptualization and diagnostic feature to address. The initial diagnostic impression for Miguel is that of Somatic Symptom Disorder, Persistent, Severe (APA, 2013). The distressing symptoms indicated by this disorder are characterized by excessive and unexplained pain that is not explained by an identified physiological pathology. If the testing results do indicate that Miguel has a medical diagnosis, his complaints are excessive and are grossly exaggerated beyond what is expected with the medical condition or explanation. Miguel meets all three *DSM-5* criteria (A, B, and C) for the diagnosis, and also two specifiers (APA, 2013).

Miguel has been complaining of severe lower back pain and chronic fatigue to his family physician. He reports his symptoms have persisted for more than 8 months. Miguel has recently been referred to a counselor due to his anxiety and fear that the back pain is not improving and could be cancer or a brain tumor. Recently, Miguel has had marked impairment with his partnership and business as a diesel mechanic because of his chronic back pain and continual fatigue. Miguel reports missing multiple days of work due to his recent physical ailments and the time he takes to manage the financial and emotional responsibilities to care for his parents. His wife, Josie, reports some anger and resentment due to his continual ailments and overall low energy level thereby indicative of some relationship distress. Although Miguel has had no history of mental health treatment, he expressed a history of child sexual abuse identified during his intake evaluation. Both family therapy and individual counseling with Miguel would be warranted in this case. The additional individual counseling in conjunction with family therapy may help Miguel mitigate how he copes and interprets stress within his perceived experiences and family.

Somatic Symptom and Related Disorders and the *DSM-5*

The *DSM-5* identified, renamed, and readdressed specifically for somatic symptom and related disorders a delineation and disconnection implied by the mind–body dualism as the previous implication of no medical diagnoses to account for the symptoms (APA, 2013). Implying that all unidentified symptoms for a medical diagnosis warrant a mental health condition/disorder stigmatizes individuals. Therefore, this particular section of the *DSM-5* includes the following diagnoses: Somatic Symptom Disorder, Illness Anxiety Disorder, Conversion Disorder (functional neurological symptom disorder), Psychological Factors Affecting Other Medical Conditions, Factitious Disorder, Other Specified Somatic Symptom and Related Disorder, and Unspecified Somatic Symptom and Related Disorder (APA, 2013). The individuals presenting with distressing somatic symptoms generally seek medical treatment instead of mental health treatment, and therefore, the *DSM-5*, in comparison to the *Diagnostic and Statistical Manual of Mental Disorders* (4th ed., text rev.; *DSM-IV-TR*; APA, 2000), attempted to more clearly differentiate the diagnoses in this chapter to aide in proper assessment and treatment. The most commonly used diagnosis within this category is SSD. The term *somatoform disorder* is no longer used in the *DSM-5* and has been replaced with Somatic Symptom and Related Disorders (APA, 2013, 2016). From a systemic perspective, it is essential, as a clinician, to get an accurate understanding as to how the family is functioning as a result of the presenting concerns of the "client." Systems perspective conceptualizes the growth and maintenance of somatic symptoms as a development beginning with family's functioning and the unresolved family challenges (Thoburn et al., 2009).

Somatic Symptom Disorder

SSD involves an individual's life being negatively impacted by a body-focused (somatic) concern that is psychologically distressing or significantly disruptive of daily life. *DSM-5* (APA, 2013) outlines diagnostic criteria for SSD and its three potential specifiers.

Criterion A indicates that the identified client must evidence symptoms that are believed to be present that are bodily in nature and cause a marked life impairment. In the example provided in this chapter, Miguel presents with chronic lower back pain and fatigue.

Criterion B proposes that the client's cognitions, affects, or actions that relate to the symptoms must be extreme and established by either the inconsistent and ongoing severity of the symptoms, extreme fears of the presenting concerns, or large amounts of time consumed with the presenting concerns. In the case of Miguel, he is continually ruminating on the prospect that his back pain is explained by cancer or a brain tumor.

Criterion C delineates that the presenting health concern need not always be present (i.e., back pain and fatigue), though it has been ongoing for more than 6 months. For our specific case, Miguel reports that his symptoms have persisted for 8 months.

Speficiers for Diagnosis: The *DSM-5* outlines several specifiers including with predominant pain, persistent, and severity (mild, moderate, or severe) depending on the client's reported concerns at the time of the diagnosis (APA, 2016).

Considering the case provided with Miguel, systems counselors may offer additional support to the family when conceptualizing how his diagnosis has impacted the family's life and the grief associated with mental health-related factors. For example, Miguel's continual worry related to his health and his subsequent job instability may cause great concern for his family. Assessing the family dynamic and identifying strategies for success is necessary.

Illness Anxiety Disorder

Illness Anxiety Disorder is characterized by excessive preoccupation with having or acquiring an illness. It has six diagnostic criteria as specified in the *DSM-5* (A–F). The first factor to consider is whether the identified client is disproportionately focused on personal health status (A). Individuals do not have to believe they have somatic symptoms; however, if such symptoms are reported, they tend to be minor in severity (B). Clients may have a significant fear that they will have or do have concern about personal health status, which contributes to disproportionate ruminations (C). The way in which individuals attend to their excessive preoccupation with having or acquiring a serious illness varies with some individuals continuously engaging in self-examination of themselves for symptoms of a health concern, whereas others avoid looking at themselves all together (D). With illness anxiety disorder, the individual's symptoms have been manifest for 6 months, although the high level of anxiety about health could have begun as something other than the current issue (E). Finally, the symptoms are not better defined by another diagnosis listed in the *DSM-5* (F).

Systemic clinicians can use the *care-seeking type* specifier to indicate individuals who frequently obtain medical services or *care-avoidant type* to indicate individuals who rarely use medical services despite the intense anxiety about having or acquiring a serious illness. It remains integral to seek collateral verification from family members to comprehensively understand the family dynamic. Additionally, this information can be used to assist the family in identifying ways to be helpful and supportive within the context of their family system.

Conversion Disorder (Functional Neurological Symptom Disorder)

Conversion Disorder is characterized by abnormal central nervous system functioning that negatively affects voluntary motor movement or sensory capability. *DSM-5* provides diagnostic criterion for this disorder using four key factors. (A) The characteristics of this particular disorder have to do with physical body movement or tactile sensations that are markedly impaired. For instance, a client may present with visible body shaking or challenges with limb positioning. (B) Symptoms more tactile in nature could present as the absence of feeling on one's skin or as problems in seeing or hearing audible sounds. Additionally, the individual's self-reported symptoms are not explained by detection of a neurological disease after examination. (C) When the diagnosis of conversion disorder is provided, the assumption is that no other medical disorder or mental health disorder better accounts for the symptoms. (D) The symptoms of conversion disorder regularly impede the client's day-to-day functioning and overall life events in more than one area of life, or the symptoms necessitate assistance from a medical professional. The *DSM-5* delineates different types of symptoms for this diagnosis; and dependent upon the symptom, the *International Classification of Diseases, Tenth Revision, Clinical Modification* (*ICD-10-CM*; National Center for Health Statistics, 2017) code will differ (with weakness or paralysis, with abnormal movement, with swallowing symptoms, with speech symptom, with attacks or seizures, with anesthesia or sensory loss, with special sensory symptom, with mixed symptoms; APA, 2013).

Systemic clinicians further specify the course of the disorder by using *acute episode* (symptoms manifest for less than 6 months) or *persistent* (system manifest for 6 months or longer) designations and they can use descriptive specifiers to indicate with or without psychological stressor (APA, 2013).

A systems framework necessitates a closer look at how this diagnosis is impacting the family. The individual suffering with a mental health disorder may experience mental, physical, and emotional suffering that impacts not only the individual but the family members and by gaining the knowledge of the disorder the family may comprehend how the somatic issues are persistent. Familial education related to this mental health diagnosis may be helpful to move the family forward in therapy.

Psychological Factors Affecting Other Medical Conditions

This is a diagnosis characterized by the presence of a nonmental health disorder medical condition or medical symptom. Psychological Factors Affecting Other Medical Conditions is defined in the *DSM-5* by three criteria and specifiers that communicate the seriousness of the diagnosis (mild, moderate, severe, or extreme). The individual may present with a medical symptom or condition that does not meet the criteria for a mental health disorder. Furthermore, the client is demonstrating behavior or psychological factors that directly exacerbate the medical condition in some respect (worsen the medical issue, impact the intervention given for the medical concern, add hazard to medical concern, and/or enhance the medical issue or require a medical intervention). Finally, these medically compromising behaviors or psychological factors are not considered a better fit for another diagnosis in the *DSM-5* (APA, 2013).

This diagnosis may impact the family system in that a medical condition may be present and the identified "patient" may appear to be doing things to sabotage his or her recovery. Education continues to be important for the family to comprehend the nuances of the diagnosis. It may be further helpful for the medical professional to confer with the systemic clinician to review the case.

Factitious Disorder

Factitious Disorder can be classified as a Factitious Disorder Imposed on Self or Another Person. Factitious Disorder is described when individuals either intentionally falsify psychological or physical symptoms or deceptively produce injury or disease. The *DSM-5* identifies Factitious Disorder into two types: Factitious Disorder imposed on self and Factitious Disorder imposed on another. The first criterion is that individuals deceptively claim to have an injury, illness, or impairment. Second, the individual presents himself or herself to others as injured, ill, or impaired independent of possible outward recompense. Most important, the falsified signs or symptoms cannot be better explained by another mental health disorder. These criteria address a Factitious Disorder that is imposed on the identified client though the physical concerns can be about another person as well (APA, 2013). Systemic clinicians can use course specifiers for this to communicate how many factitious disorder episodes the individual has displayed single episode or recurrent episode (APA, 2013).

Systems clinicians working with a family seeking therapy for a specific family member diagnosed with a factitious disorder may be struggling with embarrassment and shame. For instance, if a male partner believes that his wife has cancer, and tells others, she may feel scared that many in her life believe she is ill, when in fact, she is not. Open dialogue within the counseling session may encourage awareness and alternatives for moving forward. Critical to the family success is continued therapy.

Other Specified Somatic Symptom and Related Disorders

Other Specified Somatic Symptom and Related Disorders is a category that systemic clinicians can use when working with someone who does not necessarily meet the criteria for the somatic symptom and related disorders discussed so far but demonstrates distressing symptoms that necessitate treatment. Perhaps the client is experiencing some of the diagnostic criteria, though not nearly at the level required to be diagnosed as a different condition, or the symptoms have not gone on for the prescribed amount of time. In such cases, the diagnosis of Other Specified Somatic Symptom and Related Disorder could be a way to secure treatment or to make preliminary diagnosis that can be changed after further assessment. *DSM-5* provides systemic clinicians with four "subclinical" profiles for possible use.

Unspecified Somatic Symptom and Related Disorders

Unspecified Somatic Symptom and Related Disorders can be used for those individuals struggling with somatic-type difficulties who do not meet the diagnostic criteria of another mental health or medical diagnosis. Individuals who have this disorder experience distressing symptoms not better accounted for by a medical illness. Typically, there is not enough information available to the systemic clinician to provide a formal diagnosis in this category according to the *DSM-5* (APA, 2013). Systemic counselors are encouraged to employ a comprehensive assessment exploring the individual's excessive cognitions, behaviors, and feelings impacting mental health functioning in ways that create immobility in development. Creating a comprehensive outlook involves not only using a checklist but also exploring family interactions and relationships perceived by the individual. This offers the individual an opportunity for family counseling to enhance mental health functioning and reduce ongoing mental health symptoms. For instance, your client arrives to family counseling addressing extreme fear of an upcoming MRI viewing her tumor. The client expresses extreme pain in her head surrounding the tumor location and a resonating pain throughout her back and legs. The client shared that the physical pain is not present when she wakes up and begins her morning routine but appears after engaging with her family during the morning chores. The mother expressed that she limits her child's movement and has her child rate her pain every 10 minutes or so. In this scenario, the family counselor conceptualizes the impact of the medical condition, the obtrusive thoughts, behaviors, and feelings disproportionate to the diagnosis, and the role of the system impacting the individual's functioning. The systemic clinician has gained insight not only into the described symptoms but also the involvement of the family and perceived impact on the client within the system.

Diagnoses and Systems Theory in Review

Although the *DSM-5* provides a clear list of symptoms for particular mental health diagnoses for individuals, counselors would be remiss if they did not consider other factors when assessing clients in a holistic way, such as their family system. The shift from the *DSM-IV-TR* to the *DSM-5* in 2013 attempted to make it easier for medical and mental health care professionals to differentiate between Somatic Symptom and Related Disorders. Individuals typically present in a medical setting for treatment for these various diagnoses, and subsequently, will be referred to a mental health care professional for help. The *DSM-5* differentiates each of these diagnoses by focusing more attention on the behaviors, cognitions, and effects of the individual (APA, 2013). As a systemic clinician, it is imperative to look at the cultural context of individuals and to assess them holistically (Bitter, 2014). Approaching the client from a family systems perspective would integrate cultural and relational dynamics into counseling.

In the case study presented in this chapter, Miguel, Josie, and their two children, Marie and Rozena, would constitute the family system. Therefore, the entire family would be the client (Bitter, 2014). It would be important to collaborate closely with the entire family related to the concerns that they are presenting and draw upon the strengths of the family. This is consistent with Virginia Satir's notion of enabling members of the family to harness resources that exist specific to their unique family system in order to effectively help one another (Bitter, 2014). As distressing somatic symptoms may be emergent from or reinforced by family dynamics, it is important to consider relational and cultural components.

RELATIONAL AND CULTURAL FEATURES

The *DSM-5* clearly delineates cultural, social, and relational aspects that may influence the manifestation of Somatic Symptom and Related Disorders (APA, 2013). Trauma and violence from childhood, including abuse, can significantly affect current and later experiencing and display of somatic symptoms. Early traumatic experiences in relation to somatic disorders are discussed later, under relational influences. Level of education obtained, socioeconomic status, and the presence of recent stressful events can also influence presentation of somatic disorders. Additionally, social learning and cultural/social norms play important roles in the prevalence and severity of somatic disorders. Medical care, perception of illness and body sensations, and personal habits and routines involving seeking medical help vary among cultures, and thereby influence somatic presentations. Concisely, "somatic presentations can be viewed as expressions of personal suffering inserted in a cultural and social context" (APA, 2013, p. 310). Similarly, Kirmayer and Sartorius (2007) illuminated the "need for a social and cultural approach to the phenomenon of somatization that goes beyond the model of diseases and disorders" (p. 839). Therefore, a conceptual understanding regarding the influence of culture on an individual's experience and presentation of somatic disorders is warranted. Consider these factors within the case of Miguel. How might his specific past and current cultural and relational features be impacting the presence of his somatic symptoms?

Cultural Influences

It is important to note that culture should be conceptualized within the context of a globalizing world and is, therefore, characterized by fluidity and heterogeneity. "Current anthropological views emphasize that cultures are fluid, heterogeneous, hybrid systems of knowledge, institutions, discourse, and practices that vary over time and location" (Kirmayer & Sartorius, 2007, p. 832). An accurate understanding of one's culture would necessitate a focus on the relationship between an individual's phenomenological experiences, development, and perspective and that same individual's perception of the dominant cultural/social processes and ways of interpreting and understanding the world. In this case, that understanding would assist in elucidating the role that culture plays in one's conceptualization of illness.

In cases of somatic disorders, illnesses may become chronic and disabling when disrupting ordinary fluctuations in the somatic regulatory system. Stressful life events may produce bodily distress that becomes equivalent to the symptoms of illness. These symptoms can begin amplifying and then create a feedback loop. Different cultures may attribute various meanings to symptoms that influence the distress symptoms. Kirmayer and Sartorius (2007) explored relationships between cultural models and the magnification of somatic symptoms and disorders. Cultural models include the following three distinguishing aspects that influence the cultural context through which somatic symptoms may be experienced and presented. First, the explanations that a particular culture gives and associates with facets of pathophysiology serve to form models for understanding illness within a cultural context. Second, salient images or prototypes drawn from personal experiences, mass media, or popular culture influence culturally specific understandings of one's bodily condition. And finally, culturally embedded knowledge and manners of experiencing pain are associated with presentations of bodily distress. Cultural models convey messages about illness that are culturally encoded through rules, roles, stories, and social practices. Furthermore, when cultural knowledge is communicated through narratives and stories, it may become more vivid and meaningful, proving it to be a powerful influencer in the manifestation, prevalence, and presentation of somatic symptom and related disorders.

Certain cultures and operating systems within societies may place more stigmatization on psychological symptomatology and less on physical ailments. Somatic symptom and related disorders may be more predominant in non-Western cultures where the expression of emotional distress in a psychological manner is stigmatized and is, therefore, less accepted socially and culturally. For example, some Asian cultures may consider mental illness to be a sign of weakness, resulting in emotions being suppressed. Individuals may be culturally reinforced to somaticize rather than psychologize emotional pain and duress.

Research has shown connections between depression, somatic symptoms, and cultural effects (Um, Huh, Kim, & Chae, 2014).

The criticality of understanding cultural influences as related to one's presentation of somatic disorders has been established. Within this understanding, the influence of relational and familial factors must be taken into account, as relationships play a vital part in contributing to individuals' cultural understanding of themselves in connection with their social environment and personal circumstances. Problems related to the social and relational environment, from an early age, may be associated with the manifestation of somatic symptoms. In the case of Miguel, he perceives his role within his culture to care financially for his parents, wife, and children. Miguel appears to be struggling with his perceived rigid cultural roles and he believes that communicating openly with his family is a taboo and an expression of weakness. Miguel has been carrying the responsibilities of his family, and he appears to be struggling to adjust to the problems brought about during transitions to a different life cycle stage with his aging and medically ill parents, maturing daughter, and career changes with his wife. Z codes are used in the case of Miguel to indicate services rendered or referral to the person for a health examination regardless of abnormal or without abnormal findings. Z codes offer an understanding of Miguel's somatic symptoms by exploring other problems related to the social environment; Phase of Life Problem: Clinical attention is given to a particular developmental transition impacting the client's intrapersonal and his family's interpersonal functioning. Specific treatment methods are constructed to identify these challenges impacting the family system (see "Family Systems Interventions" section in this chapter).

Relational and Environmental Influences

As previously noted, trauma, abuse, and violence experienced in childhood have been associated with the presentation of somatic symptoms (APA, 2013; Barsky, Peekna, & Borus, 2001; Kugler, Bloom, Kaercher, Truax, & Storch, 2012; Sansone, Wierderman, Tahir, & Buckner, 2009). Afari et al. (2014) found that individuals who were exposed to trauma were almost three times as likely to display somatic symptoms compared with their counterparts who did not experience trauma. Kugler et al. (2012) cited the connection between childhood traumas, increased rate of somatic symptomatology, and decreased daily functioning. Sansone et al. (2009) found specific relevance among physical and emotional childhood trauma and somatic symptoms in adulthood.

Research has also determined differences in reporting and experience of abuse and later somatic symptoms in regard to gender. Barsky et al. (2001) found that the incidence of abuse is higher in both girls and women, and that current abuse is more likely to result in somatic symptom reporting (Gini & Pozzoli, 2009). These authors explored the potential impact that socialization had within boys and girls and somatic symptoms. As a result of socialization and social roles, women may have a greater awareness of somatization in general, be more encouraged to acknowledge distress, and use external cues to process somatic experiences. Again, it is important to note that as culture, gender roles, and society continue to evolve and flux, the influence of these relational differences will vary as well. Furthermore, as exemplified within the case of Miguel, the manifestation of somatic symptoms following abuse can certainly occur in males, as well as females.

Psychosocial and interpersonal wellness are important and impactful relational factors in regard to somatic symptomatology. Gini and Pozzoli (2009) found that children who were victimized by peers, thereby being psychosocially disadvantaged, showed a higher incidence of somatic symptoms. A developmental and interpersonal disruption in the form of bullying was shown through a meta-analysis to be detrimental to children socially, psychologically, and physically. These detriments were extended to include all parties involved in the incidences of bullying, including the victims, bullies, and those who vacillated between being bullied and victimized. This relational conflict was associated with symptoms such as headaches, backaches, abdominal pain, sleeping problems, lack of appetite, and bed-wetting.

Trauma, abuse, socialization effects, and interpersonal, psychosocial conflicts may all lead to current or later manifestations of somatic symptoms (APA, 2013; Barsky et al., 2001; Gini & Pozzoli, 2009; Kugler et al., 2012; Sansone et al., 2009). However, there are ways to mitigate these impacts and strengthen one's ability to cope and experience resilience in dealing with somatic symptom and related disorders. The following section outlines protective factors that may lead to resilience within the identified population.

Strengths: Protective Factors and Resilience

Focus on Wellness

Myers and Sweeney (2008) purported that individuals should seek to focus upon and increase their sense of wellness through developmental, preventative, and holistic methods. Wellness is a construct oriented toward optimal well-being, in which body, mind, and spirit are integrated. Wellness is relative to all people within a global society, and can be applied broadly toward understanding and celebrating the uniqueness of people from varied cultural and geographical backgrounds. There are several dimensions of wellness, of which the physical, social/emotional, and cognitive/mental aspects are discussed further in application toward developing resilience within populations presenting somatic symptoms and related disorders.

As discussed previously, trauma, stress, and other barriers to healthy development have been found to play roles in the development of somatic symptoms (APA, 2013; Barsky et al., 2001; Fischer, Lemmer, Gollwitzer, & Nater, 2014; Gini & Pozzoli, 2009; Kugler et al., 2012; Sansone et al., 2009). Although the risks have been outlined, it is important to recognize the protective factors within the context of wellness that may lead to resilience. Fazel, Reed, Panter-Brick, and Stein (2012) examined the risk and protective factors of refugee children in relation to their mental health, namely posttraumatic stress disorder, depression, and somatic symptoms. This meta-analysis discovered that the protective factors for this population included a perceived sense of safety, sense of belonging, school connectedness, proximity to other children who are similar (same ethnic origin), and familiar cohesion, all of which took place through the context of education. In essence, the structure of school and education became a protective factor, which facilitated these children's cognitive/mental as well as social/emotional wellness and development. Walker et al. (2011) examined protective factors in some of the world's poorest children. Poverty may cause distress within the brain and affect neurodevelopment. Lack of nutrition and exposure to infectious diseases and toxins can also impair overall health and mental processes. Yet, even for the most impoverished children on the globe, there are still protective factors that facilitate physical and cognitive/mental wellness, including maternal education, breastfeeding, and cognitive and social–emotional stimulation from the earliest age possible.

Mikolajczak, Menil, and Luminet (2007) examined the relationship among emotional intelligence, burnout, and somatic symptoms. A higher level of emotional intelligence was found to protect individuals from burnout and decrease somatic symptoms. Psychoeducation through the form of emotional intelligence trainings was found to be beneficial in facilitating social/emotional wellness, which in turn led to increased positive coping and resilience for individuals experiencing somatic symptoms and related disorders. The following section expands on the benefit of psychoeducation focused on coping through stress management as it applies to decreasing somatic symptoms.

Coping Through Stress Management

Stress has been defined as the "transaction between the person and the environment, whereby individuals appraise environmental demands as outweighing their abilities to meet those demands" (Steinhardt & Dolbier, 2008, p. 445). Fischer et al. (2014) purported that "decades of (mostly biological) research have documented the effects of childhood trauma on heightened stress reactivity and subsequent adverse health outcomes" (p. 2). Conversely, resilience involves individuals recovering from decreased abilities to function as a result from stress and returning to established levels of functioning (Steinhardt & Dolbier, 2008). Coping with stress productively leads to resilience. Stress has been found to be a significant influencer in the development and manifestation of somatic symptoms and related disorders. Thus, efforts toward coping with stress that lead to resilience can be beneficial in alleviating somatic symptoms (Fischer et al., 2014; Steinhardt & Dolbier, 2008).

Fischer et al. (2014) clearly established "a role for stress management training in the prevention and treatment of functional somatic syndromes" (p. 1). Steinhardt and Dolbier (2008) examined the effectiveness of a 4-week resilience promoting program aimed at reducing stress and symptomatology in college-aged students. The program included a total of 8 hours, consisting of four biweekly sessions of psychoeducational interventions. The psychoeducational sessions included information regarding how to transform stress into resilience, take responsibility, focus on empowering interpretations, and create meaningful connections. These sessions helped participants explore a variety of negative responses to stress, such as giving up or feeling that their well-being had been compromised. The result of the sessions included decreased symptomatology and increased effective coping strategies. Psychoeducational stress management training may be a worthwhile consideration to promote resilience or even thriving after stressful events and count as beneficial in reducing somatic symptoms.

Case of Miguel Side Bar

Case of Miguel	
Conceptualization Questions	**Response**
Describe how a focus on wellness and resilience benefit Miguel and his family.	
What role might education play in supporting Miguel and his family, and how?	
What forms of psychoeducation could be introduced and utilized within the context of family counseling sessions?	
Identify the diversity and cultural considerations when conceptualizing the case of Miguel.	
Explore and identify the training and preparation you perceive you need prior to providing competent family therapy.	
Consider and address the personal challenges/ biases you may experience when treating Miguel and his family.	

FAMILY SYSTEMS ASSESSMENTS

Somatic symptom and related disorders are considered by many mental health profession-als to be a challenging diagnosis given the difficulty in assessing how the individual and family are functioning. With more than 80% of individuals reporting debilitating somatic symptoms in the last week, clinicians need assessment tools that will help them develop a more comprehensive and clear understanding of what is occurring. With the recent sub-stantial change to how somatic symptoms are classified in the *DSM-5*, researchers and men-tal health professionals have placed greater focus on developing assessment tools to assess somatic symptoms and differential diagnostic criteria. The existing assessment tools are primarily individual client focused and require self-report of symptom experience. Despite the emphasis on individual-level assessment, systemic clinicians must focus on how every assessment process provides an opportunity for them to collaborate and build partnerships with families. By engaging family members in the assessment process and asking for their perspectives on what has been happening, counselors can dimensionalize their conceptual-ization of somatic symptoms and the emotional, cognitive, and behavioral correlates.

When working with a child or adolescent, counselors need to engage the family imme-diately and consult with early professional contacts including the family physician or pedi-atrician. Many parents/caregivers are not able to differentiate between clinically relevant and developmentally appropriate behaviors for their child. Also, parental anxiety around somatic symptom can be especially heightened, which could complicate the assessment pro-cess. Approaching assessment from a systems perspective can reduce gaps in identification of symptoms and contextual factors. Two assessment domains will be explored, namely clinician-administered diagnostic interviews and instrumentation.

Diagnostic Interviewing

A structured clinical interview for *DSM-5* disorders helps mental health professionals deter-mine an accurate diagnosis for Somatic Symptom and Related Disorders. A structured clini-cal interview uses standardized questions to ensure that each person is offered the same experience to accurately diagnose the symptoms and client experience. Upon conducting the structured clinical interview, family counselors can complete the Clinician-Rated Severity of Somatic Symptom Disorder, which is a three-item assessment of the degree of excessive con-cern, preoccupation, and disproportionate focus (APA, 2016). Engaging family members in this process can provide contextual information that can facilitate an accurate and compre-hensive diagnosis.

Instrumentation

There are many assessment tools available to assist clients and families in providing self-report data on somatic symptoms. The most-well-established measures are the Patient Health Questionnaire-15 (PHQ-15; Kroenke, Spitzer, & Williams, 2002) and the Symptom Check-list-90 (SCL-90) somatization scale (Derogatis, 1994). This section provides an introduction and overview to seven common and emergent assessment instruments that counselors uti-lize when working with clients and families. Many of the assessment instruments have been recently developed to reflect the revisions emergent in the *DSM-5*, and thus, researchers and mental health professionals are continuing to establish the reliability and validity of many of the instruments. Also, as the assessment instruments are focused on individual clients, sys-temic clinicians will have to be creative in identifying ways to include family members in the evaluative process. For a quick reference guide of the assessment instruments, see Table 9.1.

TABLE 9.1 Summary of Assessment Instruments

Assessment	Domains/Foci	Format	Completion Time
Clinician-Rated Severity of Somatic Symptom Disorder	Misattributions, preoccupation, and excessive concerns Recent (past 7 days)	Clinician Evaluation 3 items 5-point response sets	5–10 minutes
Four-Dimensional Symptom Questionnaire (4DSQ; Terluin, 2012)	Somatization, depression, anxiety, and distress Recent (past 7 days)	Client Self-Report 50 items 5-point response sets	20 minutes
Patient Health Questionnaire-15 (PHQ-15; Kroenke et al., 2002)	Presence and severity of common somatic symptoms Chronic (past 4 weeks)	Client Self-Report 15 items 3-point response sets	5–10 minutes
	Level 2-Somatic Symptom, Adult (Patient Health Questionnaire-15 Somatic Symptoms Severity Scale) Age 17 through adulthood Recent (past 7 days)	Client or Informant Self-Report 15 items 3-point response sets	5–10 minutes
	Level 2-Somatic Symptom, Parent/Guardian of Child Ages 6 to 17 Recent (past 7 days)	Parent/Guardian Report 13 items 3-point response sets	5–10 minutes
	Level 2-Somatic Symptom, Child Ages 11 to 17 Recent (past 7 days)	Child/Adolescent Self-Report 13 items 3-point response sets	5–10 minutes

(continued)

TABLE 9.1 Summary of Assessment Instruments (continued)

Assessment	Domains/Foci	Format	Completion Time
Somatic Symptom Disorder-B Criteria Scale (SSD-12; Toussaint et al., 2016)	Psychological features of somatic symptom disorder	Client Self-Report 12 items	2–5 minutes
Somatic Symptoms Experiences Questionnaire (SSEQ; Herzog et al., 2015)	Psychological, behavioral, and interactional components of somatic symptoms Chronic (past 6 months)	Client Self-Report 15 items 6-point response sets	10–15 minutes
Somatic Symptom Scale-8 (SSS-8; Gierk et al., 2014)	Symptom severity burden Recent (past 7 days)	Client Self-Report 8 items 5-point response sets	1 minute
Symptoms and Perceptions (SaP; Yzermans, Baliatsas, van Dulmen, & Van Kamp, 2016)	Nonspecific physical and psychological symptoms Symptom prevalence, duration, and health care use Perceptions of treatment effectiveness, impact, and concern Chronic (past month)	Client Self-Report 39 items Variable response rates across diverse item types	10–15 minutes
Symptom Checklist-90 (SCL-90) somatization scale (Derogatis, 1994)	Somatization, Obsessive-Compulsive, Interpersonal Sensitivity, Depression, Anxiety, Hostility, Phobic Anxiety, Paranoid Ideation, and Psychoticism Global Severity Index	Client Self-Report 90 items	12–15 minutes

Four-Dimensional Symptom Questionnaire (4DSQ; Terluin, 2012)

The 4DSQ is a 50-item assessment instrument that examines complaints and symptoms across the last 7 days. The domains of focus are distress, depression, anxiety, and somatization. The somatization scale assesses a range of common physical symptoms with higher scores reflecting constructs of health anxiety, sensitization, and illness features. Example items are: "During the past week, did you suffer from a vague feeling of fear?" "During the past week, did you suffer from painful muscles?" "During the past week, did you have to avoid certain places because they frightened you?" The 4DSQ has alpha reliability coefficients ranging from 0.84 to 0.94 with slightly higher test–retest reliability ranging from 0.89 to 0.94. Correlations among the scales of the 4DSQ range from 0.35 to 0.71 (Terluin, 2012; Terluin & Verbraak, 2014).

Patient Health Questionnaire-15 (PHQ-15; Kroenke et al., 2002)

The PHQ-15 is a well-established assessment for somatic symptom presence and severity (Zijlema et al., 2013). The PHQ-15 measures somatic symptoms across the last 4 weeks. Typically, the PHQ-15 is completed prior to a client's visit with the family counselor. There are 15 items on the scale with scores for each item ranging from 0 ("not bothered at all") to 2 ("bothered a lot"). Thresholds of severity range from minimal (0–4) and low (5–9) to medium (10–14) and high (15–30).

There are three adaptations of the PHQ-15 that family counselors can integrate into the assessment process. The Level 2-Somatic Symptom, Adult and Level 2-Somatic Symptom, Child Age 11 to 17 are administered based on age of the client experiencing somatic symptoms. The threshold levels and administration protocol are comparable to the PHQ-15. The third adaptation, Level 2-Somatic Symptom, Parent/Guardian of Child Age 6 to 17, is identical to the Level 2-Somatic Symptom, Child Age 11 to 17, but the assessment is completed by a parent or caregiver as opposed to the child. Given the involvement of the parent or guardian, this assessment can be used with younger children beginning at age 6.

Systemic clinicians can use the PHQ-15 and the three adapted versions to provide initial assessment data, termination assessment data, and ongoing assessment of stability of symptoms across treatment (Gierk, 2015). Addressing the assessment and integrating the family's report of the symptoms will assist the family counselor in developing a comprehensive conceptualization of the client's presenting needs. The family unit functions as an evolving system supporting the need for the family members to be provided the opportunity to self-assess and engage in the treatment process to promote all family members as active agents in counseling rather than isolating the diagnosed family member in the treatment process (Gierk, 2015).

Somatic Symptom Disorder-B Criteria Scale (SSD-12; Toussaint et al., 2016)

The SSD-12 is a 12-item instrument focused on assessing the psychological features of the *DSM-5* SSD. The SSD-12 was recently developed to examine the client's cognitions, affects, or actions that relate to the symptoms as part of Criterion B in the *DSM-5* diagnostic classification. The instrument is scored across three dimensions, namely cognitive aspects, affective aspects, and behavioral aspects. Initial reliability and validity measures seem promising (Toussaint et al., 2016), and clinicians may find the brevity and unique focus on Criterion B to be an advantages to use in clinical settings.

Somatic Symptoms Experiences Questionnaire (SSEQ; Herzog et al., 2015)

The SSEQ was developed to measure the psychological aspects of somatic symptoms (Herzog et al., 2015). The SSEQ has a total of 15 items, 13 of which measure psychological processes, one of which measures the experience of physical complaints, and one of which measures number of doctor visits. Example items include: (a) "I have _____ felt desperate because of my physical complaints"; (b) "While I have physical complaints, I _____ have to think about them"; and (c) "During the last 6 months, I have _____ experienced physical complaints." The authors of the SSEQ utilized results from a factor analysis to define four components captured in the instrument, namely health worries, experience of illness, problems while interacting with physicians, and consequences of illness.

Systemic clinicians may use the SSEQ to measure the degree of debilitating thoughts, feelings, or actions that a client is experiencing. The instrument provides data related to the impact of somatic symptoms on thinking, feeling, and health-based actions. The information gained from the instrument assists the family counselor in constructing meaningful treatment goals and establishing systemic interventions for the family therapy process.

Somatic Symptom Scale-8 (SSS-8; Gierk et al., 2014)

The SSS-8 is a recently created instrument that measures somatic symptom burden. The SSS-8 abridges the PHQ-15 and emerged in field trials for the DSM-5 (APA, 2013; Gierk, 2015). The instrument is client reported and includes eight items that translate into threshold measures of low, medium, high, or very high. The cutoff scores are categorized as "no to minimal" (0–3), "low" (4–7), "medium" (8–11), "high" (12–15), and "very high" (16–32) somatic symptom burden.

In a German study of 2,510 individuals older than 13 years, the SSS-8 had a Cronbach's alpha coefficient of 0.81 (Gierk et al., 2014). In this study, the SSS-8 had significant correlations with measures of depression ($r = 0.57$), anxiety ($r = 0.55$), and general health status ($r = -0.24$). The researchers found that as severity across threshold categories increased, there was a corollary increase in health care visits at rates around 50%.

Gierk et al. (2014) recommend coupling the administration of the SSS-8 with the administration of a brief depression and anxiety scale. Preliminary recommendations for the usage of the SSS-8 include the collection of data that could facilitate a family counselor assessing Criterion A for SSD and that could provide information on efficacy of treatment.

Symptoms and Perceptions (SaP; Yzermans et al., 2016)

The SaP is a 39-item questionnaire that focuses on 28 nonspecific psychological and physical symptoms. The instrument measures three dimensions of the 28 symptoms, namely symptom prevalence, symptom duration, and health care usage due to symptoms. Higher scores indicate higher levels of prevalence, duration, and health care use. In addition to the 28 symptom items, the remaining items require the respondent to identify the most important complaint and then rate how much it impacts daily life, perceptions of anticipated duration, perceived helpfulness of treatment, level of concern, degree of understanding, and emotional impact of symptom. The systemic clinician can gain significant clinical information from this instrument based on the data about the most salient symptom and its resultant impact. Systemic clinicians can assess family members' perceptions of these same questions (most important, impact, perceived helpfulness of treatment, level of concern, emotional impact) in order to develop a contextualized understanding of how the symptom is influencing the overall family system.

Symptom Checklist-90 Somatization Scale (SCL-90; Derogatis, 1994)

The SCL-90 is a well-established and commonly used instrument in clinical, medical, educational, and research settings. The SCL-90 has nine areas of focus, namely somatization, obsessive-compulsive, interpersonal sensitivity, depression, anxiety, hostility, phobic anxiety, paranoid ideation, and psychoticism. The scales are reported individually, and also there are three global indices assessing overall psychological distress and intensity of symptoms. The age range for the SCL-90 is 13 years and older. Interpretive reports provide age-normed data. The subscale focused on somatization can provide useful treatment information to a clinician that is contextualized in the other eight foci and the global severity index (Gierk, 2015).

FAMILY SYSTEMS INTERVENTIONS

The systemic perspective offers a holistic conceptualization of Miguel in his family, culture, community, and the societal system (see Figure 9.1). Miguel's family is viewed as a network of relationships working to regulate the interactions among the family members and at some point the system became unstable as the family attempted to create solutions for the breakdown of the emotional interactions. Given that Miguel's family is viewed as a dynamic whole and operates to regulate behaviors for the family to function with stability, the systemic clinician's conceptualization explores how the family became stuck in repetitive cycles of unproductive interactions (Nichols & Schwartz, 2006). The systemic clinician may select a battery of assessments addressed earlier to generate treatment procedures and best-practice methods for Miguel and engage the family in the interview process as a method to integrate the systemic perspective into the treatment process.

Feedback offered to Miguel by his wife and doctors works to regulate his behaviors and interactions, indicating that he has no medical and physical reason to feel fatigue and physical pain. The perceived messages Miguel internalizes from this feedback impact him in various ways, as shown in Table 9.2. The family therapist may mitigate the emotional, mental, and physical impact of the messages by reframing Miguel's interpretation of the messages and offering a connection between his interpretations, contextual environmental factors, and the intended communication.

As you have conceptualized, Miguel interprets the messages in ways that impact his mental and emotional health as he feels hopeless and helpless with no solution or faith in others to understand. The physical and mental symptoms experienced by Miguel are

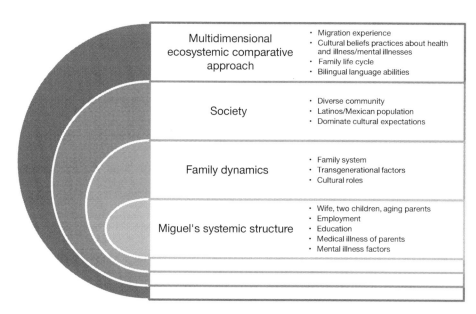

FIGURE 9.1 Systemic conceptual lens.

TABLE 9.2 Miguel's Perceived Feedback Cycle

	Miguel	Wife	Doctors	Children
Symptoms	- Back pain, fear of serious medical illness (tumor, cancer); - Fatigue, sleeping, unable to physically move with comfort			
Feedback		"Toughen up and work through the pain."	"All the tests indicate you are well and provide excellent results for good health."	"Dad is not available for me."
Perceived/ interpreted message		"Nothing is wrong and you are weak if you cannot complete your responsibilities." "Miguel, you are inadequate when you do not work to financially support the family." "You are not reliable and you are unable to be responsible for our needs." "You are weak and you are making up your pain."	"You should be feeling great, we cannot find anything wrong." "I am not being heard and I cannot communicate well my illness." "No one understands me and my pain."	"Dad limits my fun with friends." "Life is different. Now that my Dad is sick, we no longer has fun." "Dad is not reliable and he does not follow through."
Internalized impact		"I am not a provider for my family." "I am not good enough for my wife, children, and parents." "I am not being heard and others cannot find the truth."	"I cannot work and care for my family because no one can truly hear my concerns." "I am not good enough because professionals do not believe me." "I will never get better and I fear that I will lose everything from being sick."	"My children do not trust me to be there for them." "Life will always be this way from now on and I feel helpless and hopeless." "I can no longer have fun because the pain is too severe."

described by systems theorists as the family's functioning to promote the development and continuance of his somatic systems. The unresolved family conflict, rules of Miguel's responsibilities and roles, and stressors impacting the family system are kept in balance by the somatic symptoms (Bowen, 1978; Haggerty, 1983; Minuchin, 1974; Minuchin, Rossman, & Baker, 1978; Roy, 1982; Thoburn et al., 2009; Turk & Kerns, 1985; Waring, 1986). Miguel's expression of his physical and mental pain offers him an acceptable outlet to express emotional needs that are not tolerated under different circumstances within the family structure. Miguel's expression of his pain has been accepted and tolerated until more recently due to the response and communication of his wife, doctors, and children that he needs to move forward and stop complaining. The following three interventions will offer a conceptualization of Miguel and his family dynamics, steps to engage Miguel and his family to experience and process communication openly, and the systemic clinician's role within the counseling process.

Family Balloons: Carrying the Family Load

Conceptualization of the Family Dynamic

Miguel may perceive his family to be intolerant of open communication of needs. Systemic clinicians work in session to help the family think in new ways rather than working to stop the problem behavior and symptom; the family counselor works to take the symptom behaviors energy and redirects the focus in more productive ways to benefit the family dynamic. The systemic clinician's lens sees the family strengths and utilizes these to engage the family in adjusting to the developmental and contextual demands (Gehart, 2013).

Potential Emotional and Mental Benefit From the Intervention

The family will be offered an opportunity to individually express the responsibilities each member perceives he or she experiences. This will offer the family an opportunity to break down the covert rule not to openly express feelings and thoughts by enhancing communication of perceived stress and roles. The benefit and purpose of this activity offers the family real-life practice communicating thoughts and feelings, and visually shatters the perception that the problem lands solely with Miguel (Gehart, 2013).

Intervention

The systemic clinician creates an enactment for the family to alter existing communication patterns that are ineffective, maintaining problem-laden interactions. In this case, the clinician hears that Miguel feels unheard and not understood. The systemic clinician uses the physical space of balloons to help Miguel be physically/visually heard by his family members. To create an effective interactive enactment, the systemic clinician needs to help the client/family do something different regarding communication, clarifying boundaries, and sharing feelings and thoughts otherwise not acceptable to express.

Logistics

Provide the family with options to select numerous balloons of different colors and one indelible marker—a different color for each family member.

- 100 balloons, all of different colors
- Balloon pump, if needed
- Indelible markers, different colors

Counselor Communicates These Directions

- Precede the exercise by addressing Miguel: "Miguel, you appear to have no options to handle the stress of your physical pain. I wonder if you have considered all you manage and roles you take on within your family and house. Let's consider for a moment all the roles you have within the family."
- Ask each family member to select one balloon for each responsibility he or she has within the family (all family members will do this at the same time).
- Give each family member a color marker and ask them to blow up their balloons and write one responsibility on each.
- Next, have the family members select balloons that represent the stresses they have experienced and ask each family member to write each stress on a blown up balloon or draw an image to represent the stress.
- Ask the family to stand in a circle with their balloons.
- Have each family member pick up a balloon and name the balloon along with expressing how the responsibility impacts his or her role in the family.
- After each family takes a turn, ask the other members to consider what may be missing and have them add the newly generated ideas to the collection of balloons. Ask each family member to hold all of his or her balloons and the new balloons during the entire time of the activity.
- When you notice a family member struggling to hold the balloons, notice how other family members respond (take a mental note to process later).

Counselor's Processing Guide

As the activity is being conducted, the counselor softly states the directions and helps the family begin the activity by generating ideas of responsibilities. Spelling on balloons is challenging so let the family know abbreviations will work so the word fits on the balloon (this may help the member honestly write rather than writing only what each person believes he or she can spell). The counselor facilitates the activity by giving the basic instructions: "Please take a moment to explore the responsibilities you hold at work, school, home, as a Dad, Mom, sister, home owner, student, parent, spouse, child, financial provider, business owner, and duties to manage your property (list what fits with the family dynamics)." Have the family generate a few roles following a few of the clinician's thoughts.

Assist the family in collecting a pile of balloons to begin. Allow the family to select a marker color to write roles on the balloons. After the roles are written, ask the family to also write stress or concerns faced. The systemic clinician processes with the family:

- Have the family members describe what they experienced with the activity (make sure the family members use "I" language).
  - Explore the similar experiences expressed by family members and/or the different experiences communicated by everyone.
  - Validate the emotional struggles with feeling reflections.
    - "Miguel, you realize you have more roles and stressors than you can hold at one time by yourself. You realize how overwhelmed you feel and scared with each changing role."
- Have family members identify the roles they find easy to communicate and describe the roles that are more challenging to express or share.
- Explore what you observed: For instance, "Miguel, I noticed you struggled to carry all of the responsibilities you were holding . . ." (see if he responds).

- "Miguel, when your balloons were falling, what led you to continue struggling to hold on?"
- Ask the children:
  - When did you notice when Dad held on to his responsibilities and began to struggle?
  - How does the struggle Dad faces impact you?
  - Describe ways to communicate your need for help?
  - Who noticed someone needed help in the family?
  - What held you back from reaching out to offer support?
- Help the family see how holding onto balloons with no help becomes an overwhelming burden—physically painful, tiring, and evoking fears that your balloons will fall.
- Connect the balloons to real life: Explore: "How are the balloons representative of the struggles you face each day?" "How do you feel?"
- Have each family member describe the physical appearances of the other members as they held their balloons and what the impact of the responsibilities is on those family members as well as on himself or herself.
- Ask the family members to describe what they have learned from this experience.

Open Communication Strategies

Conceptualization of the Family Dynamic

The systemic clinician views family members' symptoms and problems as maintaining a sense of regularity and homeostasis within the family dynamic. Even though Miguel and his family perceive his symptoms as unwanted, they require the problems to mask an even greater distressing factor impacting the family (Gehart, 2013). The family has gained years of experience developing and maintaining the existing communication and family dynamic. Working to shift and alter the interactions will be scary for the family and unfamiliar. The family counselor will help the family experience new interactions and roles.

Potential Emotional and Mental Benefit From the Intervention

Unhealthy family systems are characterized by ridged boundaries, covert rules, ineffective communication, avoidant communication, enmeshment, and an unclear parental hierarchy (Thoburn et al., 2009). The potential benefit of the intervention is for the family members to experience a flexible interaction and behavioral pattern that provides opportunity to express thoughts and beliefs without perceived judgment of failure and rejection. The family will identify how they control one another with symptoms and withdrawing behaviors and how, having coping skills to recognize emotional distress, to express distress in more adaptive interactions rather than physical symptoms.

Intervention

The family will be sitting in a circle and will be offered to select one card (each card will have a "feeling" word and action). The intervention is to offer the family insight into dynamics and maintenance of roles, to enhance the family's expression and understanding of feelings and concerns, and to clarify unresolved issues (Kozlowska, English, & Savage, 2012).

Logistics

- The systemic clinician will create a list of feelings and actions for the group to express. The feeling and responding action will be placed on an index card.

- Or the group will collaboratively identify emotions and actions to match. The systemic clinician will place these on an index card.
- Each family member will select an index card addressing the role he or she will act out in the group dynamic.

Counselor Communicates These Directions

"The activity we will experience today will explore actions based on feelings and others' communication. Please take one index card and keep the feeling and action to yourself. Think to yourself: If you were feeling this way, what would be your action toward your other family members?" After handing out the cards, ask the family to discuss a topic that offers challenge to the family, such as: How will the weekend be spent? or What is a recent conflict the family endured over the past week? The family therapist recognizes that the process of the activity generates the meaning and not the outcome leading the family to solve the task. Therefore the process for deciding may be the intervention (unknown to the family), and require the family to be in their natural communication role when exploring the topic for the activity.

Feeling Card Statements (Comments will reflect the feelings and actions.)

- *Feeling sad*—Withdrawan, quiet, and hopeless
- *Feeling scared*—Nervous, fidgety, speaks tentatively, and anxiously looks for others' approval
- *Feeling happy*—Offers alternative solutions, responds with consideration of others, confident, and content with ideas
- *Feeling angry*—Responds with frustration and communicates with a mad tone toward others' comments; does not think they nor others are capable
- *Feeling hopeful*—Offers positive options and ideas with the group; believes others are helpful; presents as excited and with positive energy and acceptance of others

Counselor's Processing Guide

Helping the family identify emotions and process feelings with each other will be a new role and interaction for the family. Beginning this process with a less stressful topic may be a helpful plan, and the counselor can then move into discussing a recent issue the family endured. The counselor may begin processing the experience with the family during the event by tracking what he or she observes and the communication patterns that are present. The benefit to the family is to experience immediate feedback and new communication interactions.

Family therapists sequence questions to integrate the family more broadly by creating generally questions with less pressure for an emotionally driven response to questions that generate insight and family connections, such as:

Broad general questions:

- What do you think about this experience?
- What challenged you regarding your role?
- How was your index card role similar and different to the role you normally play communicating with your family?
- Describe the role you think your father, mother, and siblings played in this activity.

- What worked in this communication and what did you find to be ineffective communication?
- How is this similar to the communication experiences you have at home?
- Describe the actions you demonstrated differently while communicating here?
- Identify what behaviors, responses, and communication will be different at home the next time a similar event occurs?
  - Creativity and flexibility of the family therapist demonstrates movement and change for the family. An example of the therapist's role facilitating creative change for the family may be to have the family reenact the event they describe to be different—help the family effectively communicate differently and work to identify roles and how roles shift in family dynamics/situations.
  - Creatively facilitating this interaction of flexible behavior and role shifts assists the family in generating new comfortable interactions that will become more familiar and a more natural response when communicating.
  - To end, have each family member describe the behavioral sequence/role that he or she will demonstrate next week when pulled into a situation similar to what was experienced in session. Ask each member how he or she will be accountable for his or her change in action (have each person speak for himself or herself). Discuss how the family will communicate and disengage when building in a new behavioral interaction structure.

ETHICAL AND LEGAL IMPLICATIONS

In terms of SSD, there are ethical considerations with which a counselor should be familiar when working with individuals and families. According to the American Counseling Association (ACA) *Code of Ethics*, counselors need to be knowledgeable of and competent in the various areas in which they work. If a counselor is incompetent regarding a specific disorder or area of practice, the counselor should not engage in the counseling relationship or should refer the client/family to another professional who does have the competence and knowledge needed to treat that disorder (ACA, 2014). The systemic clinician is charged with gaining skills to be competent providing sound treatment. Supervision offers a great resource to the clinician offering observation of sessions to gain feedback on interventions, conceptualizations of the family dynamic and clinical needs, and treatment methods integrating family theory, the developmental transition needs, and diagnoses. As SSD is not highly prevalent within the general adult population (APA, 2013), professional responsibilities of the counselor require extra training and knowledge to be attained before working with clients presenting with this disorder. The clinician will need to be particularly familiar with the *DSM-5* to know the specific nuances of the diagnostic criteria and learn appropriate treatment strategies.

Another ethical concern when working with individuals/families diagnosed with this disorder is the importance of counselors being aware of their own personal beliefs and biases so as to not impose those beliefs and biases onto a client (ACA, 2014). The American Association for Marriage and Family Therapy (AAMFT, 2012) also addresses the importance of family therapists not discriminating against clients due to health issues. In the case of SSD, it is important that the family counselor be aware of beliefs and potential biases regarding this disorder before engaging in a counseling relationship with a client who has been diagnosed with this disorder. Some systemic clinicians may struggle with the lack of a medical diagnosis to support the presence of the client's symptoms and concerns. The lack of a medical diagnosis may lead the counselor to want to tell the client that his or her symptoms are not "real" (AAMFT, 2012, Standard 3.10). If a systemic clinician believes he or she may be biased regarding this disorder, the clinician should examine his or her beliefs and seek direct supervision when working with individuals who are diagnosed with this particular disorder (AAMFT, 2012 Standard 3.3; ACA, 2014).

Legal implications for this disorder are not clearly communicated and will vary from state to state. One area with which a clinician may need to be familiar is the documentation and professional status one may need to assist a client in attaining disability benefits. According to the Social Security Administration (2016), there are a number of medical conditions and mental health disorders that may qualify an individual and his or her family members to receive disability benefits. Depending on the severity of the case and the level of impact this disorder may have for a client and his or her family, a counselor may be asked to complete supplemental paperwork in support of a client receiving disability benefits. Before engaging in any supplemental paperwork provided by a client, a counselor would be wise to review the paperwork with his or her own legal counsel to ensure that no negative legal implications may fall upon the clinician. In the case of Miguel, the counselor will need to be clear with the family about addressing all informed consent and treatment procedures and how this process works with multiple clients and not one identified patient as indicated in Standards 1.2, 2.1 (AAMFT, 2012).

As you think about the ethical and legal implications of this case, reflect on the following:

- Consider your beliefs about physical illness and expression of physical pain. Do you hold bias due to the desire to tell the client that these symptoms may not be "real"?
- As the systemic clinician in this case, have you experienced physical pain or do you have a diagnosed physical condition that may lead you to self-disclose meeting your need rather than offering treatment that meets the client's needs? Consider how your self-disclosure may impact the counselor–client relationship.
- The systemic clinician role may involve legal implications for Miguel's business. Are you prepared to sit trial to state your views of Miguel's illness impacting his ability to work? How will you or will not disclose your clinical views of Miguel's missed work and the legitimate reasons?
- Consider the educational, clinical, and counseling practice you will be required to have to be prepared and ethically responsible to offer family counseling given this case.
- Address areas of the *DSM-5* you, the family counselor, will need to be particularly familiar with regarding the specific nuances of the diagnostic criteria and treatment methods you will need to learn.

CASE CONCEPTUALIZATION

Miguel has been discussed throughout the chapter in an effort to further the reader's understanding of somatic symptoms and related disorders. The authors have included a more detailed case conceptualization of Miguel and his family to assist the reader further in conceptualizing Miguel from a systemic framework. The following section on Miguel's Systemic Ecology provides a rich depiction of how his disorder impacts the family system.

Miguel's Systemic Ecology

Miguel and his family were referred to counseling by their family doctor. Miguel has been struggling with severe lower back pain and fatigue over the last 8 months. He has seen a chiropractor, general physician, and a back specialist with no resulting medical diagnosis for his lower back pain. A number of medical diagnostic screenings (e.g., MRI of the lower back) have been conducted with no evidence of physical issues that would be causing Miguel's lower back pain. As Miguel's physical pain is not improving, he frequently expresses concerns of the pain being cancer or a possible brain tumor. Miguel's family doctor thought it would be helpful for Miguel and his family to see a counselor to help address some of the fear, anxiety, and frustrations Miguel and his family are experiencing.

Miguel is currently 30 years old and was born and raised in a rural town within the western region of the United States. His parents immigrated to the United States from Mexico before he was born. Miguel takes his parents back to Mexico for 2 weeks every year to visit extended family. Miguel is fluent in both Spanish and English with Spanish being his identified native language. Miguel's mother's health has been a bit of a roller coaster. His mother is a breast cancer survivor and is now demonstrating symptoms of dementia. Miguel's father's health is failing as a result of years of manual labor. Miguel's father was diagnosed with prostate cancer last year and has just completed his cancer treatments.

Miguel and his wife (Josie) met while they were in high school. Josie became pregnant with their first daughter during their senior year in high school. Miguel and Josie married just after graduation. Josie is a 29-year-old Caucasian daughter of a fifth generation farmer. Initially, her parents were unsupportive of Miguel and Josie's relationship. However, over the years, Josie's parents have come to accept and appreciate Miguel. There is no significant medical history in Josie's extended family.

Miguel did attend the local vocational school to be a diesel mechanic and is currently a partner of a successful diesel mechanic shop. As the children have gotten older and are both in school, Josie has recently enrolled as a college student. Josie is in her first year of college and intends to focus on elementary education. Josie does not currently work outside of the home as Miguel has been able to successfully support their family financially until recently. However, due to Miguel's chronic back pain and fatigue, the business and his partnership have started to show signs of financial strain.

Miguel and Josie have two children. The oldest daughter (Marie) is 12 years old and the younger daughter (Rozena) is 6 years old. The two girls both attend public school in their area. Josie has experienced a number of miscarriages with the last miscarriage resulting in Josie being hospitalized due to hemorrhaging. Although Miguel and Josie would like to have more children, the family has decided to stop trying for more children. Marie is starting to show physical signs of puberty and has been more emotional than normal recently.

Concurrent Problems

Miguel's fatigue and lower back pain have caused a significant change in his work performance recently. Although Miguel spends most of his time in the office rather than working on machines, he has been missing a number of days of work as he reports he "just can't find the energy" to go into work. Miguel has been working with a number of medical professionals to figure out what is causing the problems with no success. Miguel currently believes that he has cancer or possibly a brain tumor that is causing the problem, but no medical test is able to confirm this belief. In fact, the medical tests have consistently shown no signs of medical illness, and each medical professional has commented on how good Miguel's test results are. Miguel has undergone blood tests, x-rays, MRIs, and even nerve studies. All tests have shown positive health results with no found cause of his back pain or fatigue.

Background History and Stressors

As Miguel is the oldest son in his family, the care of his parents falls on him. Miguel and Josie have been the main supporters of his parents, financially and emotionally. As Josie is a stay-at-home mom, she takes on the responsibility of driving her in-laws to doctors' appointments. Miguel and Josie have started discussing having his parents move in with them as Miguel's mother's mental status is worsening.

Miguel has never received counseling before but has reluctantly agreed to attend counseling as the family medical doctor is the one who recommended it. When asked about any past traumas during intake, Miguel alluded to being sexually abused by an older male in his family, but then refused to discuss it further. He stated that he has only ever told one other person, his mother, and he has never received counseling for the abuse. Josie received counseling in high school after becoming pregnant. Due to the small community where they live, Josie's parents were concerned for how Josie would handle the extra negative attention during her pregnancy. Josie speaks very highly of her experience with counseling and is hopeful that family counseling will help with Miguel's condition.

Strengths

The family is actively engaged in their community and church. The family attends a non-denominational church weekly where Josie sings in the choir. Miguel is an assistant coach, when he feels well enough, of his oldest daughter's soccer team and has done so for the last 3 years. Josie's parents are very involved with Miguel and Josie's family. Josie's parents will take the girls on occasional weekends to allow Miguel and Josie some time alone as Josie's parents recognize the strain Miguel is under with the deteriorating health of his parents.

Miguel and Josie proudly report having a very loving relationship and appear to be supportive of one another. During the intake, the couple stated that they have worked hard "to beat the odds" in staying together after a rough start to their marriage. Marie and Rozena are both engaged in extracurricular activities and report having a number of friends. The couple expressed no additional concerns at this time.

Relational Problems

Miguel and Josie have worked hard to maintain their relationship. Both Josie and Miguel report feeling frustrated by Miguel's health but for different reasons. Miguel is frustrated with the medical professionals, "not taking me seriously" and Josie reports feeling frustrated that Miguel does not just "get over it or work through the pain." Josie characterizes Miguel as "a worrier" but does not share his concern that he has cancer or an undiagnosed brain tumor. Josie does believe he is tired and in pain, but does not know how to best help him.

Miguel reports that his business partner is becoming impatient and starting to demand that Miguel show up to work or decrease the percentage of income that Miguel receives from the business. Josie reports some relational strain between her and Marie. Josie believes this may be due to Marie coming into puberty; however, Marie stated that it is because "no one in this family gets me." Rozena stated that she enjoys kindergarten and has lots of friends but expressed her disappointment that she has not been able to have a play date because dad needs to rest.

DISCUSSION

As you continue to reflect on the case study and the overall approach, contemplate these questions:

- What might be some initial concerns/reactions for you as the systemic clinician working with this family?
  - Conceptualization of general concerns
  - Competency and training considerations and potential concerns

- ▪ Ethical factors and concerns
- ▪ Personal experiences similar to the client
- ▪ Biases

- Given the lack of medical support, how might you reframe this family's presenting problem to be more supportive with less attention on problems?

- What are the developmental life stages that you see within the different individuals of this family and how might these life stages be impacting your clients?

- How might culture play into the perception of what is going on for Miguel?

- Consider and describe the resources in your community that may benefit this family and meet their presenting needs.

SUMMARY

With more than 80% of the general population experiencing problematic somatic symptoms within the last week, counselors must be prepared to meet the needs of clients and their families who are impacted by such symptoms (Hiller et al., 2006). Appropriately assessing and diagnosing somatic symptom and related disorders is critical for counselors due to the complex intersection between physical and mental health. The changes reflected in *DSM-5* (APA, 2013) are emergent from concerns with how previous models reified dualistic separation between the mind and the body and framed somatic disorders as being medically unexplainable (Dimsdale et al., 2013). Engaging in multisystemic conceptualization is essential so that counselors can provide effective and transformative systems-level interventions.

To provide effective treatment, clinicians must champion the exposition of strengths as a method for fostering wellness and resiliency. Families must be understood from a systemic conceptual lens that optimizes the relational and cultural protective factors while affirming the multitude of variables influencing the development and maintenance of distressing somatic symptoms. We, as counselors, are uniquely positioned to join with clients and their families as they may feel distrust in the health care system (Stone, 2014). Focusing on empowerment and family dynamics has the potential to impact the homeostasis in a positive way and to disrupt the systemic factors influencing the distressing somatic symptoms. Our role as clinicians is to provide empathy, share resources, confront unhealthy communication and interaction styles, encourage pathways for wellness and healthy relationships, and empower individuals and families. Such focus will provide the needed treatment and support to clients experiencing distressing somatic symptoms.

REFERENCES

Afari, N., Ahumada, S. M., Wright, L. J., Mostoufi, S., Golnari, G., Reis, V., & Cuneo, J. G. (2014). Psychological trauma and functional somatic syndromes: A systematic review and meta-analysis. *Psychosomatic Medicine, 76*(1), 2.

American Association for Marriage and Family Therapy. (2012). *AAMFT code of ethics*. Alexandria, VA: Author. Retrieved from http://www.aamft.org/imis15/Documents/Legal%20Ethics/Board%20Approved%20Code%20 for%20Weeb%20Secured.pdf

American Counseling Association. (2014). *ACA code of ethics*. Alexandria, VA: Author. Retrieved from http://www.counseling.org/knowledge-center/ethics

American Psychiatric Association. (2000). *Diagnostic and statistical manual of mental disorders* (4th ed., text rev.). Washington, DC: Author.

American Psychiatric Association. (2013). *Diagnostic and statistical manual of mental disorders* (5th ed.). Arlington, VA: American Psychiatric Publishing.

American Psychiatric Association. (2016). Clinician-rated severity of somatic symptom disorder. Retrieved from https://psychiatry.org/psychiatrists/practice/dsm/dsm-5/online-assessment-measures

Barsky, A. J., Peekna, H. M., & Borus, J. F. (2001). Somatic symptom reporting in women and men. *Journal of General Internal Medicine, 16*(4), 266–275.

Bitter, J. (2014). *Theory and practice of family therapy and counseling* (2nd ed.). Belmont, CA: Brooks/Cole Cengage.

Bowen, M. (1978). *Family therapy in clinical practice*. Northvale, NJ: Aronson.

Dale, R. C., Singh, H., Troedson, C., Pillai, S., Gaikiwari, S., & Kozlowska, K. (2010). A prospective study of acute movement disorders in children. *Developmental Medicine and Child Neurology, 53*, 739–748. doi:10.1111/j.1469-8749.2009.03598.x

Derogatis, L. R. (1994). *SCL-90-R: Symptom Checklist-90-R: Administration, scoring, and procedures manual* (3rd ed.). Minneapolis, MN: National Computer Systems.

Dimsdale, J. E., Creed, F., Escobar, J., Sharpe, M., Wulsin, L., Barsky, A., . . . Levenson, J. (2013). Somatic symptom disorder: An important change in DSM. *Journal of Psychosomatic Research, 75*, 223–228.

Fazel, M., Reed, R. V., Panter-Brick, C., & Stein, A. (2012). Mental health of displaced and refugee children resettled in high-income countries: Risk and protective factors. *Lancet, 379*(9812), 266–282.

Fischer, S., Lemmer, G., Gollwitzer, M., & Nater, U. M. (2014). Stress and resilience in functional somatic syndromes: A structural equation modeling approach. *PLoS ONE, 9*(11), 1–10. doi:10.1371/journal.pone.0111214

Gehart, D. (2013). *Theory and treatment planning in counseling and psychotherapy*. Belmont, CA: Brooks/Cole.

Gierk, B., Kohlmann, S., Kroenke, K., Spangenberg, L., Zenger, M., Brahler, E., & Lowe, B. (2014). The Somatic Symptom Scale-8 (SSS-8): A brief measure of somatic symptom burden. *Journal of the American Medical Association Internal Medicine, 174*, 399–407. doi:10.1001/jamainternmed.2013.12179

Gierk, B., Kohlmann, S., Toussaint, A., Wahl, I., Brunahl, C. A., Murray, A. M., & Lowe, B. (2015). Assessing somatic symptom burden: A psychometric comparison of the Patient Health Questionnaire-15 (PHQ-15) and the Somatic Symptom Scale-8 (SSS-8). *Journal of Psychosomatic Research, 78*, 352–255.

Gini, G., & Pozzoli, T. (2009). Association between bullying and psychosomatic problems: A meta-analysis. *Pediatrics, 123*(3), 1059–1065.

Haggerty, J. J. (1983). The psychosomatic family: An overview. *Psychosomatics, 24*, 615–619.

Herzog, A., Voight, K., Meyer, B., Wollburg, E., Weinmann, N., Langs, G., & Lowe, B. (2015). Psychological and interactional characteristics of inpatients with somatoform disorders: Validation of the Somatic Symptoms Experiences Questionnaire (SSEQ) in a clinical psychosomatic population. *Journal of Psychosomatic Research, 78*, 553–562.

Hiller, W., Rief, W., & Brahler, E. (2006). Somatization in the population: From mild bodily misperceptions to disabling symptoms. *Social Psychiatry and Psychiatric Epidemiology, 41*, 704–712.

Kirmayer, L. J., & Sartorius, N. (2007). Cultural models and somatic syndromes. *Psychosomatic Medicine, 69*(9), 832–840.

Klaus, K., Rief, W., Brahler, E., Martin, A., Glaesmer, H., & Mewes, R. (2015). Validating psychological classification criteria in the context of somatoform disorders: A one-and four-year follow-up. *Journal of Abnormal Psychology, 124*(4), 1092–1101.

Korber, S., Frieser, D., Steinbrecher, N., & Hiller, W. (2011). Classification characteristics of the Patient Health Questionnaire-15 for screening somatoform disorders in a primary care setting. *Journal of Psychosomatic Research, 71*, 142–147. doi:10.1016/j.jpsychores.2011.01.006

Kozlowska, K., English, M., & Savage, B. (2012). Connecting body and mind: The first interview with somatising patients, and their families. *Clinical Child Psychology and Psychiatry, 18*(2), 224–245. doi:10.1177/1359104512447314

Kroenke, K., Spitzer, R. L., & Williams, J. B. W. (2002). The OHQ-15: Validity of a new measure for evaluating the severity of somatic symptoms. *Psychosomatic Medicine, 64*, 258–266.

Kugler, B., Bloom, M., Kaercher, L., Truax, T., & Storch, E. (2012). Somatic symptoms in traumatized children and adolescents. *Child Psychiatry and Human Development, 43*(5), 661–673.

Mikolajczak, M., Menil, C., & Luminet, O. (2007). Explaining the protective effect of trait emotional intelligence regarding occupational stress: Exploration of emotional labour processes. *Journal of Research in Personality, 41*(5), 1107–1117.

Minuchin, S. (1974). *Families and family therapy*. Cambridge, MA: Harvard University Press.

Minuchin, S., Rossman, B., & Baker, L. (1978). *Psychosomatic families: Anorexia nervosa in context*. Cambridge, MA: Harvard University Press.

Myers, J. E., & Sweeney, T. J. (2008). Wellness counseling: The evidence base for practice. *Journal of Counseling and Development, 86*, 482–493.

National Center for Health Statistics. (2017). *International classification of diseases, tenth revision, clinical modification*. Retrieved from https://www.cdc.gov/nchs/icd/icd10cm.htm

Nichols, M. P., Schwartz, R. C. (2006). *Family therapy: Concepts and methods* (7th ed.). Boston, MA: Allyn & Bacon.

Roy, R. (1982). Marital and family issues in patients with chronic pain. *Psychotherapy and Psychosomatics, 37*, 1–12.

Sansone, R. A., Wierderman, M. W., Tahir, N. A., & Buckner, V. R. (2009). A re-examination of childhood trauma and somatic preoccupation. *International Journal of Psychiatry in Clinical Practice, 13*(3), 227–231. doi:10.1080/13651500802621551

Social Security Administration. (2016). Disability benefits. Retrieved from https://www.ssa.gov/pubs/EN-05-10029.pdf

Steinhardt, M., & Dolbier, C. (2008). Evaluation of a resilience intervention to enhance coping strategies and protective factors and decrease symptomatology. *Journal of American College Health, 56*(4), 445–453.

Stone, L. (2014). Managing the consultation with patients with medically unexplained symptoms: A grounded theory study of supervisors and registrars in general practice. *BMC Family Practice, 15*, 192–208.

Terluin, B. (2012). Four-Dimensional Symptom Questionnaire (4DSQ): Measurement instrument database for social science. Retrieved from http://www.midss.ie

Terluin, B., & Verbraak, M. (2014). Validity of the Four-Dimensional Symptom Questionnaire (4DSQ) in community mental health. *Journal of Clinical Psychology, 44*, 198–211.

Thoburn, J., Hoffman-Robinson, G., Shelly, L. J., & Sayre, G. (2009). Collaborative treatment for the psychosomatic couple. *The Family Journal, 17*(1), 6–13. doi:10.1177/1066480708328347

Toussaint, A., Murray, A. M., Voight, K., Herzog, A., Gierk, B., Kroenke, K., . . . Lowe, B. (2016). Development and validation of the Somatic Symptom Disorder-B Criteria Scale (SSD-12). *Psychosomatic Medicine, 78*, 5–12.

Turk, D. C., & Kerns, R. D. (1985). The family in health and illness. In D. C. Turk & R. D. Kerns (Eds.), *Health, illness and families* (pp. 1–22). New York, NY: Wiley.

Um, Y., Huh, H., Kim, S., & Chae, J. (2014). Possible cultural effects on the increments of somatic symptoms in subjectively resilient depressed patients. *Asia-Pacific Psychiatry, 6*(3), 259–266. doi:10.1111/appy.12143

Walker, S. P., Wachs, T. D., Grantham-McGregor, S., Black, M. M., Nelson, C. A., Huffman, S. L., & Gardner, J. M. M. (2011). Inequality in early childhood: Risk and protective factors for early child development. *Lancet, 378*(9799), 1325–1338.

Waring, E. M. (1986). Marriages of psychosomatic patients. *Medical Aspects of Human Sexuality, 20*, 142–146.

Yzermans, J., Baliatsas, C., van Dulmen, S., & Van Kamp, I. (2016). Assessing non-specific symptoms in epidemiological studies: Development and validation of the Symptoms and Perceptions (SaP) questionnaire. *International Journal of Hygiene and Environmental Health, 219*, 53–65.

Zijlema, W. L., Stolk, R. P., Lowe, B., Rief, W., White, P. D., & Rosmalen, J. G. M. (2013). How to assess common somatic symptoms in large scale studies: A systematic review of questionnaires. *Journal of Psychosomatic Research, 74*, 459–468.

FEEDING AND EATING DISORDERS: A SYSTEMIC MODEL

Margaret Clark Zappitello

*I*n 2004, the World Health Organization (WHO, 2004) reported that there had been an "apparent increase in eating disorders" (p. 43) during the previous 50 years, and identified the need to develop effective treatments for individuals who suffer from eating disorders. It may well seem strange that something as fundamental and routine, for most people, as eating and drinking can be such a struggle for others. After all, these are basic life-sustaining activities that human beings engage in instinctively and habitually from birth. This can be, however, a life-threatening reality for those who suffer from feeding and eating disorders.

Although feeding and eating disorders have been the subject of clinical research and treatment for some time, it has only been recently that a more accurate understanding of their causality and effects has been achieved. For example, families of individuals with feeding and eating disorders were often viewed as part of the problem, yet not necessarily the solution. As Whitney and Eisler (2005) observed:

> Previous theoretical models regarding family functioning have proposed that dysfunctional family interactions may play a causal role in the development of eating disorders. Such models, while historically important, have been unhelpful in blaming families and are poorly supported by empirical evidence. (p. 575)

Currently, treatment of individuals with eating disorders involves systems work, whether it is the individual's biological family, or another system with which they are involved. Whoever might be part of their family system, individuals with feeding or eating disorders experience reciprocal influences with their family members. Consequently, the family system is appropriately involved in both assessing and treating those mental health disorders. Other systems, such as agencies that provide custodial or supervisory care for clients, are also part of the overall systems approach to treating feeding and eating disorders. The purpose of this chapter is to provide information about the *Diagnostic and*

Statistical Manual of Mental Disorders (5th ed.; *DSM-5*; American Psychiatric Association [APA], 2013) feeding and eating disorders in terms of diagnoses and criteria, relational and cultural features, family systems assessments, family systems interventions, ethical and legal implications, and a case conceptualization.

DSM-5 AND FAMILY SYSTEMS

The *DSM-5* (APA, 2013) can be a useful tool in the diagnostic and assessment portions of treatment for feeding and eating disorders. The research underlying the *DSM-5* diagnostic criteria provides the foundation of a reasonable working model for understanding these mental and physical health challenges. This section provides a description of the feeding and eating disorders in the *DSM-5* within the framework of the related diagnostic criteria. General information regarding the etiology of each disorder is included. Relational and cultural features, including those involving family systems, are detailed in the next section.

Feeding and Eating Disorders and the *DSM-5*

The *DSM-5* (APA, 2013) identifies six specific Feeding and Eating Disorders: Pica, Rumination Disorder (RD), Avoidant/Restrictive Food Intake Disorder (ARFID), Anorexia Nervosa (AN), Bulimia Nervosa (BN), and Binge Eating Disorder (BED). In the *DSM-5* (APA, 2013), the older *International Classification of Diseases, Ninth Revision, Clinical Modification (ICD-9-CM)* codes are correlated with the *International Classification of Diseases, Tenth Revision, Clinical Modification (ICD-10-CM*; National Center for Health Statistics, 2017) codes that are now in use for each of these disorders. In addition to an *ICD-10-CM* code, the diagnostic code for the feeding and eating disorders may also include specifiers for the status of remission and severity. As with other *DSM-5* disorders, Feeding and Eating Disorders should not be confirmed as a diagnosis if they are better explained by a medical condition or another mental disorder. An additional diagnosis for a feeding or eating disorder is appropriate if the symptoms are substantial enough to warrant specific treatment.

Interestingly, three of the specific feeding and eating disorders (i.e., Pica in Adults, Avoidant/Restrictive Food Intake Disorder, and Binge Eating Disorder), along with Other Specified Feeding or Eating Disorder, have the same *ICD-10-CM* code (APA, 2013). Notably, obesity is not identified as a mental health disorder because of the many and varied factors that can contribute to its etiology, although it often co-occurs with certain mental health disorders and some psychotropic medications. Overweight or Obesity is categorized under Other Conditions That May Be a Focus of Clinical Attention.

Pica in Children and Adults

The primary symptom of pica is consistently eating substances that are not food and have no nutritional value for a period of at least 1 month (APA, 2013). These substances can be many and varied, including wood, paper, paint, dirt, and ice. For the pica diagnosis, this behavior cannot be consistent with the individual's developmental level (less than 2 years old), and cannot be part of a cultural or social ritual. This behavior can occur concurrently with a different mental health disorder, but should be separately diagnosed only if it is significant enough to require specific clinical attention. Pica is sometimes diagnosed only after a consequent medical condition brings it to light.

Pica behaviors can begin at any age (APA, 2013). For example, Pica in Children can be found with children otherwise developing normally. Pica in Adults is more common among adults with intellectual disabilities, and occurs more frequently if the disability is more severe. An *in remission* specifier is used for this disorder if behaviors have not met the diagnostic criteria for an extended amount of time.

Rumination Disorder

For a diagnosis of Rumination Disorder (RD), the ruminating behaviors must occur for at least a month, multiple times a week, even daily (APA, 2013). In rumination, food that has been chewed and swallowed is regurgitated. The regurgitated food is chewed again, then swallowed again or spit out. An important point to note is that these behaviors are not the result of nausea or vomiting, and that the individual does not show an aversion to the behaviors. This ruminating behavior can seem to have a self-calming or stimulating effect.

RD occurs at any age, and, among adults, more often with those who are intellectually disabled (APA, 2013). Infants with RD may suffer from malnutrition, weight loss, and failure to meet expected developmental gains. In infants, the disorder typically begins between 3 and 12 months of age, and often stops on its own. Older children and adults can also experience malnutrition, especially if they restrict eating before or during social situations to avoid being observed engaging in the rumination behavior. Weight loss and social dysfunctions can be additional consequences of this disorder. As with pica, an *in remission* specifier is available for RD.

Avoidant/Restrictive Food Intake Disorder

Avoidant/Restrictive Food Intake Disorder (ARFID is a more extensive version of the Diagnostic and Statistical Manual of Mental Disorders (4th ed., text rev.; DSM-IV-TR; APA, 2000) feeding disorder of infancy or early childhood (APA, 2013). AFRID typically begins in infancy and early childhood, the individual's developmental level if the individual is less than 2 years of age, with an equal distribution between male and female. When AFRID co-occurs with autism spectrum disorder, it occurs more often in males. Restrictive eating from lack of interest (begins in infancy or early childhood), aversion to characteristics of food (texture, taste, and so forth, beginning in the first 10 years of life), and avoidance of anticipated negative effects of eating (e.g., choking, vomiting) based on prior experience (any age) are criteria for this disorder. These behaviors can result in failure to meet nutritional needs, substantial weight loss, and malnutrition, to the point of having to rely on enteral feeding or oral supplements. Problems with psychosocial functioning, such as refusal to eat in the presence of others, might also result from these eating problems.

In order to diagnose this disorder, the related behaviors cannot be a result of unavailability of food or a cultural practice, or due only to anorexia nervosa or bulimia nervosa (APA, 2013). There is no evidence of Body Dysmorphic Disorder with AFRID, which is an important distinction between AFRID and AN or BN. There is not enough information available at this time to connect AFRID with later development of eating disorders. The development of AFRID may be related to medical problems, including gastrointestinal issues. As with Pica and RD, an *in remission* specifier is available for this disorder.

Anorexia Nervosa, Restricting Type and Binge-Eating/Purging Type

There are three basic criteria for Anorexia Nervosa (AN): restrictive calorie intake resulting in very low weight for their body type, age, and so forth; a strong fear of gaining weight, or consistently interfering with gaining weight; and an inaccurate perception of their body with an overemphasis of the importance of bodily perception on self-esteem, or a failure to acknowledge the potential dangers associated with their significantly low body weight (APA, 2013). For individuals with AN, the behaviors are manifestations of a self-control issue. In addition, individuals perceive their whole body or parts of their body as being fat, no matter what their weight may be. Paradoxically, losing weight can actually intensify their obsession with, and anxiety about, weight loss.

AN has obsessive-compulsive characteristics, which may include collecting recipes and hoarding food (APA, 2013). Depression symptomatology is also common, which could be secondary to malnutrition. Suicidal ideation is not unusual, and should be assessed as part of the diagnostic process. Additionally, individuals with AN have been known to use medications to manipulate (reduce) body weight.

AN typically does not start before puberty or after 40 years of age (APA, 2013). The onset can be due to a stressful life event or trauma, and is more likely if a first-degree biological relative has AN. In addition, there is a higher incidence of bipolar disorder and depressive disorders in first-degree relatives of individuals with anorexia nervosa, occurring more frequently with the binge-eating/purging type than the restricting type. A 10 to 1 ratio of females to males has been observed among those who have AN.

For a diagnosis of Anorexia Nervosa, Restricting Type, the required criteria must be met for at least 3 months (APA, 2013). The restricting and weight control behaviors include dieting, fasting, and/or excessive exercise. Characteristics also include control and rigidity manifesting in various ways, including emotionally and socially. For example, flat affect and/or withdrawal from social interactions can be symptomatic of AN. Binge eating or purging cannot be present for this type to be diagnosed.

A diagnosis of Anorexia Nervosa, Binge-Eating/Purging Type, requires that certain behaviors, including binge eating, last for at least 3 months (APA, 2013). Binge eating is clinically defined as consuming an amount of food that is clearly more than a person would typically eat within a specific amount of time, usually a 2-hour period. The possible binge eating behavior has to be considered within the associated circumstances. For example, many people may eat more on a holiday, but doing so does not necessarily meet the criteria for this diagnosis. A single episode of binging may involve the individual eating in more than one location, which could include different homes, eateries, and so forth. In this disorder, the binging is then followed by purging, which includes overuse of laxatives, diuretics, or enemas, or self-induced vomiting. Individuals with the binge-eating/purging type of AN tend to display impulsivity and to misuse substances.

An *in partial remission* specifier is used with AN when restrictive eating has not occurred for a substantial amount of time, but one of the other criteria is still met (APA, 2013). The *in remission* specifier for AN is used if behaviors have not met any of the diagnostic criteria for a substantial amount of time. *In full remission* is appropriate when none of the criteria have been met for a prolonged amount of time.

The severity specifier for both types of AN is based on body mass index (BMI) or a BMI percentile for children and adolescents, and can reflect the extent of functional disability, symptoms, and supervisory needs (APA, 2013). Because of the medical consequences of AN behaviors, medical professionals are usually involved in cases of AN, and they would determine a client's BMI. Mild, moderate, severe, and extreme levels of severity are possible, based on specific BMI criteria in the *DSM-5* (APA, 2013, p. 339).

Bulimia Nervosa

Bulimia Nervosa (BN) does not involve restrictive eating practices (APA, 2013). Instead, BN involves binge eating (as described in the previous section on AN, binge-eating/purging type). During the binge eating, individuals will feel that they do not have control over how much or what they eat. After binge eating, individuals will attempt to avoid weight gain from the binge eating by purging through misusing laxatives, diuretics, and other medications; self-induced vomiting; fasting; or extreme exercising. Another criterion for this disorder is that the binge eating and purging must happen an average of at least once a week for 3 months. Similar to AN, a diagnostic criterion for BN is that the individuals' self-esteem is unreasonably based on their perceptions, or misperceptions, of their own body in terms of weight and other factors. Additional characteristics common to both of these disorders are an inordinate fear of gaining weight, an obsessive determination to lose weight, and negative perceptions of their own bodies.

The *in partial remission* specifier for BN means that some of the diagnostic criteria are no longer met (APA, 2013). *In full remission* indicates that none of the diagnostic criteria are met. The severity specifier is based on the number of times that purging occurs in a week. Mild, moderate, severe, and extreme indicate a range from between one to three episodes a week up to 14 or more incidents of purging in a week.

Individuals with BN are generally normal weight or overweight, but not obese (APA, 2013). BN can be fatal from damage caused by purging behaviors, including gastrointestinal and cardiac problems. This eating disorder is most common among older adolescents and young adults, with a 10 to 1 ratio of female to male. It often begins after a dieting attempt, and can be related to multiple life stressors and events. Individuals with this eating disorder are at a higher risk for death from suicide and other causes. BN does not usually develop into AN. The purging behaviors will sometimes stop, whereas the binge eating continues. This would require a change in diagnosis to binge eating disorder. Concerns about weight, depressive symptomatology, and anxiety can be precursors of BN. Bipolar disorder (mood issues) and substance misuse can also be related to BN.

Binge Eating Disorder

The criteria for Binge Eating Disorder (BED) include incidents of binge eating (defined under AN, binge-eating/purging type) at the average rate of once a week for 3 months (APA, 2013). This disorder does not include purging behaviors, but does involve a significant sense of discomfort regarding the binging behavior. Also, three out of the following five specific elements are required to make this diagnosis: eating more quickly than usual; eating until discomfort results; eating a lot of food when not hungry; eating alone so that the binging will not be observed by others; and experiencing negative emotions after binging.

Individuals with BED can be obese, overweight, or of normal weight (APA, 2013). BED can be triggered by stress and negative emotions about self and body, food, and so forth. This disorder can occur in children, although it typically starts during adolescence or young adulthood. Individuals who seek treatment for BED are usually older than individuals who seek treatment for AN or BN, and the remission rate is higher for BED than AN or BN. Like AN and BN, BED tends to occur in combination with Bipolar Disorder, Depressive Disorders, Anxiety Disorders, and, less frequently, Substance/Medication Abuse.

The specifier for *in partial remission* indicates that the binge eating occurs an average of less than one incident a week (APA, 2013). *In full remission* means that no criteria have been met for a significant period of time. The severity specifier is the same as for BN.

Other Specified Feeding or Eating Disorder

Other Specified Feeding or Eating Disorder have some symptoms of feeding and eating disorders to the point of impairing healthy daily functioning, but do not meet all of the criteria for those disorders (APA, 2013). Some examples of these disorders include, but are not limited to, atypical anorexia nervosa; bulimia nervosa (of low frequency and/or limited creation); binge eating disorder (of low frequency and/or limited duration); purging disorder; and night eating syndrome. As indicated by the name of this category, diagnosis does require that specific characteristics be used in the identifying language.

Unspecified Feeding or Eating Disorder

This designation of Unspecified Feeding or Eating Disorder is used when symptoms do not meet the criteria for a specific feeding and eating disorder, and the clinician chooses not to identify the reason that the criteria are not met (APA, 2013). This category also covers those circumstances in which there are not adequate data to determine a clear diagnosis. Specific language regarding characteristics of the disorder is not necessary when using this diagnostic category.

RELATIONAL AND CULTURAL FEATURES

As with other mental health disorders, feeding and eating disorders do not develop in a vacuum. In addition to potential physiological factors, including genetics, relational and cultural influences can be involved in both the etiology and treatment of those disorders. The following sections review each of the *DSM-5* feeding and eating disorders in terms of associated relational and cultural features. Information regarding these features in the treatment of feeding and eating disorders is discussed later in this chapter in the section on Interventions.

Pica

"Pica" is appropriately derived from the Latin term for magpie, a scavenging bird that feeds indiscriminately on even nonfood substances (Sinha & Mallick, 2010, p. 21). Although this same behavior is generally considered to be dysfunctional in human beings, it can also be a cultural-based practice for spiritual, medicinal, or social reasons (APA, 2013). In such cases, pica is not diagnosed. Other culturally accepted pica-type behaviors, such as chewing gum or ice, sometimes rise to the level of a diagnosis of pica. This is typically more common among pregnant women.

For young children and developmentally delayed individuals, deficits in supervision by caregivers can contribute to the development of pica behaviors (APA, 2013). That kind of relationship factor can have a profound impact on the course of this illness. The pica behaviors and symptoms may also be exacerbated should the caregiver relationship be disrupted by dependency and neglect or other legal interventions that change the minor child or dependent adult's living situation.

Rumination Disorder

RD is an uncommon disorder, and its causes are not clear (Talley, 2011). However, it has been observed that parent–child relationship problems, neglect, and stress may be precursors of this disorder in infants and younger children (APA, 2013). As with pica, possible side effects of RD, including malnutrition and weight loss (Chial, Camilleri, Williams, Litzinger, & Perrault, 2003), could lead to legal actions that might disrupt the caregiver relationship and exacerbate the RD symptomatology.

Avoidant/Restrictive Food Intake Disorder

As with pica, ARFID is not diagnosed if the subject behaviors are solely related to cultural or religious practices (APA, 2013). Relational risk factors for this disorder are anxiety in the family, or having a mother with an eating disorder. Conversely, physical and social problems of this disorder may adversely affect family, particularly around activities that involve eating. Certain types of parent–child relationships may also contribute to the etiology of

AFRID. If a child with this disorder does better with a caregiver other than the child's parents, neglect or abuse may be indicated.

Anorexia Nervosa, Restrictive and Binge-Eating/Purging Types

Both types of AN occur cross-culturally, and each has some connection to societal, occupational, or avocational values of being thin (APA, 2013). An individual with AN may express the related fear of being overweight in terms that are acceptable for his or her culture, such as gastrointestinal complaints. It is often the family of someone with AN who reports the illness since the individual either does not recognize or acknowledge the problem. The family is also an important source of information regarding the course of illness because the family member with AN is generally not willing or able to do so.

Bulimia Nervosa

A societal emphasis on slender body types can be a risk factor for BN, along with the relational issue of physical or sexual abuse (APA, 2013). There is evidence that BN occurs cross-culturally and internationally at similar rates of prevalence. Transmission between family members and genetic predispositions are also possible with BN. It is not uncommon for individuals with BN to experience adverse effects on their social lives and relationships.

Binge Eating Disorder

The percentage of females with BED is consistent across cultures, and, in terms of gender diversity, more males are diagnosed with BED than the other eating and feeding disorders (APA, 2013). There is evidence that there may be some genetic predisposition related to this disorder as it appears to be more common in family groups. It is not uncommon for individuals with BED to experience problems with adjustment to social roles.

Cross-Cultural Considerations

Thus far, studies have shown the cross-cultural and international nature of eating disorder features, as well as their similarity across gender. For example, while researching the use of cognitive-behavioral therapy with Mexican American women suffering from BED, Shea, Cachelin, Gutierrez, Wang, and Phimphasone (2016) discovered that "The prevalence of bulimia nervosa (BN) and binge eating disorder (BED) among Latinas is comparable to those of the general population; . . ." (p. 31). In another study on self-identified Black, Hispanic, and White women with BED, Lydecker and Grilo (2016) determined that, although some factors varied in intensity and severity, "associated eating disorder psychopathology levels were similar across racial/ethnic groups" (p. 88).

There are also numerous studies that demonstrate the international nature of eating disorders, confirming that the related features are constant across nationalities. These studies include research on the following related topics: multifamily eating disorder treatment in the Czech Republic (Mehl, Tomanová, Kuběna, & Papežová, 2012); adult AN in couples in Australia (Murray, 2014); specific factors affecting eating disorders in Italy and Sweden (Sassaroli et al., 2015); and the role of media in relation to eating disorders in Indian adolescents (Singh, Parsekar, & Bhumika, 2016). Additionally, research on gender differences in the treatment of BED (Shingleton, Thompson-Brenner, Thompson, Pratt, & Franko, 2015) resulted in a similar finding that "No main effects of gender were found in treatment outcome" (p. 382). Clearly, eating disorders do not discriminate based on culture, nationality, or gender.

FAMILY SYSTEMS ASSESSMENTS

Inclusion of the family system is essential when dealing with feeding and eating disorders, for the health of both the identified client and his or her family, all of whose well-being is inextricably interconnected. As Whitney and Eisler (2005) observed:

> The impact of the illness on the family is immediately evident through the influence that the symptoms hold within the household. Just as issues around food, eating, and weight dominate the sufferer's thoughts and behaviours, food may also take a predominant role within family life and interactions. (p. 577)

Understanding that an individual's eating-disordered behaviors impact every member of his or her family is key to effective assessment. Evaluating the needs of each family member is necessary in order to achieve an accurate and thorough conception of the family system and the case (Treasure et al., 2008).

The assessment of family systems includes two basic components: Evaluating the identified client and other family members individually, and evaluating the family system as a whole, which also involves the evaluation of family subsystems. One step in this process is to evaluate client symptoms within the framework of the *DSM-5* (APA, 2013) criteria for specific feeding and eating disorders. Evaluating the client and his or her family members for other mental health disorders is also important. Anxiety, depression and suicidality, obsessive-compulsive behaviors, and substance misuse are not uncommon comorbid disorders for individuals with eating disorders (APA, 2013; National Eating Disorders Association [NEDA], 2015). Violent victimization has also been associated with eating disorders in women and children (WHO, 2013, 2016). Therefore, trauma disorders are another diagnosis that is not unusual among individuals with eating disorders. More information on specific assessments for these diagnostic categories can be found in the chapters on those issues.

Obtaining a thorough biological/psychological/social history from family members, most particularly from the identified client, is another step in this process. If this is done through an interview process, additional information can be obtained through interactions between the mental health professional and the family members. Observation of the interactions between family members is another fundamental and enlightening assessment technique.

The following sections review specific assessment strategies and instruments for each of the *DSM-5* (APA, 2013) eating and feeding disorders. Most of the identified assessment tools are self-report measures, some of which explore relationships. Because of assessment differences, pica and RD are examined separately. Because of assessment similarities, ARFID, AN, BN, and BED are discussed together in one section.

A general caution to keep in mind when assessing for feeding and eating disorders is that there are medical conditions with symptoms that overlap with eating disorders. Therefore, it is important that those medical conditions are accurately diagnosed and receive prompt medical attention. Although restrictive eating and vomiting might be accurately identified as meeting eating disorder criteria in some cases, these can also be symptoms of achalasia. Additionally, they can be evidence of physiological swallowing issues and some degree of *aperistalsis*, which is a medical problem involving the body's inability to move food through the gastrointestinal tract. To avoid misdiagnosis of medical illnesses such as achalasia, and to monitor clients for medical issues that can accompany feeding and eating disorders (APA, 2013), it is imperative that mental health professionals assessing for eating disorders collaborate with medical professionals throughout the assessment, diagnosis, and treatment processes.

Pica

Pica behaviors are generally assessed through self-report or observation by parents or other family members or caregivers, particularly in cases with younger clients (APA, 2013). Sometimes, assessment for pica is part of medical testing consequent to gastrointestinal, nutritional, and other medical problems that can occur because of pica behaviors. Regardless of how pica might be diagnosed, medical evaluation is an important part of addressing its potential medical complications.

Rumination Disorder

Like pica, RD is typically identified through self-report or observation by parents and others, including caregivers (APA, 2013). RD has historically been diagnosed primarily in children and adults with developmental delays or intellectual disabilities (Chitkara, Van Tilbur, Whitehead, & Talley, 2006; Talley, 2011). However, there has been an increasing number of recognized cases of RD (Talley, 2011) and RD has been seen more often in all ages of individuals who are healthy other than having RD (Chitkara et al., 2006). It is not clear whether this is because there are actually more individuals with RD, or if greater awareness of RD symptomatology among medical providers has led to the condition being recognized more frequently (Talley, 2011).

Medical assessment and monitoring may be necessary, particularly with infants and younger children, although "Extensive diagnostic testing is unnecessary" (Chial et al., 2003, p. 158). Two assessment tools, the Diagnostic Interview Schedule for Children and the Rome III Diagnostic Questionnaire for the Pediatric Functional GI Disorders (Delaney et al., 2015) can be used to assess children for RD. Similar assessments for adults are not yet available.

RD is often misdiagnosed because the individual with RD does not accurately observe or report his or her own symptoms (Talley, 2011). Consequently, the complete history that is necessary for diagnosis may be better obtained through information from a family member or other reliable source. A prompt and accurate diagnosis allows for timely intervention and improvement of the condition.

Avoidant/Restrictive Food Intake Disorder, Anorexia Nervosa, Bulimia Nervosa, and Binge Eating Disorder

As indicated at the beginning of this section on family systems assessments, ARFID, AN, BN, and BED assessment typically begins with self-report and observation by others, including parents and other caregivers (APA, 2013). As also previously stated, medical assessment and monitoring may become necessary. This is particularly true for infants and younger children with AFRID, and extreme or advanced cases of individuals with any of the eating disorders in this section. When purging is involved, related dental care may also become necessary because of the damage that can be caused by recurrent vomiting.

Although eating-disordered behaviors are often first identified by family members, particularly in younger clients, a variety of formal assessments have been developed for use in the clinical identification and treatment of eating disorders. How and when these assessment tools are used depends largely on the severity and treatment setting of the case.

In general, assessments in eating disorder cases are used to gather the following four categories of information: eating-disordered behaviors of the identified client; the general mental health status of the identified client; the identified client's family relationships and dynamics; and the interrelationship between the eating disorder, as well as the related treatment, and the identified client's parents or caregivers.

When assessing eating-disordered behaviors, different assessment instruments are used for different age groups. Two widely used assessments for children and adolescents, ages 8 through 18, are the Child Eating Disorder Examination (ChEDE) and the Child Eating Disorder Examination-Questionnaire (ChEDE-Q; Van Durme, Craeynest, Craet, & Goossens, 2015). These assessments are versions of the widely used Eating Disorder Examination that were developed specifically for use with children and adolescents. The ChEDE is a semistructured 28-question clinical interview that evaluates eating-disordered behaviors and cognitions. The ChEDE-Q is a 30-question self-report version of the ChEDE. For adults, the Eating Disorder Inventory-2 (Abbate-Daga et al., 2013) is a self-report assessment that evaluates behaviors, cognitions, and personality characteristics that are typically associated with eating disorders.

In addition to assessments that specifically target symptoms of eating disorders, clinicians also use assessments to develop a more complete understanding of the general mental health of the identified client. For example, depression, anxiety, self-esteem, self-efficacy, and temperament are often explored with the client experiencing eating disorders. A commonly used personality inventory is the Temperament and Character Inventory (TCI; Abbate-Daga et al., 2013). The TCI includes seven dimensions. Four of the dimensions evaluate temperament (novelty seeking, harm avoidance, reward dependence, and persistence), which includes genetically predisposed emotional patterns. The other three dimensions assess character (self-directedness, cooperativeness, and self-transcendence), which is defined as personality traits developed through life experience. In addition to providing greater understanding of a client's personality traits, TCI results can also be used to identify certain family-related characteristics and to explore a connection between those characteristics and the severity of the client's eating disorder.

Other assessments elicit information from the identified client and his or her family about family relationships and dynamics. One of these instruments is the Family Questionnaire (Sepulveda et al., 2014). The Family Questionnaire, which is also available in Spanish, itemizes 45 behavioral symptoms. The frequency of occurrence of each symptom is rated by family members of the identified client on a 3-point Likert scale, ranging from "never" to "often." When the symptom is identified as occurring, the family member also responds to two questions that focus on the impact of the symptoms on that family member. The data gathered by this instrument can provide valuable information on both the status of symptoms for the client, and the impact of the client's disorder on his or her family members.

There are also assessments specifically for parents and caregivers of clients who have been diagnosed with eating disorders. Two of these are the Accommodation and Enabling Scale for Eating Disorders (AESED; Sepulveda, Kyriacou, & Treasure, 2009) and the Eating Disorders Symptom Impact Scale (Sepulveda, Whitney, et al., 2008). The AESED is a 33-item self-report instrument for family members of individuals with eating disorders (Sepulveda et al., 2009). Five behavioral categories are explored in the AESED: "Avoidance and Modifying Routine, Reassurance Seeking, Meal Ritual, Control of Family, and Turning a Blind Eye" (p. 1). The results of the AESED are useful in assisting caregivers to develop healthy coping behaviors, and in evaluating the efficacy of family therapy strategies.

The EDSIS (Sepulveda, Whitney, et al., 2008) is a self-report instrument of 30 items that identify ways in which caregivers of individuals with eating disorders are impacted by their caregiving activities. Those impacts are incorporated into four categories: "nutrition, guilt, dysregulated behaviour, and social isolation" (p. 1). Each item has a 0 to 4 Likert scale, ranging from "never" to "nearly always" (p. 3). In addition to identifying caregivers' needs, this assessment is also used to review the helpfulness of family therapy.

There are a number of other assessment instruments that have been developed for particular use with eating disorders. Mitchell and Peterson's 2005 book entitled *Assessment of Eating Disorders* (Berg, Peterson, & Frazier, 2012) is a reliable source of information about eating disorder assessments. This book may be more helpful for mental health professionals who work with eating disorder issues on a regular basis.

FAMILY SYSTEMS INTERVENTIONS

Just as feeding and eating disorders develop under the influence of internal and external factors, strategies that successfully treat those disorders include both intrapersonal and interpersonal interventions that necessarily include family systems (Lantzouni, Cox, Salvaator, & Crosby, 2015). Those family systems interventions vary in type and degree depending on the exact nature of the case and the treatment setting. As in the previous section on assessment, pica and RD are discussed separately because of their specific and distinct treatment approaches. AFRID, AN, BN, and BED are discussed together in a later section.

Pica

Behavioral strategies within a family systems structure have been consistently effective in the treatment of pica. For example, Reed-Knight, Thompson, Bigham, Sil, Griffin, and Johnson (2015) reported success with "behavioral strategies for addressing pica within the home" (p. 173). Sinha and Mallick (2009) also described cases of pica that were resolved with the use of behavioral therapy in conjunction with occasional use of pharmacotherapy and nutritional supplements, and the involvement of immediate family members. Although in-home therapy is preferred for addressing pica behaviors because of the effectiveness of familial involvement, in-home caregivers of significantly impaired individuals might not be able to provide the intense supervision that is required for effective implementation of behavioral interventions for pica. In those situations, an institutional kind of systemic structure can be effective. For example, adolescents diagnosed with autism and significant intellectual disabilities also experienced reduction in pica behaviors through an inpatient behavioral modification program (Hagopian, González, Rivet, Triggs, & Clark, 2011).

Rumination Disorder

Outpatient behavioral therapy with emphasis on diaphragmatic breathing has been largely successful in managing RD (Chial et al., 2003; Chitkara et al., 2006; Talley, 2011). Diaphragmatic breathing is a simple technique that is used to relax the diaphragm throughout and after meals. RD regurgitation cannot occur when the diaphragm is relaxed in this way, which makes it possible to manage and, ultimately, extinguish the RD behaviors. Including the client's family in education about RD and the diaphragmatic breathing training enhances client support at home, and is an essential component of this treatment strategy.

Avoidant/Restrictive Food Intake Disorder, Anorexia Nervosa, Bulimia Nervosa, and Binge Eating Disorder

When considering the impact of family influences on a client's recovery from a feeding or eating disorder, common sense dictates that informed, deliberate, constructive familial support is a vital component of an effective treatment plan (National Alliance on Mental Illness, 2015a, 2015b, 2015c, 2015d, 2015e). It is imperative that mental health professionals develop an effective working relationship with the entire family in order to assist the family in identifying and accessing their own strengths while addressing their treatment challenges (Whitney & Eisler, 2005, p. 575). As a foundational part of this process, it is important to "Help families understand that they did not cause the illness; neither did their child/family member choose to have it" (Academy for Eating Disorders, 2012, p. 15). Even when family is not physically present for psychotherapy, awareness of systemic influences is important for effective treatment. "While family work may not be ideal or possible in all cases, the ability of therapists to think systemically in this work is critical to ensuring effective outcome in many cases" (Downs & Blow, 2011, p. 21).

Continuum of Care for Eating Disorders

There are five basic levels of care available for individuals struggling with eating disorders (NEDA, 2015), all of which can and do incorporate a systems perspective and family involvement. In general terms, outpatient treatment is indicated for eating disorder cases where the client is medically stable and his or her behaviors do not put him or her at immediate risk. Intensive outpatient or day treatment is the next higher level of care for clients with more significant symptoms, requiring several hours of psychotherapy each week, including group work. Partial hospitalization is essentially a full-time version of intensive outpatient treatment, where the client goes home at night instead of actually living at the facility. When a client's symptoms and medical status deteriorate to the point that constant supervision of eating, drinking, exercising, and bathroom use is necessary in order for the client to engage productively in therapy and become more healthy, residential treatment is indicated. The highest level of care, inpatient treatment, becomes necessary when, in addition to residential structure and supervision, the client is in need of a hospital standard of medical monitoring and care.

Although the *DSM-5* severity specifiers for AN, BN, and BED do not directly correlate with the above-stated levels of treatment, there are some general parallels in actual practice. For example, severe or extreme AN is based solely on BMI, and would probably require residential or inpatient treatment for medical reasons. A severe or extreme specifier for BN, based on the number of incidents of compensatory behavior per week, might result in at least partial hospitalization, depending in part on the overall medical status of the client. With respect to BED, the number of binge eating episodes could result in a severe or extreme specifier, which might necessitate partial hospitalization or a higher level of care if there is sufficient medical symptomatology. Mild or moderate severity specifiers for these disorders would usually lead to an outpatient or an intensive outpatient/day treatment level of care. ARFID does not have severity specifiers, and the level of treatment would be dictated primarily by the medical status of the client.

As stated, all of these levels of care are enhanced by a systems perspective and appropriate involvement of the client's family. In outpatient treatment, family work is conducted by the client's psychotherapist. The higher levels of care are program centered, and family work is done in different ways depending on the given program. When the client's family lives near where the program is run, more options are available for holding family sessions. When client families do not live close to the program facility, technical-assisted distance counseling is sometimes used. In order to give all client families the opportunity to learn about and participate in the client's eating disorder treatment program, some residential and inpatient treatment centers invite family members to travel to the center for "family days." These family-oriented events provide psychoeducation and psychotherapy in various formats as part of the client's overall treatment plan.

Family-Based Therapy (Maudsley Family Therapy)

Family-based therapy (FBT), also known as the Maudsley method or Maudsley approach (NEDA, 2015, p. 31), originated at the Maudsley Hospital in London, the United Kingdom (Downs & Blow, 2013). This systemic approach to the treatment of eating disorders is widely considered to be "the gold standard treatment for adolescent patients in the early stage of illness" (Treasure, Rhind, Macdonald, & Todd, 2015, p. 366), and has been endorsed by the APA (Couturier, Kimber, & Szatmari, 2013, p. 3). FBT includes a basic structure of three phases, each of which includes a primary focus and other specific family therapy goals to be accomplished during the phase.

During the first phase of FBT, the primary goal is for the parents to take control of the eating-disordered behaviors of their child or adolescent, which also leads the family to become fully engaged in the treatment process (Downs & Blow, 2013). The second phase involves assisting the identified client to start eating on his or her own, along with beginning to identify client issues that are related to the disordered eating. In the third phase, control over eating transitions from the parents back to the identified client, and the family therapy focus continues to shift away from the eating disorder itself to broader issues for the purpose of developing healthier family functioning (Ciao et al., 2015).

As noted, FBT has been shown to be effective when treatment begins in the early stages of eating disorders in adolescents. In response to the continued need for a treatment approach for later stage eating disorders in adolescents, and eating disorders in adults, FBT has been adapted into the New Maudsley, Collaborative Care model (Treasure et al., 2015). This model has been specifically designed for clients and their families who enter treatment during later stages of eating disorders, and clients with adult onset eating disorders.

Family-Based Day Treatment and Multifamily Treatment With Adolescents

Variations on the Maudsley FBT approach have been created for specific use in centers and hospitals that provide higher levels of care for eating disorders. For example, Henderson et al. (2014) described a day treatment program where parents engaged in family therapy with the adolescent client and learned to supervise the client's meals at home. That program resulted in "positive outcomes," which could be "maintained 6 months post-treatment" (p. 2). Additionally, a study by Girz, Robinson, Foroughe, Jasper, and Boachie (2012) also concluded that family-based day treatment results in positive outcomes effective for adolescents struggling with eating disorders.

Multifamily therapy has also shown promise in the treatment of adolescents with eating disorders. Gelin, Fuso, Hendrick, Cook-Darzens, and Simon (2015) conducted a study on an FBT-derived multifamily model, and reported that, "This study suggests that Multiple Family Therapy may benefit adolescents with eating disorders, with improvement on several outcome measures . . ." (p. 160). Depestele, Claes, and Lemmens (2014) found that clients and their families achieved a more accurate and healthier perspective through group work with other families. The clients felt that they received "more understanding and support from their parents," and the parents felt "more involved" in the treatment process (p. 37).

Support and Treatment for Parents/Caregivers

A vital theme woven through the previously discussed interventions is that the well-being of parents and caregivers has a significant impact on treatment outcomes for clients facing disordered eating. Fischer, Luiselli, and Dove (2015) shared a case study of a 16-year-old male with AFRID in which the mother was involved in her son's treatment at the clinic and at home. In that case, parent-inclusive treatment "improved consumption of previously avoided foods and lowered subjectively perceived anxiety" (p. 154). Also of note was that the client's gains "were maintained posttreatment, and both the participant and his mother rated the procedures and outcome favorably" (p. 154). In another case of ARFID, where the client was a 6-year-old girl (Murphy & Zlomke, 2016), the parents were actually trained and coached through the treatment process for their daughter. This case also resulted in substantial improvement in the client's behaviors, and the improvement remained stable at a 6-week follow-up.

Robinson, Strahan, Girz, Wilson, and Boachie (2012) described a Maudsley-type program for adolescents with family-based therapy where parental self-efficacy was a primary focus. The author observed that, throughout treatment, as the parents achieved an improvement in self-efficacy, the symptoms in their adolescent children reduced. Consequently, the author concluded that those treatment results supported the perspective that family therapy is efficacious in the treatment of eating disorders.

Abbate-Daga et al. (2013) targeted parental counseling as part of an FBT-type treatment program for adolescent females. The authors stated that the parental counseling component of the program "aimed to help parents better understand their daughters' illness and to improve family relationships and coping abilities with ED behaviours" (p. 380). The authors also reported that their "preliminary findings support the effectiveness of parent counselling in ED" (p. 375). In summary, the authors concluded that "this study showed that parent counselling can be a useful and versatile therapeutic instrument with informative, emotional and relational functions" (p. 389).

Of course, not all clients end up in a treatment center program. Sepulveda, Lopez, Todd, Whitaker, and Treasure (2008) reviewed a Maudsley workshop series that was developed for parents who were providing care at home as part of an outpatient treatment program for their children with eating disorders. Parents reported that the workshop series helped with stress and responsibilities of caring for the identified client. Other parental helps include a motivational interviewing skills assessment and training model for caregivers of minor children with eating disorders (Sepulveda, Wise, Zabala, Todd, & Treasure, 2013). The Motivational Interviewing Scenarios Tool for Eating Disorders was developed to assist parents in identifying and developing communication and relationship skills in order to facilitate the recovery process for the client and family.

Treatment for Couples

Although it is true that most eating disorder research and treatment has historically focused on younger clients, it is also true that adults also suffer from eating disorders (Linville & Oleksak, 2013). Those adults need effective treatment, including couples and family work, as much as children and adolescents (Murray, 2014). In fact, evidence indicates that couple relationships in particular can provide "support and motivation" for adults recovering from eating disorders (Linville & Oleksak, p. 266). Conversely, problems in their couple relationships adversely affected the treatment and recovery of adult clients in treatment for eating disorders (Zak-Hunter & Johnson, 2015).

Dick, Renes, Morotti, and Strange (2013) performed a research review specifically regarding heterosexual couples in which the female had been diagnosed with an eating disorder. Their conclusions demonstrated how failure to resolve relationship issues through couple and family therapy could adversely affect the female client beyond the scope of the eating-disordered behaviors. Consequently, the authors recommended that providing treatment for a couple's relationship issues was an important part of addressing the eating disorder experienced by a member of the couple.

ETHICAL AND LEGAL IMPLICATIONS

When working with family systems, the ethical codes that would typically apply are those of the American Association for Marriage and Family Therapy (AAMFT, 2015) and the American Counseling Association (ACA, 2014). These ethical codes, in conjunction with applicable state and federal laws, govern the practice of psychotherapy as it relates to the systemic treatment of individuals with feeding and eating disorders, and their families. This section highlights ethical and legal issues that tend to arise in cases involving eating disorders.

There are a variety of potential ethical and legal dilemmas related to feeding and eating disorders. Matusek and Wright (2010) summarized these issues as:

> [E]thical questions relevant to medical, nutritional and psychological treatment of clients with eating disorders including imposed treatment, enforced feeding, the duty to protect minors and adults, the determination of competence and capacity among medically comprised clients, and the effectiveness of coercive treatment for clients with eating disorders. (p. 434)

For example, parents of children with Pica may be reported for neglect because of safety concerns related to allowing children to consistently ingest nonfood substances, including leaded paint (APA, 2013). Adults with intellectual disabilities who engage in pica behaviors might also need supervision. Legal processes might also become necessary in order to establish guardianship and arrange for living situations with appropriate structure and oversight.

For young children and developmentally delayed individuals, deficits in supervision by caregivers can contribute to the development of pica behaviors (APA, 2013). That kind of relationship factor can have a profound impact on the course of this illness. Particularly with respect to minor children, neglectful caregiving can lead to dependency and can neglect legal actions against the parents or other caregivers. Although such actions may result in improved circumstances for the minor child or dependent adult, the stresses accompanying that process could at least temporarily exacerbate the pica behaviors.

RD in adults with intellectual disabilities (APA, 2013) might also lead to legal proceedings for the purpose of appointing an appropriate guardian and providing effective supervisory care. There is also a possibility that parents might be erroneously accused of neglect because of apparent failure to thrive in infants and children with RD. Both of those situations could also occur with individuals with ARFID.

The above-stated situations demonstrate the need for accurate legal and ethical decision making by mental health professionals. In addition to the fundamental expectation of focusing on the well-being of clients and doing no harm to clients (AAMFT, 2015; ACA, 2014), psychotherapists are also responsible for knowing applicable legal requirements, including exceptions to confidentiality in cases of abuse and neglect. Advising clients of these exceptions at the inception of the counseling relationship, making informed and accurate use of those exceptions, and facilitating the appropriate placement of clients in need of special supervisory care are essential to the effective treatment of individuals and families dealing with feeding and eating disorders.

In more severe cases, BN and BED behaviors might lead to ethical and legal issues regarding guardianship or conservatorship (NEDA, 2015), compulsory treatment, or legal involvement related to substance misuse. However, guardianship and compulsory treatment issues have been reported more frequently for cases of AN. Because of the risks of fatality associated with AN, intensive medical care may become necessary in order to preserve life (Holm, Brixen, Andries, Hørder, & Støving, 2012). In such cases, it is not uncommon for the individual suffering from AN to refuse treatment. Health care providers for these individuals then have to make ethical and legal determinations about whether or not it is appropriate to take the necessary legal steps to provide compulsory treatment (Born et al., 2015), which might include mental health holds of appropriate durations (NEDA, 2015).

Compulsory treatment or refeeding may be essential to prevent a fatal outcome (Holm et al., 2012), and there is an ongoing discussion among mental health professionals in this specialty about whether or not compulsory treatment is actually effective (Elzakkers, Danner, Hoek, Schmidt, & van Elburg, 2014). Professionals have also asked if forcing someone to accept treatment is ethical (Kendall & Hugman, 2013), or if the individual should have the right to refuse care (Campbell & Aulisio, 2012). A proposed alternative is to provide palliative care for individuals who do not want to undergo refeeding treatment (Lopez, Yager, & Feinstein, 2010). Although the AAMFT (2015) *Code of Ethics* and ACA (2014) *Code of Ethics* do not directly address this specific issue, Section B.2.b of the ACA *Code of Ethics* does discuss end-of-life decisions for terminally ill clients. This section states that counselors should be aware of "applicable laws," and seek "consultation or supervision from appropriate professional and legal parties" (p. 7) before making clinical decisions regarding such cases.

Another potential challenge in providing treatment for feeding and eating disorders can arise in cases with minor children if both of the parents of a minor child do not agree that there is a need for treatment. If both parents have decision-making authority for the minor child, whether they are married or not, and both of them do not give consent for treatment of a minor child, then mental health professionals could be violating ethical and legal standards if they were to proceed with treatment. It is also true that, in some states, minor children can seek counseling without the knowledge or consent of their parents after they reach a certain age. Again, the AAMFT (2015) *Code of Ethics* and ACA (2014) *Code of Ethics* require counselors to act in accordance with applicable laws, and to advocate for the welfare and appropriate treatment of clients, including minor clients and their families, within the framework of those laws. Consent from clients, or the parents or guardians of minor clients, is also needed in the form of releases of information so that all of the professionals (mental health, medical, educational, and so forth) who are involved in the case can freely communicate with each other in order to provide effective treatment for the client and his or her family.

CASE CONCEPTUALIZATION

As is stated in various ways throughout this chapter, employing a systemic lens is an important part of providing effective psychotherapy for individuals and families dealing with feeding and eating disorders. For the purpose of more fully understanding this concept, the following case is presented. This case study involves a somewhat unusual example of restrictive eating. Reviewing all of the symptoms within the family context is essential for accurately diagnosing this case. Successful treatment planning is also dependent on a thorough understanding of the factors of this case.

Presenting Concerns

Jamie Walters is a 14-year-old Caucasian female who is currently in counseling for assistance with restrictive eating-disordered behaviors. She entered treatment with her current counselor almost 2 years ago upon discharge from an inpatient eating disorder treatment center. Although Jamie's illness first became severe enough for inpatient treatment when she was 10 years old, she has experienced difficulty eating since she was 10 months old. Jamie's mother attributes this in part to jaw size and bite problems, which are now being corrected with dental procedures including extraction of some adult teeth and orthodontia.

She has also received speech therapy services throughout her earlier school years due primarily to pronunciation challenges occasioned by the dental problems. Historically, Jamie has struggled with understanding, completing, and submitting her schoolwork on time, often resulting in unsatisfactory grades.

Recently, Jamie has again begun to restrict her intake of both food and fluids, resulting in the loss of approximately five pounds. Her expressed goal is to stop the eating-disordered behaviors, regain the lost weight, and avoid going back to inpatient treatment. Although she demonstrates more insight into her own thoughts and feelings, and her health situation, it will be necessary to continue close monitoring of Jamie's food and fluid intake at home, along with her weight and orthostatic status (blood pressure and pulse rate) through her pediatrician, in the event that she may again need to be admitted to inpatient treatment.

Concurrent Problems

During her last inpatient treatment, Jamie's assessment results indicated that she might be experiencing Autism Spectrum Disorder (APA, 2013, pp. 50–59) in addition to having Attention-Deficit/Hyperactivity Disorder, predominantly hyperactive/impulsive presentation (ADHD; pp. 59–65) and mild Dyspraxia (some difficulty with fine and gross motor coordination). She is currently taking 80 mg of Strattera daily for the ADHD, which has resulted in better focus and grades at school, as demonstrated by the fact that she is currently on the honor roll in her first semester of high school. For the last several years, she has also been involved in ballet classes, the school band, and other extracurricular activities that have aided in the development of muscle coordination and social skills. She uses her Ventolin inhaler for asthma as needed.

Background History and Stressors

In terms of Jamie's immediate family, her mother has been almost entirely responsible for Jamie's care, including daily supervision of food and fluid intake. This is particularly true as Jamie's father is out of town for his employment approximately 50% of the time. This responsibility for Jamie, and the other family members, in conjunction with some gastro-intestinal medical problems, has resulted in Jamie's mother becoming worn down physically and emotionally.

According to Jamie's mother, Jamie's father and two older siblings have been diagnosed with "higher functioning autism." Her older sister has shared a bedroom with Jamie, and frequently displayed behavior that was very disruptive to the family. Jamie, her mother, and her brother have all reported that the family environment has improved significantly since the older sister moved out of state to live with relatives after graduating from high school earlier in the year.

Strengths

Jamie wants to be "normal" and is actively engaged in family, school, and other life activities. The family demonstrates commitment and caring between members, and is willing to participate in treatment and to support Jamie at home. Jamie's mother has consistently been willing and able to supervise her food and fluid intake. Jamie's mother also manages the related resources, including Social Security Disability, Medicaid, and school accommodations that have been established consequent to the eating disorder and ADHD diagnoses.

DSM-5 Impressions and Implications

Unspecified Feeding and Eating Disorder

Rule out Anorexia Nervosa, Restricting Type
Rule out Avoidant/Restrictive Food Intake Disorder
(NOTE: The preceding diagnostic information is from the discharge summary for Jamie
   when she completed her most recent inpatient treatment.)
Attention-Deficit/Hyperactivity Disorder, predominantly hyperactive/impulsive presen-
   tation, in partial remission
Asthma
Dyspraxia
Academic or Educational Problem
Sibling Relational Problem

Jamie continues to struggle with restrictive eating behaviors that seem to be attributable, at least in part, to physiological factors that surfaced when she was only 10 months
old. The related symptoms were exacerbated to the point of inpatient admission and treatment at the ages of 10, 11, 12, and 13. Currently, she has been out of inpatient treatment
longer than before, and seems to have more control over the eating-disordered behaviors,
as evidenced by her increased intake of food and fluids in response to concerning orthostatic and weight loss information obtained through her weekly check-in with her pediatrician. At this point, it seems clear that the diagnosis for this would be ARFID, ruling out
AN. A primary reason for this is that Jamie has not expressed a fear of being "fat" or
gaining weight either verbally or behaviorally. In fact, Jamie and her mother have both
reported that Jamie has consistently demonstrated an enjoyment of eating her favorite
foods without concern for the related calorie intake.

Relational Problems

The level of stress in Jamie's family environment has been consistently elevated due in
large part to emotional outbursts from her older sister. Jamie's mother has also experienced
some health challenges, including gastrointestinal problems that have contributed to a
higher level of family stress at meal times. As mentioned earlier, the older sister moved out
during the previous summer, which has resulted in a significantly lower stress level at
home, particularly as Jamie had shared a bedroom with the older sister. Jamie's mother
worked with Jamie and Jamie's counselor to determine ways to reduce the stresses around
mealtime due to her (the mother's) medical issues. Jamie and her mother report that these
strategies have been effective in creating a more relaxed experience at meals. It is possible
that this reduction of stress at home will make it more possible for Jamie to successfully
reverse the recent downward trend in her eating behaviors and avoid another admission
to inpatient treatment.

Assessments

Jamie has already completed a number of assessments at school and while in residential
treatment, including the Wechsler Intelligence Scale for Children, the Woodcock Johnson
Tests of Achievement, the Minnesota Multiphasic Personality Inventory-Adolescent, and
the Behavior Assessment System for Children. At this point in Jamie's life and treatment,
a personality inventory such as the TCI (Abbate-Daga et al., 2013) would be an appropriate assessment. Reviewing the TCI results with her counselor could help Jamie develop a

greater understanding of and appreciation for self. As Jamie continues her recovery and makes plans for graduating from high school and moving into an adult life away from her family, having that kind of self-awareness and self-esteem could be empowering in her ongoing recovery.

Interventions

Jamie has received treatment in patient programs a total of four times, the first two times in a program affiliated with the local children's hospital, and the last two times at a hospital specializing in the treatment of eating disorders in children and adolescents. Jamie was first admitted to treatment when she was 10 years old, the second time was 7 months later at age 11, and the third time was 6 months later at age 12. The fourth time was approximately 1 year later when she was 13. At present, she has been out of inpatient treatment for almost 1 year. The possibility of an emotional anniversary was explored because of the timing of some of the returns to inpatient treatment, but neither Jamie nor her family members could identify any underlying reason for the timing of the inpatient treatment. Through therapy with her current counselor, Jamie has identified that school stressors do negatively impact her eating at times, but this is not as common now that she is on Strattera for ADHD and is feeling more confident and successful at school.

Although in inpatient treatment, Jamie participated in individual, family, and group counseling sessions. With her current counselor, Jamie has continued to engage in both individual and family therapy. At this time, Jamie is considerably more verbal and easier to understand than when first entering treatment with her current counselor. She has responded well to Cognitive Behavioral Therapy (CBT) and Rational Emotive Behavior Therapy (REBT) techniques, including homework regarding eating behaviors and her related thought and emotional processes. DBT self-management skills have also been a focus of treatment, particularly emotional regulation, along with some ACT values clarification work. Family therapy has also been conducted with various combinations of family members, and Jamie's mother typically participates in at least part of each session, reporting regarding Jamie's food and fluid intake, and weekly check-in information from Jamie's pediatrician.

Ethical and Legal Implications

The ethical codes of the AAMFT (2015) and ACA (2014), along with related federal and state law, provide a valuable framework for reviewing this case for potential ethical issues. At this point, because Jamie is a minor child and has a collaborative relationship with her parents, particularly her mother, there are no ethical or legal issues regarding her willingness to engage in treatment. Jamie's parents and siblings have also engaged in family therapy. The systemic clinician in this case has ensured that all required documentation (i.e., informed consent and disclosure forms, releases of information, and so forth) has been completed, is using appropriate psychotherapeutic practice strategies in treating Jamie and her family, and is maintaining effective communication with the rest of the treatment team working on this case. In short, there are no current ethical or legal issues in this case.

DISCUSSION

As you continue to reflect on the case study and the overall approach, contemplate these questions:

- Based on the information presented for this case, do Jamie's symptoms meet the criteria for AFRID? Why, or why not?

- Considering the successful results of Jamie's inpatient treatment, what might be some approaches or techniques from inpatient treatment that could also be utilized in outpatient treatment? For example, might a group be helpful at some point? How might one be found?

- Although Jamie and her mother have been working with Jamie's counselor to shift responsibility for Jamie's eating behaviors to her from her mother, what would be reasonable goals regarding the complete transfer of accountability for Jamie's eating behaviors to Jamie?

- Jamie's interest in ballet has served as motivation for recovery because she cannot participate in such a physically demanding activity if she is not at a healthy weight. What might be some concerns about Jamie continuing to participate in ballet as she transitions from active treatment into a maintenance stage of recovery? What strategies might be helpful in planning and implementing her relapse prevention with respect to ballet, particularly from a family systems treatment perspective?

- Up to this point, Jamie is the only family member who has been receiving individual counseling. Might individual counseling for other family members be appropriate? How might the needs of other family members in this respect be determined?

SUMMARY

The purpose of this chapter has been to demonstrate the potentially effective interaction between the *DSM-5* diagnostic data for feeding and eating disorders, and family systems theoretical orientations and treatment options for those disorders. Although eating disorders ". . . are complex conditions that can arise from a combination of long-standing, biological, emotional, psychological, interpersonal, and social factors" they can be successfully treated with effective individual, couple, and family therapy (NEDA, 2015, p. 10). Even individuals with pica and RD, which are substantially different from the other feeding and eating disorders in terms of both etiology and psychotherapeutic strategies, benefit greatly from systems-based treatment. As demonstrated by the research presented in this chapter, family systems treatment is uniquely effective at empowering individuals affected by eating disorders, and their families, in order to achieve long-term recovery.

Of course, there is still much that can be done to refine and enhance treatment for these potentially fatal disorders. As Ciao et al. (2015) affirmed, researchers need to continue examining the connection between family functioning and effective treatment of eating disorders, along with developing improved strategies for helping individuals with eating disorders and their families. Considering the significant improvements in treatment outcomes for eating disorders resulting from related research in recent years, there is every reason to anticipate that meaningful research will lead to a continuation of this trend in the future.

REFERENCES

Abbate-Daga, G., Quaranta, M., Marzola, E., Cazziniga, G., Amianto, F., & Fassino, S (2013). Effectiveness of parent counselling in eating disorders. *British Journal of Guidance and Counselling, 41*(4), 375–394. doi:10.1080/03069885.2012.729025

Academy for Eating Disorders. (2012). *Eating disorders: Critical points for early recognition and medical risk management in the care of individuals with eating disorders* (2nd ed.). Reston, VA: Author. Retrieved from http://www.aedweb.org

American Association for Marriage and Family Therapy. (2015). *AAMFT code of ethics.* Alexandria, VA: Author. Retrieved from http://dx5br1z4f6n0k.cloudfront.net/imis15/Documents/Legal%20Ethics /AAMFT-code-of-ethics.pdf

American Counseling Association. (2014). *ACA code of ethics*. Alexandria, VA: Author. Retrieved from https://www.counseling.org/resources/aca-code-of-ethics.pdf

American Psychiatric Association. (2000). *Diagnostic and statistical manual of mental disorders* (4th ed., text rev.). Washington, DC: Author.

American Psychiatric Association. (2013). *Diagnostic and statistical manual of mental disorders* (5th ed.). Arlington, VA: American Psychiatric Publishing.

Berg, K. C., Peterson, C. B., & Frazier, P. (2012). Assessment and diagnosis of eating disorders: A guide for professional counselors. *Journal of Counseling and Development, 90*, 262–269.

Born, C., de la Fontaine, L., Winter, B., Müller, N., Schaub, A., Früstück, C., . . . Meisenzahl, E. (2015). First results of a refeeding program in a psychiatric intensive care unit for patients with extreme anorexia nervosa. *BMC Psychiatry, 15*(57). doi:10.1186/s12888-015-0436-7

Campbell, A. T., & Aulisio, M. P. (2012). The stigma of "mental illness": End stage anorexia and treatment refusal. *International Journal of Eating Disorders, 45*(5), 627–634. doi:10.1002/eat.22002

Chial, H. J., Camilleri, M., Williams, D. F., Litzinger, K., & Perrault, J. (2003). Rumination syndrome in children and adolescents: Diagnosis, treatment, and prognosis. *Pediatrics, 111*(1), 158–162.

Chitkara, D. K., Van Tilburg, M., Whitehead, W. E., & Talley, N. J. (2006). Teaching diaphragmatic breathing for rumination syndrome. *American Journal of Gastroenterology, 101*, 2449–2452. doi:10.1111/j.1572-0421.2006.00801.x

Ciao, A. C., Accurso, E. C., Fitzsimmons-Craft, B., Lock, J., & Le Grange, D. (2015). Family functioning in two treatments for adolescent anorexia nervosa. *International Journal of Eating Disorders, 48*(1), 81–90. doi:10.1002/eat.22314

Couturier, J., Kimber, M., & Szatmari, P. (2013). Efficacy of family-based treatment for adolescents with eating disorders: A systemic review and meta-analysis. *International Journal of Eating Disorders, 46*(1), 3–11. doi:10.1002/eat.22042

Delaney, C. B., Eddy, K. T., Hartmann, A. S., Becker, A. E., Murray, H. B., & Thomas, J. J. (2015). Pica and rumination behavior among individuals seeking treatment for eating disorders or obesity. *International Journal of Eating Disorders, 48*(2), 238–248. doi:10.1002/eat.22279

Depestele, L., Claes, L., & Lemmens, G. M. D. (2014). Promotion of an autonomy-supportive parental style in a multi-family group for eating-disordered adolescents. *Journal of Family Therapy, 37*, 24–40. doi:10.1111/1467-6427.12047

Dick, C. H., Renes, S. L., Morotti, A., & Strange, A. T. (2013). Understanding and assisting couples affected by an eating disorder. *American Journal of Family Therapy, 41*, 232–244. doi:10.1080/01926187.2012.677728

Downs, K. J., & Blow, A. J. (2011). A substantive and methodological review of family-based treatment for eating disorders: The last 25 years of research. *Journal of Family Therapy, 35*, 3–28. doi:10.1111/j.1467-6427.2011.00566.x

Elzakkers, I. F. F. M., Danner, U. N., Hoek, H. W., Schmidt, U., & van Elburg, A. A. (2014). Compulsory treatment in anorexia nervosa: A review. *International Journal of Eating Disorders, 47*(8). doi:10.1002/eat.22330

Fischer, A. J., Luiselli, J. K., & Dove, M. B. (2015). Effects of clinic and in-home treatment on consumption with feeding-associated anxiety in an adolescent with avoidant/restrictive food intake disorder. *Clinical Practice in Pediatric Psychology, 3*(2), 154–166. doi:10.1037/cpp0000090

Gelin, Z., Fuso, S., Hendrick, S., Cook-Darzens, S., & Simon, Y. (2015). The effects of a multiple family therapy on adolescents with eating disorders: An outcome study. *Family Process, 54*(1), 160–172. doi:10.1111/famp.12103

Girz, L., Robinson, A. L., Foroughe, M., Jasper, K., & Boachie, A. (2012). Adapting family-based therapy to a day hospital programme for adolescents with eating disorders: Preliminary outcomes and trajectories of change. *Journal of Family Therapy, 35*, 102–120. doi:10.1111/j.1467-6427.2012.00618.x

Hagopian, L. P., González, M. L., Rivet, T. T., Triggs, M., & Clark, S. B. (2011). Response interruption and differential reinforcement of alternative behavior for the treatment of pica. *Behavioral Interventions, 26*, 309–325. doi:10.1002/bin.339

Henderson, K., Buchholz, A., Obeid, N., Mossiere, A., Maras, D., Norris, M., . . . Spettigue, W. (2014). A family-based eating disorder day treatment program for youth: Examining the clinical and statistical significance of short-term treatment outcomes. *Eating Disorders, 22*, 1–18. doi:10.1080/10640266.2014.857512

Holm, J. S., Brixen, K., Andries, A., Hørder, K., & Støving, R. K. (2012). Reflections on involuntary treatment in the prevention of fatal anorexia nervosa: A review of five cases. *International Journal of Eating Disorders, 45*(1), 93–100. doi:10.1002/eat.20915

Kendall, S., & Hugman, R. (2013). Social work and the ethics of involuntary treatment for anorexia nervosa: A postmodern approach. *Ethics and Social Work, 7*(4), 310–325. doi:10.1080/17496535.2013.833275

Lantzouni, E., Cox, M. H., Salvaator, A., & Crosby, R. D. (2015). Mother-daughter coping and disordered eating. *European Eating Disorders Review, 23*(2), 126–132. doi:10.1002/erv.2343

Linville, D., & Oleksak, N. (2013). Integrated eating disorder treatment for couples. *Journal of Couple and Relationship Therapy, 12*(3), 255–269. doi:10.1080/15332691.2013.806709

Lopez, A., Yager, J., & Feinstein, R. E. (2010). Medical futility and psychiatry: Palliative care and hospice care as a last resort in the treatment of refractory anorexia nervosa. *International Journal of Eating Disorders, 43*(4), 372–377. doi:10.1002/eat.20701

Lydecker, J. A., & Grilo, C. M. (2016). Different yet similar: Examining race and ethnicity in treatment-seeking adults with binge eating disorder. *Journal of Consulting and Clinical Psychology, 84*(1), 88–94. doi:10.1037/ccp0000048

Matusek, J. A., & Wright, M. O. (2010). Ethical dilemmas in treating clients with eating disorders: A review and application of an integrative ethical decision-making model. *European Eating Disorders Review, 18*, 434–452. doi:10.1002/erv.1036

Mehl, A., Tomanová, J., Kuběna, A., & Papežová, H. (2012). Adapting multi-family therapy to families who care for a loved one with an eating disorder in the Czech Republic combined with a follow-up pilot study of efficacy. *Journal of Family Therapy, 35*, 82–101. doi:10.1111/j.1467-6427.2011.00579.x

Murphy, J., & Zlomke, K. R. (2016). A behavioral parent-training intervention for a child with avoidant/restrictive food intake disorder. *Clinical Practice in Pediatric Psychology, 4*(1), 23–34. doi:10.1037/cpp0000128

Murray, S. B. (2014). A case of strategic couples therapy in adult anorexia nervosa: The importance of symptoms in context. *Contemporary Family Therapy: An International Journal, 36*, 392–397. doi:10.1007/s10591-014-9301-y

National Alliance on Mental Illness. (2015). Eating disorders. Retrieved from https://www.nami.org/Learn-More/Mental-Health-Conditions/Eating-Disorders

National Center for Health Statistics. (2017). *International classification of diseases, tenth revision, clinical modification*. Retrieved from https://www.cdc.gov/nchs/icd/icd10cm.htm

National Eating Disorders Association. (2015). *Parent toolkit*. New York, NY: Author. Retrieved from www.nationaleaatingdisorders.org

Reed-Knight, B., Thompson, B., Bigham, L., Sil, S., Griffin, A., & Johnson, A. (2015). Identification of pica behaviors in youth with sickle cell disease: A quality improvement (QI) project. *Clinical Practice in Pediatric Psychology, 3*(2), 167–174.

Robinson, A. L., Strahan, E., Girz, L., Wilson, A., & Boachie, A. (2012). "I know I can help you": Parental self-efficacy predicts adolescent outcomes in family-based therapy for eating disorders. *European Eating Disorders Review, 21*(2), 108–114. doi:10.1002/erv.2180

Sepulveda, A. R., Anastasiadou, D., Rodríguez, L., Almendros, C., Andrés, P., Vaz, F., & Graell, M. (2014). Spanish validation of the Family Questionnaire (FQ) in families of patients with an eating disorder. *Psicothema, 26*(3), 321–327. doi:10.7334/psicothema2013.310

Sepulveda, A. R., Kyriacou, O., & Treasure, J. (2009). Development and validation of the Accommodation and Enabling Scale for Eating Disorders (AESED) for caregivers in eating disorders. *BMC Health Services Research, 9*(171), 1–13. doi:10.1186/1472-6963-9-171

Sepulveda, A. R., Lopez, C., Todd, G., Whitaker, W., & Treasure, J. (2008). An examination of the impact of "the Maudsley eating disorder collaborative care skills workshops" on the well-being of carers. *Social Psychiatry and Psychiatric Epidemiology, 43*, 584–591. doi:10.1007/s00127-008-0336-y

Sepulveda, A. R., Whitney, J., Hankins, M., & Treasure, J. (2008). Development and validation of an Eating Disorders Symptom Scale (EDSIS) for carers of people with eating disorders. *Health and Quality of Life Outcomes, 6*(28), 1–9. doi:10.1186/1477-7525-6-28

Sepulveda, A. R., Wise, C., Zabala, M., Todd, G., & Treasure, J. (2013). Development and reliability of a Motivational Interviewing Scenarios Tool for Eating Disorders (MIST-ED) using a skills-based intervention among caregivers. *Eating Behaviors, 14*, 432–436. doi:10.1016/j.eatbeh.2013.07.010

Sassaroli, S., Veronese, G., Nevonen, L., Fiore, F., Centorame, F., Favaretto, E., & Ruggiero, G. M. (2015). Autonomy and submissiveness as cognitive and cultural factors influencing eating disorders in Italy and Sweden: An exploratory study. *Europe's Journal of Psychology, 11*(2), 233–243. doi:10.5964/ejop.v11i2.902

Shea, M., Cachelin, F. M., Gutierrez, G., Wang, S., & Phimphasone, P. (2016). Mexican American Women's perspectives on a culturally adapted cognitive-behavioral therapy guided self-help program for binge eating. *Psychological Services, 13*(1), 31–41. doi:10.1037/ser0000055

Shingleton, R. M., Thompson-Brenner, H., Thompson, D. R., Pratt, E. M., & Franko, D. L. (2015). Gender differences in clinical trials of binge eating disorder: An analysis of aggregated data. *Journal of Consulting and Clinical Psychology, 83*(2), 382–386. doi:10.1037/a0038849

Singh, M. M., Parsekar, S. S., & Bhumika, T. V. (2016). Body image, eating disorders and role of media among Indian adolescents. *Journal of Indian Association for Child and Adolescent Mental Health, 12*(1), 9–35.

Sinha, M., & Mallick, A. K. (2009). Pica in the backdrop of psychiatric disorders: A complex etiology. *International Medical Journal, 17*(1), 21–23.

Talley, N. J. (2011). Rumination syndrome. *Gastroenterology and Hepatology, 7*(2), 117–118.

Treasure, J., Rhind, C., Macdonald, P., & Todd, G. (2015). Collaborative care: The new Maudsley model. *Eating Disorders, 23*(4), 366–376.

Treasure, J., Sepulveda, A. R., MacDonald, P., Whitaker, W., Lopez, C., Zabala, M., . . . Todd, G. (2008). The assessment of the family of people with eating disorders. *European Eating Disorders Review, 16*, 247–255. doi:10.1002/erv.859

Van Durme, K., Craeynest, E., Craet, C., & Goossens, L. (2015). The detection of eating disorder symptoms in adolescence: A comparison between the Children's Eating Disorder Examination and the Children's Eating Disorder Examination Questionnaire. *Behaviour Change, 32*(3), 190–201. doi:10.1017/bec.2015.10

Whitney, J., & Eisler, I. (2005). Theoretical and empirical models around caring for someone with an eating disorder: The reorganization of family life and inter-personal maintenance factors. *Journal of Mental Health, 14*(6), 575–585. doi:10.1080/09638230500347889

World Health Organization. (2004). *Prevention of mental disorders: Effective interventions and policy options.* Geneva: Author. Retrieved from http://www.who.int

World Health Organization. (2013). How can violence against children be prevented? Retrieved from http://www.who.int/features/qa/44/en

World Health Organization. (2016). Violence against women: Intimate partner and sexual violence against women. Retrieved from http://www.who.int/mediacentre/factsheets/fs239/en

Zak-Hunter, L., & Johnson, L. N. (2015). Exploring the association between partner behaviors and eating disorder symptomology. *Families, Systems, and Health, 33*(4), 405–409. doi:10.1037/fsh0000147

11

ELIMINATION DISORDERS: A DEVELOPMENTAL SYSTEMS PERSPECTIVE

Carol Pfeiffer Messmore, Alyssa Weiss Quittner, and Kaisha A. Thomas

*I*n 1952, over 60 years ago, the initial publication of the American Psychiatric Association's (APA) *Diagnostic and Statistical Manual of Mental Disorders* was released. Since that time, it has undergone several revisions; the most recent edition is the *Diagnostic and Statistical Manual of Mental Disorders* (5th ed.; *DSM-5*; APA, 2013), which was released in May 2013 (APA, 2013). However, there were no changes to the diagnostic classification of elimination disorders from the *Diagnostic and Statistical Manual of Mental Disorders* (4th ed.; *DSM-IV*; APA, 1994) to the *DSM-5*. Whereas these disorders were previously listed as a subcategory in the chapter titled Disorders Usually First Diagnosed in Infancy, Childhood, or Adolescence in the *DSM-IV*, elimination disorders are now listed in an independent chapter in the *DSM-5*.

The traditional process of diagnosing a mental health disorder using the *Diagnostic and Statistical Manual of Mental Health Disorders* identifies symptoms and behaviors that make daily life difficult for an individual, but more so can have an impact on one's family. These symptoms and behaviors, in a checklist format, are then linked to a diagnosis that can determine treatment for the atypical behaviors of the person being diagnosed. This deficit-based understanding of the individual ignores the family system and the concept of variability in behavior (Messmore, 2012). Further, a review of the literature (Carr, 2014) suggests that systemic interventions are effective treatments for disorders of childhood including elimination disorders. However, systemic family therapy is not the primary treatment for elimination disorders despite the common factors of poor family functioning, transgenerational occurrence, and comorbid mental health disorders. Given the social, environmental, and family transgenerational factors, using a family systems approach when working with children diagnosed with an elimination disorder would be an effective treatment protocol.

DSM-5 AND FAMILY SYSTEMS

Typically seen as an individual problem, elimination disorders are problematic for the entire family. The shame and embarrassment felt by the child can be a result of a frustrated parent who is unsure of what to do or a guilty parent who has felt that same way as a child. Either way the parent and the child feel like failures, which is why this disorder is so disruptive to the family system.

Elimination disorders include encopresis and enuresis; both conditions can have medical as well as emotional origins. Typically, these diagnoses occur in children 4 to 5 years and older who have already mastered toilet training. These disorders are not atypical in early childhood; a European study of 7-year-olds found that 10% of males and females combined experienced *nocturnal enuresis* (wetting during sleeping) and 2% to 3% experienced *diurnal urinary incontinence* (wetting during waking hours). This same study found that 1% to 3% of the children experienced *encopresis* (soiling during waking or sleeping periods; von Gontard, 2013). These disorders typically occur separately, but co-occurrence is common. Interestingly, the vast majority of elimination disorders are functional, and not due to neurological, structural, or medical causes (von Gontard & Neveus, 2006).

Diagnostic Features of Elimination Disorders

According to the *DSM-5* (2013), and the *International Statistical Classification of Diseases and Related Health Problems, 10th Revision (ICD-10*; World Health Organization, 2008), diagnostic criteria for Enuresis and Encopresis include involuntary or purposeful passing of urine or stools in children who have already mastered toileting. Enuresis is diagnosed in children who are at least 5 years old chronologically or developmentally and the behavior must be consistent over 3 months of time with a frequency of a minimum of two occurrences per week over 3 months. Enuresis has three specification criteria: nocturnal only (passing urine only while sleeping at night, also called *monosymptomatic enuresis*), diurnal only (passing urine only when awake), and a combination of nocturnal and diurnal (happening while sleeping and awake).

Encopresis includes involuntary or purposeful passing of urine or stools in children who have mastered toileting and are at least 4 years old chronologically or developmentally with a frequency of at least of one occurrence per month over 3 months. Furthermore, the behavior cannot be a result of medications (e.g., diuretic) or other medical disorders (e.g., diabetes, spina bifida, epilepsy) as those would be the primary diagnosis. Encopresis has two specification criteria: with constipation and overflow incontinence (the child is experiencing constipation and a history of constipation) or without constipation and overflow incontinence (the child is not experiencing constipation nor is there a history of constipation). If a child is experiencing considerable distress (impacting social, academic, emotional functioning) from symptoms similar to enuresis or encopresis but does not meet the diagnostic criteria, then the diagnosis of Other Specified Elimination Disorder is used for urinary incontinence and for fecal incontinence.

Research demonstrates comorbidity of elimination disorders in children already diagnosed with sensory processing disorder (Pollock, Metz, & Barabash, 2014); attention deficit/hyperactivity disorder (Mellon et al., 2013; Yuce, Zoroglu, Ceylan, Kandemir, & Karabekiroglu, 2013); anxiety, depression; and conduct disorder or oppositional defiant disorder (Akdemir, Kültür, Temizel, Zeki, & Dinç, 2015). Children born with neurological deficits such as Spina Bifida are also at high rates of diagnosis of elimination disorders. Children diagnosed with autism spectrum disorder and intellectual disability are also found to have higher than typical co-occurring diagnosis of elimination disorders (Coehlo, 2011). This latest research lends consideration of the neurodevelopment of children and additional treatment modalities such as occupational and psychoeducational therapy be supplementary to the behavioral health or medical treatment. Medication prescribed for coexisting medical issues has also been linked to children experiencing elimination disorders including antipsychotics (Barnes, Drake, & Paton, 2012) and stimulants (Robaey, 2011).

However, research in the United States has also indicated that there are social and environmental links to the development of elimination disorders such as child abuse, sexual abuse, bullying, lack of access to bathroom facilities (including classroom rules, lack of hygiene products, and privacy), and nutrition. Children experiencing these social and environmental risk factors may withhold urine and bowel movements or have painful, large bowel movements and as a result develop medical conditions such as chronic constipation, ulcerative colitis, anal fissures, urinary tract infections, and damage to the kidneys (Coehlo, 2011; Kistner, 2009). These risk factors are indicative of the need to assess a child presenting with an elimination disorder in the full context of his or her environment and family system.

Enuresis

Enuresis occurs in a higher frequency with rates as high as 16% of 5-year-olds, 11% of 9-year-olds, and 3% of 16-year-olds; it is also seen more commonly in boys than girls (Mellon et al., 2013). A hereditary component has also been found through research of families with children diagnosed with enuresis; 75% were found to have other family members across generations also diagnosed with this disorder (Bayoumi et al., 2006). Treatment typically includes both behavioral (urine alarms, positive reinforcement with rewards), bladder exercises, and pharmacological (antidepressants, antidiuretics; M. L. Brown, Pope, & Brown, 2010).

von Gontard and Neveus (2006) note that enuresis is two to three times more common than daytime urinary incontinence and one and a half to two times more common in boys than in girls. The frequency of bed wetting decreases as the child gets older: 20% in 4-year-olds, 10% in 7-year-olds, 1% to 2% in adolescents, and 0.3% to 1.7% among adults (von Gontard & Neveus, 2006). From a family systems perspective, this affords a great point of entry into intervention with the children and families who are faced with these challenges. However, despite the evidence that enuresis is common in children who have experienced stressful life events, inconsistencies across studies as well as the limited research in this area have precluded the identification of a definite relationship between nocturnal enuresis and psychological problems (Wolfe-Christensen, Veenstra, Kovacevic, Elder, & Lakshmann, 2012).

In fact, some professionals theorize that the emotional and behavioral problems that arise from enuresis are more connected with the embarrassment, stress, and stigma associated with the bed wetting than the involuntary nature of nocturnal enuresis. Additional research suggests that the emotional and psychological difficulties that arise in children with nocturnal enuresis are less associated with the condition than with the parents' negative response to the child's bed wetting (Sharf & Jennings, 1988). Interestingly, some studies report no increase in psychological distress at all for children with enuresis, while others have demonstrated clinically significant elevated rates of internalizing, externalizing, and attentional problems, as reported by parents (De Bruyne et al., 2009; Friman, Handwerk, Swearer, McGinnis, & Warzak, 1998; Hirasing, van Leerdam, Bolk-Bennink, & Bosch, 1997; Joinson, Heron, Emond, & Butler, 2007).

In a research study of 8,151 children aged 7½ years, 15.5% had nocturnal enuresis (boys 20.2%, girls 10.5%). Frequent enuresis, defined by two or more wet nights per week, affected only 2.6% of them (boys 3.6%, girls 1.6%; Butler, Golding, Northstone, & ALSPAC Study Team, 2005). Monosymptomatic enuresis, defined as children who do not have daytime symptoms, rather only wet during sleep, suggesting a disturbance of bladder function, is twice (68.5%) as common as nonmonosymptomatic enuresis (31.5%)—children who have lower urinary tract symptoms and may have gastrointestinal symptoms (Butler, Heron, & ALSPAC

Study Team, 2006). Children with symptoms of monosymptomatic enuresis typically are deep sleepers and are difficult to arouse (Wolfish, Pivik, & Busby, 1997), and have increased urine volume at night. In contrast, their bladder function during the day is normal. Children with non monosymptomatic enuresis include the symptoms of monosymptomatic enuresis in addition to symptoms of those with daytime urinary incontinence. There is strong evidence that nocturnal enuresis is inherited, as research has demonstrated that as many as 77% of youth with enuresis have a first-degree relative with a history of the condition (Bayoumi et al., 2006; von Gontard, Schaumburg, Hollmann, Eiberg, & Rittig, 2001).

Encopresis

Encopresis is more commonly diagnosed in boys than girls (Coehlo, 2011) and occurs in 4.1% of 5- to 6-year-olds going down to 1.6% by the time the child reaches the age of 11 (Mellon et al., 2013). Children diagnosed with encopresis were found to have higher rates of mothers diagnosed with psychiatric disorders such as anxiety and depression and live in poorly functioning family systems (Akdemir et al., 2015). Treatment commonly includes changes in the child's diet and pharmacological (laxatives or stool softeners) and behavioral management (reward charts, positive praise, and support).

Van der Wal, Benninga, and Hirasing (2005), in their research, found that 4.1% of 5- to 6-year-olds and 1.6% of 11- to 12-year-olds were affected by encopresis. Further, in a long-term follow-up study, it was found that encopresis can persist into adolescence and even young adulthood. Forty-nine percent of 12-year-old children continued to have episodes of soiling, and 15% at 18 years of age were found to have encopresis without constipation. However, encopresis with constipation has a less positive prognosis. Eighty percent had a good outcome by age 16, with 75% to 80% at 16 to 27 years of age (Bongers, van Wijk, Reitsma, & Benninga, 2010).

More stigmatized than enuresis, encopresis is usually associated with high levels of distress for both children and their parents, and the rate of comorbid emotional disorders is higher, affecting 30% to 50% of all children with encopresis (von Gontard, Baeyens, Van Hoecke, Warzak, & Bachmann, 2011). There is significant evidence to indicate that children with encopresis are three to five times more likely to have additional comorbid emotional or behavioral disorders than nonsoiling children. In a large study of children aged 7½ years old, it was found that 11.9% of children with encopresis were also diagnosed with oppositional defiant disorder, attention deficit/hyperactivity disorder (9.2%), generalized anxiety (3.4%), specific phobias (4.3%), and separation anxiety (4.3%; Joinson et al., 2007).

Furthermore, parenting stress related to the child's encopresis is frequently reported. According to Fishman, Rappaport, Schonwald, and Nurko (2003), many parents assume the child's stubbornness or lack of effort to get to the bathroom is the primary cause of the child's incontinence. As such, they blame or punish the child. However, upon understanding the physiological factors that are involved with encopresis, they often feel guilt for taking such a hard stance (Campbell, Cox, & Borowitz, 2009). Likewise, children, especially those who are older, are at risk for being teased in school and called names, resulting in low self-esteem, rejection, and social isolation (Campbell et al., 2009). Given the psychological, social, and familial risk factors associated with elimination disorders—addressing feelings of guilt, shame, low self-esteem, parenting styles, and frustrations—a systemic family therapy approach to assessing and treating these clients would be effective.

RELATIONAL AND CULTURAL FEATURES

Research suggests that there is very little variation in the prevalence of elimination disorders across countries and cultures (van der Wal et al., 2005). According to a large meta-analysis, the median prevalence was 9% worldwide (van den Berg, Benninga, & DiLorenzo, 2006). The discrepancies could be accounted for by differences in definition, data collection, sample size, modes of reporting, and possible underreporting due to societal norms. Earlier research noted that the prevalence of elimination disorders was higher among children from depressed and lower socioeconomic groups (Equit, Klein, Braunbither, Gräber, & von Gontard, 2014). In the first study of its kind to examine the prevalence of elimination disorders across varying ethnic groups, van der Wal et al. (2005) found that encopresis among Turkish and Moroccan children was lower than their Dutch counterparts. A possible explanation for this is that the Turkish and Moroccan parents did not report the encopresis due to their beliefs that urine and feces are regarded as impure in Islamic culture.

Similarly, the prevalence of nocturnal enuresis is comparable worldwide. Research conducted by Liu, Sun, Uchiyama, and Okawa (2000) found 4.3% of Chinese children and adolescents aged 6 to 16 years suffer from enuresis, in Taiwan, 8% of children aged 6 to 11 years (Chang, Chen, Tsai, & Chin, 2001). Further, 14.9% of children aged 5 to 7 years in Turkey (Erdogan et al., 2008), 15% of children and adolescents in Saudi Arabia, and 20.8% of children and adolescents aged 6 to 15 years in Ethiopia are challenged with enuresis, including daytime incontinence (Desta, Hägglöf, Kebede, & Alem, 2007). Of interest, only a few studies have reported daytime urinary incontinence—16.6% of Korean children aged 5 to 13 years had overactive bladder, 4.5% daytime incontinence, and 6.4% enuresis (Chung et al., 2009).

Research has demonstrated that in the early years of development, having a relationship with a caregiver who is responsive and available to the child's needs is more likely to have positive outcomes and maintain competent functioning. Werner and Smith (2001) found that the young children who are able to garner support and positive responses from their caregivers may be at an advantage. Consequently, children who do not have a supportive relationship with a caregiver can be impacted negatively by the absence of the relationship in addition to the elimination disorder. Clinicians may assign a diagnosis using the V or Z codes for relational problems such as Parent–Child Relational Problem. As such, when working with this population, it is important to have parental involvement in the treatment of elimination disorders.

There is also evidence that parental stress and anxiety may be a significant factor in the treatment of elimination disorders (R. T. Brown, Connelly, Rittle, & Clouse, 2006; Janick, Finney, & Riley, 2001; Spurrier et al., 2000). Therefore, it is crucial not only to assess the parents for potential barriers that may impede working with the children, such as marital discord, mental health issues, and environmental factors, but to also assess their willingness to cooperate and collaborate with the clinician to overcome these barriers. As such, clinicians working with children diagnosed with an elimination disorder who are experiencing parental marital discord may assign Child Affected by Parental Relationship Distress. If a child is being blamed or shamed for the elimination episodes, it can cause high levels of emotional distress for the child who may then be diagnosed with High Expressed Emotion Level Within Family. Systemic family therapy is uniquely poised to address these issues by exploring the entire family system and focusing on strengths and using those strengths to minimize risks and resolve the issues using a contextual lens.

FAMILY SYSTEMS ASSESSMENTS

Assessment is a critical part of clinical treatment as it guides the therapeutic process. Laird (1995) suggests that family systems approaches have a basic tenet that "every human system needs to be understood in its sociocultural context" (p. 153). Given the social and environmental risks factors related to elimination disorders, it is consistent to utilize a systemic focus for assessment and treatment. Incorporating the critical contextual and social discourse that is intertwined with presentation of behavior lessens the judgmental diagnostic discourse of problem definition. Systemic family assessment involves understanding the problem through a relational lens. The assessment is completed with the family system as a whole while being curious about the interactional patterns of the parts of the system (which are the family members) and realizing that the problem is larger than the individual (Kazak, Simms, & Rourke, 2002). Systemic assessment is a fluid process as well; discussion with the family continually provides new contextual information for the presenting problem, allowing for further assessment (Williams, Edwards, Patterson, & Chamow, 2011). This circular process is isomorphic with the systemic concept of circularity; the process of systemic assessment does not have defined beginning or end (Gunn, Haley, & Prouty Lyness, 2007). The interaction of the assessment process with the presenting problem is a cyclical progression of deconstruction of patterns and context related to the problem.

Young children are often the symptom bearer for family problems as they are not as complex in their thought processes and less able to self-regulate or understand the rules of the system as are the older family members (Lund, Zimmerman, & Haddock, 2002). In addition, influence of the family history and the social environment can also impact a child's behavior and how a parent may conceptualize or understand that behavior (Bricker, Davis, & Squires, 2004). While theory defines the process of treatment, assessment transcends theory in that the basic concepts of assessment for effective practice are central across different theoretical constructs (Sparks & Duncan, 2010; Sprenkle, 2009). The fundamental focus of systemic assessment depends on the therapeutic alliance and understanding the structure and function within the family system in relation to the problem (Thomlison, 2016).

The relationship between the therapist and the entire family system is a critical part for successful outcomes in therapy (Sparks & Duncan, 2010). This encompasses a respectful relationship with each family member, which incorporates being curious about each family member's perspective of the problem. In this way the therapist is able to gather contextual information about the problem and the system members as each interacts with the problem in his or her own way. A supportive and trusting relationship between a client and a therapist allows the clients to feel safe; clients may be fearful of disclosing sensitive events, beliefs, or feelings in a therapeutic setting that is not supportive. Effective assessment is dependent on the client family being able to share the full context of the problem as well as the therapist being able to ask uncomfortable questions. Through the utilization of curiosity, the therapist is able to step outside of judgment and assumptions to wonder about the problem with the family (Williams et al., 2011).

Regardless of the theoretical model used in the work with a family, a therapist must evaluate and assess the functionality of the family system. This may entail the structure and organization of the family hierarchy, the qualities of the family relationships, and the recurring patterns of interaction in the family system (verbally and nonverbally). This assessment is done through observation and the clinical interview process and can also involve the family using standardized self-reporting instruments and/or role-play experiential activities. Systemic clinicians may also use a graphic mapping or diagramming tool as well, such as an ecomap, genogram, or family map (Thomlison, 2016). The systemic assessment process develops the presenting problem from the individual level to the family level.

Assessment of an Elimination Disorder

Children are often brought into therapy to be "cured" by a frustrated parent. The parent of a child experiencing symptoms associated with an elimination disorder may be profoundly distressed due to the many different associated risk factors (e.g., chaotic homes, child abuse) and comorbid disorders (e.g., maternal depression, attention deficit/hyperactivity disorder, conduct disorder; Akdemir et al., 2015; Coehlo, 2011; Kistner, 2009; Mellon et al., 2013). Frequent punishment is applied at the onset of the behavioral symptoms as well; this intervention is not effective and further frustrates the parent and child (Coehlo, 2011). While there are many different standardized assessment tools for childhood disorders, none of them are directly applicable to the assessment of an elimination disorder. Consequently, the assessment of an elimination disorder is done through clinical interviewing and observation of the family interactional patterns. While the elimination disorder may be presenting as a symptom of one family member, systemically the problem is seen as a family-level problem, not as an individual-level problem (Kazak et al., 2002).

There can be medical reasons for the symptoms of an elimination disorder, which necessitates a child being referred for a pediatric medical assessment prior to the mental health assessment. Research has indicated that in some instances, a combination of medical intervention (pharmacological) and mental health intervention results in successful treatment of elimination disorders (M. L. Brown et al., 2010; Coehlo, 2011). Therefore, it would be helpful for the therapist to request that the family pediatrician become involved for evaluation of muscle tone, diet and nutritional habits, gastrointestinal functioning, and any developmental or neurological delay. If these issues can be ruled out, the therapist can focus on the social, environmental, and familial history.

The therapist also needs to learn about the developmental milestone achievements of the child as an indicator of typical or atypical development. Therefore, the therapist must also possess an awareness of typical development of infants and children. The history of the toilet training process for all children in the family offers information as to any negative impact that might be influencing the child currently, as well as any other contextual fears or concerns that might be occurring with any family member. Gathering this information can be done through the clinical interview process, and family maps and genograms can help document patterns and historical transmission of behaviors related to the elimination disorder pathology. Given the hereditary component of enuresis, a genogram can be particularly helpful in the assessment process.

The Genogram—A Visual Diagram as an Assessment of the Family System

The systemic perspective views the individual within the framework of family and social context. Typically including three generations, the genogram depicts historical patterns across the family, which lend insight into the present situation of the family system (McGoldrick, Gerson, & Petry, 2008). The genogram is a visual diagram of the family system similar to a family tree. However, the genogram differs from a family tree because it not only includes the family structure, but also includes pertinent factors such as age, gender, sexuality, marital status and history, education, medical issues, and relational functioning. Information is gathered through clinical discussions with all family members; frequently information not known by all clients is disclosed, making the process very fluid. It grows and changes across clinical sessions. According to McGoldrick et al. (2008), "families repeat themselves. What happens in one generation will often repeat itself in the next—that is, the same issues tend to be played out from generation to generation, though the actual behavior may take a variety of forms" (p. 15).

The clinician utilizes the genogram to identify patterns of family functioning that continue across generations, as well as developing hypotheses about the meaning of the presenting problem within the family system. The collaborative nature of the genogram development process is also a valuable tool as families have often not thought about family patterns of behavior, and the information-gathering process can stimulate thoughtful consideration of the problem in a broader context.

The Clinical Interview—A Narrative Descriptive Assessment

The initial client session is the time not only for the clinician to begin the development of a therapeutic relationship, but is also a critical time to start the assessment process. Gathering information about the presenting problem, family dynamics, and functioning is key to the development of the client goals. This process of information gathering during an initial session can be considered a clinical interview (Williams et al., 2011).

The clinical interview process begins with the clinician discussing reasons the family has entered therapy (what has happened and why) and what the family hopes to see happen as a result of therapy (how will the family know when therapy can end). All family members are a part of the interview as all perspectives of the system must be included—they may be very different.

Questions may take an investigative format; however, it is essential that the process happen in a conversational way with the clinician taking a stance of curiosity to encourage everyone's participation (Williams et al., 2011). Information gathered includes details of the problem: when, where, and why each member thinks the problem is happening; how the family is coping; the family value system; the cultural and social context of the problem; any medical or developmental issues in the family; any changes in the family; as well as the timeline of the problem. Also important information to gather is the relational family structural information, which offers insight into family alliances and who holds the power to make decisions in the family (Bitter, 2014; Williams et al., 2011).

The clinical interview should include all members of the family; Williams et al. (2011) state, "all individuals are shaped by the relational context in which they live. . . . A failure to include the family dynamics in the assessment of children and adolescents provides an incomplete picture and is a disservice to the youth you are treating" (p. 103). The clinician's observations are also part of the clinical interview; this may include observation of relational interaction and family dynamics (Berg & Steiner, 2003). For example, the clinician may note who presents the problem and who is most impacted by the problem as this tells who in the family is most invested in change. Other observations may include how family members interact with each other—who is supportive, who is blamed, who is engaged or not engaged. The clinician should remain curious about these observations and bring them to the family for insight into the system dynamics.

It is essential that the therapist also engage in a discussion about the child's history of trauma including physical abuse and sexual abuse; enuresis can be presenting pathology as a developmental regression. Research indicates that children with a history of trauma who are experiencing symptoms of enuresis also rated their families with higher levels of conflict than those children without a trauma history (Faust, Kenny, & Runyon, 1997). The clinical interview presents the opportunity for the clinician and family to begin a collaborative exploration and assessment of the problem.

Instruments and Assessment Scales or Checklists

There are many different assessment and screening tools used with families; a distinction must be drawn as to the difference between an assessment tool and a screening tool. A screening tool is used to identify the need for further evaluation such as a behavioral checklist or self-report instrument. As assessment tool is an evaluative measure that determines functioning and is administered by a clinician trained to use the tool. Both tools are valuable and both should be used in collaboration with clinical observation and interview narratives as a part of the assessment decision-making process (Glascoe, 2005).

Assessment from a family systems perspective includes evaluative data from all system members in order to gather a broader description and understanding of the family and the presenting problem. Some common tools that assess individual functioning and family functioning which could be used when working with children with a diagnosis of encopresis or enuresis are included in the following sections.

EDHB: Early Development and Home Background Form

This measurement tool was developed by the APA in conjunction with the *DSM-5* and is to be used during the initial client interview session for children aged 6 to 17. The tool comprises two documents: one is a 19-question form to be completed by the parent or guardian, which asks about early development, language skills, and the home environment. The other form has eight questions and is completed by the clinician after reviewing the parent's/guardian's responses. The information gathered from this tool is suggested to be used to augment other clinical evaluation methods (Shaffer, 2013).

FACES IV: Family Adaptability and Cohesion Scale IV

This assessment tool measures family communication and satisfaction using six different scales assessing family flexibility and cohesion. It is a self-report of 42 items completed individually by family members (Olson, 2011; Williams et al., 2011).

FAD: Family Assessment Device

This assessment tool uses six scales to assess satisfaction with family functioning including involvement, communication, problem solving, and roles of the family members. It is a self-report questionnaire (60 questions) completed by all family members (Mansfield, Keitner & Dealy, 2015; Williams et al., 2011).

ASQ: Ages and Stages Questionnaires

This is a parent-completed screening tool that can be completed quickly and divided into nine age categories from birth to age 5. This tool identifies children at risk for developmental and motor delays. The areas screened include gross motor, fine motor, communication, personal–social, and problem solving (Landy, 2009).

ASQ-SE: Ages and Stages Questionnaires: Social Emotional

This is a parent-completed screening tool that can be completed quickly and divided into nine age categories from birth to age 5. This tool identifies children at risk for behavioral and emotional areas that require further evaluation and intervention such as self-regulation, communication, affect, interaction with others, and autonomy (Landy, 2009).

ASEBA: Achenbach System of Empirically Based Assessment

This system contains multiple assessments by age level (preschool, school age, adults, older adults) and within each age level are assessments completed by those who interact daily with the individual being assessed such as parents, teachers, caregivers, or peers. It is suggested that all members of the family receive the appropriate assessment when working with a family system (Achenbach, 2009; Williams et al., 2011).

The systemic assessment of an elimination disorder does not focus on the pathology of the individual experiencing the symptoms but rather as a presentation of a larger family problem (Faust et al., 1997). Due to the multiple factors related to elimination disorders that are across assessment dimensions—medical, emotional, and environmental/social—the most effective assessment of the family system is done using a combination of tools, both interview and self-report instruments. Research indicates that effective treatment for elimination disorder has been found using multiple systemic family therapy approaches (Bitter, 2014; Carr, 2014; Lindblad-Goldberg & Northey, 2013; White, 1984).

FAMILY SYSTEMS INTERVENTIONS

Systemic clinicians use a variety of interventions based on their theoretical focus and framework such as: ecosystemic structural family therapy (ESFT), narrative therapy, behavioral family therapy, and intergenerational family therapy. This section addresses interventions associated with the various therapeutic approaches for elimination disorders.

Ecosystemic Structural Family Therapy

"ESFT is a systemic, strength-based and trauma-informed family therapy model that has evolved from structural family therapy" (Lindblad-Goldberg & Northey, 2013). ESFT therapists are guided by five principles that assist their consideration of clinical problems. Some theoretical assumptions of ESFT include the following: (a) all behavior communicates within the defined culture and assumptions occur within social interactions; (b) causes are seen to be circular and not linear; and (c) families function within multiple micro- and macrosystems that affect the family's integrity and structure.

When working from ESFT framework, therapists utilize various approaches to address Elimination Disorder. Therapists center interactions on the clients, whereas the client needs to resolve the presenting problem and to eliminate undesirable interaction cycles. They seek to move the development of a child in the direction of self-control and increasing social–emotional skills comfort. Lastly, the family needs to learn to consolidate and connect emotionally in order to work together.

There are four treatment stages in the ESFT model (Lindblad-Goldberg & Northey, 2013). The first stage of treatment requires the therapist to develop the relationship with the clients. Therefore, the therapist works on joining and inviting the participants who want and need to become part of the therapeutic system. The second stage emphasizes creating a significant therapeutic focus. ESFT approach is predicated on the therapist understanding how strengths and challenges among the identified client and the family members are demonstrated. It also requires the therapist to understand the biodevelopmental systemic context where the symptoms manifest; an example that a therapist might use in this stage would be an ecomap.

The third stage is developing key growth. The main focus of this stage is to create interactional experiences to encourage growth or change. The therapist attempts to alter previous behaviors rather than accept a repetition of inappropriate behaviors.

Therapists during this stage work with the client to limit the undesirable interactional patterns that cause stress within the family system. These interventions are directed at the following: (a) strengthening parental skills, (b) promoting alliances, self-regulation, and (c) creating appropriate parent–child connection and attachment (Lindblad-Goldberg & Northey, 2013). Actions taken during this stage include creating boundaries, enactments, reframing, and unbalancing. The therapist involves the family members whose interactions seem to preserve the problem as well as those who are impacted by it.

The individuals involved in the therapeutic system work collaboratively to establish specific goals focused on the resolution of the problem and directing the child's development toward self-control and social–emotional skill and comfort. The family system in turn needs to learn to consolidate and connect emotionally in order to work together and allow community systems to organize the family's effort toward growth. The final stage emphasizes the change in behavior, family dynamic, and termination of therapy. In this stage the therapist helps the family members incorporate the different ideas that surfaced during therapy and develop a clear theoretical understanding of the effects of their behaviors.

Narrative Therapy

Narrative therapists want to formulate ideas about the family life that are not immersed in the problem. They employ a form of externalization when working with their clients. The purpose of externalization shows clients how to separate themselves from the problem. The use of narrative therapy allows the child to avoid concentrating on the problem at first. The therapist wants the child to be able to distance himself or herself from the problem. The child can objectify the problem of the "poo" (Silver, Williams, Worthington, & Phillips, 1998, p. 413).

The narrative therapist helps the family develop a narrative or story where the family sees themselves as accomplished, competent, and determined to teach the problem (not the child) a lesson and overcome the problem. Joining is important in narrative therapy, as it allows the therapist and the child to come together in the experience. White (1984) in working with children states, "One way of joining with the child is to help him/her identify the experiences when in the grip of the symptoms" (p. 153). This allows the therapist to make observations when the problem surreptitiously appears.

The therapist determines the extent of how much power the problem exerts over the child and to what degree the child is in charge. To determine this a therapist might ask, "Are you more of the boss over the sneaky poo or is it more the boss over you" (White, 1984, p. 154)? Through this process the therapist takes time to help the child see the extent to which the problem holds the role of "boss" and not the child. Once the child views the situation through this perspective, the therapist can move forward using questions such as: "Who should be the boss?" "Do you want to stand up to the problem?" "Do you want the problem to completely give in and let it reign over you and your parents?" (White, 1984, p. 154). Engaging in this dialog allows the family to develop the new narrative and escape the old narrative facilitating change.

Behavioral Family Therapy

A major component of Behavioral Family Therapy includes responsibilities that clients carry forward in their daily lives, or homework assignments. Change occurs prior to or simultaneously with accepting oneself, and that engaging in these behavioral changes may lead to an increased level of self-understanding. The goal of behavioral therapy is to increase personal choice and to construct new conditions for learning. The client and the therapist work together to develop mutually agreed upon goals These goals need to be clear, concrete, understood, and attainable (Corey, 2013).

Behavioral therapy focuses on supporting positive family interactions and learning to modify and change behaviors to function better. When working from a behavioral therapy perspective, the therapist's primary focus is on observable behavior. Behavioral therapists work the client's current problems and ways these issues impact that influence them (Corey, 2013). The therapist engages with the family and discusses the environmental occurrences related to the present behavior. During the sessions the family members remain keenly involved through participation in certain actions directed at confronting their problems. The family members learn to monitor their behavior both during and outside of therapy sessions. They gain practice with coping skills, and role-play new behavior.

The purpose of the questions derived from a behavioral perspective is to help the therapist gain a true picture of the pattern that surrounds the client's behavior (Winek, 2010). The therapist directs some questions toward quantifying the frequency of the problem. For example, when working with a family that reports an elimination disorder, the therapist might ask: How many times during a day or week does the client eliminate in his or her pants?

Intergenerational Family Therapy

Bowen's Intergenerational Family Therapy theory views the family through both the individual and systemic lens. The therapist who utilizes this approach observes how "individuals function within a family system, how they develop dysfunctional patterns, and how they can repair and enhance their relationships with members of their family" (Bitter, 2014, p. 171). The premise of the theory is promotion of differentiation and the therapist looks at intergenerational roles and behaviors. Intergenerational therapists feel the main goal for clients is to change within the context of the system. They use various methods to determine the participants in the system and their roles. Therapeutic approaches include: "genograms, going home again, detriangulating, engaging in person-to-person relationships, differentiating self and asking questions" (Gladding, 2015, p. 242).

Relationship patterns from the family of origin need to be recognized and addressed. "Bowen assumes that multigenerational patterns and influences are central in understanding present nuclear family functioning" (Bitter, 2014, p. 171). He developed a tool called the *genogram* as a way to gather information about the family and previous generations. The genogram allows for a visual picture of the individual's family.

Intergenerational therapists sit with the family and construct a genogram through information provided by them. The purpose is to assist the therapist and the family to gather information about the family structure and look at relationships within the family context. Both the therapist and family view the information together through this pictorial diagram. Through this diagram, the therapist directs questions to the client to gain more information about the family dynamics and patterns. Therapists use this tool in different ways depending on what the client brings to the session. When looking at the case of a family coming in with elimination disorder, an intergenerational therapist may focus on medical condition questions and place the details on the genogram to locate a pattern. Through that information, the therapist formulates other questions in order to clarify and expand familial relationships, interactions, and history.

Systemically, the intergenerational family therapist understands the elimination disorder as a representation of anxiety in the child, transmitted from the parents as a result of the conflict in their relationship. Questions start more on the objective and structural level and then move toward the emotional level. The therapist uses process questions to gain an understanding of the family members and their perspectives. These questions help the family think about the roles they play as they interact with the other members of the family (Bitter, 2014).

ETHICAL AND LEGAL IMPLICATIONS

Therapists need to always consider ethical and legal issues when engaging with clients. This holds more importance when dealing with children who come with vulnerabilities. The therapeutic role requires adherence to the ethical principles that guide practice. When working with clients, therapists need to remember their ethical responsibilities to the clients.

An important part of being the therapist working with these families is to screen for any trauma and physical or sexual abuse when working with children with elimination disorder. The elimination disorder may be the effect of the trauma or abuse. Many parents become frustrated with the elimination disorder because they do not understand why this is happening and the children do not understand. Out of frustration, some parents use physical punishment (Coehlo, 2011; Kistner, 2009). Another role of therapists is to explore the parenting style of these parents. Therapists need to ask questions: How do you punish your child? What does communication look like with your child? When the elimination occurs, how do you react to your child?

According to the American Association for Marriage and Family Therapy (AAMFT) *Code of Ethics* (2015) and the American Counseling Association (ACA) *Code of Ethics* (2015), therapists have a responsibility to their clients to establish a foundation for the therapy process. The ACA *Code of Ethics* states that core professional values include:

1. Enhancing human development throughout the life span
2. Honoring diversity and embracing a multicultural approach in support of the worth, dignity, potential, and uniqueness of people within their social and cultural contexts
3. Promoting social justice
4. Safeguarding the integrity of the counselor–client relationship
5. Practicing in a competent and ethical manner (counseling.org)

The core values support the mission of the ACA and provide the foundation for the code of ethics. The ACA code goes beyond the ethical principles and further delineates the expectations of ethical practice based on six principles and nine sections that address areas from the therapeutic relationship to research.

The AAMFT *Code of Ethics* begins with core values, outlines the ethical principles, and expands on the concepts that relate to ethical practice. Although defined somewhat differently, both associations address the ethical considerations that guide therapeutic relationship building, interactions among colleagues, and research.

The most important principles in working with clients who come with elimination problems are autonomy, beneficence, and nonmaleficence. Autonomy requires the therapist to respect the client's decisions and to include the client in the decision-making process, even when the client is a child. Beneficence states that therapists need to promote the best possible solutions to assist the client and family in reaching positive outcomes while in turn not increasing client distress or harm (nonmaleficence). Whether the clinician is working within the framework of the ACA or AAMFT *Codes of Ethics*, the clinician must address the known risk factors related to the elimination disorders such as trauma, physical abuse, and sexual abuse.

CASE CONCEPTUALIZATION

In order to understand elimination disorders from a systemic framework, a case study is presented. The counselor had been working with a blended family that started therapy when it merged its households. The therapeutic work was coming to a close when it became apparent that the youngest child was having some additional difficulties that were also seen to be impacting the family system.

Presenting Concerns

The case involving Lucas (age 6) and his family was about to be closed when his mother, Sophia, and her boyfriend, Keith, announced in the last session that she was pregnant.

Keith's daughters, Addison and Avery, were thrilled about the news; however, Lucas ran from the therapy room and locked himself in the bathroom. He could be heard crying loudly and after a few minutes Sophia was able to get him to open the door and calm him down. It was decided to keep the case active so that they could call to schedule if need be. A few months later Sophia did call and asked to bring "just Lucas" in for a session as he had several "incidents" at school and at home of "not making it to the bathroom." Sophia reported finding "messy clothes" in his backpack and hidden in his room. Lucas denied that anything was wrong and would cry whenever Sophia or Keith attempted to talk with him about the incidents that had been happening several times a month for the few months that had passed since the last visit. At that time Sophia reported that Addison and Avery were doing well and that things between her and Keith were "OK" although they continued to disagree about marriage (Keith wanted to legalize their relationship; Sophia did not feel it was "necessary." This disagreement had started soon after the announcement of the pregnancy). They felt that Lucas was "acting out" as a result of the pregnancy and the increased focus on the planning for the new baby.

The blended family had first entered therapy as a preventative action when Sophia and Keith, who had been in a relationship for 6 months at that time, decided to move in together. At the time of the first session, Keith had already moved into Sophia's home with his twin 15-year-old daughters, Addison and Avery. Neither parent reported having any behavioral concerns for any of the children at that time; however, after the first session Lucas told his mother that he wanted to live with his biological father. Sophia and Keith felt that this was "attention getting" behavior and that family therapy would be a positive preventative measure not just for Lucas but also for Addison and Avery. The family attended six sessions of family therapy discussing household rules, parental responsibilities and managing relationships with extended family members including Sophia's ex-husband and Keith's mother. Lucas no longer talked about moving in with his biological father; however, he would frequently become upset during the sessions. He would engage in games with the girls and it appeared that all three children had playful and supportive relationships. Sophia and Keith continued to label his behavior as "attention getting" and would sometimes ignore it, sometime punish it, and sometimes give positive attention to it.

Prior to the blending of the family, Lucas and his mom lived alone in a large single family home. Sophia had moved to the United States from Argentina when she was 30 years old and pregnant with Lucas. The move was prompted by a separation and subsequent divorce from her husband and father of Lucas, Manuel. Manuel continues to be in their lives as he travels frequently between the United States and Argentina for business. Both Sophia and Lucas report positive relationships with Manuel who has remarried; Lucas looks forward to spending holidays and summers with his father in Argentina. Lucas is bilingual and prior to Keith and his daughters moving in, only Spanish was spoken in the home. Sophia and Manuel feel strongly that Lucas should grow up rooted in his Argentinian culture; Keith agrees but does not want Spanish spoken exclusively as he and his daughters do not understand the language. Keith reports no interest in learning Spanish.

Lucas attends a private school, excels academically but not socially according to his mother. He is soft spoken and prefers to play alone or be with his mother rather than participate in group activities at school. Sophia does not work outside of the home and has been a frequent classroom volunteer at Lucas's school and serves on the school's board of trustees. She is financially stable as a result of her divorce settlement as well as her own family resources. She will continue to receive financial support from the divorce settlement as long as she does not remarry.

Keith, a 50-year-old Caucasian male, lost his wife 5 years ago to breast cancer when the twins were 10 years old. As an attorney, Keith works long hours and prior to moving in with Sophia, depended on his mother, Julia, to help him with the twins who attend the same private school as Lucas. Sophia and Keith met at the children's school where he has also been active on the board. Keith was raised in a very close family and his mother has always been actively involved in his life. Until recently she was responsible for the girls' activities and making dinner each night for them. Keith sold the home he had been living in after moving into Sophia's home, which was larger and accommodated all of the children more easily. However, the new house is located over 30 minutes from Julia and she has become less involved with Keith and the twins since the move according to Keith.

Addison and Avery excel academically, athletically, and socially; the transition to the new house has been exciting for them as they were allowed to decorate their new rooms themselves. Sophia has also started taking the girls to their sport practices after school, which means Lucas must also come along. During these times Lucas speaks to his mother in Spanish, which upsets Addison and Avery because they do not understand. Lucas complains about having to attend the sport practices; however, he reports that he does enjoy being with his "sisters" as he calls Addison and Avery.

Concurrent Problems

When Sophia brought Lucas in for the session he became upset and ran under a desk in the waiting room and defecated in his shorts. Sophia was visibly upset and stated that Lucas and Keith were not getting along; this behavior was getting worse and he had "incidents" at school and at home. Keith feels that she "babies" Lucas and is reinforcing this behavior as he believes that Lucas should be punished for defecating in his clothes and be forced to wear them throughout the school day or else he should be put "back into diapers." Sophia does not want to punish him and is trying to understand what is causing the regression and thinks it has to do with tension that has been happening in the household.

Lucas and the twins have witnessed arguments between their parents about marriage. Keith wants to be legally married when the baby arrives. She is not concerned about marriage and does not want to "rush into anything." She wanted Keith to attend the session so this could be discussed but he refused to attend the therapy session because he felt it would "reinforce the attention-seeking behavior" he feels is prompting the encopresis. Sophia clearly thought that if Keith would "back off," Lucas would adjust to what is happening.

Lucas had seen a pediatrician to rule out any medical issues. Sophia discussed his diet and toileting habits with the doctor who determined that there was no obvious medical reason for the "constipation" which caused the involuntary soiling. Lucas had a balanced diet of fiber and hydration; there was no report of straining when attempting to empty his bowels either. Lucas reported not realizing he needed to have a bowel movement and also recognized that he was usually upset before the elimination happened and often did not remember the unfolding of events subsequent to moving his bowels. The pediatrician offered a prescription of laxatives, however, and encouraged Sophia to seek behavioral intervention due to Lucas reporting that the incidents happened when he was upset. Sophia first tried using a laxative with Lucas and monitoring his bowel movements; however, it seemed to exacerbate the situation.

Background History and Stressors

Lucas had typical development and milestone achievements; walking at 13 months, potty trained at 38 months. He was cared for at home by his mother until attending a half-day prekindergarten program at age 4. Lucas's kindergarten teacher suggested that he be tested for the gifted classroom program that year. Sophia arranged for the testing and learned that Lucas has an IQ of 152 and was moved halfway through the year into the gifted program at the same private school. Manuel was concerned that this would put too much stress on Lucas, but agreed with Sophia's decision. Education is very important in their family; both Manuel and Sophia have graduate degrees from a university in Argentina. Sophia stated that Manuel continues to be concerned that the accelerated academic program might be putting too much stress on Lucas and that the encopresis is the result of the stress.

Sophia and Keith continue to argue about marriage. She thinks that Keith fears she is not committed to him and that is why she would not marry him. Sophia says she just does not see the reason to marry and he just has to "understand." She knows that the kids have heard them argue and the girls even talked with her about it after school one day. Addison and Avery are glad that their father is "happy again" and are worried that this will come to an end if Sophia would not marry him.

Sophia has also stopped volunteering at school in Lucas's classroom; she reported that the pregnancy is tiring her plus the demands of having three kids to run around afterschool take much of her time. Julia has offered to help; however, Sophia feels that she needs to spend the time with the girls now and is focusing on developing a supportive relationship with them. She is upset that Julia has told Keith that she is "keeping her away" from the girls and he wants Sophia to not do so much with them so that Julia can be involved again. She stated that she wished Keith would put more time into developing a relationship with Lucas as she is doing with Addison and Avery.

Strengths

The family is supportive of Lucas and provides needed structure and nurturing; despite Keith's frustrations there has been no shaming or physical punishment for the encopresis episodes as he is following Sophia's lead. Additionally, Lucas's teacher at school has been very watchful and reassuring with Lucas. When he becomes upset at school and "misses the toilet," as the teacher calls it, she quickly contacts Sophia about the incident and keeps spare clothing in her desk for him. Addison and Avery are also attentive to Lucas, watchful over him at school, and clearly enjoy having a "baby brother." The family is financially secure with no history of trauma or abuse.

DSM-5 Impressions and Implications

Lucas had been cleared of any medically related issues to the encopresis by his pediatrician who told her that it was a "behavioral issue." There was no history of trauma or abuse associated with the symptoms. Sophia was confused because the incidents happen when he is awake, never at night, so she knows he has control of his bowels and he never wets the bed or urinates in his pants during the day and the teacher reports that he is using the bathroom at school. Lucas had not experienced any painful bowel movements or constipation issues that might have developed into withholding the bowel movements until leakage occurred. The episodes continued several times a month for over 3 months. The diagnosis given for this case was: Encopresis without constipation and overflow continence. The family attended four sessions following the session when Lucas came alone with his mother.

Relational Problems

While Lucas had been raised living in a household separate from his biological father, his father had always been present for holidays and important events. Keith and Sophia clearly explained to the children that they would never look to replace his father or their mother;

however, Addison and Avery had started calling Sophia "mom." This confused Lucas as she was his mom; he did at times call Keith "dad" but would become upset afterward. The relationship between Keith and Lucas had become very strained as a result of the encopresis. Keith was frustrated with Lucas and while he did not verbally communicate his displeasure, he avoided Lucas and stopped tucking him in at night. Keith also began talking about Lucas as a "big boy" and a "big brother." Lucas in return avoided Keith to the point of not making eye contact and not wanting to be in the same room with Keith. The evident distress was consistent with Other Conditions That May Be a Focus of Clinical Attention, such as Parent–Child Relational Problem.

Assessments

A genogram was completed, which revealed that Lucas was an only child and only grandchild for both families of Sophia and Manuel. He received much attention as such, and enjoyed the title of "the baby." Sophia's family was overjoyed about the prospect of the new baby and had begun talking with Lucas about being a "big brother." Keith's family was also excited about the new baby and, while Addison and Avery called Lucas their "baby brother," they also talked with him about being the "big brother" to the new baby. The genogram also indicated that the families interacted in positive relationships across the generations and subsystems. Particularly interesting was the positive interaction between the family members of Manuel toward Keith and the new baby. There was no history of encopresis evident across the family system.

The genogram also indicated that Sophia and Lucas had a very close and overly involved relationship until Keith moved into the house. Lucas had been sleeping in bed with his mom most nights because she reported being "worried" about him alone in his bedroom on the other side of the house. Sophia indicated that she felt the relationship with Lucas had become conflictual at that time and she realized she had also withdrawn from the relationship because she was unsure how to handle him. She was more comfortable now with him sleeping alone in his room because it was near to Addison's and Avery's rooms. Sophia also reported that she had stopped volunteering in Lucas's classroom because she was tired but also because she knew Lucas needed to become more "independent" of her.

The assessment clinical interview revealed that many changes had happened in a short time period for Lucas: He had changed classes at school; his new class was more academically challenging; his mother became involved in an intimate relationship (which had not happened before); Keith and his daughters moved into the home; his private time with his mother was disrupted by new responsibilities with Addison and Avery; his mother's pregnancy meant that another child was coming and he would lose his "baby of the family" status. His mother was pulling back from her relationship with him to support his development of "independence." Keith was also withdrawing from him due to his frustrations with the encopresis and the stress it was placing on Sophia.

Interventions

The process of creating the genogram was an intervention as well; the blended family enjoyed learning about each other. Of particular note was conversation between the children. Addison and Avery recognized that they never had the opportunity to be "only" children as twins. However, the girls talked about the benefits and value of having a sibling and let Lucas know that while being the "baby" and an "only" child seemed great, having a sibling was much more fun. This prompted "siblings-only" activities for the three children, planned by the children as well. Lucas even started teaching the girls Spanish and wanted them to travel to Argentina with him during the summer to stay at his father's home; the girls were excited to do that because they had never been out of the country. All of the parents were considering this and thought it might be a nice break for Sophia who would be just home with the new baby.

Creating the genogram also allowed Sophia and Keith to recognize the many changes that had happened in a short time for all of the children. While Addison and Avery responded easily due to their age, they had thought Lucas would as well; however, that was developmentally inconsistent. At his age Lucas is very concrete in his thinking and adjusting to change can be difficult. Lucas wants to be the "big boy" and be independent as others are telling him; he still needs the cuddles and nurturing that the "baby boy" received. This struggle between the two sides of Lucas is frustrating for him and hard to handle. This struggle opened the discussion in the family of Lucas the "big boy" and Lucas "the baby." They were all able to talk about parts of themselves which were babies too and that it is hard to always be the "big boy" or "big girl." This helped Lucas understand that his struggle to be a "big boy" but also wanting to be "the baby" was OK and even normal.

Discussing times when Lucas the "big boy" made decisions and showed up to school and when Lucas "the baby" was in charge occurred. Since soiling pants is what babies do it was decided that Lucas "the baby" was in charge on those days that the soiling incidents happened at school or home, externalizing the problem and avoiding the blaming of the problem on Lucas. There were plenty of days each month when Lucas the "big boy" was in charge so the family was able to talk about what was different about those days. Further discussion happened for the family to brainstorm how to keep Lucas the "big boy" in charge during times that need those "big boy" decisions like going to the bathroom. This process elevated Lucas the "big boy" to a highly desirable status; over time it was only Lucas "the big boy" showing up to school and at home. Lucas stated that since there was a new baby coming he needed to be able to help the new baby the way Addison and Avery were helpful to him. Lucas became excited about being a big brother yet still relished the attention from the girls as their "little brother." He was careful to correct anyone who called him a "baby" or their "baby brother."

Ethical and Legal Implications

Consent for treatment was needed from Manuel as the biological and legal father of Lucas, which was not problematic since a supportive relationship existed between the three parents. Acknowledging Keith as a parental figure for Lucas in the family was also important from a treatment standpoint to provide structure in the blended family system. The therapist, knowing that abuse and trauma could be associated with elimination disorder, explored the family history and was prepared to respond legally if maltreatment was disclosed. The State in which the therapist practices mandates mental health providers as reporters of child abuse and/or child neglect. Both the ACA and the AAMFT *Code of Ethics* address the responsibility of the clinician to disclose confidential information when such disclosure is necessary to protect the client from serious harm and required by state law (AAMFT, 2015; ACA, 2015). As part of the consent of treatment intake, the family was made aware of this mandate. Fortunately, in this case there was no disclosure or indication of abuse or neglect.

DISCUSSION

As you continue to reflect on the case study and the overall approach, contemplate these questions:

- How could the disagreement between Sophia and Keith play into the diagnosis?
- If Manuel had refused to consent for treatment of Lucas, how would the therapist proceed?
- Would having Lucas wear pull-ups or another protective undergarment be an effective systemic intervention?
- If Sophia had not been pregnant, would the "big boy" Lucas still be an effective intervention?
- If there had been a medical issue responsible for the encopresis, would the intervention have been different?
- What are the ACA and AAMFT ethical codes that pertain to the treatment of this family?

Utilizing a genogram to explore the history of presenting symptoms in the family actually brought the family together; the parents were unaware that elimination disorders had a hereditary component. While this was not the situation for this family, the process of talking about family members and learning that everyone has some "issue" helped change the identification of the "problem that Lucas has" to a confusing behavior that Lucas is having, through which the family wanted to support him. The genogram discussion also allowed the family to walk through the many changes that had occurred for all family members in the past year; each member talked about how he or she worked through the changes and how they impacted him or her.

Watching his girls interact so joyfully with Lucas, Keith realized that he had unrealistic developmental expectations of Lucas and then further challenged the relationship by distancing himself from Lucas. He was thankful to have three children who supported each other unconditionally and that as a parent it was his responsibility to do so as well. The family ended up making a blended family tree to display in their home as a result of the genogram discussions. This was a family activity that included researching family albums for photos and Keith's mother Julia became involved as well.

Externalizing the problem outside of Lucas through identifying the episodes as times when "Lucas the baby" was in charge helped Lucas talk about his feelings related to the incidents and the changes that had happened to the family over the past year. Sophia was able to see that she had distanced herself from Lucas and felt torn between Keith and Lucas. She also felt that she was worried that Keith's mother would interfere with her relationship with Addison and Avery because she was a "bad mom" since Lucas was displaying this "problem behavior." From this case it is easy to see how the context of the family is involved with the presenting problem of encopresis. The family continued to engage in therapy and used the sessions to strengthen their sense of family unification through interactive exercises including playing team board games, creating the blended family tree, and writing questions/issues that each wanted to talk about in session. The externalization of the problem through using "Lucas the baby" was an important process for the family; recognizing his struggle to become a "big boy" yet still desiring to be "the baby," the family was able to be empathetic and reassuring to Lucas when incidents happened.

However, a month or so after the family sessions started, the episodes of encopresis stopped happening. As Sophia's pregnancy became more apparent, Lucas seemed more comfortable as the new big brother. Sophia and Keith were more comfortable in their coparenting roles and trusted each other's commitment to the family; the arguments stopped between them. With less tension between the parents, the children also felt more comfortable that the family was moving forward together. Family therapy ended before the birth of the new baby and the family was planning for the new baby girl, working together to choose the name. The children were also excitedly planning for a summer trip to Argentina where Lucas's father thrilled that Lucas was doing so well, was happy to have all of the children visit, and promised that Addison and Avery would be able to teach their dad how to speak Spanish after the trip.

SUMMARY

Elimination disorders are not atypical for young children and adolescents; with the multiple contributing factors of the pathology, it can be challenging for a family and clinician to determine the cause. Given the social, environmental, family functioning and transgenerational factors, using a family systems approach when working with children diagnosed with an elimination disorder would seem to be an acknowledged treatment practice and review of the research has demonstrated that systemic treatment is effective (Carr, 2014).

The case presented illustrates how the interaction of family members influences behaviors in the system. It is not possible to address the symptoms or pathology of one system member (Lucas) without addressing the symptoms in the whole system or family. Once the "problem" was elevated from the individual level to the family level, everyone was able to participate in the resolution process.

REFERENCES

Achenbach, T. M. (2009). *The Achenbach System of Empirically Based Assessment (ASEBA): Development, findings, theory, and applications.* Burlington: University of Vermont Research Center for Children, Youth, & Families.

Akdemir, D., Çengel Kültür, S. E., Saltık Temizel, İ. N., Zeki, A., & Şenses Dinç, G. (2015). Familial psychological factors are associated with encopresis. *Pediatrics International, 57*(1), 143–148.

American Association for Marriage and Family Therapy. (2015). *AAMFT code of ethics.* Alexandria, VA: Author. Retrieved from http://www.aamft.org/iMIS15/AAMFT/Content/Legal_Ethics/Code_of_Ethics.aspx

American Counseling Association. (2015). 2014 *ACA code of ethics: As approved by the ACA Governing Council.* Alexandria, VA: Author. Retrieved from http://www.counseling.org/docs/ethics/2014-aca-code-of-ethics.pdf?sfvrsn=4

American Psychiatric Association. (1994). *Diagnostic and statistical manual of mental disorders* (4th ed.). Washington, DC: Author.

American Psychiatric Association. (2013). *Diagnostic and statistical manual of mental disorders* (5th ed.). Arlington, VA: American Psychiatric Publishing.

Barnes, T. R. E., Drake, M. J., & Paton, C. (2012). Nocturnal enuresis with antipsychotic medication. *The British Journal of Psychiatry: The Journal of Mental Science, 200*(1), 7.

Bayoumi, R. A., Eapen, V., Al-Yahyaee, S., Al Barwani, H. S., Hill, R. S., & Al Gazali, L. (2006). The genetic basis of inherited primary nocturnal enuresis: A UAE study. *Journal of Psychosomatic Research, 61*(3), 317–320.

Berg, I. K., & Steiner, T. (2003). *Children's solution work.* New York, NY: W. W. Norton.

Bitter, J. R. (2014). *Theory and practice of family therapy and counseling* (2nd ed.). Belmont, CA: Brooks/Cole Cengage.

Bongers, M., van Wijk, M., Reitsma, J., & Benninga, M. (2010). Long term prognosis for childhood constipation: Clinical outcomes in adulthood. *Pediatrics, 126*, e156–e162.

Bricker, D., Davis, M., & Squires, J. (2004). Mental health screening in young children. *Infants and Young Children, 17*(2), 129–144.

Brown, M. L., Pope, A. W., & Brown, E. J. (2010). Treatment of primary nocturnal enuresis in children: A review. *Child: Care, health and development, 37*(2), 153–160.

Brown, R. T., Connelly, M., Rittle, C., & Clouse, B. (2006). A longitudinal examination predicting emergency room use in children with sickle cell disease and their caregivers. *Journal of Pediatric Psychology, 31*, 163–173.

Butler, R. J., Golding, J., Northstone, K., & ALSPAC Study Team. (2005). Nocturnal enuresis at 7.5 years old: Prevalence and analysis of clinical signs. *BJU International, 96*(3), 404–410.

Butler, R. J., Heron, J. & The ALSPAC Study Team. (2006). Exploring the differences between mono- and polysymptomatic nocturnal enuresis. *Scandinavian Journal of Urology and Nephrology, 40*, 313–319.

Campbell, L. K., Cox, D. J., & Borowitz, S. M. (2009). Elimination disorders: Enuresis and encopresis. In M. C. Roberts & R. G. Steele (Eds.), *Handbook of pediatric psychology* (4th ed., pp. 481–490). New York, NY: Guilford Press.

Carr, A. (2014). The evidence base for family therapy and systemic interventions for child-focused problems. *Journal of Family Therapy, 36*, 107–157.

Chang, P., Chen, W. J., Tsai, W. Y., & Chiu, Y. N. (2001). An epidemiological study of nocturnal enuresis in Taiwanese children. *British Journal of Urology International, 87*, 678–681.

Chung, J. M., Lee, S. D., Kang, D. I., Kwon, D. D., Kim, K. S., Kim, S. Y., . . . Han, S. W. (2009). Prevalence and associated factors of overactive bladders in Korean children 5–13 years old: A nationwide multicenter study. *Urology, 73*, 63–69.

Coehlo, D. P. (2011). Encopresis: A medical and family approach. *Pediatric Nursing, 37*(3), 107–112.

Corey, G. (2013). *Theory and practice of counseling and psychotherapy* (9th ed.). Belmont, CA: Brooks/Cole Cengage.

De Bruyne, E., Van Hoecke, E., Van Gompel, K., Verbeken, S., Baeyens, D., Hoebeke, P., & Vande Walle, J. (2009). Problem behavior, parental stress, and enuresis. *Journal of Urology, 182*, 2015–2021.

Desta, M., Hägglöf, B., Kebede, D., & Alem, A. (2007). Socio-demographic and psychopathologic correlates of enuresis in urban Ethiopian children. *Acta Paediatrica, 96*, 556–560.

Equit, M., Klein, A., Braun-bither, K., Gräber, S., & von Gontard, A. (2014). Elimination disorders and anxious-depressed symptoms in preschool children: A population-based study. *European Child and Adolescent Psychiatry, 23*(6), 417–423.

Erdogan, A., Akkurt, H., Boettjer, N. K., Yurtseven, E., Can, G., & Kiran, S. (2008). Prevalence and behavioural correlates of enuresis in young children. *Journal of Paediatrics and Child Health, 44*, 297–301.

Faust, J., Kenny, M., & Runyon, M. (1997). Differences in family functioning of sexually abused vs. nonabused enuretics. *Journal of Family Violence, 12*(4), 405–416.

Fishman, L., Rappaport, L., Schonwald, A., & Nurko, S. (2003). Trends in referral to a single encopresis clinic over 20 years. *Pediatrics, 111*, e604–e607.

Friman, P. C., Handwerk, M. L., Swearer, S. M., McGinnis, C., & Warzak, W. J. (1998). Do children with primary nocturnal enuresis have clinically significant behavior problems? *Archives of Pediatric and Adolescent Medicine, 152*, 537–539.

Gladding, S. T. (2015). *Family therapy: History, theory and practice*. Boston, MA: Pearson.

Glascoe, F. P. (2005). Screening for developmental and behavioral problems. *Mental Retardation and Developmental Disabilities Research Reviews, 11*(3), 173–179.

Gunn, W., Haley, J., & Prouty Lyness, A. (2007). Systemic approaches to family therapy. In H. Thompson Prout & D. T. Brown (Eds.), *Counseling and psychotherapy with children and adolescents: Theory and practice for school and clinical settings* (pp. 388–418). Hoboken, NJ: Wiley.

Hirasing, R. A., van Leerdam, F. J., Bolk-Bennink, L. B., & Bosch, J. D. (1997). Bedwetting and behavioural and/or emotional problems. *Acta Paediatrica, 86*, 31–34.

Janicke, D. M., Finney, J. W., & Riley, A. W. (2001). Children's health care use: A prospective investigation of factors related to care-seeking. *Medical Care, 39*, 990–1001.

Joinson, C., Heron, J., Emond, A., & Butler, R. (2007). Psychological problems in children with bedwetting and combing (day and night) wetting: A UK population-based study. *Journal of Pediatric Psychology, 32*, 605–616.

Kazak, A., Simms, S., & Rourke, M. (2002). Family systems practice in pediatric psychology. *Journal of Pediatric Psychology, 27*(2), 133–143.

Kistner, M. (2009). Dysfunctional elimination behaviors and associated complications in school-age children. *The Journal of School Nursing, 25*(2), 108–116.

Laird, J. (1995). Family-centered practice in the post-modern era. *Families in Society, 76*(3), 150–160.

Landy, S. (2009). *Pathways to competence: Encouraging healthy social and emotional development in young children*. Baltimore, MD: Brookes.

Lindblad-Goldberg, M., & Northey, W. F., Jr. (2013). Ecosystemic structural family therapy: Theoretical and clinical foundations. *Contemporary Family Therapy, 35*, 147–160.

Liu, X., Sun, Z., Uchiyama, M., & Okawa, M. (2000). Attaining nocturnal urinary control, nocturnal enuresis, and behavioral problems in Chinese children aged 6 through 16 years. *Journal of the American Academy of Child and Adolescent Psychiatry, 39*, 1557–1564.

Lund, L. K., Zimmerman, T. S., & Haddock, S. A. (2002). The theory, structure and techniques for the inclusion of children in family therapy: A literature review. *Journal of Marital and Family Therapy, 28*(4), 445–454.

Mansfield, A. K., Keitner, G. I., & Dealy, J. (2015), The family assessment device: An update. *Family Process, 54*, 82–93.

McGoldrick, M., Gerson, R., & Petry, S. (2008). *Genograms: Assessments and intervention*. New York, NY: W. W. Norton.

Mellon, M. W., Natchev, B. E., Katusic, S. K., Colligan, R. C., Weaver, A. L., Voigt, R. G., & Barbaresi, W. J. (2013). Incidence of enuresis and encopresis among children with attention-deficit/hyperactivity disorder in a population-based birth cohort. *Academic Pediatrics*, 13(4), 322–327.

Messmore, C. (2012). Diagnosis in infants and very young children: A review of the two classification systems. *Counseling and Human Development*, 44(5), 1–8.

Olson, D. H. (2011). FACES IV and the circumplex model: Validation study. *Journal of Family Therapy*, 3(1), 64–80.

Pollock, M. R., Metz, A. E., & Barabash, T. (2014). Association between dysfunctional elimination syndrome and sensory processing disorder. *The American Journal of Occupational Therapy*, 68(4), 472–477.

Robaey, P. (2011). Commentary: Enuresis and ADHD in older children and an adolescent treated with stimulant medication: A case series. *Journal of the Canadian Academy of Child and Adolescent Psychiatry*, 20(1), 56.

Shaffer, D. (2013). Early development and home background. American Psychiatric Association. Retrieved from https://www.psychiatry.org/psychiatrists/practice/dsm/dsm-5/online-assessment-measures

Sharf, M. B., & Jennings, S. W. (1988). Childhood enuresis: Relationship to sleep, etiology, evaluation, and treatment. *Annals of Behavioral Medicine*, 10, 113–120.

Silver, E., Williams, A., Worthington, F., & Phillips, N. (1998). Family therapy and soiling: An audit of externalizing and other approaches. *Journal of Family Therapy*, 20, 413–422.

Sparks, J. A., & Duncan, B. L. (2010). Common factors in couple and family therapy: Must all have prizes? In B. L. Duncan, S. D. Miller, B. E. Wampold, & M. A. Hubble (Eds.), *The heart and soul of change: Delivering what works in therapy* (pp. 357–391). Washington, DC: American Psychological Association.

Sprenkle, D. H. (2009). *Common factors in couple and family therapy: The overlooked foundation for effective practice*. New York, NY: Guilford Press.

Spurrier, N. J., Sawyer, M. G., Staugas, R., Martin, A. J., Kennedy, D., & Steiner, D. L. (2000). Association between parental perceptions of children's vulnerability to illness and management of children's asthma. *Pediatric Pulmonology*, 29, 88–93.

Thomlison, B. (2016). *Family assessment handbook: An introduction and practical guide to family assessment*. Boston, MA: Cengage.

van den Berg, M. M., Benninga, M. A., & Di Lorenzo, C. (2006). Epidemiology of childhood constipation: A systematic review. *American Journal of Gastroenterology*, 101, 2401–2409.

van der Wal, M. F., Benninga, M. A., & Hirasing, R. A. (2005). The prevalence of encopresis in a multicultural population. *Journal of Pediatric Gastroenterology and Nutrition*, 40, 345–348.

von Gontard, A. (2013). The impact of DSM-5 and guidelines for assessment and treatment of elimination disorders. *European Child and Adolescent Psychiatry*, 22, 61–67.

von Gontard, A., Baeyens, D., Van Hoecke, E., Warzak, W., & Bachmann, C. (2011). Psychological and psychiatric issues in urinary and fecal incontinence. *Journal of Urology*, 185, 1432–1437.

von Gontard A., & Neveus T. (2006) *Management of disorders of bladder and bowel control in childhood*. London, UK: Mac Keith Press.

von Gontard, A., Schaumburg, H., Hollmann, E., Eiberg, H., & Rittig, S. (2001). The genetics of enuresis: A review. *Journal of Urology*, 166, 2438–2443.

Werner, E. E., & Smith, R. S. (2001). *Journeys from childhood to midlife: Risk, resilience, and recovery*. Ithaca, NY: Cornell University Press.

White, M. (1984). Pseudo-encopresis: From avalanche to victory, from vicious cycle to virtuous cycles. *Family Systems Medicine*, 2(2), 150–160.

Williams, L., Edwards, T., Patterson, J., & Chamow, L. (2011). *Essential assessment skills for couple and family therapists*. New York, NY: Guilford Press.

Winek, J. L. (2010). *Systemic family therapy: From theory to practice*. Thousand Oaks, CA: Sage Publications.

Wolfe-Christensen, C., Veenstra, A. L., Kovacevic, L., Elder, J. S., & Lakshmanan, Y. (2012). Psychosocial difficulties in children referred by pediatric urology: A closer look. *Urology*, 80, 907–913.

Wolfish, N. M., Pivik, R. T., & Busby, K. A. (1997). Elevated sleep arousal thresholds in enuretic boys: Clinical implications. *Acta Paediatrica*, 86, 381–384.

World Health Organization. (2008). *Multiaxial classification of child and adolescent psychiatric disorders: The ICD-10 classification of mental and behavioural disorders in children and adolescents*. Cambridge, England: Cambridge University Press.

Yuce, M., Zoroglu, S., Ceylan, M., Kandemir, H., & Karabekiroglu, K. (2013). Psychiatric comorbidity distribution and diversities in children and adolescents with attention deficit/hyperactivity disorder: A study from Turkey. *Neuropsychiatric Disease and Treatment*, 9, 1791–1799.

MULTISYSTEMIC DIMENSIONS OF SLEEP–WAKE DISORDERS

Rachel M. O'Neill and Brandy L. Gilea

Sleep is vital to multiple physiological systems that maintain health (Buckhalt, 2011; Dahl & El-Sheikh, 2007); however, approximately 35% to 40% of the U.S. population experiences a sleep disturbance (Hossain & Shapiro, 2002). Adults should sleep approximately 7 to 8 hours per night; sleeping less than 7 hours per night is associated with adverse health conditions (e.g., weight gain, diabetes, hypertension, heart disease; Watson et al., 2015). Sleep disturbances may result in functional impairment, such as diminished cognitive capacity, daytime sleepiness, and fatigue. Certainly, disturbed sleep has the potential to impact the family system in a myriad of ways. In this chapter, the authors discuss multisystemic dimensions of sleep–wake disorders.

DSM-5 AND FAMILY SYSTEMS

As noted previously, restful sleep is crucial to the well-being of individuals. Research (e.g., Durmer & Dinges, 2005) has found that attention, cognition, and memory are impacted by sleep deprivation. Sleep impairment may also increase negative effect and mood deterioration (Kahn-Greene, Killgore, Kamimori, Balkin, & Kilgore, 2007). In addition to the impact on physical and mental well-being, sleep disorders have the potential to impact work place productivity. Poor sleep affects the workplace through employees' compromised physical and mental health, impaired cognition, and increased workplace absences (Gaultney & Collins-McNeil, 2009). Fullerton (2006) estimated that the annual sleep disorder–related costs (i.e., medical costs, workplace costs) exceed $100 billion in the United States. In addition to the consequences experienced by individuals with disturbed sleep, there may also be broader implications for the family unit. Individuals who experience sleep disturbances may struggle in their relationships with partners, children, and friends.

Alterations in sleep patterns can be due to a variety of factors. Some individuals experience disrupted sleep as a result of another mental health disorder (e.g., depression, anxiety). Disordered sleep can also be a symptom of a medical condition (e.g., recent surgery, diabetes). Still other individuals may experience issues with sleep due to a variety of lifestyle factors (e.g., diet, exercise, stress). The *Diagnostic and Statistical Manual of Mental Disorders* (5th ed.; *DSM-5*; American Psychiatric Association [APA], 2013) identifies 10 sleep–wake disorders: Insomnia Disorder (a dissatisfaction with the quality and/or quantity of one's sleep), Hypersomnolence Disorder (excessive sleepiness), Narcolepsy (irrepressible need to sleep), Breathing-Related Sleep Disorders, Circadian Rhythm Sleep–Wake Disorders, Non–Rapid Eye Movement (NREM) Sleep Arousal Disorders, Nightmare Disorder, Rapid Eye Movement (REM) Sleep Behavior Disorder, Restless Legs Syndrome (RLS; unpleasant sensations in the legs, especially when at rest), and Substance/Medication-Induced Sleep Disorder (sleep-related problems experienced as a result of the direct physiological consequences of a substance).

Insomnia Disorder

Insomnia Disorder is characterized by dissatisfaction with sleep quality or quantity and/or difficulty falling or staying asleep (APA, 2013). There are two types of insomnia: *Primary insomnia* (insomnia without a co-occurring physical or mental health complaint) and *comorbid insomnia* (insomnia in conjunction with a mental disorder; van de Laar, Pevernagie, van Mierlo, & Overeem, 2015). Insomnia disorder appears to be a relatively common condition; it is estimated that 33% of the adult population has met criteria for insomnia disorder (APA, 2013). Although there is no single casual pathway for the development of insomnia disorder, there may be numerous risk factors. Poor sleep habits, work schedule, anxiety, and overuse of caffeinated substances may all contribute to the development of an insomnia disorder (APA, 2013). Family issues (stress, divorce, child-rearing) may also contribute to the development and maintenance of insomnia. Insomnia is a common feature of other mental disorders (e.g., major depressive disorder) and a thorough assessment is needed to determine whether the sleep disturbance meets clinical significance. A diagnosis of Insomnia Disorder can be assigned to those who meet criteria for another mental health disorder provided that the symptoms of insomnia are sufficient to warrant a separate diagnosis (APA, 2013). Insomnia disorder can have far-reaching impacts on the entire family system. Although bed partners may be most impacted by the insomnia disorder, it is not uncommon for children and coworkers of the individual with insomnia disorder to also experience effects of the disorder.

Hypersomnolence

Individuals diagnosed with Hypersomnolence experience symptoms of excessive sleep and deteriorated quality of wakefulness (APA, 2013). Individuals with hypersomnia experience daytime sleepiness and short sleep latency (the length of time it takes to transition from full wakefulness to sleep) not attributable to a physical or mental health condition (Jennum, Ibsen, Avlund, & Kjellberg, 2014). Although hypersomnolence shares some features with narcolepsy, the two disorders differ in several key ways. Both conditions are characterized by excessive sleepiness; however, individuals with Narcolepsy have cataplexy (i.e., sudden bilateral muscle tone loss) and recurrent intrusions of elements of REM sleep into the transition between sleep and wakefulness (e.g., sleep-related hallucinations, sleep paralysis; APA, 2013). Individuals with hypersomnia may experience difficulty engaging with family and friends, and may be reluctant to participate in activities that require sustained concentration.

Breathing-Related Sleep Disturbances

Breathing-related sleep disorders (i.e., Sleep Apnea Hypopnea, Central Sleep Apnea [Idiopathic Central Sleep Apnea, Cheyne–Stokes Breathing, Central Sleep Apnea Comorbid With Opioid Use], and Sleep-Related Hypoventilation [Idiopathic Hypoventilation, Congenital Central Alveolar Hypoventilation, Comorbid Sleep-Related Hypoventilation) are characterized by abnormalities in the breathing process during sleep that result in disrupted sleep–wake cycles. Obstructive Sleep Apnea, the most common type of sleep apnea (APA, 2013), is characterized by upper airway collapse, resulting in intermittent hypopnea (shallow breathing) or apnea (absence of breathing) followed by awakening (Reishtein et al., 2006). Obstructive sleep apnea commonly occurs with other sleep-related disorders (Bjorvatn, Pallesen, Gronli, Siversten, & Lehmann, 2014). Sleep apnea may contribute to dissatisfaction in the quality of sleep for bed partners of those with the condition. For example, an individual with sleep apnea may experience several episodes of sleep-related breathing and waking issues per night, which may, in turn, impact the bed partner's ability to engage in his or her own restful sleep.

Circadian Rhythm Sleep–Wake Disorder

The primary feature of circadian rhythm sleep–wake disorders (Delayed Sleep Phase Type, Advanced Sleep Phase Type, Irregular Sleep–Wake Type, Non-24-Hour Sleep–Wake Type, Shift Work Type, Unspecified Type) is the inability to sleep during a designated sleep time (Sharma & Feinsilver, 2009). Individuals with a Circadian Rhythm Sleep Disorder experience a recurrent sleep disruption due to an alteration of the circadian system (the body's internal clock) and the sleep–wake schedule required by an individual's physical environment (e.g., work schedule; APA, 2013). Depressive symptoms may also be associated with delayed sleep–wake and activity rhythms (Robillard et al., 2014). Visually impaired individuals are at particular risk for developing the non-24-hour sleep–wake type of circadian rhythm sleep disorders due to their inability to synchronize their circadian clock to external day–night cycle (Warman et al., 2011). Those with circadian rhythm sleep–wake disorders may experience disturbances in the quality of relationships with friends and family due to their impaired sleep schedule. For example, an individual may struggle to sleep during the night time hours when the rest of family is asleep and, as a result, may sleep during the day when the rest of the family members are engaged in family activities.

Parasomnias

Parasomnias (i.e., Non-Rapid Eye Movement Sleep Arousal Disorders and Rapid Eye Movement Sleep Behavior Disorder) are characterized by abnormal behavioral, experiential, or physiological events occurring in association with the sleep cycle (APA, 2013). All parasomnias occur most commonly in the early part of the sleep period, usually in connection with slow wave sleep, and individuals are usually amnesic or partially amnesic for the event the next day (Bjorvatn, Gronli, & Pallesen, 2010). In both subtypes of NREM Sleep Arousal Disorders (Sleepwalking Type and Sleep Terror Type), an individual experiences incomplete arousals during the sleep cycle (APA, 2013). Individuals with sleepwalking-type NREM sleep arousal disorder may engage in other behaviors in addition to sleepwalking, such as sleep eating or sleep sexual behavior. Sleepwalking episodes usually occur abruptly within the first 3 hours of sleep and individuals demonstrate a blank facial expression with a low level of awareness and reactivity (Plazzi, Vetrugno, Provini, & Montagna, 2005). Sleepwalking and sleep terrors appear to be more prevalent in children and adolescents, yet when these episodes occur in adults they may result in injury to self and occasional violence toward bed partners (Attarian & Zhu, 2013). Of all the sleep disturbances, parasomnias may be the most intrusive to bed partners because of the potentially aggressive or violent parasomnia-related behavior.

Individuals with Nightmare Disorder experience repeated dreams that usually involve threats to survival or security (APA, 2013). Schredl (2010) suggested that around 2% to 5% of the adult population report one or more nightmares a week. Nightmares are experienced as story-like sequences of imagery that seem real and that incite anxiety, fear, or other dysphoric emotions (APA, 2013). Individuals with nightmare disorder report experiencing distress the following day as a result of the nightmare (Lancee & Schrinjnemaekers, 2013). Nightmare disorders may also be potentially uncomfortable for bed partners and family members of the individual who experiences the nightmare. Family members may feel powerless to help the individual who is experiencing the nightmare-related concerns.

REM Sleep Behavior Disorder is characterized by repeated episodes of arousal, often reflecting motor responses to the content of action-filled or violent dreams of being attacked or trying to escape from a threatening situation (APA, 2013). Sleep behaviors can include screaming, grasping, punching, kicking, and occasionally jumping out of bed, which may be harmful for the client and his or her bed partner (Fantini & Ferini-Stambi, 2007). Those with sleep behavior disorders may also experience other parasomnia behaviors; Godin, Montplaisir, and Nielsen (2015) found a prominent presence of nightmares in individuals who also met criteria for REM sleep behavior disorder.

Restless Legs Syndrome

Restless Legs Syndrome is a neurological sleep disorder in which the individual feels a compelling desire to move the legs or arms (APA, 2013). RLS is a common disorder that usually results in sleep disturbance (Mackie & Winkleman, 2015). Symptoms are usually worse when the individual is at rest (APA, 2013). RLS may impact the overall quality of an individual's ability to fully experience relaxing sleep. It may also contribute to difficulty in bedtime routines as the individual's bed partner may experience discomfort as a result of the compulsion the individual with RLS has to move his or her arms or legs.

Substance/Medication-Induced Sleep Disorder

Substance/Medication-Induced Sleep Disorder occurs when an individual experiences a sleep-related disturbance due to the intoxication or withdrawal associated with a particular substance (APA, 2013). Individuals may experience sleep-related concerns during intoxication or withdrawal. It is important for clinicians to be aware of the potential for substances to interfere with a client's sleep processes. Biological testing (e.g., urine drug screens, blood tests) can help rule out or confirm the presence of substances. It can also be helpful to seek information from family members to determine whether the individual has engaged in any recent substance use.

RELATIONAL AND CULTURAL FEATURES

The family system can influence the development and continuation of sleep disorders in numerous ways. A thorough understanding of the impact of family and systematic contributors to sleep is necessary for effective assessment and intervention of sleep-related concerns. Krueger and Friedman (2009) suggested that family relationship variables may be associated with sleep disturbances in adults. It is also important to note the impact of the individual's sleep problem on the entire family system; bed partners (i.e., those who sleep with the individual experiencing a sleep disorder) and children may experience negative consequences as a result of the individual's sleep-related concerns.

In general, cosleeping with a partner is beneficial to both individuals' sleep (Krueger & Friedman, 2009). However, in relationships where one partner experiences a sleep disorder, the negatives of the sleeping arrangement may far outweigh the positives. For example, individuals who share a sleep space with a partner with insomnia may also experience difficulty sustaining sleep if the partner tosses and turns, gets up and out of bed frequently, or otherwise disturbs his or her partner's sleep. Bed partners of those with sleep-related difficulties may be at particular risk for experiencing negative consequences related to their partner's sleep–wake concerns. In some cases, there is concern about potential physical harm. For example, REM behavior sleep disorders may place clients and their bed partners at a high risk for injuries (Olson, Boeve, & Silber, 2000). In addition to safety-related concerns, there may also be concerns related to the development of partner's health-related concerns. Jennum et al. (2014) found that hypersomnia had a significant influence on clients' partners in several ways: health care contacts in the secondary health care system were elevated, and partners had a greater demand on the social care system.

The relationship itself may contribute to the development of sleep disorders; relationships that are characterized by psychological abuse tend to result in sleep problems for both men and women (Rauer, Kelly, Buckhalt, & El-Sheikh, 2010). Considering the cessation of awareness required for deep sleep, it makes sense that those who are in potentially unsafe living situations may feel uncomfortable accepting the vulnerability necessary to engage in sleep. Individuals must feel safe within the family environment in order to obtain quality sleep (Dahl & El-Sheikh, 2007).

It is an important task of parenthood to help children establish an appropriate sleep schedule and promote effective sleep hygiene (Gradinger et al., 2011). Parents who struggle with impaired sleep may inadvertently contribute to their children's sleep-related concerns and thus create a pattern of difficulty within the family as it relates to sleep practices. Additionally, responsibilities associated with the parental role may also contribute to sleep impairment. Although the responsibilities associated with being a new parent are inherently stressful, nighttime infant crying significantly impacts parental sleep as well as the quality of the marital relationship (Meijer & van den Witenboer, 2007), and mothers of children with sleep problems may experience impairments in sleep quality, mood, stress, and fatigue (Meltzer & Mindell, 2007).

Family roles, responsibilities, and other variables may affect an individual's overall quality of sleep. For example, research on female caregivers for a family member with dementia found that the caregiver's sleep quality was highly correlated with the sleep quality of their care recipient (Castro et al., 2009). Increased family stressors (e.g., health concerns, financial problems) may contribute to the development of sleep-related problems. A thorough assessment of family-related stressors can help the counselor identify the extent to which these stressors may be impacting the individual.

Sleep disorders may also have an impact on an individual's social functioning. Individuals who experience daytime sleepiness as a result of their sleep disorder may experience impairment in social interactions, especially family-related interactions (Reishtein et al., 2006). Diminished quality of sleep can lead to impairments in leisure activities. Individuals who do not obtain enough quality sleep may be too fatigued to participate in previously enjoyed social activities. This decrease in social participation may lead to difficulty in the client's social and romantic relationships.

Sleep-related difficulties affect individuals from all cultural backgrounds. Though Gaultney (2010) found no significant race/ethnicity differences in sleep disorders, Krueger and Friedman (2009) found that non-Hispanic Black race/ethnicity, low levels of socioeconomic status, depression and physical health issues (i.e., cardiovascular disease and diabetes) were associated with impaired sleep (i.e., sleeping too little or sleeping too much). Socioeconomic status appears to be related to sleep in a number of important ways. Individuals from low-socioeconomic status families may have less available sleep space (i.e., fewer and more crowded bedrooms), lower quality heating, cooling, and ventilation systems, lower quality bedding, and higher levels of allergens, all of which may contribute to impairments in the quality and quantity of sleep (Buckhalt, 2011).

Some sleep disorders (e.g., insomnia disorder, nightmare disorder, restless leg syndrome) are more likely to occur in females, whereas others (e.g., obstructive sleep apnea) occur more frequently in males (APA, 2013). Other cultural considerations may be related to the individual's willingness to seek help for the sleep-related problems. For example, an individual's culture may dictate the kinds of dream content that can be shared and with whom it may be shared (Hollan, 2009). It may also be relevant to inquire about the significance of sleep, dreaming, and nightmares within the client's culture.

As with other *DSM-5* disorders, it is important to consider the potential for other conditions that may be a focus of clinical attention noted as Z codes in the *DSM-5* to impact both the presentation and treatment of Sleep–Wake Disorders. Systemic clinicians should be mindful of the potential impact of these conditions including housing problems, problems related to the client's primary support system, and educational concerns. For example, in situations where a family member is experiencing a significant sleep–wake disorder, his or her partner may experience Relationship Distress With Spouse of Intimate Partner (APA, 2013). As has been noted throughout the chapter, sleep–wake disorders have the potential to impact the family, especially bed partners, in a number of ways. Thus, systemic clinicians should thoroughly assess the impact of the sleep–wake concern on the individual's intimate relationships.

FAMILY SYSTEMS ASSESSMENTS

In many cases, a thorough medical evaluation is a necessary first step to rule out medical-related concerns that might be contributing to the client's sleep difficulties. Once medical concerns have been ruled out, formal assessment tools in conjunction with clinical interviews are generally a logical starting point in the assessment process (Gilea, Nate, & Paylo, 2015). In some situations, mental health professionals may refer the client to a sleep disorder specialist for an all-night polysomnography (a sleep study that records EEG activity; Gilea et al., 2015) or another diagnostic sleep exam.

Sleep disorders are often comorbid with depression, anxiety, and cognitive changes and sleep-related disturbances increase an individual's risk of mental illnesses and Substance Use Disorders (APA, 2013); a thorough mental health examination (e.g., assessment, mental status examination) is often indicated before treating sleep-related concerns. In particular, it is important to note the severity of the sleep-related concerns (e.g., frequency, duration, and urgency of sleep-related concerns). Involving the client's bed partner in the assessment process can help the counselor gather important diagnostic information. Bed partners are usually the first observers to note and recognize sleep problems so it can be helpful to encourage sleep-disordered clients to bring their bed partners to consultations (Gradinger et al., 2011). Family counseling may be especially helpful for those individuals who experience nightly problems as a result of a partner's sleep disorder.

A thorough assessment of the impact of sleep-related concerns is an important consideration for mental health professionals who work with this population. Sleep and circadian rhythms change dramatically throughout the normal aging process (Robillard et al., 2014) though it is possible that an individual may develop sleep-related problems at any age. Inquiring as to whether an individual has previously experienced normative sleep can help the systemic clinician to determine the longevity of the sleep-related problems.

The following assessment questions may prove to be a useful starting point in the assessment of sleep-related disturbances:

- Are you having trouble falling asleep? Staying asleep? Awakening too early?
- On average, how many hours of sleep do you get per night? Would you like to sleep more? Less?
- Do you feel rested upon waking in the morning or do you tend to feel groggy?
- On average, how much caffeine are you consuming per day? Do you feel that you *need* caffeine in order to function?
- Do you find yourself getting anxious close to bedtime? Do you worry about not being able to sleep?
- How long do you lie in bed before falling asleep?
- How many times per night do you awaken? How long does it take you to fall back to sleep?
- To what extent, if any, have your sleep problems impacted your bed partner?
- Do you worry that you might inadvertently harm yourself or your bed partner due to your sleep-related concerns?
- Do you have disturbing dreams? Do you worry about having disturbing dreams?
- How long have you been experiencing sleep-related concerns?

Gradinger et al. (2011) also encouraged practitioners to assess the client's home and work life as recent research (e.g., Niedhammer et al., 2009) found workplace bullying to be associated with sleep-related disturbances. Inquiring about workplace expectations, number of hours worked, and overall satisfaction associated with work can help the practitioner develop an understanding of any potential workplace influences on sleep. Additionally, it may be helpful to determine the extent of time, if any, that the individual spends working from home (e.g., answering e-mails, making phone calls). Individuals who lack a strong boundary between work and personal life may be more likely to demonstrate difficulty detaching from their daily workplace stressors and thus may be more at risk for sleep-related disturbances.

Self-Report Measures

Self-report measures can also be a helpful tool in the assessment process. For individuals who experience symptoms of insomnia, the Insomnia Severity Index (ISI; Gagnon, Belanger, Ivers, & Morin, 2013) can assess the degree to which the insomnia is affecting their daily lives. The ISI is a self-report questionnaire that assesses the severity of sleep disturbance through rating symptoms on a scale of 0 (none) to 5 (very severe). The ratings are added to get a total score of the client's sleep dissatisfaction. The ISI can serve as a useful starting point to assist the systemic clinician in assessing a client's sleep-related disturbance.

Sleep Log

A *sleep log*, also referred to as a *sleep diary*, is discussed in more detail in the section "Family Systems Interventions" of this chapter; however, its utility as an assessment tool is worth noting here. Sharma and Feinsilver (2009) recommended the use of a sleep log as part of a comprehensive assessment of circadian rhythm sleep disorder. Although Sharma and Feinsilver's (2009) use of the sleep log as an assessment tool was specific to circadian rhythm sleep disorder, it would seem that it may also be a useful assessment measure for other sleep disorders. Overall, the sleep log can provide a tangible indication of how often the individual is experiencing sleep-related concerns. It can also assist the client and systemic clinician in determining patterns, antecedents, and functional consequences of the sleep-related disturbance.

Understanding the social impact of the sleep-related concern is another consideration in the assessment process. A study of those with sleep apnea–related concerns found individuals tended to avoid situations in which sleepiness would be inappropriate or embarrassing (Reishtein et al., 2006). Thus, it is important to inquire as to whether the client has experienced any negative social consequences as a result of his or her sleep-related issue. The following questions can be helpful to determine the extent, if any, that the client has experienced social consequences as a result of his or her sleep disorder:

- Have you experienced any restriction in daily activities?
- Do you find yourself avoiding activities in which you feel too tired to participate?
- Are you embarrassed by your sleepiness? Do you go to lengths to avoid appearing sleepy?
- Do you find yourself engaging in any compensatory behaviors (e.g., drinking large amounts of caffeine, taking caffeine pills) to hide your sleepiness from others?
- Has your sleep issue affected your work at all? If so, how?
- Do you find yourself avoiding social situations (e.g., dating) for fear that someone may learn about your sleep-related problems?

A final assessment consideration is related to the assessment of the client and the client's bed partner's physical safety. Some sleep disorders (e.g., REM behavior disorder) place clients and their bed partners at a high risk for injuries as a result of the dream enacting associated with the disorder (Olson et al., 2000). Mental health counselors must be prepared to assess the degree to which the sleep behaviors may be placing the client, or the client's partner, at risk for harm. In some cases, it may be necessary to develop a safety plan to ensure that the bed partner is not at risk for harm. A safety plan may include information on how the bed partner can safely wake the client if he or she is experiencing a sleep-related issue and/or a temporary alternate sleeping location for the bed partner in the event that the client's sleep issues become too difficult to tolerate.

FAMILY SYSTEMS INTERVENTIONS

Individuals experience changes in sleep patterns and requirements throughout their lives. These changes may result in significant distress resulting in the diagnosis of a sleep–wake disorder (Paylo, Kress, & Kelly Gilea, 2014). Sleep–wake disorders are commonly experienced throughout the lifetime with approximately 10% to 15% of individuals impacted by Insomnia (APA, 2013) and other clinically significant sleep–wake disorders. Most clients with a sleep–wake disorder present for treatment with complaints regarding the quality (e.g., restlessness, nightmares) and quantity (e.g., not enough hours of sleep per night) of their sleep that impairs daytime functioning (e.g., results in sleepiness during the day; APA, 2013). The most common sleep–wake disorders are sleep apnea, insomnia, and restless leg syndrome (Ram, Seirawan, Kumar, & Clark, 2010). Some sleep–wake disorders may be treated by a systemic clinician (e.g., insomnia, hypersomnolence disorder) while others may be better treated by a medical doctor or sleep specialist (e.g., restless leg syndrome, sleep apnea).

Sleep disturbances impact the individual as well as others in their life (e.g., spouse, child, and coworker) due to resulting daytime symptoms such as restlessness, fatigue, and sleepiness that may impact the relationship. For example, a fatigued spouse may be more irritable and frustrated than usual. These feelings may be imparted on the other spouse who may now be the recipient of negative emotions and behaviors. It is known that treatment may be more effective when all family members actively participate in the recovery process (Thompson, Bender, Cardoso, & Flynn, 2011). A multisystemic treatment approach may be recommended due to the impact of sleep–wake disorders on all family members.

Medical treatment modalities (e.g., ventilators, mouth guards) are often used to treat sleep–wake disorders, as well as cognitive behavioral therapy (CBT) and behavioral therapy (Moul, Morin, Buysse, Reynolds, & Kupfer, 2007) and pharmacological approaches. The interventions in this chapter focus on those that can be implemented by systemic clinicians. Systemic clinicians may treat some sleep–wake disorders but must be able to identify when a referral to a sleep specialist is necessary or appropriate (APA, 2013). They may not be competent to prescribe medications or apply medical treatment modalities. The symptoms that characterize sleep–wake disorders overlap many medical and neurological conditions, suggesting the need to be able to know when to make a referral to a medical provider (APA, 2013). Treatment considerations in this chapter focus on the most common sleep–wake disorders treated by systemic clinicians using a multisystemic approach that considers familial and relational variables.

Treatment Considerations

Systemic clinicians should consider changes in clients' sleep patterns and requirements throughout their life spans when selecting treatment interventions. It is necessary to develop a sleep baseline to assist in the establishment of realistic treatment goals and objectives. Interventions should be selected that assist clients in returning to their premorbid level of sleep functioning. Interventions also need to be selected that address confounding factors such as symptoms of depression or anxiety that often overlap with sleep disturbances (Suh et al., 2012). A Family Systems Model may be used to determine the treatment approach because it is likely that all members are impacted by the sleep disturbance, as well as changes in sleep baseline (e.g., earlier bedtime and longer hours of sleep) and improved confounding factors (e.g., decreased depressed mood).

Cognitive Behavioral Therapy

Interventions grounded in CBT are likely to be used by systemic clinicians along with medications to treat sleep–wake disorders (Gellis, Arigo, & Elliott, 2013; Jernelov et al., 2012). Common CBT interventions involve the use of a sleep diary, sleep hygiene routines, sleep restriction therapy (SRT), progressive muscle relaxation, and thought stopping (Paylo et al., 2014). CBT has proven to be effective because sleep-related beliefs and attitudes impact sleep disturbances and the symptoms of sleep–wake disorders (Jansson-Fröjmark & Linton, 2008). A reduction in negative beliefs and attitudes is correlated with improvement of some symptoms (e.g., sleep quality). All family members may be involved in the application of CBT interventions.

Sleep Diary

A sleep diary can be a useful intervention for identifying sleep patterns and changes. It is used to establish a baseline of sleep behavior and can assist a systemic clinician in identifying symptoms, patterns, and severity. A sleep diary is a log of an individual's sleep (www .sleepfoundation.org). The diary may include quantitative (e.g., wake time, bedtime, times when difficult falling to sleep or waking) and qualitative (e.g., description of nightmares or how tired or awake one feels) information. Data can be tracked for varying lengths of times ranging from weeks to months. Duration of tracking may depend on quality of data and symptom severity (e.g., greater symptom severity may lead to a need to track data for a longer period of time). The data assist the client and systemic clinician in obtaining an increased awareness and understanding of the sleep disturbance. Once additional interventions are integrated into treatment, the sleep diary can be used as a measure of progress (e.g., increased periods of sleep for 3 consecutive days may suggest a positive response to interventions). Family members are encouraged to keep a separate sleep diary of the client's sleep behaviors to add a richer context to the information collected. Family members may choose to include an additional column that addresses the impact of the sleep disturbance on their relationship with the client. Table 12.1 offers an example of a sleep diary. Rows and columns may be adapted to best fit the client's issues and needs.

TABLE 12.1 Sample Sleep Diary

	Monday	Tuesday	Wednesday	Thursday	Friday	Saturday	Sunday
Week 1							
Bedtime	I went to bed at 10:30 p.m. but lay awake in bed. I fell asleep at 1:00 a.m.	I went to bed at 9:00 p.m. and watched TV for 1 hour. I turned off the TV and stared at the ceiling until 12:00 a.m. I fell asleep at 12:00 a.m.	I fell asleep on the couch at 8:00 p.m. while watching TV. I woke at midnight and went to bed. I lay awake in bed until 3:00 a.m.	I went to bed late because I was out with friends yesterday. I went to bed at 2:00 a.m. and fell asleep right away. I woke at 5:00 a.m. and fell back to sleep at 5:30 a.m.	I went to bed at 10:30 p.m. and looked at social media on my phone until midnight. I fell asleep at midnight and slept until 4:00 a.m. I was awake until I had to get up at 7:00 a.m. for work.	I went to bed at 3:00 a.m. and fell right to sleep. I slept until 9:00 a.m. I got up and went to lie on the couch.	I lay on the couch all day yesterday and into the night. I went to bed at 1:00 a.m. I fell asleep right away but woke at 2:00 a.m. and lay there until 3:30 a.m. I slept until my alarm went off at 8:00 a.m. for breakfast with my family.
Number of times sleep interrupted Times awake Total amount of time	I woke three times through the night at 2:00 a.m. (awake 30 minutes), 4:35 a.m. (awake 15 minutes), 6:00 a.m. (awake 30 minutes), woke to alarm at 7:00 a.m.	I woke twice during the night at 3:30 a.m. (awake 1 hour) and 6:00 a.m. (I could not fall back to sleep and got out of bed at 7:00 a.m. to get ready for work.	I slept on the couch from 8:00 p.m. to midnight and in bed from 3:00 a.m. to 6:00 a.m. I woke twice through the night: (a) at midnight (awake 3 hours) and (b) at 6:00 a.m. (awake 1 hour). I got up at 7:00 a.m. to get ready for work.	I woke once through the night from 5:00 a.m. to 5:30 a.m. (awake 30 minutes). I heard my alarm go off at 7:00 a.m. for work. I turned it off and slept until 10:00 a.m.	I slept 4 hours and woke once through the night (at 4:00 a.m. for 3 hours). I felt stressed out and could not fall back to sleep. I got up at 7:00 a.m. to get ready for work.	I slept 6 hours and did not wake through the night.	I woke once through the night (awake from 2:00 a.m. to 3:30 a.m., 1.5 hours).

316

Difficulty falling asleep	I lay awake in bed from 10:30 p.m. to 1:00 a.m. (2.5 hours). I watched TV for 1 hour (9 p.m.–10 p.m.) and lay awake in bed for an additional 2 hours (10:00 p.m.–12:00 a.m.).	I was exhausted and fell asleep on the couch but could not go back to sleep once I went to bed.	I felt stressed out after seeing a mean post on social media from my ex-girlfriend and could not fall asleep.	I fell asleep right away.	I fell asleep right away.	I fell asleep right away.
Technology used at bedtime (type and length of use)	I watched TV from 8:00 p.m. to 10:30 p.m. I went to bed at 10:30 p.m. I felt tired but could not sleep. After 20 minutes awake, I looked at pictures and websites on my smartphone for 1 hour.	I fell asleep watching TV. I sat on the couch at 7:30 p.m. and dozed off at 8:00 p.m.	I read social media posts on my phone for 1.5 hours from 10:30 pm to midnight.	None.	None.	I watched TV until I went to bed.
Difficulty waking Wake time	I woke to my alarm at 7:00 a.m., feeling very tired. 7:00 a.m.	I woke early and could not fall back to sleep. I felt angry and restless. 6:00 a.m.	I could not wake up for work because I was too tired. I slept longer and woke, feeling anxious and tired. 10:00 a.m.	I woke early and could not fall back to sleep. 4:00 a.m.	I woke up feeling tired and hung over. 9:00 a.m.	I woke up to my alarm at 8:00 a.m. I felt tired and wanted to sleep longer. 8:00 a.m.

(continued)

TABLE 12.1 Sample Sleep Diary (continued)

	Monday	Tuesday	Wednesday	Thursday	Friday	Saturday	Sunday
Number of hours slept	7.5 hours in bed, 6 hours of sleep time but interrupted three times.	10 hours in bed, 6 hours of sleep but interrupted twice.	7 hours (4 hours on the couch and 3 hours in bed).	8 hours but interrupted once.	4 hours but woke early; trouble falling asleep.	6 hours.	7 hours but interrupted once.
Nightmares	None.	None.	None.	None.	None but I kept thinking about the posts I read on my social media page.	None.	None.
Daytime naps Total:	None.	None.	I suppose that sleeping on the couch from 8:00 p.m. to midnight could be considered a nap. I could not stay awake any longer.	I napped on the couch from noon to 3:00 p.m.	None.	I lay on the couch all day watching TV. I napped from noon until 2:00 p.m. on the couch. I continued to lie on the couch after I woke.	None.
Length:	I slept on the couch for 30 minutes after work from 5:30 p.m. to 6:00 p.m.						
Sleep-wake daily rating (1 = most tired, 10 = most awake) 1–10 scale	I rate today's feelings of sleepiness at a "5." I feel tired but I was able to stay at work today.	I rate today's feelings of sleepiness at a "6." I was tired but able to go to work today.	I rate today's feelings of sleepiness at a "5." I need a solid night of sleep.	I felt tired all day. I rate today's feelings of sleepiness at a "2." I was not able to go to work and I lay on the couch all day.	I felt exhausted all day. I rate today's feelings of sleepiness at a "1." I felt like I could barely function.	I felt tired and hung over all day. I rate today's feelings of sleepiness at a "4." I just lay around all day.	I felt tired all day but was able to spend time with my family. I rate today's feelings of sleepiness at a "5."
Feelings experienced during sleeplessness	I was angry and frustrated because I was tired and wanted to sleep.	I was angry and restless. I wanted to be able to sleep.	I felt nauseous from lack of sleep. I was sad and angry.	I felt tired all day. I was anxious and frustrated.	I felt stressed out and angry.	I felt nauseous and frustrated.	I just felt tired.

Caffeinated beverages consumed (type and amount)	I drank two large cups of coffee in the morning, a soda beverage at lunch and dinner.	I drank two large cups of coffee in the morning, a soda beverage at lunch and dinner.	I drank two large cups of coffee in the morning, a soda beverage and energy drink at lunch and a soda at dinner.	I drank three large cups of coffee when I woke up and had an energy drink after my nap. I drank iced tea with dinner.	I drank two large cups of coffee and an energy drink in the morning, another energy drink at lunch, and a soda beverage at dinner.	I drank two large cups of coffee and an energy drink in the morning, water at lunch and dinner.	I drank two large cups of coffee in the morning, a soda beverage at lunch and dinner.
Alcoholic beverages consumed (type and amount)	None.	I drank a glass of wine at 7:00 p.m. I was hoping it would make me tired.	I had three beers and a shot of whiskey with my friends after dinner.	None. None.	I drank three beers after dinner and had another two beers and three shots of whiskey with my friends at the bar.	None.	None.
Exercise (include length of time)	None.	None.	None.	None.	None.	None.	None.

Sleep Hygiene Routines
Sleep routines and practices may help decrease the symptoms of mental health disorders, such as behavioral outbursts and aggression. Given the comorbidity of sleep–wake disorders and other mental health conditions, it is suggested that the implementation of a sleep routine may have a positive impact on sleep disturbances. Sleep routines lead to a greater sense of adjustment for clients and family members through a decrease in negative symptoms (Pressman & Imber, 2011). Sleep routines may consider ritualistic pre-bedtime practices (e.g., taking a bath, reading a book, avoiding television), bedtime, hours of sleep, wake time, sleeping arrangements (e.g., own bedroom in bed, on couch, shared room, cosleeping). A review of the sleep diary in Table 12.1 demonstrates lack of a structured sleep routine and pattern. The client has varying bedtimes, pre-bedtime practices, and hours of sleep. A mental health professional may review the sleep diary and assist the client with developing a sleep routine. For example, the client appears to wake daily at 7:00 a.m. for work. An 11:00 p.m. bedtime would allow for 8 hours of sleep before waking. The client complains of stress induced by technology use. A suggestion might be to restrict technology use 3 hours before bedtime and introduce reading or listening to calming music 1 hour before bed.

The family environment has an impact on sleep hygiene. Family dynamics may impact sleep time, daytime sleepiness, and sleep onset latency. An organized family routine, including a sleep routine, is likely to result in greater sleep time, less daytime sleepiness, and an ability to fall asleep as wanted (Billows, Gradisar, Dohnt, Johnston, & McCappin, 2009). Family members may consider implementing the same sleep routine for consistency within the family and to minimize disruption of the individual with the sleep–wake disorder.

Sleep Restriction Therapy
Systemic clinicians may recommend sleep restriction therapy (SRT) to assist in the establishment of a sleep routine and healthier sleep practices. The intervention is most often used to treat insomnia as the goal is to establish a bed and wake time and experience uninterrupted nightly sleep. Systemic clinicians may take unique approaches to implementing SRT. Consideration may also be given to working collaboratively with a sleep specialist to ensure working within one's area of training and competency. The most common SRT intervention involves prescribing a specific number of hours of sleep each night to a client. The number of prescribed hours is typically set below 8 to ensure sleepiness at bedtime. As quality of sleep increases and a sleep routine is established, the amount of hours prescribed may increase (Miller et al., 2014). One example includes the prescription of 6 hours of sleep for 3 consecutive nights with an increase of 30 minutes per night thereafter until 8 hours of sleep is achieved (see Table 12.2). The prescribed sleep hours would be increased only if the client is able to report a consistent bed and wake time, as well as rested sleep through the night. A sleep diary may be useful to develop a baseline of a client's sleep before using SRT. In Table 12.2, the client reported an average of 6 hours of sleep per night. The systemic clinician would prescribe less time in bed than originally spent with the overall goal of spending time in bed only when sleeping. When implementing SRT, naps and rest are not encouraged through the day because they are likely to impact the sleep routine. SRT may be used with additional CBT interventions to address a larger spectrum of sleep–wake disorder symptoms. For example, thought stopping may be used to challenge irrational beliefs about sleep that may impact the sleep routine (Suh et al., 2012). Family members can help the client challenge his or her irrational beliefs about sleep and offer support as adjustments are made to the typical sleep routine. However, they may not want to engage in SRT if not diagnosed with a sleep–wake disorder.

Progressive Muscle Relaxation
Sleep–wake disorders are often comorbid with other mental health disorders and have overlapping symptoms such as stress and muscular tension (Sadock & Sadock, 2007).

TABLE 12.2 Sample Sleep Restriction Therapy Schedule						
	Monday	Tuesday	Wednesday	Thursday	Friday	Saturday	Sunday
Bedtime	1:00 a.m.	1:00 a.m.	1:00 a.m.	12:30 a.m.	12:30 a.m.	12:30 a.m.	12:00 a.m.
Hours of sleep	6	6	6	6.5	6.5	6.5	7
Wake time	7:00 a.m.	7:00 a.m.	7:00 a.m.	7:00 a.m.	7:00 a.m.	7:00 a.m.	7:00 a.m.

Progressive muscle relaxation techniques can be used to decrease symptoms that may interfere with healthy sleep patterns. The goal is to decrease arousal and tension prior to bedtime (Lundh & Broman, 2000). A systemic clinician assists the client with progressive muscle relaxation by helping the individual move through a series of tensing a specific muscle group followed by a period of relaxing the same muscle group. The client experiences an increased awareness of the muscular tension followed by a sense of relaxation of both the body and mind. The process is continued as each muscle group experiences both tension and relaxation. A client may employ this procedure at home as well. Family members are encouraged to participate in the exercise with the client. The gesture offers support for the individual with the sleep–wake disorder while simultaneously experiencing tension reduction. All family members may benefit from decreased stress and a regular sleep pattern.

Thought Stopping
Irrational fears, beliefs, and anxiety surrounding sleep (e.g., "I will never sleep again." or "I am going to die if I don't sleep tonight.") may be correlated with sleep–wake disorders (Suh et al., 2012). Addressing these thoughts with a systemic clinician can help decrease sleep-defeating beliefs and lead to a more restful night of sleep. Thought stopping is a CBT intervention that teaches an individual to take control of his or her negative thoughts. The goal is to learn to identify a negative thought and decrease the frequency and intensity of the thought. For example, when a client has the thought, "I will never sleep again," he or she is encouraged to intervene and stop the thought immediately by yelling "stop" silently or out loud and/or visualizing a stop sign (Bakker, 2009). Family members are encouraged to help the client achieve the goal of thought reduction by engaging in the thought-stopping process. For example, a spouse may hold up a stop sign when his or her significant other shared a negative, sleep-interfering thought.

CBT interventions may be used to treat sleep–wake disorders and symptoms of sleep–wake disorders that may need medical interventions (e.g., ventilator). A systemic clinician should begin with a comprehensive understanding of the client's sleep disturbance and develop a sleep-baseline before implementing interventions. The overarching goal of all interventions is increased quality of sleep. Family members are encouraged to engage in treatment to support the client and address their own symptoms (e.g., irritability) triggered by the client's sleep disturbance.

ETHICAL AND LEGAL IMPLICATIONS

Sleep–wake disorders may require treatment by an interdisciplinary team of professionals including systemic clinicians, sleep specialists, and medical doctors. Systemic clinicians may treat some sleep–wake disorders or symptoms of them (e.g., anxiety, frustration, fatigue) but must be able to identify when interdisciplinary consultation or a referral to another provider is necessary (APA, 2013). Systemic clinicians must consider competency before diagnosing, assessing, and treating a sleep–wake disorder.

Competency Considerations

Competence embraces the moral principle of nonmaleficence, meaning to not harm a client (Remley & Herlihy, 2016). "Counselors act to avoid harming their clients, trainees, and research participants and to minimize or to remedy unavoidable or unanticipated harm" (American Counseling Association [ACA], 2014, Section A.4.a). Incompetent practice through the provision of services when a systemic clinician lacks knowledge and skill is among the most common causes of harm to a client. A harmed client may sue the systemic clinician for malpractice, highlighting competency as both an ethical and legal issue (Remley & Herlihy, 2016). Very few mental health training programs train systemic clinicians to use counseling techniques to treat sleep–wake disorders (e.g., insomnia; Puterbaugh, 2011). Scope of practice may be limited to the use of CBT interventions unless the systemic clinician received specialized training in the use of interventions specific to sleep–wake disorders (e.g., mouth ventilator).

Systemic clinicians are encouraged to treat sleep–wake disorders within the boundaries of their competence. Both the ACA and American Association of Marriage and Family Therapy (AAMFT) address competency in their codes of ethics. "Counselors practice only within the boundaries of their competence, based on their education, training, supervised experience, state and national professional credentials, and appropriate professional experience" (ACA, 2014, Section C.2.a.). The *AAMFT Code of Ethics* supports the *ACA Code of Ethics* asserting that "marriage and family therapists do not diagnose, treat, or advise on problems outside the recognized boundaries of their competencies" (AAMFT, 2012; Standard 3.11). As stated, most training programs do not prepare systemic clinicians to use specialized interventions for sleep–wake disorders, requiring professionals to seek education and training postgraduation. Even when a systemic clinician is competent to treat sleep–wake disorders, it is necessary to note that many symptoms of sleep–wake disorders may be connected to physical illness (e.g., sleep apnea) and therefore it is recommended that counselors consult with medical professionals to determine a need for treatment (Puterbaugh, 2011) beyond a mental health practitioner's scope of practice.

Family Systems Considerations

A multisystemic approach to treating sleep–wake disorders may be recommended due to the impact that the disorders have on all members of the family. Thompson et al. (2011) affirmed that treatment may be more effective when all family members are involved in the process. The inclusion of multiple family members in treatment, albeit recommended, can lead to ethical and legal issues. Counselors are able to guarantee only that the client's confidentiality is kept by him or her. Other family members are encouraged to respect confidentiality but are not legally or ethically required to do so. When incorporating family members into the treatment of a sleep–wake disorder, "counselors clearly define who is considered 'the client' and discuss expectations and limitations of confidentiality" (ACA, 2014, Section B.4.b.). Clients need to understand that family members may choose to breach confidentiality and share personal information with others not involved in treatment.

CASE CONCEPTUALIZATION

A case study is presented in order to understand sleep–wake disorders from a systemic framework. The case of Frederick is reviewed as diagnostic and treatment approaches are explored. A family systems perspective is considered.

Presenting Concerns

Frederick, a 42-year-old Caucasian business man, husband and father of two young boys, self-referred for outpatient counseling services presenting with complaints of "not being able to sleep" and "always feeling tired." Frederick works 40 hours a week as a computer software specialist and spends evenings and weekends with his wife, Rebecca, and sons, Jonathan (10) and Wiley (7). He reported "always" struggling with sleep recalling periods in college when he would "lie in bed all night watching television and hoping to fall asleep." He added, "Back then I would actually get sleep a few nights a week though, and now I don't even get that."

The client noted that his sleep issues intensified several months ago when he was unemployed. He reported being laid off from his previous position due to funding cuts and was able to secure a new position within 2 months. He added feeling hopeful that sleep would return to normal patterns once he secured employment. Frederick defined his normal sleep as "tossing and turning, snoring, and waking a few times but falling back to sleep." He added, "Even though it wasn't the best night's sleep, I still felt rested."

Frederick indicated that he spends "hours" trying to fall asleep at night often watching television, reading, or "staring at the ceiling" hoping to "doze off." "From time to time I even have a glass of wine to try to relax." He indicated that it takes 2 hours on average to fall asleep "only to keep waking up all night long." Frederick wakes up three to four times per night and "tosses and turns" until falling back to sleep. He elaborated that he "even wakes up before my alarm goes off for work" feeling tired but unable to resume sleep. The client indicated that it is "rare to get one good night of sleep a week."

Frederick indicated concern for his wife who is often woken from her sleep by his restlessness. He indicated feeling "sad and guilty that he makes her so tired and irritable because she doesn't get the sleep she needs." He described feeling worried that his sleep is impacting the quality of their relationship providing an example of his wife sleeping in the guest bedroom to achieve a rested night of sleep. The sleep issues have led to marital discord indicated by Frederick, "We are both so tired that we just snap and yell at each other all the time."

Frederick consistently presents for work and fulfills job responsibilities adding that "about all I can do is make it through the work day without falling asleep but I get my work done." The client reported doing so with "lots of coffee and energy drinks to keep me awake." When questioned about medical issues, Frederick reported seeking services from his primary care physician and a sleep specialist. Both were unable to identify a medical cause for his sleep disturbance. He added, "I don't even really feel stressed out; I have a job and a great family; if I could sleep everything would be okay."

Concurrent Problems

Frederick does not have a prior medical or mental health history. He reported sleep disturbances in college but did not seek professional treatment. He is not taking any prescribed or over-the-counter medications. Following his self-initiated intake, he was referred by the systemic clinician for outpatient counseling services.

Background History and Stressors

Frederick did not report a history of mental health treatment. He indicated that he sought medical services from his primary care physician and a sleep specialist. Both were unable to identify a cause for his sleep disturbance. He agreed to participate in outpatient counseling services, stating, "I hope counseling works; I just want to feel awake and enjoy my life."

Strengths

Frederick is employed and married with two children. He reports enjoying leisure time with his family on evenings and weekends (e.g., barbequing, attending children's softball games). He has experienced sleep dissatisfaction for the majority of his adult life and has been able to achieve personal goals (e.g., graduate from college, secure employment, get married, and raise a family).

DSM-5 Impressions and Implications

Frederick described a long-standing history of sleep disturbance beginning in college and intensifying 7 months ago. He indicated a desire to achieve more sleep and a better night of rest. While he attempts to go to bed at a reasonable hour, Frederick lays awake for extended periods of time willing himself to fall asleep. Once Frederick falls asleep, he reported waking through the night and often experiencing a failure to return to sleep. He often wakes earlier than needed (e.g., before his alarm goes off for work) and lays in bed awake without being able to return to sleep. During his college years, Frederick experienced sleep disturbances a few nights a week but identified that he currently experiences sleep difficulties most if not all nights. The symptoms presented qualify Frederick for Insomnia, Persistent.

For all sleep–wake disorders it is necessary to rule out medical issues or physiological effects of a substance. During his initial interview, Frederick indicated that both a medical doctor and sleep specialist were unable to identify a medial cause for his sleep disturbance. Frederick reports an occasional glass of wine but does not indicate that the alcohol use has a negative impact on his life, suggesting the absence of the substance impacting his disorder. Insomnia is often comorbid with other mental and emotional disorders (e.g., anxiety). Frederick reported some frustration and irritability. However, he does not meet full diagnostic criteria for a comorbid disorder.

Relational Problems

Frederick is employed full time as a computer software specialist and indicated feeling content with his position and career. He disclosed an ability to fulfill his work roles and responsibilities but added struggling to stay alert through the day due to exhaustion. He is married with two children. Frederick's sleep disturbance has led to marital discord that he attributes to frustration and irritability due to lack of sleep (i.e., Relationship Distress With Spouse or Intimate Partner). Although the sleep disturbance began 7 months ago when Frederick was unemployed, he was able to secure employment 5 months ago without any relief to his sleep issues.

Assessments

A detailed clinical interview revealed the disclosure of enough symptoms to qualify Frederick for Insomnia. The diagnosis was further confirmed through the Insomnia Severity Index (ISI; Gagnon et al., 2013). Frederick was encouraged by the systemic clinician to complete the self-report questionnaire designed to assess the severity of his sleep disturbance using a scale ranging from 0 (none) to 5 (very severe). The ratings for each question are added to yield a total score that defines the severity of the client's sleep dissatisfaction (Gagnon et al., 2013). Frederick's final score suggested a severe rating of his sleep dissatisfaction from insomnia. The systemic clinician reviewed Frederick's answers with him and his wife to gather qualitative information (i.e., enhanced description) of Frederick's sleep issues.

Interventions

Frederick's responses during the clinical interview suggested an inadequate sleep routine. A consistent sleep routine can lead to a decrease in symptoms and a more restful night's sleep. The systemic clinician recommended a ritualistic practice to employ before bedtime. Frederick was encouraged to stop using all forms of technology (e.g., television, smart phone) 2 hours prior to bedtime. Rebecca and his children agreed to do the same to support Frederick in his efforts to treat his insomnia. The family agreed to spend time together exchanging stories from their day, playing board games, and reading together. Following social time, the family was prescribed a daily progressive muscle relaxation routine to decrease negative feelings (e.g., tension, frustration) that interfere with sleep patterns. Frederick agreed to select a progressive muscle relaxation technique from the self-help book recommended by the systemic clinician. Each activity required the family to move through a series of tensing a muscle group followed by relaxation of the muscle group. The process was implemented until all muscle groups were tensed and relaxed, culminating in a feeling of relaxation.

Frederick was directed to continue his sleep routine by taking his shower 1 hour before bedtime followed by drinking a cup of chamomile tea while reading a book of choice. His bedroom was limited to activities conducive to sleep (e.g., relaxing, reading, sleeping). Frederick agreed to go to bed and wake at the same time every day, including weekends. A total of 8 hours of sleep was recommended without any naps during the day to ensure sleepiness at bedtime. Frederick's family agreed to employ the same sleep routine to minimize any disturbance of Frederick and implement consistent sleep practices for all involved.

Ethical and Legal Implications

The systemic clinician would need to use assessments, techniques, and interventions within his or her scope of practice. Specialized training in interventions specific to sleep–wake disorders may be needed to avoid providing services outside scope of practice. Consideration would also need to be given to the limits of confidentiality. Frederick's wife, Rebecca, was involved in his treatment. While encouraged to maintain his confidentiality, she is not required to do so by law. This limit to confidentiality would need to be discussed with Frederick prior to his wife's involvement in services.

DISCUSSION

As you continue to reflect on the case study and the overall approach, contemplate these questions:

- Symptoms of anxiety appear to play a role in Frederick's insomnia. Although Frederick does not meet diagnostic criteria to warrant a comorbid diagnosis, how would you address his frustration, tension, and irritability? How can his family help him address these symptoms?

- What sections of the *ACA* and *AAMFT Codes of Ethics* apply regarding confidentiality in this case?

- How would you adjust Frederick's sleep routine if he did not respond positively to the initial recommendation? How would you encourage Frederick's family members to adjust their sleep routines?

- Sleep restriction therapy (SRT) could be an additional component to Frederick's sleep routine. How would you implement SRT? How could Frederick's family help him implement SRT?

- Rebecca, Jonathan, and Wiley are not experiencing insomnia but are impacted by Frederick's sleep disturbance. How would you encourage the family to maintain involvement in Frederick's treatment?

- What type of training and supervision would you engage in to guarantee working within your scope of practice when treating sleep–wake disorders?

SUMMARY

Family may play an important role in the development and maintenance of sleep-related concerns. A close and warm family environment should promote safe and healthy sleep (Dahl & El-Sheikh, 2007). Treatment that incorporates a relational family approach may be beneficial for the long-term benefit of the client. The family environment can be experienced as a facilitator or a barrier in the life of persons with sleep disorders (Gradinger et al., 2011); treatment providers should take reasonable steps to incorporate family interventions into the counseling process. Perhaps more than any other mental disorder, bed partners of those with sleep-related disorders are affected in numerous ways, including increased morbidity and use of medication, and reduced work ability and income (Jennum et al., 2014). Incorporating a family systems perspective into the assessment of sleep–wake disorders can provide mental health counselors with another perspective on the degree to which the sleep-related issues are impacting the client's life. Likewise, a family-oriented perspective to the treatment of sleep-related disorders may contribute to enhanced treatment gains.

REFERENCES

American Association for Marriage and Family Therapy. (2012). *AAMFT code of ethics.* Alexandria, VA: Author. Retrieved from https://www.aamft.org/imis15/Documents/AAMFT%20Code_11_2012_Secured.pdf

American Counseling Association. (2014). *ACA code of ethics.* Alexandria, VA: Author. Retrieved from http://www.counseling.org/docs/ethics/2014-aca-code-of-ethics.pdf?sfvrsn=4

American Psychiatric Association. (2013). *Diagnostic and statistical manual of mental and emotional disorders* (5th ed.). Arlington, VA: American Psychiatric Publishing.

Attarian, H., & Zhu, L. (2013). Treatment options for disorders of arousal: A case series. *International Journal of Neuroscience, 123,* 623–625. doi:10.3109/00207454.2013.783579

Bakker, G. M. (2009). In defence of thought stopping. *Clinical Psychologist, 13*(2), 59–68.

Billows, M., Gradisar, M., Dohnt, H., Johnston, A., & McCappin, S. (2009). Family disorganization, sleep hygiene and adolescent sleep disturbance. *Journal of Clinical Child and Adolescent Psychology, 38*(5), 745–752.

Bjorvatn B., Gronli, J., & Pallesen, S. (2010). Prevalence of different parasomnias in the general population. *Sleep Medicine, 10,* 1031–1034.

Bjorvatn, B., Pallesen, S., Gronli, J., Siversten, B., & Lehmann, S. (2014). Prevalence and correlates of insomnia and excessive sleepiness in adults with obstructive sleep apnea symptoms. *Perceptual and Motor Skills: Physical Development and Measurement, 118,* 571–586.

Buckhalt, J. A. (2011). Insufficient sleep and the socioeconomic status achievement gap. *Child Development Perspectives, 5,* 59–65.

Castro, C. M., Lee, K. A., Bliwise, D. L., Urizar, G. G., Woodward, S. H., & King, A. C. (2009). Sleep patterns and sleep-related factors between caregiving and non-caregiving women. *Behavioral Sleep Medicine, 7,* 164–179.

Dahl, R. E., & El-Sheikh, M. (2007). Considering sleep in a family context: Introduction to the special issue. *Journal of Family Psychology, 21,* 1–3.

Durmer, J. S., & Dinges, D. F. (2005). Neurocognitive consequences of sleep deprivation. *Seminars in Neurology, 25,* 117–129.

Fantini, M. L., & Ferini-Strambi, L. (2007). Idiopathic rapid eye movement sleep behavior disorder. *Neurological Sciences, 28,* S15–S20. doi:10.1007/s10072-007-0734-z

Fullerton, D. (2006). The economic impact of insomnia in managed care: A clearer picture emerges. *American Journal of Managed Care,12,* 246–252.

Gagnon, C., Belanger, L., Ivers, H., & Morin, C. M. (2013). Validation of the Insomnia Severity Index in primary care. *Journal of the American Board of Family Medicine, 26*(6), 701–710.

Gaultney, J. F. (2010). The prevalence of sleep disorders in college students: Impact on academic performance. *Journal of American College Health, 59*(2), 91–97. doi:10.1080/07448481.2010.483708

Gaultney, J. F., & Collins-McNeil, J. (2009). Lack of sleep in the workplace: What the psychologist-manger should know about sleep. *The Psychologist-Manager Journal, 12,* 132–148.

Gellis, L. A., Arigo, D., & Elliott, J. C. (2013). Cognitive refocusing treatment for insomnia: A randomized controlled trial in university students. *Behaviour Therapy, 44,* 100–110.

Gilea, B. L., Nate, R., & Paylo, M. J. (2015). Treating insomnia. American Counseling Association. Practice briefs. Retrieved from https://www.counseling.org/knowledge-center/practice-briefs

Godin, I., Montplaisir, J., & Nielsen, T. (2015). Dreaming and nightmares in REM sleep behavior disorder. *Dreaming, 25,* 257–273. doi:10.1037/drm0000011

Gradinger, F., Glassel, A., Gugger, M. Cieza, A., Braun, N., Khatami, R., . . . Mathis, J. (2009). Identification of problems in functioning of people with sleep disorders in a clinical setting using the International Classification of Functioning Disability and Health (ICF) Checklist. *Journal of Sleep Research, 20,* 445–453.

Hollan, D. (2009). The influence of culture on the experience and interpretation of disturbing dreams. *Culture, Medicine and Psychiatry, 33,* 313–322. doi:10.1007/s11013-009-9137-3

Hossain, J., & Shapiro, C. (2002). The prevalence, cost implications, and management of sleep disorders: An overview. *Sleep and Breathing, 6,* 85–102.

Jansson-Fröjmark, M., & Linton, S. (2008). The role of sleep-related beliefs to improvement in early cognitive behavioral therapy for insomnia. *Cognitive Behaviour Therapy, 37,* 5–13.

Jennum, P., Ibsen, R., Avlund, K., & Kjellberg, J. (2014). Health, social and economic consequences of hypersomnia: A controlled national study from a national registry evaluating the societal effect on patients and their partners. *European Journal of Health Economics, 15,* 303–311.

Jernelov, S. Lekander, M., Blom, K., Rydh, B., Ljotsson, B., Axelsson, J., & Kaldo, V. (2012). Efficacy of a behavioural self-help treatment with or without therapist guidance for comorbid and primary insomnia: A randomized controlled trial. *BioMed Central Psychiatry, 12.* Retrieved from http://www.biomedcentral.com/1471-244X/12/5

Kahn-Greene, E. T., Killgore, D. B., Kamimori, G. H., Balkin, T. J., & Killgore, W. D. (2007). The effects of sleep deprivation on symptoms of psychopathology in healthy adults. *Sleep Medicine, 8,* 215–221.

Krueger, P. M., & Friedman, E. M. (2009). Sleep duration in the United States: A cross-sectional population-based study. *American Journal of Epidemiology, 169,* 1052–1063.

Lancee, J., & Schrijnemaekers, N. L. (2013). The association between nightmares and daily distress. *Sleep and Biological Rhythms, 11,* 14–19. doi:10.1111/j.1479-8425.2012.00586.x

Lundh, L., & Broman, E. (2000). Insomnia as an interaction between sleep-interfering and sleep-interpreting processes. *Journal of Psychosomatic Research, 49,* 299–310.

Mackie, S., & Winkelman, J. W. (2015). Long-term treatment of restless legs syndrome (RLS): An approach to management of worsening symptoms, loss of efficacy, and augmentation. *CNS Drugs, 29,* 351–357. doi:10.1007/s40263-015-0250-2

Meijer, A. M., & van den Witenboer, G. L. H. (2007). Contribution of infants' sleep and crying to marital relationship of first-time parent couples in the 1st year after childbirth. *Journal of Family Psychology, 21*, 49–57.

Meltzer, L. J., & Mindell, J. A. (2007). Relationship between child sleep disturbances and maternal sleep, mood, and parenting stress: A pilot study. *Journal of Family Psychology, 21*, 67–73.

Miller, C. B., Espie, C. A., Epstein, D. R., Friedman, L., Morin, C. M., Pigeon, W. R., & Kyle, S. D. (2014). The evidence base of sleep restriction therapy for treating insomnia disorder. *Sleep Medicine Reviews, 18*(5), 415–425.

Moul, D. E., Morin, C. M., Buysse, D. J., Reynolds, C. F., & Kupfer, D. J. (2007). Treatment of insomnia and restless leg syndrome. In P. E. Nathan & J. M. Gorman (Eds.), *A guide to treatments that work* (pp. 611–640). New York, NY: Oxford University Press.

National Sleep Foundation. (2016). Retrieved from http://sleepfoundation.org

Olson, E. J., Boeve, B. F., & Silber, M. H. (2000). Rapid eye movement sleep behavior disorder: Demographic, clinical and laboratory findings in 93 cases. *Brain: A Journal of Neurology, 123*, 331–339.

Paylo, M. J., Kress, V. E., & Kelly Gilea, B. L. (2014). Sleep-wake disorders, sexual dysfunctions, paraphilic disorders, and gender dysphoria. In V. Kress & M. Paylo (Eds.), *Treating mental disorders: A strength-based, comprehensive approach to case conceptualization and treatment* (pp. 498–521). Columbus, OH: Pearson.

Plazzi, G., Vetrugno, R., Provini, F., & Montagna, P. (2005). Sleepwalking and other ambulatory behaviors during sleep. *Neurological Science, 26*, s193–s198.

Pressman, R. M., & Imber, S. C. (2011). Relationship of children's daytime behavior problems with bedtime routines/practices: A family context and the consideration of faux-ADHD. *The American Journal of Family Therapy, 39*, 404–418.

Puterbaugh, D. (2011). Searching for a good night's sleep: What mental health counselors can do about the epidemic of poor sleep. *Journal of Mental Health Counseling, 33*, 312–326.

Ram, S., Seirawan, H., Kumar, S. K. S., & Clark, G. T. (2010). Prevalence and impact of sleep disorders and sleep habits in the United States. *Sleep Breath, 14*, 63–70.

Rauer, A. J., Kelly, R. J., Buckhalt, J. A., & El-Sheikh, M. (2010). Sleeping with one eye open: Marital abuse as an antecedent of poor sleep. *Journal of Family Psychology, 24*, 667–677.

Reishtein, J. L., Pack, A. I., Maislin, G., Dinges, D. F., Bloxham, T. J., George, C. F. P., . . . Weaver, T. E. (2006). Sleepiness and relationships in obstructive sleep apnea. *Issues in Mental Health Nursing, 27*, 319–330.

Remley, T. P., Jr, & Herlihy, B. (2016). *Ethical, legal, and professional issues in counseling* (5th ed.). Upper Saddle River, NJ: Pearson.

Robillard, R., Naismith, S. L., Smith, K. L., Rogers, N. L., White, D., Terpening, Z., . . . Hickie, I. B. (2014). Sleep-wake cycle in young and older persons with a lifetime history of mood disorders. *PLOS ONE, 9*(2), e87763. doi:10.1371/journal.pone.0087763

Sadock, B. J., & Sadock, V. A. (2007). *Kaplan and Sadock's synopsis of psychiatry: Behavioral sciences/clinical psychiatry* (10th ed.). Philadelphia, PA: Lippincott Williams & Wilkins.

Schredl, M. (2010). Nightmare frequency and nightmare topics in a representative German sample. *European Archives of Psychiatry Clinical Neuroscience, 260*, 565–570.

Sharma, B., & Feinsilver, S. (2009). Circadian rhythm sleep disorders: An update. *Sleep and Biological Rhythms, 7*, 113–124.

Suh, S., Ong, J., Steidtmann, D., Nowakowski, S., Dowdle, C., Willett, E., . . . Manber, R. (2012). Cognitions and insomnia subgroups. *Cognitive Therapy and Research, 36*(2), 120–128.

Thompson, S. J., Bender, K., Cardoso, J. B., & Flynn, P. M. (2011). Experiential activities in family therapy: Perceptions of caregivers and youth. *Journal of Child and Family Studies, 20*, 560–568.

van de Laar, M., Pevernagie, D., van Mierlo, P., & Overeem, S. (2015). Subjective sleep characteristics in primary insomnia versus insomnia with comorbid anxiety or mood disorder. *Sleep and Biological Rhythms, 13*, 41–48.

Warman, G. R., Pawley, M. D. M., Bolton, C., Cheeseman, J. F., Fernando, A. T., III, Arendt, J., & Wirz-Justice, A. (2011) Circadian-related sleep disorders and sleep medication use in the New Zealand blind population: An observational prevalence survey. *PLOS ONE, 6*(7), e22073. doi:10.1371/journal.pone.0022073

Watson, N. F., Badr, M. S., Belenky, G., Bliwise, D. L., Buxton, O. M., Buysse, D., . . . Tasali, E. (2015). Recommended amount of sleep for a healthy adult: A joint consensus statement of the American Academy of Sleep Medicine and Sleep Research Society. *Journal of Clinical Sleep Medicine, 11*, 591–592.

SEXUAL DYSFUNCTIONS:
A RELATIONAL UNDERSTANDING

Anne S. Cabanilla and Roxanne Bamond

Health care providers have used the *Diagnostic and Statistical Manual of Mental Disorders (DSM)* to support communication of essential characteristics of mental health disorders among professionals since its inception by the American Psychiatric Association (APA) in 1952 (2013). The developers of the original *DSM* intended to increase uniform understanding of patient presenting concerns, and support effective patient care.

Previous editions of the *DSM*, including the revised fourth edition, *Diagnostic and Statistical Manual of Mental Disorder* (4th ed., text rev.; *DSM-IV-TR*; APA, 2000), minimally addressed mental health concerns from a family systems perspective (APA, 2013). Sexual disorders were bundled together in a broad chapter that included disorders of sexual dysfunction, paraphilias, and gender identity disorders. These were not discussed in relational terms, other than to acknowledge that when an individual experiences a problem with sexual dysfunction, this often involves a partner.

Changes were made to the *DSM- IV-TR* chapter on sexual disorders when the *Diagnostic and Statistical Manual of Mental Disorder* (5th ed.; *DSM-5*; APA, 2013) was developed. There was wide discussion among mental health professionals about the need for specific changes in diagnostic criteria and overall perspective on what genuinely constituted a sexual disorder involving mental health. For example, Female Sexual Arousal Disorder was changed to include notation of severity and duration of symptoms (Graham, 2010). Similarly, Brotto (2010) addressed recommendations for change to the Hypoactive Sexual Disorder in women diagnosis when it was revised during the development of the *DSM-5*. Regier, Narrow, Kuhl, and Kupfer (2009) suggested that one notable improvement in the *DSM-5* over the *DSM-IV-TR* should be the use of dimensional measures, although the task force responsible for the revision eventually chose not to adopt this change to the diagnostic criteria in the Sexual Disorders chapter. These changes are most concerned with precision in definition and measurement of symptoms. Balon, Taylor, and Clayton (2007) also suggested changes to the way sexual disorders are conceptualized in the *DSM-5*. These authors were recommending future changes in 2007 to the manual they hoped would be revised in the near future. Specifically, they stated that the *DSM-5* should include precision in delineating when a sexual problem becomes a sexual dysfunction, whether a specific duration criterion for sexual dysfunctions should be required (as is the case for many other mental health diagnoses), and whether marked distress should be included in diagnostic criteria. Indeed, these changes were all incorporated into the *DSM-5* Sexual Disorders chapter.

The *DSM-5* addresses sexual concerns across several chapters (APA, 2013). Whereas the *DSM-IV-TR* was organized such that a chapter titled Sexual and Gender Identity Disorders included sexual dysfunctions, paraphilia, gender identity disorders, and sexual disorder not otherwise specified, the *DSM-5* includes these topics separated into three chapters. Other Specified Sexual Dysfunction and Unspecified Sexual Dysfunction are now included in the Sexual Dysfunctions chapter, while Gender Dysphoria and Paraphilic Disorders are each in separate chapters.

DSM-5 AND FAMILY SYSTEMS

The Sexual Dysfunctions chapter in *DSM-5* includes Delayed Ejaculation, Erectile Disorder, Female Orgasmic Disorder, Female Sexual Interest/Arousal Disorder, Genito-Pelvic Pain/Penetration Disorder, Male Hypoactive Sexual Desire Disorder, Premature (Early) Ejaculation, and Substance/Medication-Induced Sexual Dysfunction, as well as Other Specified Sexual Dysfunction and Unspecified Sexual Dysfunction. These diagnoses have in common the premise that each disorder is diagnosed in an individual. One partner or the other is thought to experience the disorder. The assumption is that the problem occurs in the individual, and is not relational. However, it is important to consider sexual dysfunctions from a relational context as it often impacts relationships.

In addition to the lifelong/acquired and generalized/situational subtypes, a number of factors must be considered during the assessment of sexual dysfunction, given that they may be relevant to etiology and/or treatment and that they may contribute, to varying degrees, across individuals: (a) partner factors (e.g., partner's sexual problems; partner's health status); (b) relationship factors (e.g., poor communication; discrepancies in desire for sexual activity); (c) individual vulnerability factors (e.g., poor body image; history of sexual or emotional abuse), psychiatric comorbidity (e.g., depression, anxiety), or stressors (e.g., job loss, bereavement); (d) cultural or religious factors (e.g., inhibitions related to prohibitions against sexual activity or pleasure, and attitudes toward sexuality); and (e) medical factors relevant to prognosis, course, or treatment (see *DSM-5*, pp. 423, 425, 427, 431, 434–435, 438, and 444).

"If severe relationship distress, partner violence, or significant stressors better explain the sexual difficulties, then a sexual dysfunction diagnosis is not made, but an appropriate V or Z code for the relationship problem or stressor may be listed." (APA, 2013, p. 424).

RELATIONAL AND CULTURAL FEATURES

Sexual dysfunction in one partner inevitably affects the other partner and the quality of the relationship. Physical distress during sexual encounters that prevents mutually satisfying sexual experience can result in emotional distress within each individual and between the two partners. Once this emotional distress has occurred, it is not unusual for either or both partners to fear reoccurrence. This worry that the problem "could happen again" can lead to avoidance of sexual interactions. Misinterpretation of the partner's motive for avoidance may result in confusion, hurt feelings, and relational distress.

Since the Sexual Disorders in the *DSM-5* are physiological in nature, they are necessarily gender based. Assuming the individual experiencing the disorder is not in the midst of transgendering (the *DSM-5* does not address transgendering in the Sexual Dysfunctions chapter), the specific diagnosis applies only to one individual based on his or her gender-based physiology. For example, a female is not diagnosed with Premature Ejaculation, and a male does not experience Genito-Pelvic Pain/Penetration Disorder.

Given the nature of emotional sexual politics in Western culture, there may, however, be some emotional impact of these disorders/disabilities on the individual and the couple. For example, male erectile dysfunction may trigger some feelings of inadequacy in the male partner based on cultural expectations about masculine sexuality. Likewise, females in Western culture may worry that they lack femininity or are not attractive if they are not sexually responsive. Culturally based values around sexuality and gender may have a powerful impact on the emotional well-being of the individual client, and therefore the family system or couple.

Many of the sexual disorders can be linked to advancing age or life stage. For example, the likelihood of erectile dysfunction increases with age. Likewise, female sexual interest/arousal disorder can occur as women age and enter menopause. Women who have recently given birth may experience hormonal shifts that limit sexual desire, or they may have culturally derived beliefs about sexuality and motherhood that reduce sexual drive. Beliefs and values related to aging, life stage, and sexuality must be considered when working with the individual and the couple experiencing the problem. Both partners' beliefs and values about sexuality and aging must be explored and reconciled.

Because sexual relationships involve both physical and emotional intimacy, the ability of partners to trust each other is an important factor. Trust can be based on each partner's confidence that the other is respectful and compassionate. If there is an imbalance of power in the relationship, there can be challenges to the development of trust and intimacy, which can affect the sexual relationship. This can, further, affect the individual's sexual functioning.

Finally, religion can play a significant role in the development of each individual's sexual values. Many religious orientations include proscriptions around sexual behaviors. These religiously imposed values can easily affect the individual's emotional experience related to sexuality, resulting in physical barriers to healthy sexual functioning.

All in all, sexual functioning is cyclical and systemic. Problems that affect the mind's perceptions about sexuality can affect the body's sexual functioning. When there is a physical sexual dysfunction, the individual is likely to respond with emotional distress. Likewise, problems that affect the individual often affect the couple or system. When the physical intimacy is disrupted, the couple's emotional intimacy is likely to be affected. This can result in further emotional distancing, which continues the cycle of disorder.

Alarcon (2014) notes that significant efforts to address cultural considerations, including gender, were undertaken during the development of the *Diagnostic and Statistical Manual of Mental Disorder* (4th ed.; *DSM-IV*; APA, 1994), *DSM-IV-TR*, and *DSM-5*. Notably, the team involved in the development of each of these manuals included a task force to review cultural considerations and included Culture Bound Syndromes, at least in the Appendices of the *DSM*. There is no mention of efforts to specifically include family systems concepts; however, relational concerns are addressed in the section, Other Conditions That May Be the Focus of Clinical Attention. The broad categories of Relational Problems, Abuse and Neglect, Educational and Occupational Problems, Housing and Economic Problems, Other Problems Related to Social Environment, Problems Related to Crime or Interaction Related to the Legal System, Other Health Service Encounters for Counseling and Medical Advice, Problems Related to Other Psychosocial, Personal, and Environmental Circumstances, and Other Circumstances of Personal History all include subcategories that take into consideration relational and life challenges that could affect the client's well-being and ability to function successfully. These Z codes could be used to formulate an understanding of the client's relationships and other life experiences on emotional distress, including sexual dysfunction.

FAMILY SYSTEMS ASSESSMENTS

Many assessments have been created to help clinicians understand the sexual satisfaction or dissatisfaction experienced by couples (Fischer & Corcoran, 2013). From a systemic perspective, however, assessments are performed in service to therapeutic treatment, and all therapeutic treatment is based on a therapeutic model (Gehart, 2014). A therapist does not first assess the client system, devoid of a therapeutic orientation, and then treat the client system in a linear way. Rather, the practitioner understands assessment through the lens of a treatment model. A therapist, a priori, holds beliefs about the formation and resolution of problems. Those beliefs are usually predicated on his or her treatment model. So, if a therapist utilizes a model that posits that difficulties in human relationships are created and exacerbated through problematic or dysfunctional interactional cycles, he or she will begin to assess, through a therapeutic interview, for those interactional cycles (Watzlawick, Weakland, & Fisch, 1974). In the initial therapeutic assessment interview, the questions the practitioner asks the clients, and the assessment that she or he utilizes, are informed by the search for behavioral interactions that continue to create, perpetuate, or exacerbate the dysfunction (Fisch, Weakland, & Segal, 1982; McGoldrick, Gerson, & Petry, 2008). Likewise, if a practitioner holds the theoretical position that difficulties occur when the clients' experiences, in this case their sexual (dys)functioning, are markedly different than the dominant culture's story about optimal or normal sexual functioning, the therapist will juxtapose that dominant cultural story with that of the clients' experiences (White & Epston, 1990). The practitioner seeks, from this perspective, to prompt the clients to self-assess their adherence to, or rejection of, that dominant cultural story in their lives. So for as many models of treatment that exist, there are just as many ways to assess the couple and the couple's difficulties.

For most therapists, working from systemic models, the assessment is integrated into an initial intake interview with the client(s). Rarely do therapists simply administer a paper and pencil assessment, or if they do, they generally follow up by assessing the clients' perspectives of the difficulties in the initial therapeutic intake or session. In some circumstances, though, it would benefit the therapist and clients to administer a written assessment so as to gather additional information about the nature and etiology of the sexual difficulties the couple is experiencing. The therapist or counselor who may be inclined to utilize, or recommend to his or her clients, a written assessment might consider Gottman's *Quality of Sex, Romance, and Passion in the Relationship Questionnaire* (Gottman & Gottman, 2010). This 28-item self-assessment identifies issues that may affect the couples' sexual relationship. It clearly delineates couples that may have a declining level of sexual satisfaction.

Clients usually present to therapy wanting to gain something they do not have or to be rid of something that is bothersome. Clients who present to treatment have likely already assessed their needs and have come to the conclusion that something is "wrong" with their sexual relationship. They are usually experiencing something they do not want, such as reaching orgasm too quickly or not at all, or they are missing something that they do want, like a sense of feeling connected and loved. The practitioner, utilizing a systemic model, is listening through her or his theoretical perspective to what is and what is not working for the clients, while also assessing the clients' beliefs about the difficulties. The information that the clients offer is being funneled through the practitioner's theoretical model: some of the information the clients offer is essential in the therapist's assessment, while other information is disregarded as tangential to the treatment of the difficulty. Systemically informed therapists want to understand their clients' desires, goals, and treatment concerns while also understanding the clients' beliefs about the etiology of these difficulties. This type of collaborative relationship between therapists and clients is essential so that clients come away from therapy having gained new behaviors, skills, and perceptions that will help them in the resolution of their presenting concerns.

An important note on this topic is that in accordance with a systemic orientation and treatment, the couple's sexual functioning cannot be understood separately from its overall relationship (Schnarch, 1991; Weeks, Gambescia, & Hertlein, 2016). From a systemic perspective everything connects, and as one aspect of the relationship changes it has positive or negative effects on other parts of the relationship. Therefore, assessing a couple's sexual functioning is done within the larger context of their entire relationship. Often sexual difficulties are understood as a symptom of an overarching problem in the relationship. Sexual difficulties can also be understood as a gateway into the couple's overall functioning (Schnarch, 1991). As the relationship improves, so may the sexual difficulties, and the inverse is also true: As the couple's sexual difficulties resolve, they often find a better way of relating to each other outside of the bedroom. The question for systemic therapists becomes the point of entry; do systemically informed therapists begin by helping clients improve the overall functioning of their relationship, knowing that improved functioning will have a systemic effect on their sexual relationship, or do they begin with the focus on the couple's sexual relationship? As the sexual relationship improves, couples often report an overall satisfaction in their partnership. Most systemic therapists find themselves doing both, working to help improve the couple's experiences both inside and outside of the bedroom.

From a relational and systemic perspective it is crucial to understand how the symptom, or sexual difficulty, makes sense in the overall relationship of the couple. Assessment of how the symptom is integral to the person (or persons) who bear the symptom(s) is also important (Green & Flemons, 2004). Most clients say they want to rid themselves of the disturbing symptom. Yet when the practitioner can understand the symptom from a position of respect and curiosity, a new relationship can occur between the clients and their sexual difficulties. In this new relationship, the symptom can remain for as long as needed or "the couple [can] make it possible for the symptom to wander away" (Green & Flemons, 2004, p. 129). When the symptoms of sexual dysfunction are seen through a lens of integrity, curiosity, and respect they often inform the treatment team (the clients and the therapist) of possible resolutions to the overarching difficulties in the relationship.

Prior to presenting for treatment, the client(s) likely tried to diminish or extinguish the sexual difficulty but found either the symptom remained or became more pronounced. In any assessment it is important to understand the measures the client(s) took to extinguish the problem and if or how the symptom changed. As is common in couples therapy, the problem that brought them into treatment had been happening for quite a while and couples tried many things on their own or in prior treatment to rid themselves of the difficulty. The therapist must assess all prior attempts at resolving the presenting problem. If some approaches helped, or helped briefly, while other approaches and interventions failed or exacerbated the difficulties, this must be examined and understood by the counselor. This is important to assess so the treating practitioner does not attempt to implement *more of the same* unhelpful interventions (Fisch et al., 1982).

The therapist must also assess each client's motivation to change. Therapists may assume that if a couple presents for treatment, both partners are motivated to do something differently to change their sexual relationship. Often in couples therapy, one person is more motivated to change, while the other may be ambivalent or leans clearly toward the side of things remaining the same. A common mistake a couples therapist can make is siding with the partner who wants to change or failing to fully understand one partner's ambivalence around change. Another common mistake the therapist can make is believing that if clients merely understood each other, or communicated better, they would want the same thing. Since sexual dysfunction, by definition, is understood systemically as a relational diagnosis (this is true even when a physical diagnosis is ruled out), a therapist must assess for what both individuals see as therapeutic success. Even when both partners want their sexual relationship to be different or better, their definitions of "better" may vary.

Common to all systemic approaches is the importance of assessing each individual's belief about the sexual dysfunction; what it looks like in his or her perception, and how the dysfunction both benefits and hurts them individually and as a couple. The therapist must also thoroughly assess all attempts the couple, both together and individually, has made to change the sexual relationship. Assessing for the motivation to change and what might be lost or gained if change occurs is also important. A good assessment must also include a clear description of what specific changes each partner is seeking. If these descriptions are different, if the individuals want different things out of their sexual relationship, therapy must begin with a discernment stage to fully understand if common goals exist (Doherty, 2011).

Approaches: Assessment Tools and Interventions

For the sake of brevity we condense and discuss three overarching approaches to systemic treatment: the *natural systems approach*, the *cybernetic systems approach*, and the *language systems approach*. Most models of couples therapy and family therapy treatment reside within these three systems. Further, we discuss key assessment techniques in these approaches, demonstrating the differences and similarities in what and how couples' sexual difficulties are understood, assessed, and treated. Since interventions cannot be understood apart from assessment in systemic approaches, interventions are also discussed.

Natural Systems Theory

Natural systems theory is predicated on the belief that families are biological systems that evolve over time, and dysfunctions within couples and families are intergenerational. What was unresolved in one generation is passed down, and patterns of behavior occur from one generation to the next until individuals within those systems resolve those difficult patterns (Kerr & Bowen, 1988). Perhaps the most prominent assessment tool put forth from a natural or biological systems approach is the genogram (McGoldrick, 2011; McGoldrick et al., 2008). The genogram is a tool that allows for the clinician to interview the couple, sketch out family patterns of relating through generations, and assess the couple's present difficulties from a historical point of view. By creating a genogram with the couple, the therapist is able to pinpoint patterns of enmeshment, cutoff, and emotional triangulation in their relationship (McGoldrick et al., 2008). These relational patterns give rise to the symptoms the couple is presently experiencing. Through this process of assessment using a genogram, the couple can begin to enact new, more functional patterns of relating. In this way, the genogram is both an assessment tool for the therapist and an intervention for the clients (McGoldrick et al., 2008). From a natural systems approach, the couple's sexual difficulties are understood as patterns of relating that are left over and handed down by both of their respective families. Until the couple recognizes these intergenerational patterns of triangulation, cutoff, and enmeshment, and choose to relate differently, they will not evolve into more psychologically healthy individuals. Sexual difficulties are merely the symptom of a larger relational dance wherein one or both individuals are reactive to each other. The therapist's position is to help clients recognize how these intergenerational patterns are active in their present difficulties, and to coach them into a more responsive, rather than reactive, pattern of relating to each other.

Cybernetic Systems Theory

From a cybernetic understanding of systems theory, all communication makes sense in the context in which it is taking place (Gehart, 2014), and what may be understood as individual or couple/family dysfunction is actually a logical reaction to covert or overt relationship rules. Practitioners, informed by this manner of understanding human behaviors, are looking for the logic in which the dysfunctional behavior or behaviors occur. They seek out the relational rules that allow the dysfunction to occur and make sense. The practitioner understands that the symptom or difficulty is actually a way that the participants are communicating. Sexual dysfunction, seen as a communication device, does not shift or change as long as the context in which those behaviors take place remains hidden, unexpressed, or unchanged. The therapist then goes in search of the logic of the dysfunction and attempts to give voice, again either overtly or covertly, to the dysfunction. By doing so, the context in which those behaviors made sense no longer exists and therefore new, more satisfying behaviors can emerge.

Assessment from this perspective is done in conversation with the client(s). The therapist attempts to get a complete behavioral interactional cycle that maintains the problem and to understand the rules or beliefs that keep those behaviors in place. Clients may believe "good girls do not ask for what they want" or "men are supposed to be sexually dominant." Once those beliefs and meanings are challenged, usually in a behavioral way, and the clients accept new rules around them, the dysfunction no longer makes sense in context anymore and the communication, in the form of new behaviors, shifts. Before any attempt to shift the couple's behaviors, it is crucial that the practitioner understand the logic those behaviors maintain. The therapist asking sense-making questions such as, "When is this most likely to occur?" "Who notices it first?" "What happens right before and right after?" "Who initiates sex and how?" seeks to get a complete behavioral interaction of how the problem is maintained.

As in the case with the genogram in a natural systems approach, much of the intervention stage of cybernetically informed approaches involves the therapist assessing the problem. The therapist seeks to intervene by either shifting the meanings of the behaviors or interrupting the behavioral loops or cycles. This can be done by paradox, wherein the practitioner tells the client to do "more of the same" and thereby controlling what might have been understood as uncontrollable; it can also be done by shifting the meaning of the difficulty by reframing it. For example, no longer is it sexual dysfunction but rather a way of expressing ambivalence around being parents again. Once the dysfunction is reframed or the problematic behavior is enacted purposefully, a shift is likely to occur in the interactional cycle between partners. The context has shifted, the rules are different, and therefore the dysfunctional behaviors no longer make sense in the new context.

Language Systems

With the rise of postmodern theory, family therapists began to move away from a biological or mechanistic understanding of human systems and alighted more on an understanding that problems are created and "dissolved" through language (Anderson & Goolishian, 1988). Practitioners began to question their expert role and aligned themselves more with a relative understanding of what it meant to even be dysfunctional. Questions began to emerge as to who defines "normal" and how do culture, gender, socioeconomic status, race, and other identity factors influence the definition of "abnormal" behavior. Therapy became a political endeavor wherein ultimate truth was challenged and all problems were understood through multiple lenses. From this perspective, assessment emphasized the discovery of how clients came to decide or understand that they had a dysfunction. Who defined it? How does the dominant culture create the understanding that the couple is experiencing "dysfunction" rather than their own unique kind of "functioning"? Who in the couple decided that therapy was needed? And who is defining the behavior as problematic? The practitioner, alongside the clients, is much more likely to assess the larger cultural–political systems for the creation of the problem than he or she is to attribute the difficulty to the clients themselves. In this codiscovery process, the clients and the therapist collaborate to find a way for the clients to create an affirming sexual relationship with each other.

While the assessment is generally done collaboratively, so are the interventions. The practitioner may be looking for opportunities to "externalize the problem" (White &

Epston, 1990) from a position of internal pathology to a relational understanding. No longer are the clients dysfunctional but rather they are creating and living alternative and affirming stories. Practitioners can cocreate "dialogical space" wherein the couple can deconstruct the problematic story of sexual dysfunction and reconstruct a positive sexually affirming story (Anderson & Goolishian, 1988; Rober, 2002).

FAMILY SYSTEMS INTERVENTIONS

Interventions are natural extensions of assessments. Often interventions are offered simultaneously with assessment, rather than sequentially. Often the particular type of exploration of the problem, which we are labeling *the assessment*, is the point at which the therapist is already intervening to change the presenting problem. However, in this section we seek to focus more closely on the tools of intervention in these three relational approaches.

Natural/Biological Systems Interventions

A practitioner utilizing a biological or natural systems approach believes that patterns of difficulties that are experienced in the present are handed down intergenerationally. By creating, minimally, a three-generational genogram of the client system, the therapist can begin to get a sense of the patterns of behaviors that are contributing to the presenting problem. Generally the therapist begins with the clients' immediate families in the present generation, then he or she branches out generationally. The therapist asks questions regarding the relationships between people, developmental life cycle transitions, and important nodal events. All of this information is noted on the genogram, with particular attention to utilizing certain symbols for people, patterns of relating, and life cycle events. Through the creation of the genogram, family functioning can be seen and understood both across the life cycle and throughout generations (McGoldrick et al., 2008).

The genogram is used as an intervention tool. By illustrating and understanding the historical reactivity in a family, the clients can then, with the help of the practitioner, identify and enact more responsive ways to approach their difficulties. Therapists seek to help clients to increase their level of differentiation, or the ability each has to be both connected and independent in relationships. "Therapists promote differentiation by coaching [clients] to maintain his/her emotional state without undue influence from the other" (Gehart, 2014, p. 237). As clients increase their abilities to respond thoughtfully to the presenting difficulty and to each other, their levels of differentiation increase. With this increase, clients are then able to approach their difficulties as invitations to relate in ways that are more affirming to their relationships. They can create a new interconnected way of being which both affirms their independence from and connection to each other.

Cybernetic Systems Interventions

Approaches informed by a cybernetic understanding encourage alteration of clients' behaviors or beliefs so that they can have a different subjective experience. After assessing the clients' attempts at getting rid of their problems, the therapist, through directives (or behavioral tasks), encourages the clients to do something other than what they have been doing (O'Hanlon, 2004). Directives, informed by the clients' goals, can be either straightforward or indirect (Gehart, 2014). Straightforward directives overtly instruct the clients to position themselves differently, vis-a-vis their difficulties. For example, after finding out that the difficulty always follows a predictable pattern, the therapist may intervene by telling the clients to change where they have sex or who initiates it. This change in how the clients relate to each other necessarily changes how they view the difficulty. By directing the clients to do something differently, the habitual cycle of the problem is undermined. The therapist may also use indirect directives like paradox, or the introduction of a metaphor to shift the underlying context of the problem. In these interventions, the clients no longer see their difficulties in the same way. Therefore, they will act or behave differently toward the problem. For example, when a client who may be avoiding sex is told to "go slow," his or her reluctance has now become the *appropriate response* rather than the problematic one. Ultimately, in these cybernetic approaches, the underlying beliefs and actions (or nonactions) that keep the clients stuck in a problem are challenged, and in so doing, the clients' relationship with the problem is altered. Their old ways of relating no longer make sense because the context has shifted.

Language Systems Interventions

The main intervention used in language systems approaches is the question. The manner in which therapists ask questions, and to what intended outcome, may determine the trajectory of the problem. Often therapists intervene by juxtaposing the dominant beliefs that keep the problem in place with alternative beliefs that may not yet be realized or articulated. Through therapeutic conversations, the practitioner seeks to deconstruct the problem and reconstruct client-generated solutions (Anderson, 1997). The therapist seeks to position himself or herself as a nonexpert in the clients' lives and solutions. He or she is more an expert at generative conversations that produce alternative approaches to client conundrums. By allowing clients to participate in a curious stance toward their difficulties and to choose alternative ways of understanding and interacting, the therapist allows problems to *dissolve* (Anderson & Goolishian, 1988). An underlying belief in postmodern language systems approaches is that problems are socially constructed and often are perceived by clients as being internal. The postmodern therapist, grounded in a language systems approach, seeks to highlight those socially constructed perceptions and to invite the clients to choose more affirming narratives for their lives (Freedman & Combs, 1996). They do this by seeking rich descriptions of the problem, by asking meaning-making questions, and through curious reflection. Between the clients' and the therapist's exploration of the difficulty, alternative realities, understandings, and ways of relating can be realized.

ETHICAL AND LEGAL IMPLICATIONS

As is the case whenever clinicians are attempting to help clients resolve presenting concerns, there are ethical considerations to keep in mind when applying assessment, diagnosis, and treatment interventions to a family system presenting with Sexual Dysfunction. Practitioners must remain mindful of the clients' privacy and confidentiality, as well as the impact of diagnostic labeling.

Privacy and confidentiality are an important ethical consideration in every case of mental health treatment, and when the presenting problem revolves around sexuality, this seems especially important. Western culture has long deemed matters of sexuality to be extremely personal, and potentially embarrassing or even shameful. Practitioners who help clients with sexual problems must be committed to being mindful of maintaining the clients' confidentiality and privacy.

There are implications to assigning a formal diagnosis, whether it is a *DSM-5* diagnosis, an *International Statistical Classification of Diseases and Related Health Problems, 10th Revision (ICD-10;* World Health Organization, 2016) diagnosis, or a nonpathologizing Z code to any single member of the system. Clinicians and their clients must clearly communicate goals, priorities, and rationale for the decision to apply a diagnosis, as well as an understanding of the impact of sharing this diagnosis with an outside source such as a health insurance company. Whereas insurance companies often fail to offer reimbursement for family systems treatment, many do cover treatment for individual mental health problems. This fact has led some practitioners to suggest identifying an individual to "carry the label" for the problem in order to obtain coverage for services. In many cases, the couple would not otherwise be able to afford services, and the problem would go untreated. The ethical concern, therefore, is twofold. Are the couple and the clinician deliberately falsifying a claim for financial gain? This, of course, is illegal as well as unethical, even if the intent is to provide services for a need that would otherwise go unmet. Additionally, applying a mental health diagnosis to either partner, for a condition that might be considered by many to be relational and "normal, under the circumstances" may stigmatize the clients, which could actually harm the client. Finally, when a formal diagnosis of sexual dysfunction goes on record, there is always a risk that this information could be leaked. In other words, confidentiality could be compromised.

When faced with an ethical dilemma, the counselor's only recourse is to consult the appropriate ethical codes and guidelines, and choose a course of action that is in line with guidelines. Seeking supervision or professional consultation is also advised. In the case of confidentiality, the American Counseling Association (ACA) *Code of Ethics* Section B clearly states that all information concerning clients is held in the strictest confidence. B.6.g specifically states that "steps are taken to ensure that receivers of counseling records are sensitive to their confidential nature." In addition ACA E.5.d instructs that "counselors may refrain from making and/or reporting a diagnosis if they believe that it would cause harm to the client or others. Counselors carefully consider both the positive and negative implications of a diagnosis." For one or both partners to be diagnosed with a sexual dysfunction could have serious effects on them both individually and relationally. If one partner is diagnosed, he or she could be blamed for the relational issue and be held individually responsible for changing the sexual relationship. The implications of the diagnosis would likely compromise the couples' relationship as a whole.

In addition, it is unethical and illegal to submit a claim for third-party reimbursement from a health insurance provider using a diagnostic code that does not actually apply to the client, simply because the diagnosis is one that is covered or reimbursed. The American Association for Marriage and Family Therapy (AAMFT) *Code of Ethics* 8.4 specifically states, "Marriage and family therapists represent facts truthfully to clients, third-party payors, and supervisees regarding services rendered" (AAMFT, 2015). So in order to justify the diagnosis, counselors must accurately document that *DSM-5* symptom criteria for a specific diagnosis are actually met. When considering the reality that the sexual dysfunction is relational, it would be unethical and harmful to diagnose only one person in the partnership.

Additional ethical concerns about *systems* treatment for Sexual Dysfunctions might include the need to balance competing agendas if the two partners have different goals for the counseling process. For example, the clinician needs to work diligently to avoid siding with one or the other client if one partner wants change while the other partner wants things to remain the same. When working with more than one client in a family system, it is important to understand what both, or all, want to accomplish in treatment. Marriage and family therapists' ethical codes are built around the idea that clients, not the therapist, get to decide the focus of treatment and the decisions regarding their relationships (AAMFT, 2015, 1.8). The American Counseling Association's ethical codes also state that the clients' goals and relationships are the focus of treatment (ACA, 2014, A.1.). When working with one client, or the client who is more invested in change, the marriage and family therapist must understand that any and all changes that the individual client makes have systemic effects in the relationships in which the client participates. Change may not always be welcome from partners and other relations. A key component of an ethical therapeutic posture is the idea of fairness and nonmaleficence (Wilcoxen, Remley, & Gladding, 2012). When both partners may want very different outcomes from therapy, how does the ethical practitioner understand what "doing no harm" could look like to both partners with competing agendas? When assessing and treating a couple, the therapist, adhering to an ethical standard of care, must side with both of the clients. Often, when couples want different outcomes in treatment, an ethical dilemma is present for the therapist. Making these competing agendas overt in treatment is the first step to providing autonomy in treatment for each participant in the treatment system.

Other ethical considerations specific to treating sexual dysfunctions from a systems perspective include attending to diversity in the expression of sexual behaviors. Systemic therapists must account for their own biases and beliefs and not impose them on clients. All behaviors are understood to be an expression of context, and sexuality is firmly rooted in each person's ethnicity, gender, sexual orientation, and family culture. An ethical systemic therapist must be very aware and be careful to avoid the propensity to infuse his or her own values into the clients' choices, actions, and beliefs (Wilcoxen et al., 2012). Remaining open and accepting of individual expressions of sexuality is crucial for therapists who work with couples' sexual difficulties.

CASE CONCEPTUALIZATION

When a couple presents for treatment for sexual issues, it is imperative for the therapist or counselor to understand both clients' perspectives of the presenting difficulties as well as a relational conceptualization of the sexual problems. Systemic therapists are going to gather information about the etiology of the presenting problem, the length of time that the difficulties have been present, all attempts to resolve the issue(s), and other contributing factors influencing the presenting problem. Often, when couples present with sexual dysfunction, there can be many factors contributing to their difficulties. Couples may have attempted many things to mitigate or eliminate the dysfunction, often resulting in little or no change and occasionally exacerbating the difficulties. In this case study, a history of the presenting sexual dysfunction is presented along with a conceptualization of treatment from the three systemic approaches.

Presenting Concerns

Wife Tara and husband Clive, the parents of a 2-year-old daughter, have stopped having sexual intercourse due to issues with sexual arousal, penetration, and ejaculation. While both acknowledge wanting to be sexual and having sexual thoughts and fantasies at times, neither has been able to fully discuss or act on these desires with the other. Neither is engaged in an outside intimate or sexual relationship.

The couple has presented to therapy after both have been medically assessed and neither has a medical sexual issue. Both want to have another child, but they have not been able to complete sexual intercourse since right before the birth of their daughter 2 years ago. Tara reports that she does not experience sexual urges as often as she did before the birth of her child. However, she occasionally initiates sex when she "feels like it" or thinks she is ovulating. Her preoccupation with concerns about the ongoing failure to have satisfying sexual relations usually causes Tara to lose interest in sex and experience little to no sexual excitement or pleasure during these encounters. Clive, while becoming initially aroused, finds himself losing his erection soon after. Tara apologizes to Clive and says that she is "tired too," making excuses for both of them so that Clive does not feel guilty or embarrassed. Generally, Tara finds herself waiting several weeks before initiating sex again. Tara is waiting longer before initiating sex with Clive as their sexual difficulties persist. While Clive is affectionate with Tara, he rarely ever initiated sex with Tara once she refused his approach early in the relationship, prior to marriage. He acknowledges that as time goes by he is less and less interested in sex in general. Both report enjoying closeness with each other by hugging and cuddling.

Tara is Caucasian, non-Hispanic, and Clive is Japanese American (Clive's father is American and his mother is from Japan, and Clive was raised in the United States). Both have high school diplomas and some college courses but neither has a college degree. Tara is a successful working professional in a large financial organization having risen through the ranks as a computer programmer. After being fired from a technical company 3 years ago, Clive works two part-time manual labor jobs. Initially, after losing his job, Clive actively searched for further professional employment but in the past 2 years he has stopped looking for a career even though the couple often argues about him getting a "good" job. Presently, Tara has been paying nearly all the family bills and is solely responsible for most of the housework, cooking, and child care of their toddler. Clive contributes financially by covering his own expenses for his vehicle and work-related costs.

Concurrent Problems

Clive is currently taking medication (statins) for elevated cholesterol and a heart condition. Clive had a hospitalization for a cardiac event 2 years ago, shortly after the birth of their child. Presently, Clive has checkups every 6 months with his cardiologist who has given him the "all clear" to enjoy sex.

Tara is morbidly obese after the birth of their daughter. She is addressing this medical concern by attending a local weight loss program and walking for ½ hour during her lunch break at work. Tara is under the care of her OB/GYN for fibroid cysts. She is being monitored for the possibility of surgery if she continues to have problems conceiving.

Background History and Stressors

Tara and Clive were both raised in "traditional families" where the father was the fully employed "bread winner" and both of their mothers had the primary responsibility for raising the family. Tara's mother went back to work as a teacher after Tara's last sibling entered elementary school and continued to work full time after the death of Tara's father from cancer when Tara was 12 years old.

Clive's father was a "manly man," by Clive's description, and was the dominant parent in the household. Although Clive's mother was the full time parent, his father was the one who disciplined him and his younger brother.

Both were raised Roman Catholic but neither Clive nor Tara espouse a religion now as adults.

Both Tara and Clive currently smoke tobacco, and have since young adulthood. Clive has used recreational drugs (cocaine and marijuana) off and on but has reported that since his cardiac event, he has cut back on smoking significantly, and is not using any street drugs now.

Tara reports drinking about one to two glasses of wine during and after dinner on most nights.

Strengths

This is a second marriage for Tara and a third marriage for Clive. They met and became friends at work, and both described finding their "soul mates" in each other. They married after a long friendship and a brief romance of less than 1 year. Tara and Clive see themselves as each other's "best friend" and enjoy many of the same things. Both like going to movies together, playing cards, taking family vacations, and cooking together on special occasions.

Lately, their difficulties with their sexual relationship are leading to feelings of personal inadequacy and a growing dissatisfaction with shared time together. They both report wanting to get back to being "best friends." Both describe, since the birth of their daughter, they have spent less time alone together.

Clive's parents are still together after 30 years of marriage and Tara reports that her parents were "happily married" until her father's death.

Tara has a strong support system in her extended family and friends, and Clive, while more socially isolated, reports feeling emotionally supported by his parents. Clive's parents have recently loaned him money to start a handyman business.

DSM-5 Impressions and Implications

Individually, both Tara and Clive meet criteria for a diagnosis of Sexual Dysfunction. Tara could be diagnosed with Female Sexual Interest/Arousal Disorder. Since she is experiencing significantly reduced sexual interest/arousal, reduced initiation of sexual activity, and reduced sexual excitement or pleasure during sexual activity, Tara could be diagnosed with Female Sexual Interest/Arousal Disorder. She has been experiencing these problems for nearly 2 years, while the minimum duration for symptoms is 6 months. The problem is causing significant distress, as both Tara and Clive are upset and wondering: "What is wrong with me?" The problem has become so persistent they have sought couples' counseling. The problem is not the result of another mental disorder, severe relationship distress such as partner violence, or significant stress. It also does not appear to result from medication use or substance abuse.

Clive meets criteria for two sexual dysfunction disorders. He could be diagnosed with Male Hypoactive Sexual Desire Disorder. He is experiencing deficient sexual/erotic thoughts and desire for sexual activity, and this has been occurring for much longer than the minimum 6 months required duration threshold. This is causing him significant distress, and the problem is not better explained by another mental disorder, severe relationship distress, other significant stressors, or substance use.

Clive could also be diagnosed with Erectile Disorder. He has marked difficulty maintaining an erection until the satisfying completion of sexual activity, and marked decreased erectile rigidity. Once again, the duration of these symptoms is greater than 6 months, the problem is causing him significant distress, and his symptoms are not better accounted for by another explanation, such as a medical condition, medication, or substance use.

Alternatively, the treating clinician could choose to apply one of the ICD-9-CM (V codes) or ICD-10-CM (Z codes) from the list of Other Conditions That May Be a Focus of Clinical Attention. The Relationship Problems section includes Relationship Distress With Spouse or Intimate Partner under Other Problems Related to Primary Support Group. This diagnosis is intended for use when the focus of the clinical treatment is on the quality of the intimate partnership when the couple is experiencing relationship distress. The DSM-5 guidelines on applying this diagnosis include the caveat, "Typically, the relationship distress is associated with impaired functioning in behavioral, cognitive, or affective domains" (p. 716). Examples include conflict resolution difficulty, withdrawal, overinvolvement, chronic negative attributions of the other's intentions, or chronic sadness, apathy, or anger toward the partner. Tara and Clive's relational problems come close to fitting this description, but may be just outside the boundaries of the definitions. This could leave the treating clinician with the dilemma of deciding whether to "push the limits" on expanding the literal interpretation of this DSM-5 Z code diagnosis. Further complicating this decision, the

Relationship Distress diagnosis excludes clinical encounters for mental health services for sex counseling. Tara or Clive could be seeking sex counseling. The *DSM-5* reserves this diagnosis for *individuals* who seek counseling related to sexual enjoyment, as well as other sex-related issues. Their problems could be considered more relational than sexual, depending on the perspective of the treating clinician.

Applying a *DSM-5* diagnosis to Tara and Clive's case is neither simple nor uncomplicated. Lebow (2006) explores the inherent challenges of integrating the *DSM* system of diagnosis with family systems treatment, when systems theory was not part of the conceptualization for the *DSM* model in the first place. The decision about which diagnosis is most appropriate for Tara and Clive requires the treating clinician to use clinical judgment and informed experience. This decision is affected by the clinician's professional perspective. It is also important to communicate with the clients to determine their needs and preferences, and their original intent when they sought treatment. The determination of the appropriate diagnostic code also hinges on who is the end recipient of the diagnostic information. The treating clinician may view the diagnosis and treatment plan through the lens of his or her professional orientation. A family systems–oriented counselor may see no utility in diagnosing Clive and Tara with individual sexual functioning disorders, for example, since this will not impact the treatment plan. Clive and Tara may also feel stigmatized if their problem is construed as pathological, which could impede their recovery. If the need to make a formal diagnosis is based on the requirement that the nature of the clients' problems be standardized so that it can be communicated to other professionals, which was the original purpose for the development of the *DSM*, then the diagnosing clinician must keep this communication in mind as well. Ultimately, the diagnosis the clinician chooses may be influenced by the knowledge of who eventually sees it, and the reason for the diagnosis in the first place. The clinician asks herself or himself, "What does this recipient need to know about my clients?"

Relational Problems

Clive's confidence, both professionally and sexually, has decreased since he was fired from his job. While he tells Tara that he is afraid for his health or tired from working manual labor, in the therapeutic interview he says he feels less like a "man" and just like another one of Tara's girlfriends. Tara blames her weight for Clive's lack of arousal and "lets him off the hook" when he loses interest in sex because she believes that she is to blame for his disinterest in her sexually. Both Clive and Tara demonstrate a conflict-avoiding style of relating.

Since the onset of their sexual difficulties, both have reported less satisfaction in their overall relationship and have spent more time apart. Tara says that their toddler is requiring more attention but she feels relieved when she does not have to "deal with their issues." She says she rarely asks Clive to help with the care of their child because she knows "he is tired" from working in the sun all day. Often Clive falls asleep on the couch watching television after a late dinner and comes to bed in the middle of the night. More nights than not, their daughter has found her way to the couple's bed and has fallen asleep next to Tara.

Assessments

From a Natural Systems Perspective

During the first session, a family history is gathered using a three-generational genogram. What became evident in both Clive's and Tara's histories were the responsibility put on both of their mothers for the raising of the children. While both Clive and Tara reported that their fathers were the "breadwinners" and the "disciplinarians," in reality their mothers both raised the children and were significant in financially supporting the family. Tara's mother returned to full-time work nearly immediately upon the death of Tara's father and Clive's mother supported the family by "working under the table" at a local family-owned restaurant. Through assessing the family system, it became evident via the genogram that there were primary and close relationships between mothers and their children, especially the female children, and a distant relationship between the fathers and the children, either through death, in Tara's relationship with her father, or a significant cutoff between Clive and his father. This family pattern of distance and triangles seems to happen at the birth of the first child in both Tara's and Clive's families of origin. The mothers became close to the children and, at times, fused with them, while the fathers became more distanced and cutoff. While both mothers would speak kindly of the fathers, the day-to-day interactions were few and distant. After the death of Tara's father, Tara's mother became somewhat emotionally dependent on Tara. Tara described the mother–daughter relationship as very strong and, at times, suffocating.

Tara and Clive began to notice the same pattern reenacting in their own nuclear family. At the birth of their daughter, and shortly thereafter losing his corporate job, Clive began pouring his attention and effort into manual labor, often working two jobs or more, while Tara, the significant breadwinner in the family, focused her attention on their daughter. Tara and Clive were not demonstrating outright conflict in their relationship, yet the pattern of cutoff with each other and closeness between the mother and the child was beginning to become evident. They also began to demonstrate ambivalence toward having more children and having an intimate sex life.

The creation of a genogram, and the subsequent therapeutic conversations that ensued, allowed the couple to reflect overtly on their family patterns and more recent nodal life events. This reflection contributed to the couple creating decidedly more differentiated positions, allowing them to grow in connectedness with each other. This began with both of them speaking about the nature of the relationship that was developing, their fears around the distance that was creeping into their relationship, and the way they were handling (or not handling) the responsibility for financial support and child care. A "turning toward each other" (Saks, 2004, p. 101) position began to ensue in their relationship. They began to speak about what they wanted sexually and in their family. Rather than become overly focused on their child, Tara began to focus more on herself and her health goals, while also discussing her concerns about their family and her sexual relationship with Clive. She began to move away from making excuses for herself, and overfunctioning in the relationship. She was able to give voice to her expectations of herself and in her partnership with Clive. Clive began to recognize and address his pattern of underfunctioning, and how that pattern was eroding his confidence in himself, in his work, and in his sexual relationship with Tara.

Cybernetic Systems Approach

While a cybernetic systems approach was not actually utilized overtly in this case, it became evident that Clive and Tara were communicating a pattern of ambivalence about having another child. They both present to counseling saying they want a better sexual relationship and another child, but what they are not saying is that their current family situation is difficult. Tara is deeply resentful of having to "carry all the weight" in their finances and child care and Clive is demonstrating how emasculated he has felt since being fired from his job. Tara's overfunctioning in their relationship only made Clive feel more inept and rejected. Clive's underfunctioning in the family prompted Tara to carry the weight of the child rearing and finances. This recursive pattern was playing out in their sexual relationship too. At first, Tara's sexual rejection early in the relationship was viewed from a position of virtue, and her subsequent initiation let them both know that she was ready to be sexual with Clive. Later his reliance on her being the initiator in bed mimicked the pattern in their overall relationship. Tara began to resent having to "ask for sex" and Clive perceived Tara's initiating as just another way she was in control of things in their lives. His burgeoning sexual rejection of her, through his remaining flaccid or losing his erection, created a symmetrical pattern between them in that she began to back down from initiating sex with him. The more Clive failed to become aroused the less Tara asked for sex; the less she asked, the more impotent he became. She found herself, when aroused, "taking care of it herself" by occasionally masturbating. Without intervention, it is likely that this pattern would continue until a larger crisis ensues in their marriage. Presenting to therapy at this time is a good sign that things can and will change.

Language Systems Approach

From a language systems approach, the therapist would be very curious to know who sees this as a problem, how they came to view it as a problem, and what they would want to see differently in their lives. Meaning-making questions such as: What does it mean to have "good sex?" What do you both believe about "good sex?" Who taught you how sex was supposed to be? How are your roles as "man" and "woman" contributing to or taking away from "good sex?" What does your culture, age, socioeconomic status, gender, ethnicity, and sexual orientation tell you about how "good sex" is supposed to be? How do your definitions differ, and how are they the same? What happens if this situation does not improve? Who else is involved in the investment in your relationship, and you two having "good sex?"

Another area of curiosity might involve mapping the effects of the problem (White, 2007) on Tara and Clive's relationship. How has "bad sex" (or whatever name they devise for the problem) interfered with their lives or prevented them from having a better life together? How have they managed, at times, to resist the negative effects of "bad sex?" Have they ever been able to give "bad sex" the slip, or make it go away? The therapist might be deconstructing the story of "bad sex" and its effects on Tara and Clive's relationship, while helping them come up with a preferred story about their relationship and their sexuality.

Interventions

Clive and Tara presented to therapy wanting what they did not have, a better sexual relationship and another child. What they had not been able to realize by themselves, and in prior treatment, is that their current sexual dysfunctions were a way that both were covertly communicating about the politics of their relationship and their current level of individual psychological functioning. If sexual dysfunction was assessed simply at the level of behavior, and the practitioner intervened by separating out their individual sexual pathologies and treating those pathologies individually, the relational difficulties would have not been respected or addressed. Tara and Clive's sexual functioning likely would not have improved without looking at the relational context. Their sexual difficulties might possibly have worsened with the idea that one or both are individually dysfunctional. A posture of blaming self or other might have been the resulting outcome of that treatment approach. With a relational approach, the couple could make sense of their interactional patterns, and understand how their difficult sexual patterns were a result of the politics of relationships in general, and their relationship more specifically. This allows a greater freedom to change. The change in beliefs and patterns of relating were easier and more affirming for Clive and Tara to address than looking at themselves as sexually dysfunctional or deficient.

After getting a three-generational history, hearing the extent to which the current narratives in their lives were distressing, and finding that their symmetrical patterns of relating around sex were contributing to their difficulties, the therapist was able to help position the couple, vis-a-vis those difficulties, in a respectful and meaningful way. Tara and Clive began to understand their sexual difficulties as a way both were trying to unintentionally maintain the intergenerational patterns, however difficult, as well as their own sense of integrity. No longer was Clive's flaccid penis a sign that he was incompetent or dysfunctional but rather it was a protest to feeling left out and powerless. His penis was telling him very important things about the nature of his relationship with Tara and how he wanted to change himself and their relationship. Tara's diminishing sexual desire and the body weight she was finding difficult to shed was also a way that she was protesting the relationship. She was exhausted with having the full burden of the finances and child care and did not know how to ask for what she wanted, sexually or otherwise. Her body, and her sexual (dys) functioning were saying what she could not. She was shutting down to Clive, sexually and otherwise, and finding closeness in her relationship with her daughter. In this context their sexual difficulties and (dys)functioning could be valued for what it was, a sign that they both needed to relate differently.

From this sense-making position, the couple felt validated and was then able to rely on the sexual difficulties as a way to invite them into different interactions and conversations. The therapist was able to have Tara and Clive speak to their own and each other's sexual symptoms. Tara felt herself "giving up much of the weight" of the relationship to Clive. They came up with new patterns of child care and finances. In fact, Clive's earnings were dedicated specifically to child care as he looked for more self-affirming work. At the last meeting, he was taking a certification course and was becoming "passionate" about a new line of work. Clive also hired a babysitter so that he and Tara could take a martial arts class together at a local studio. Both were looking to become more "playful" together. When, occasionally, their sexual difficulties resurfaced, they were able to speak to each other and address the symptoms. They were able to ask themselves and each other about their expectations. Was Clive getting "down on himself" about his competency at work? Was Tara reverting back to an overfunctioning position? No longer could the sexual difficulties be seen as pathological but rather as an ally in their relationship. The "dysfunction" was a way that their bodies were giving voice to what was difficult to address interpersonally. The difficulties invited them to spend time alone, as "best friends," asking each other and themselves about what was needed.

After "making sense of the symptoms" and the wisdom their bodies had in voicing what was difficult to address, the therapist had Tara and Clive employ a specific position in bed. When either of their symptoms arose, Tara and Clive would turn toward each other in bed, looking into each other's eyes, and give voice to the symptom. Tara may say, "I am exhausted and overwhelmed. I do not know how to ask you for what I want. I am afraid you will see me as demanding." Clive may find himself saying, "I feel incompetent and 'not enough' for you. I am afraid that you will see me as 'soft and ineffectual'." Their symptoms demanded that they reconnect on an emotionally intimate level. No longer did the symptom make them retreat from each other; rather, it was a sign to both that it was necessary to face each other and open up. It was often difficult for Tara and Clive to listen to the other's thoughts about the relationship. Tara was very disturbed at times with the idea that she was just "too much" to handle. Clive was very frightened that he was "not enough" for his wife. Rather than let these beliefs and ideas go unchallenged, the couple brought them to each other. This allowed them a gateway into intimacy rather than isolation.

Ethical and Legal Implications

The ethical systemic therapist must address the concerns that the client brings to therapy. While the therapist may want to impose a treatment goal on the client(s) or seek to pinpoint one person in the couple as the problem, the systemic therapist understands that the relationship is the client. This makes diagnosing one or the other with a sexual dysfunction very difficult. Even though one or both may fit criteria for a sexual dysfunction, the relational nature of the symptoms precludes an individual diagnosis. Clive and Tara both present fitting criteria for an individual diagnosis. Yet in exploring their dysfunctional sexual symptoms from a relational perspective, it becomes very clear that they arise from a difficult way of relating overall. To diagnose one or both would be to ignore the relational aspect of sexual dysfunction.

In Clive and Tara's case, both wanted to remain married and to have a better sexual relationship. This common goal between the two individuals makes it relatively easy for an ethical therapist to commence treatment. If one client in a couple wants to remain in the relationship and the other is unsure, or wants to leave the relationship, the ethical therapist would have to honor both positions. A period of discernment would likely ensue in treatment (Doherty, 2011).

If a therapist posited that one (or both) of the presenting clients were deficient or dysfunctional, and diagnosed them accordingly, it could have harmed the relationship. Focusing treatment on only one half of the couple might have exacerbated the tendency to assess blame, creating more of a division in the couple. For therapists holding the values of beneficence and nonmaleficence (Beauchamp & Childress, 2009), diagnosing one or both with a sexual dysfunction could have done more harm than good. In Clive and Tara's case, the symptoms were understood and framed as a way of communicating dysfunction in the relationship rather than in the individual. From a systems perspective, by diagnosing individuals, the therapist begins under a faulty therapeutic assumption and communicates an unclear message to the clients.

Tara and Clive were seen together for each session. Yet, often in couples therapy, the therapist may decide to split the couple up and see them individually. This can be helpful but it also can create ethical and legal dilemmas. At times, even when the clients agree on treatment goals, secrets can be revealed when a therapist is seeing the members of a couple individually. Secrets in couples therapy, like an ongoing or previous affair that is unknown to the other partner, can challenge therapists. Most therapists address this at the commencement of treatment, stating their policy about secrets (Wilcoxen et al., 2011). Even withstanding a no-secrets policy, one or both individuals in couples therapy can reveal a secret and a decision about terminating treatment must be considered. This can have ethical implications for the therapist's work with the couple. One or both may leave treatment feeling more hopeless about themselves and the relationship than at the onset of treatment. Without the therapist being able to reveal the secret, doubt about the nature of the sexual dysfunction may become internalized in one or both partners.

Finally, an ethical therapist must consider his or her expertise when it comes to the treatment of sexual dysfunction. Many systemically trained therapists do not hold the theoretical belief that pathology resides inside individuals but rather is the expression of the relationship. When treating and diagnosing a sexual dysfunction, therapists are obligated to practice within the scope of their competence (AAMFT, 2015, 3.1; 3.6; 3.10; ACA, 2014, C.2.a.; C.2.b.). If Clive and Tara did not report improvements in the symptoms and in their relationship, it would be vitally important for the therapist to seek out new treatments, clinical supervision, and further education around the presenting difficulties. Within a reasonable time, with no demonstrated change in the presenting problem, an ethical therapist would look toward referring the couple to a different practitioner (AAMFT, 2015, 1.9; 1.10; 1.11; ACA, 2014, A.11.a; A.11.c.).

DISCUSSION

As you continue to reflect on the case study and the overall approach, contemplate these questions:

- As you develop your treatment plan for Tara and Clive, you will need to collaborate with them to devise treatment goals. What goals do you have in mind for your work with this couple?

- What theoretical orientation is reflected in these goals? Is it a family systems orientation? If so, what influenced your decision to take a systems approach?
- What other kinds of techniques or interventions would you consider implementing in your treatment of Clive and Tara?
- How do these techniques relate to their *DSM-5* diagnoses?
- What ethical considerations stand out to you as most important as you develop a *DSM-5* diagnosis for Tara and Clive?

SUMMARY

In this chapter, we reviewed the history of the *DSM* as it has addressed concerns related to Sexuality Disorders. The current version of the *DSM* separates Disorders of Sexual Functioning From Paraphilias and Gender Dysphoria, and addresses only male and female difficulty with sexual arousal and satisfaction. These diagnoses were explored through a systems lens.

The chapter also included a review of the case of Tara and Clive, who are currently experiencing dissatisfaction with their sexual relationship. Assessment and treatment of Tara and Clive was discussed from systemic and relational theoretical approaches, using a genogram for both assessment and treatment. The therapist also utilized nonpathologizing questions (Anderson & Goolishian, 1988; White & Epston, 1990) and assessed the interactional behavioral patterns around their sexual relationship (Watzlawick et al., 1974).

Applying the concepts of diagnosis that form the basis of the *DSM-5* to the Sexuality Disorders, viewed through the lens of family systems, can be somewhat problematic in two ways. First, these diagnoses apply to individuals, not couples or families. It is not possible to say, for example, that both partners have Erectile Dysfunction or Female Sexual Interest/Arousal Disorder, even if the condition is affecting the relationship. Diagnosing each partner, or the relationship as a discreet entity, using the *DSM-5* diagnostic criteria, is not an accepted practice. Second, a diagnosis of a Sexual Dysfunction does not mesh with the assessment and treatment concepts included in the natural, cybernetic, or language systems theoretical approaches that are the foundations by which family systems are conceptualized. Lastly, systemic therapists who seek to intervene positively in a relationship keep their focus on the interaction between clients, rather than within the individual. To see one or both individuals as the culprit of the difficulty, rather than viewing the difficulty itself as vital information about the relationship, is to miss a giant opportunity to help clients forge a better relationship. When the symptom is seen as a way the clients communicate what may be difficult or impossible in their relationship, the helping practitioner can utilize the difficulty rather than seek to extinguish it. The symptom of sexual dysfunction is very likely to diminish or disappear when the couple has addressed the underlying relational issue(s).

The founders of the original *DSM* intended this book to aid and support clarity in communication between helping professionals as they attempted to treat those presenting with emotional distress. The assumption is that common terminology and conceptualization of the nature of the distress help counselors and other clinicians to "be on the same page" in terms of treatment. Those who shaped the current *DSM-5* declared their intent to further this mission toward a standard understanding of the nature of the various mental health disorders. While it is clear that the intent was to help professionals to better help clients and patients to recover, the pathway to this goal may still be obscured. From a family systems perspective, a *DSM-5* diagnosis may still miss the mark, conceptually. This may be because systems theory has never been predicated on the notion of individual diagnosis, and no one has ever been able to develop an accepted theory that allows for diagnosis of a whole system.

If there is a way to use the increased clarity about the symptom presentation to support communication between the clients, their counselor(s), and others who might impact their recovery (e.g., a medical provider, health insurance carriers, additional family members), then this goal might be achieved. The overall goal is always the well-being of the clients. The *DSM* from its first version to its latest iteration was always intended to further this goal. The assumption is that improved clarity and communication between all involved parties is an effective pathway to achieve client well-being. To that end, practitioners who seek to help clients with emotional distress may need to continue to bridge the communication gap by including a systems thought process in the discussion, and refining the blend of individual and systems approaches.

REFERENCES

Alarcon, R. D. (2014). Cultural Inroads in DSM-5. *World Psychiatry, 13*(3), 310–313. doi:10.1002/wps.20132

American Association for Marriage and Family Therapy. (2015). *AAMFT code of ethics.* Alexandria, VA: Author. Retrieved from https://www.aamft.org/imis15/AAMFT/Content/Legal_Ethics/Code_of_Ethics.aspx

American Counseling Association. (2014). *ACA code of ethics.* Alexandria, VA: Author. Retrieved from http://www.counseling.org/resources/aca-code-of-ethics.pdf

American Psychiatric Association. (1994). *Diagnostic and statistical manual of mental disorders* (4th ed.). Washington, DC: Author.

American Psychiatric Association. (2000). *Diagnostic and statistical manual of mental disorders* (4th ed., text rev.). Washington, DC: Author.

American Psychiatric Association. (2013). *Diagnostic and statistical manual of mental disorders* (5th ed.). Arlington, VA: American Psychiatric Publishing.

Anderson, H. (1997). *Conversation language and possibilities: A postmodern approach to therapy.* New York, NY: Basic Books.

Anderson, H., & Goolishian, H. (1988). Human systems as linguistic systems: Evolving ideas about the implications for theory and practice. *Family Process, 27*, 371–393.

Balon, R. R., Segraves, R. T., & Clayton, A. (2007). Issues for DSM-V: Sexual dysfunction, disorder, or variation along normal distribution: Toward rethinking DSM criteria of sexual dysfunctions. *The American Journal of Psychiatry, 164*(2), 198–200.

Beauchamp, T. L., & Childress, J. F. (2009). *Principles of biomedical ethics* (6th ed.). New York, NY: Oxford University Press.

Brotto, L. A. (2010). The DSM diagnostic criteria for hypoactive sexual desire disorder in women. *Archives of Sexual Behavior, 39*(2), 221–239. doi:10.1007/s10508-009-9543-1

Doherty, W. (2011, November/December). Treating the mixed agenda couple. *Psychotherapy Networker.* Retrieved from https://www.psychotherapynetworker.org/magazine/article/315/in-or-out

Fisch, R., Weakland, J. H., & Segal, L. (1982). *The tactics of change: Doing therapy briefly.* San Francisco, CA: Jossey-Bass.

Fischer, J., & Corcoran, K. (2013). *Measures for clinical practice and research: A sourcebook. Volume 1 Couples, families and children* (5th ed.). New York, NY: Oxford University Press.

Freedman, J., & Combs, G. (1996). *Narrative therapy: The social construction of preferred realities.* New York, NY: W. W. Norton.

Gehart, D. (2014). *Mastering competencies in family therapy: A practical approach to theories and clinical case documentation* (2nd ed.). Belmont, CA: Brooks/Cole.

Gottman, J., & Gottman, J. S. (2010). *Level I: Bridging the couple chasm Gottman couples therapy: A new research-based approach.* Seattle, WA: The Gottman Institute.

Graham, C. A. (2010). The DSM diagnostic criteria for female sexual arousal disorder. *Archives of Sexual Behavior, 39*(2), 240–255. doi:10.1007/s10508-009-9535-1

Green, S., & Flemons, D. (Eds). (2004). *Quickies: The Handbook of Brief Sex Therapy.* New York: W. W. Norton.

Kerr, M. E., & Bowen, M. (1988). *Family evaluation: An approach based on Bowen theory.* New York, NY: W. W. Norton.

Lebow, J. (2006). Relational disorders and relational processes in mental health. *Journal of Family Psychology, 20*(3), 432–437. doi:10.1037/0893-3200.20.3.432

McGoldrick, M. (2011). *The genogram journey: Reconnecting with your family.* New York, NY: W. W. Norton.

McGoldrick, M., Gerson, R., & Petry, S. (2008). *Genograms: Assessment and intervention* (3rd ed.). New York, NY: W. W. Norton.

O'Hanlon, B. (2004). Come again: Brief possibility-oriented sex therapy. In S. Green & D. Flemons (Eds.), *Quickies: Brief sex therapy.* New York, NY: W. W. Norton.

Regier, D. A., Narrow, W. E., Kuhl, E. A., & Kupfer, D. J. (2009). The conceptual development of DSM-V. *The American Journal of Psychiatry, 166*(6), 645–650.

Rober, P. (2002). Constructive hypothesizing, dialogic understanding and the therapist's inner conversation: Some ideas about knowing and not knowing in the family therapy session. *Journal of Marital and Family Therapy, 28*(4), 467–478.

Saks, R. (2004). Sexual dysfunction. In J. S. Gottman (Ed.), *The marriage clinic casebook.* New York, NY: W. W. Norton.

Schnarch, D. M. (1991). *Constructing the sexual crucible: An integration of sexual and marital therapy.* New York, NY: W. W. Norton.

Watzlawick, P., Weakland, J. H., & Fisch, R. (1974). *Change: Principles of problem formation and problem resolution.* New York, NY: W. W. Norton.

Weeks, G. R., Gambescia, N., & Hertlein, K. M. (2016). *A clinician's guide to systemic sex therapy* (2nd ed.). New York, NY: Routledge.

White, M. (2007). *Maps of narrative practice.* New York, NY: W. W. Norton.

White, M., & Epston, D. (1990). *Narrative means to therapeutic ends.* New York, NY: W. W. Norton.

Wilcoxen, S. A., Remley, T. P., Jr., & Gladding, S. T. (2012). *Ethical, legal, and professional issues in the practice of marriage and family therapy* (5th ed.). Boston, MA: Pearson.

World Health Organization. (2016). *International Statistical Classification of Diseases and Related Health Problems, 10th Revision, Version:2016* (online). Retrieved from http://apps.who.int/classifications/icd10/browse/2016/en

GENDER DYSPHORIA AND SYSTEMIC MEANING

Deb Coolhart and Brianna Mason

*A*s transgender people are becoming more visible in the media and online, people experiencing gender dysphoria have greater access to information about transgender identities and treatments to relieve gender dysphoria. People of all ages are pursuing gender transition and thus more and more families are dealing with adjusting to a family member's new gender identity. This chapter discusses the *Diagnostic and Statistical Manual of Mental Disorders* (5th ed.; *DSM-5;* American Psychiatric Association [APA], 2013) diagnosis of Gender Dysphoria and how it relates to family systems. The impact of relational and cultural factors on gender transition, how to assess and intervene in families, and the ethical and legal implications of gender transition in families are examined. Finally, we conclude with a case conceptualization of a family dealing with gender dysphoria.

DSM-5 AND FAMILY SYSTEMS

Gender transition is often seen as a process one goes through individually, exploring and making decisions about how to express an internal sense of gender. While the process is individual in some senses, there are clear impacts of gender dysphoria and transition on the entire family system. Each family member must change the way they see and relates to his or her transgender sibling, child, parent, or partner. First, we explore some of the core concepts and common language regarding gender variance as well as diagnostic characteristics of gender dysphoria. Then we discuss the ways in which gender transition is a process that involves the whole family.

Understanding Gender Variance

To begin, let us take a look at some of the common language used to discuss gender. At birth, doctors make an initial assessment of gender as either female or male; this is referred to as *gender assignment* (APA, 2013). Thus, in this chapter, we refer to this "natal gender" as *assigned gender*. *Gender identity*, on the other hand, is "a category of social identity and refers to an individual's identification as male, female, or occasionally, some category other than male and female" (APA, 2013, p. 451). When assigned gender and gender identity match, as they often do, a person is considered *cisgender*. Sometimes people feel as though their gender identity is at odds with their assigned gender, and this is where *gender variance* enters the picture. There are many different ways people can express and identify their gender variance, such as gender nonconforming, gender queer, nonbinary, or a variety of other terms that indicate a gender identity falls outside of the traditional options of only female and male. These diverse expressions may or may not be paired with a desire to undergo a gender transition, where persons take social and often medical steps to be seen externally as their gender identity. This official, and sometimes legal, change of gender has also been referred to as *gender reassignment* (APA, 2013). In this chapter, we use the term *affirmed gender* to refer to the gender that matches a person's gender identity.

People who meet the criteria for Gender Dysphoria typically identify within the gender binary as female or male. They have the experience of being assigned female or male at birth and strongly identify as the other gender. They often have a strong desire to be seen as their affirmed gender by others; they often experience distress about their physically gendered bodies, and desire changing their bodies to more closely match their affirmed gender. People meeting criteria for Gender Dysphoria most often identify themselves as trans or transgender. *Trans* or *transgender* can be used as umbrella terms to include the broad spectrum of persons whose gender identity differs from the assigned gender (APA, 2013). The term *transsexual* is sometimes used to refer specifically to the experience of people experiencing Gender Dysphoria; in other words, for a person who has undergone or desires gender transition (APA, 2013). Many people who fall under this definition of transsexual do not prefer the term; thus, for the purposes of this chapter, the term "transgender" is used for the latter, more specific description of people who meet criteria for Gender Dysphoria.

Diagnostic Features of Gender Dysphoria

In comparison to earlier editions, the *DSM-5* (APA, 2013) includes significant changes to the diagnosis of Gender Dysphoria, which was previously called Gender Identity Disorder. This is a less pathologizing approach to understanding transgender people where the identity is no longer seen as the problem. Instead, the gender dysphoria, or the feeling of discomfort with one's assigned gender, is addressed as the clinical concern. The *DSM-5* also specifies separate criteria for Gender Dysphoria in children as compared to in adolescents and adults. While both are characterized by a feeling of incongruence between assigned and affirmed gender paired with distress or impairment due to the incongruence, the criteria for Gender Dysphoria in children are described more concretely as behaviors, such as preferences for play, dress, and peers that align with affirmed gender. For both children and adolescents/adults, there is a desire to be one's affirmed gender and a discomfort with the anatomy of one's assigned gender. Additionally, the *DSM-5* suggests that the diagnosis of Gender Dysphoria be specified if it is occurring simultaneously with a disorder of sex development or if the person is posttransition (living full time in affirmed gender and pursuing medical gender transition).

The *DSM-5* provides several useful examples of associated features that support the diagnosis of Gender Dysphoria. Gender dysphoria can be either early onset, which begins in childhood, or late onset, which emerges in adolescence or later in life. During puberty, adolescents may take actions to hide the secondary sex characteristics of assigned gender, such as by binding breasts or genitals. Additionally, adolescents often desire hormone therapy and sometimes surgeries to align their bodies with affirmed gender. For adolescents and adults who are sexually active, it is common for sexual activity to be limited by not allowing partners to see or touch genitals. While some individuals with gender dysphoria desire both hormone therapy and surgeries, some are satisfied with one or the other.

Finally, of importance to note is that the *DSM-5* states that pretransition, adolescents and adults are at increased risk for suicides as well as suicidal ideation and attempts. While suicide risk may continue posttransition, distress may be buffered by supportive environments (APA, 2013). While the *DSM-5* does not specifically discuss family systems, it is implied that these supportive environments include families and other contexts such as school and work.

Gender Transition as a Family Process

Gender transition certainly includes an individual process, where the transgender person internally solidifies and accepts their gender identity and makes choices about steps in gender transition. However, gender transition is also very much a relational process and involves the entire family system. Family members find out about the transgender identity through discovery or disclosure, and this knowledge often shifts family relationships. Sometimes, family members are shocked, do not understand, struggle to accept, outright reject, or deny this new knowledge (Bockting, Knudson, & Goldberg, 2006), causing strain in relationships. Other times, family members may have already known about, suspected, or commit to understanding and supporting the gender identity, leading to improved relationships where the transgender person can now be more authentic in relationships. Family members may differ in their reactions and levels of support (Raj, 2008), which can lead to conflict. For example, one child may find it very easy to adjust to and support a parent's gender transition, whereas another child in the same family may react with anger, embarrassment, and emotional distance. This could cause conflict between siblings and/or cause the alliance between the supportive child and the transgender parent to alienate the other child. Similarly, parents may have varying reactions to their child's transgender identity, where one supports and the other rejects, causing parents to argue about how to move forward with their child's gender expression or transition. Regardless of how families respond to the transgender member, each family member has his or her own emotional experience (Lev, 2004); family members must learn to understand and relate to their transgender member in a different way (Coolhart, 2012; Veldorale-Griffin, 2014), and family relationships are impacted.

The systemic experience of gender transition also extends beyond the family system when the gender transition is disclosed outside of the family. The transgender person comes out to others at the workplace, in religious contexts, at school, and so forth, all of which can impact the family system. For example, a transgender parent may lose a job, impacting the family's financial situation, or be rejected from a religious community, leaving other family members to decide how/whether to remain a part of that community. Family members also go through their own process of coming out, deciding who, how, and when to tell about their transgender child, partner, sibling, or parent (Lev, 2004). They may encounter being asked questions about their transgender family member and/or be faced with situations of mistreatment where they must decide whether or not to act as an advocate. In fact, the relational implications of gender transition are so profound that the process really cannot be conceptualized and effectively supported clinically without considering the family system.

RELATIONAL AND CULTURAL FEATURES

As we begin to conceptualize gender transition as a systemic process, it is important to examine the relational and cultural factors that impact a family's experience. The emotional processes families go through upon learning about their transgender family member are discussed, followed by the ways in which other cultural identities and locations can sometimes pose additional challenges. Finally, protective factors are examined, with a focus on perhaps the most important dynamic that buffers the negative experiences of transgender people: family support.

Family Emotional Processes

Although the experiences of transgender people are often portrayed through an individual lens encompassing only the focus of the transgender person, some authors have described the relational process of coming out and dealing with the complexities of gender transition. These models generally describe the emotional processes of families moving from early stages of grappling with difficult feelings after discovery of the transgender identity and then eventually moving to later stages of understanding and acceptance. Table 14.1 summarizes the stages identified by these authors with each model progressively becoming more complex and allowing for more variability of both challenging and positive experiences.

Emerson (1996) was the first to address family emotional processes and proposed stages mimicking Kübler-Ross's (1969) bereavement model. These stages of grief include denial, anger, bargaining, depression, and acceptance. While Kübler-Ross's model may be useful for beginning to understand the experiences of family members, the experience of having a transgender family member should not be viewed as being as fatalistic as a family member's death; conceptualizing it in this way pathologizes the transgender identity and

TABLE 14.1 Family Emotional Process Stage Models

	Early Stages Marked by Struggle	Later Stages Marked by Increased Acceptance
Emerson (1996)	• Denial • Anger • Bargaining depression	• Acceptance
Ellis and Eriksen (2002)	• Posttraumatic reactions and bargaining • Anger and loss • Coping and seeking support	• Family members' internal change • Acceptance and wish for transgender person's happiness • Resilience and pride
Lev (2004)	• Discovery and disclosure • Turmoil	• Negotiation • Finding balance
Raj (2008)	• Denial • Acknowledgment • Tolerance	• Acceptance • Integration • Appreciation • Celebration

negates experiences of growth and transformation some families also experience. Ellis and Erikson (2002) also based their model on Kübler-Ross's (1969) stages of death and dying, although they provided greater depth and variability in the stages. They incorporated familial experiences of growth and change as well as positive aspects of the process, such as family members wishing for the transgender person's happiness as well as family resilience and pride.

Lev's (2004) more contemporary Family Emergence Model broke away from initial conceptualizations of family emotional processes as being similar to the process of death and dying. Her model describes the developmental stages the family system moves through, which includes: Discovery and Disclosure, Turmoil, Negotiation, and Finding Balance. Discovery and Disclosure includes family members being shocked and confused about their transgender family member. Stage two is Turmoil, meaning that family members experience stress and chaos while they grapple with this new information. In stage three, Negotiation takes place in that members negotiate "what they are comfortable living with regarding transition issues and what limits the family can set on gender expression" (Lev, 2004, p. 281). Finding balance is in stage four, which involves the family members integrating the transgender family member back into their system.

Raj (2008) discussed a transformative model where families move through stages on a continuum of Denial to Acceptance to Celebration. In this model, families participate in gaining increased understanding in order to move from one stage to the next. Families start in the Denial stage, characterized by ignorance, fear, hate, anger, guilt, and shame. After they gain an initial understanding of the transgender identity, they are able to move to Acknowledgment. Consequent stages include Tolerance, Acceptance, Integration, Appreciation, and Celebration. Raj's (2008) model moves away from viewing the process as pathological and allows space for families to experience positivity regarding their transgender member.

More recently, authors have begun to explore families' experiences of ambiguous loss in the families of transgender people (Norwood, 2013; Coolhart, Ritenour, & Grodzinski, under review). *Ambiguous loss* is any loss that is incomplete or uncertain and can take two forms: (a) psychological absence and physical presence and (b) physical absence and psychological presence (Boss, 1999). It has been suggested that parents of transgender children may experience both types of ambiguous loss (Wahlig, 2015). In the first type, the child's psychological existence as a certain gender may be perceived as gone (psychological absence); however, the parents still physically have a child (physical presence). In the second type, the child's physical presence as a certain gender is gone (physical absence), while much of the child's personality and psychological sense of self are present (psychological presence). Because of the complex and uncertain feelings involved in ambiguous loss, it can be very stressful and lead to feelings of being stuck or frozen in grief (Boss, 1999). Parents may feel that they are experiencing the living death of their child or confusion because they are feeling loss even though their child is still alive. When parents are able to see that their child is the same person, that they are able to become the person they have always been, and that their child can finally be happy, transformation is experienced and the feelings of grief can become unstuck (Coolhart et al., under review).

When family relationships are complicated by other dynamics, experiencing this transformation can be particularly challenging. For example, if a mother feels very close to her assigned daughter and is overprotective, overinvolved, and overcontrolling regarding her child's choices (Parent–Child Relational Problem), it may be particularly difficult for her to accept that her child is actually a son (APA, 2013). This mother may have to therapeutically address her own investment in her child's outcomes before being able to process her grief and experience transformation. Additionally, cultural factors may impact how and if a parent can experience transformation. For example, if parents hold religious beliefs or are impacted by cultural values that invalidate transgender experiences, it may be more difficult for them to move through ambiguous loss.

Cultural Intersectionality and Risk Factors

Transgender people represent a great deal of diversity with regard to factors such as age, race, socioeconomic status (SES), and religion. These intersectional identities often have a great impact on how transgender people experience discrimination in society, in general, and often, within their families. Thus, it is important to consider the other ways in which transgender clients are privileged and/or marginalized.

Gender

It is important to recognize that the experiences of transgender women (people with an assigned male gender who identify as female) differ from the experiences of transgender men (people with an assigned female gender who identify as male). Transgender women in particular experience transphobia early on within their family systems, where feminine behavior is discouraged and often shamed, not permitted, or punished. These messages may be received overtly or subtly, but both have negative consequences on the transgender person within the family and can lead to a process of internalizing the discrimination, which consequently leads to lower self-esteem and shameful feelings of oneself (Sevelius, 2013). Transgender men also often receive early pressure around gender, where feminine behaviors and clothing are suggested and sometimes forced. However, in general, families (and society) afford little "girls" more flexibility to behave in masculine ways and even positively call them "tomboys," whereas little "boys" displaying feminine behavior get ridiculed as "sissies."

These gendered differences extend beyond the family and into adulthood. Transgender people are notoriously mistreated when seeking medical services. Transgender men report more discrimination in health care, whereas transgender women report being refused treatment more often (Grant et al., 2011). While seeking employment it is often difficult for transgender people in general; transgender women may face more discrimination in this context as well. One possible way of understanding these differences is that transgender men may "pass" more often, that is, blend in and be perceived as their affirmed male gender. Testosterone has powerful effects on the body, such as lowered voice and facial hair, which often make transgender men more difficult to identify visibly. Thus, not standing out as transgender, in addition to occupying the socially privileged position of male, may provide transgender men with more access to resources in comparison with transwomen. On the other hand, if a transgender woman's body masculinized during adolescence and adulthood, estrogen cannot reverse many of the effects, making transgender women more visible. Therefore, transgender women may be more likely to be unemployed, homeless, and forced to engage in survival sex (Sevelius, 2013). Not surprisingly then, transgender women are more likely to be HIV positive (Grant et al., 2011).

Race

Transgender people of color face marginalization, not only due to their transgender status, but also due to their ethnic minority status. Because of these multilayered levels of oppression, this population faces much greater risk of negative mental and physical health outcomes (Balsam, Molina, Beadnell, Simoni, & Walters, 2011). Additionally, transgender people of color are at increased risk for violence, mistreatment, poverty, and discrimination in employment (Grant et al., 2011) as compared to White transgender people. They also experience increased discrimination within medical health care settings, with Latinos/as transgender people expressing the most alarming rates of mistreatments by doctors. When compared to their White counterparts, African American transgender people receive significantly lower rates of health care coverage. Perhaps due to these systemic barriers, transgender people of color have higher rates of HIV infection, with African American transgender people being 10 times more likely to be HIV positive when compared to national rates of African Americans (Grant et al., 2011). As previously discussed, transgender women experience increased challenges and discrimination, so the intersection between being a transgender woman and also a person of color causes particularly detrimental mistreatment. For example, the rate of violence against transgender people is highest for transgender women of color.

Socioeconomic Status

In the lesbian, gay, bisexual, transgender, and queer community, transgender people typically experience the highest rates of employment discrimination. They often report high unemployment rates as well as earning less than $25,000 annually (Badgett, Lau, Sears, & Ho, 2007). Not only do they have higher rates of unemployment, transgender people experience harassment at work, loss of jobs or careers, and live in dire poverty (Grant et al., 2011). Lower SES status may increase the risks for other negative outcomes, such as negative self-concept, increased rates of mental disorder comorbidity, and school dropout (APA, 2013). According to the National Transgender Discrimination Survey (Grant et al., 2011), transgender people who earn less than $10,000 a year have a 54% risk of committing suicide. Level of education also impacted suicidality, where those who had less than a college degree reported over 15% more chance of a suicide attempt.

Age

The intersection in transgender identity and age presents an interesting point of discussion. Those who fall in the 18 to 44 years of age range report the highest rates of suicide attempts. These statistics are contrary to the general population, which show that older adults have the highest number of attempts (Grant et al., 2011). This could be related to family rejection as well as struggles in the school setting. Bullying can be so bad that parents sometimes have to change their children's schools (Kuvalanka, Weiner, & Mahan, 2014, p. 371). Harassment from other children and even teachers at school may occur when transgender youth express themselves in gender nonconforming ways. This may contribute to youth refusing to go to school because they do not want to experience the pressure of dressing in clothes that do not match their internal sense of gender (APA, 2013). There is a correlation between increased rates of suicide attempts and youth who report being bullied because of their transgender identity. Not only do transgender youth experience peer harassment, but also report being assaulted and bullied by authority figures in school such as teachers. If the perpetrators are in fact their teachers, suicide rates strikingly increase (Grant et al., 2011). Little is written about older transgender adults; however, it should not be assumed that they are not also experiencing discrimination and mistreatment. In one study, about 65% of transgender older adults, 50 years and older, reported experiencing emotional abuse more than once and over 40% reported having at least one experience with health care discrimination (Cook-Daniels & Munson, 2010).

Protective Factors

Transgender people face increased vulnerabilities such as family challenges, sexual and physical violence, poverty, and transgender-related discrimination in health care, housing, and employment (Bradford, Reisner, & Xavier, 2013; Grant et al., 2011; Kenagy, 2005; Nuttbrock et al., 2010). Also, transgender people often experience poorer mental and physical health outcomes, such as lower quality of life, increased suicide attempts, and higher rates

TABLE 14.2 Outcomes Associated With Parental Support and Rejection

Parental Support	Parental Rejection
Self-esteem	Suicide ideation and attempts
Social support	Depression
General health status	Illegal drug use
Higher GPAs	Alcohol abuse
School belonging	Smoking
Life satisfaction	Unprotected sex
Overall mental health	Homelessness
	Sex work

GPA, grade point averages.

Sources: Grant et al. (2011); Ryan, Huebner, Diaz, and Sanchez (2009); Ryan, Russell, Huebner, Diaz, and Sanchez (2010); Travers et al. (2012); Watson, Barnett, and Russell (2016).

of depressive symptoms and anxiety (Budge, Adelson, & Howard, 2013; Goldblum et al., 2012; Grant et al., 2011; Newfield, Hart, Dibble, & Kohler, 2006; Nuttbrock et al., 2010). Even in the face of these stressors, transgender people often demonstrate resiliency in order to survive and thrive under such stress. The Minority Stress Model (Meyer, 1995, 2003) suggests that minorities experience additional stressors, which include external/environmental discrimination, the anticipation of mistreatment, and internalized prejudice. In order to help buffer the negative effects of these stressors, transgender people may experience social support, or community resilience, which can serve as protective factors (Meyer, 2015).

Perhaps the most important protective factor for transgender people is family support. Several studies (summarized in Table 14.2) have demonstrated that parental support is associated with multiple positive mental and physical health outcomes. Conversely, parental rejection has detrimental effects such as life-threatening behaviors and overall well-being. Therefore, transgender people with supportive family members are more likely to be stable with regard to housing, mental health, school performance, and general happiness.

In addition to, or in the absence of, family support, transgender people can experience the protective factor of community resilience through other forms of social support. Friends, coworkers, families of choice, and/or connections with transgender communities can also buffer the negative effects of transgender minority stress. Also, having access to other social privileges may aid in the protection against transgender distress. As discussed previously, the intersections of other marginalized identities often complicate experiences of discrimination and oppression; experiencing other privileges, such as maleness, Whiteness, higher SES, or education, may buffer experiences of discrimination and make it easier to access resources, such as employment and medical care.

FAMILY SYSTEMS ASSESSMENTS

Because families are greatly impacted by a transgender member's gender transition, it is important to assess how different family relationships are being impacted. This section explores areas and initial questions for assessing family systems with regard to gender. For many families seeking therapy, there is also an interest in taking steps toward medical gender transition. Because receiving these medical interventions often requires the support of a clinician, the readiness process for medical gender transition is also discussed.

General Areas for Family Assessment

Oftentimes, a transgender adult initially presents alone in therapy or, when a transgender youth is involved, one parent may accompany the youth. Because access to other family members is often limited at first, it is important to ask questions to gauge how the larger family system is being impacted. There are a variety of ways family members may be affected by the transgender identity, such as a sibling being harassed by peers, a partner threatening to leave if gender transition is pursued, a grandparent rejecting a parent because they are supportive of a transgender youth, a parent refusing to see his or her child while dressed in affirming clothing, or aunts/uncles forbidding their children from seeing their cousin. Thus, it is important to broadly assess not just the immediate family system, but the extended family system as well.

Because family support is vitally important for transgender people, assessing support and opposition and their impacts is at the core of the family systems assessment. It is important to understand whether the transgender person is facing an immediate risk such as being kicked out of the home, having medical treatment or financial resources withheld, or experiencing abuse. If these threats to physical well-being are present, they must be attended to first. Other areas for assessment include finding out who in the family is being affected, if distress is present, how relationships are being impacted, and what cultural identities may be intersecting with how the family understands the transgender identity. If possible, all implicated family members should be involved in treatment in order to work toward decreased distress and increased understanding and support.

Bockting et al. (2006) suggested three areas of inquiry to discuss with loved ones when they become engaged in therapy: Disclosure, Impact on Relationships, and Support Resources. Assessing the area of Disclosure includes finding out when and how the loved one found out about the transgender person's identity, how they reacted and how they feel about it now, and whether other people know about the transgender identity and how they feel about that. Impact on Relationships includes assessing for fears or questioning about the transgender identity, the loved ones' relationship with transgender people and any impacts on their own identity, how they feel about gender-affirming behaviors (e.g., clothing and hormone treatment), and how gender is impacting other relationships. Assessing the area of Support Resources includes finding out if the loved ones have any connection to other transgender people and/or their loved ones and how they see their relationship to the transgender community in the future. Assessment in these various areas provides information about how to intervene relationally in these couples and families, attending to the relationships that are most strained and building on relationships that are supportive.

Readiness Process for Medical Gender Transition

Many clients experiencing gender dysphoria wish to take steps toward medical gender transition and seek the assistance of mental health professionals in that process. Historically, physicians and surgeons have required letters from mental health professionals, stating that clients are ready for hormones and surgeries, and many still do. Because of this requirement, transgender clients often feel like they are being "tested" by mental health professionals in order to receive medical treatments. For a more thorough discussion of this ethical issue, see the section "Ethical and Legal Implications." In order to be more client centered and transaffirmative, we advocate for the use of the term *readiness process*, rather than *assessment* for medical gender transition. The readiness process involves transgender clients and their families carefully examining the impacts of treatments and collaboratively deciding, with the assistance of a clinician, that they are ready to undergo such treatments. The result of the readiness process is the clinician's letter of "support" versus letter of "recommendation," since clinicians should not really recommend that clients undergo medical treatments; rather we should support them in their decision to do so.

Detailed therapeutic guides have been developed for navigating this readiness process, both for adults (Bockting et al., 2006; Coolhart, Provancher, Hager, & Wang, 2008) and for youth and their families (Coolhart, Baker, Farmer, Melhaney, & Shipman, 2013). See Coolhart et al.'s (2008, 2013) tools for comprehensive lists of questions to discuss with clients going through the readiness process for medical gender transition treatments. The focus here is on areas in the readiness process specifically relating to the family system. While many adults go through the readiness process individually, it sometimes makes sense to involve family members, such as partners or children, since gender transition impacts couple and parent–child relationships. When youth are going through the readiness process, it is essential for at least one parent to be involved (and sometimes other family members), as they need to be ready for their child to undergo changes. Parents also need to consent to medical treatments and facilitate youths' access to medical providers.

The first domain in the readiness process related to the family system is Early Awareness of Gender and Family Context (Coolhart et al., 2008, 2013). Transgender people and their families are often aware of gender variance in early childhood (Lev, 2004). Thus, clinicians should assess when the transgender person first experienced and/or expressed gender variance and how the family responded. Families' responses vary widely, ranging from full support to punishment and abuse. These early responses can be very informative in terms of how transgender people form their identities and internalize feelings of shame. Clinicians should ask about what clients learned from their families about gender and how they fit and/or did not fit in with these expectations. When gender variance is not supported and youth experience "gender shame," they often feel humiliation and learn to hide these parts of self (Stone Fish & Harvey, 2005). They learn to play the role that is expected of them and believe that their parents/families do not love them for who they are. Not surprisingly, transgender people who have not been supported in their gender variance may delay and fear coming out to family members. In terms of the readiness process, these fears need to be confronted because medical gender transition eventually causes physical changes that cannot be hidden, making eventual disclosure inevitable.

The second domain to be considered systemically is Parental/Family Attunement to Affirmed Gender (Coolhart et al., 2013), and refers to how ready a family system is to begin gender transition. It is especially relevant for transgender youth due to their high level of dependence on their families, and especially their parents. Because parents typically experience a host of complex emotions upon the discovery of their child's transgender identity, it is important to sort through these feelings during the readiness process. Questions should be asked to understand how each family member is coping with a new understanding of the youth, whether there are differences in how parents and/or siblings are processing the changes, and how relationships are being impacted. Also to be discussed is how family members anticipate adjusting to the use of a new name and pronouns as well as increased gender expressions that match the youth's identity, such as clothing and hairstyle. In some families, the level attunement may be very high and families are ready to move forward in gender transition. In other families, when attunement is very low and parents are not supportive of physical changes, family therapy is necessary before moving forward with gender transition (see the section "Family Systems Interventions").

Finally, while engaging in the readiness process with a systemic lens, it is essential to explore the domain of Current Intimate Relationship (Coolhart et al., 2008, 2013). The partners of transgender people are greatly impacted by gender transition and often have to consider whether or not they can remain in the relationship. While some relationships certainly weather the change of gender transition and sometimes grow closer as a result, some partners are not able to adjust to this new relationship dynamic. Also, if there are children in the family, they may have their own struggles with adjusting to a new view of their parent. Further, if the transgender identity has been hidden for some time and the partner feels betrayed by this new knowledge, sometimes they restrict access to their children. Thus, in making decisions about moving forward in gender transition, it is important to consider potential consequences on couple and parent–child relationships.

Clearly, there are many dynamics in the family system that can present obstacles in the readiness process for gender transition. While these challenges may delay taking steps in transition, in most cases they should not be viewed as reasons not to transition. Rather, challenges should be faced clinically and the family system should work toward greater understanding. When family members are highly rejecting, changes and conflicts in family relationships may be inevitable. However, it is possible to work towards tolerance and acceptance. For most transgender people who desire transition, the desire does not go away. Therefore, deciding not to transition often is just delaying the inevitable, causing ongoing distress for the transgender person. At times it may make sense to delay transition, for example, waiting until children are out of the home or until a transgender youth with unsupportive parents turns 18 years of age. Clinicians should not be making decisions about the appropriate timing of gender transition; rather they should facilitate exploring all of the areas of support and opposition and help clients make their own decisions about what is best for them.

FAMILY SYSTEMS INTERVENTIONS

As discussed earlier, transgender people with supportive families fare better with regard to mental and physical health outcomes. Thus, it is vital for clinicians to intervene in families using a gender-affirmative approach. Also, depending on where the transgender person is located in the family system (i.e., parent, youth), there are specific challenges with which families may be dealing. Therefore, we discuss important areas for intervention, first for transgender youth and their families, and then for transgender adults and their couple and parenting relationships.

The Gender-Affirmative Approach

In order to effectively intervene in the family systems of transgender people, it is essential that clinicians take a gender-affirmative approach. At the center of a gender-affirmative approach is destigmatizing and normalizing gender nonconforming expressions (Malpas, 2011). The pathology and distress associated with transgender identities is not located in the transgender individual, but rather in the social constructs that privilege heterosexuality and cisgenderism and create prejudice, discrimination, and oppression for transgender people (Coolhart, 2012). Thus, as gender-affirmative clinicians, we are assisting families to see transgender identities as a natural variation of humanity. We are aiming to help transgender clients express gender in ways that are most comfortable for them (Hidalgo et al., 2013). We are normalizing clients' gender expressions and, especially in working with transgender youth, we are assisting parents in helping their child develop self-esteem (Lev, 2004). According to Ehrensaft (2011), "Listening to children and paying attention to what they are telling you about their authentic gender self is the cornerstone of helping them grow healthy and strong" (p. 103).

Transgender adults may be apprehensive or hesitant to seek therapy due to previous experiences of discrimination and being pathologized by mental health providers. Thus, particularly with adults, it may be important for clinicians to be transparent and direct, clearly communicating a gender-affirmative stance. This may include advocating for the transgender population in a variety of ways including politically, socially, and economically. Additionally, clinicians should inform themselves about the history and evolution of the transgender community with regard to appropriate terminology (Bockting et al., 2006; Carroll, Gilroy, & Ryan, 2002; Zamboni, 2006).

Interventions With Transgender Youth and Families

When transgender youth and their families seek therapy, they may be starting from many different places. While some parents may be totally supportive of their child's gender identity, others may be struggling to accept it. First, we discuss how to decide where to start with these families, based on the level of support. We introduce the idea of family attunement and outline strategies for families to increase attunement. Finally, we discuss how to explore with families options for their child's gender expression and transition.

Deciding Where to Start

Clinicians working with transgender youth and their families must create a delicate balance between supporting parents' emotional process about their child's gender expression and creating safety for the youth (Coolhart, in press). The first step in working with these families is assessing the parents' level of support for their child's gender identity and expression. The ultimate goal is to help parents achieve attunement to their child's gender. Attunement goes beyond acceptance and tolerance of gender expression, to where parents reach harmony, understanding, and peace with their child's gender (Coolhart, in press). Parental responses can have a significant impact on youth's self-acceptance, well-being, emotional and social adjustment, and safety (Malpas, 2011). For example, parents who tell children that their gender identities are not true, that it is wrong, or that they refuse to accept it, may be setting the stage for children's development of depression, anxiety, and suicidal ideation. On the other hand, parents who respond with a desire to understand, protect, and help their child may be helping children gain confidence and comfort in who they are. Thus clinical work with parents aims to help them learn to love their children as they are, not send messages of disappointment, and become grounded in their role of positive parenting (Coolhart, 2012; Lev, 2004).

As shown in Figure 14.1, when parents are struggling to accept their child's gender identity, therapy must take a detour before exploring gender expression and transition options. While a youth may want to move forward with gender transition, such as changing their name or starting hormones, parents may not be ready for these steps. The clinician must first work to increase parents' attunement to their child's gender.

What follows are interventions to be used with youth and parents, first in the process of increasing attunement, and then in the exploration of gender transition options.

Increasing Attunement

First, it may be important to have separate sessions with the parents without the youth present (Coolhart, 2012). Parents are often working through difficult emotions and need a space to verbalize their negative feelings about their child's gender. Clinicians can listen and support this process, while at the same time coach parents about what is appropriate to discuss with their child and what thoughts and feelings may be hurtful to their child, and thus are better dealt with privately. Concurrently, clinicians can also meet with the youth alone in order to provide a space to safely express gender and gain an

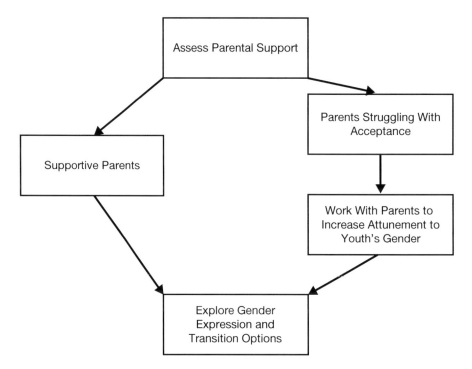

FIGURE 14.1 Courses of therapy with transgender youth and families.

understanding of their experiences and desires for gender. Once parents are able to manage their emotional reactivity and youth can feel safe in sessions, conjoint sessions can resume or begin. In other words, when parents are able to process their negative feelings (e.g., "I hate that you are doing this") and transphobic beliefs (e.g., "Being transgender is a disease") with the clinician rather than the child, they are able to send more affirming and loving messages directly to their child, preventing further damage to their child's sense of self.

A primary task in working with parents is processing their feelings of fear and loss (Coolhart, in press). Parents often fear for the safety and well-being of their child or the fear of condemnation (Brill & Pepper, 2008). These fears are understandable given that we live in a society where transgender people are often misunderstood and mistreated. Thus, clinicians can validate these fears, point out that they are grounded in parents' love for their child, and help parents understand that their child now needs even more support and protection in the face of possible discrimination. Parents can be made aware of the research on the importance of parental support (previously discussed) and the role that their support plays in their child's resiliency. When parents' anxiety is decreased, they can have more control over their fears and can recognize that their needs are separate from their child's needs (Malpas, 2011).

Processing and managing parents' fears can sometimes be complicated by cultural intersections. When religion or specific cultural beliefs reinforce transnegative thoughts and feelings, these belief systems may need to be gently challenged and expanded to make room for acceptance. For example, when families have religious beliefs that say that being transgender is wrong, some families are able to question and reevaluate these values, sometimes finding new ways to approach their faith and/or finding new faith communities. With other families that are less flexible about their beliefs, the therapeutic task may be exploring the role of unconditional love for children within their belief system and discussing how parents may be able to lead with those values.

Loss is another feeling that is common for parents and often needs to be processed clinically. For example, they may struggle with children wanting to change their birth name because it may have special meaning, or they may feel as if they are losing their son or daughter, brother, sister (Zamboni, 2006). They may even feel confused about their feelings of loss because the loss is ambiguous, where they are not actually losing a child, though it feels that way. Clinicians can validate these feelings and sit with parents through these painful emotions, helping them move forward and see that their child is not going anywhere and that they are just becoming more authentic in their self.

When parents are adjusting to their child's identity, they often do not have a lot of knowledge about transgender people, and what they do know may not be accurate; thus clinicians should provide accurate psychoeducational information about gender diversity and transgender identities to help parents become more aware (Lev, 2004; Malpas, 2011). Part of this process may involve helping parents deconstruct their own beliefs about transgender people, examining where they come from and whether they hold up against accurate information (Coolhart, in press). Education can lead to transformation for parents, moving from being uneducated to experts, and this transformation can lead to advocacy for their child (Kuvalanka et al., 2014).

In working to increase attunement, it may also be necessary to consider other relational dynamics within the family (see Box 14.1). For example, parents might be in conflict around their level of support (Raj, 2008) and this could be causing conflict or confusion in the family. Sometimes, the relationship distress may reach such difficulty resolving these conflicts that it causes chronic sadness and anger in the relationship, meeting criteria for Relationship Distress With Spouse or Intimate Partner. In this case, couples therapy should be utilized to seek common ground and compromise in order to better support the child. Other times, parents may have concerns about siblings being told about the transgender identity or about how they are responding to it. In some families, siblings' responses to the gender identity may be so extreme that they are abusive to the transgender sibling, causing impairment in family functioning and meeting criteria for Sibling Relational Problem. Clinicians can coach parents about how to talk with siblings and/or engage them in family therapy. Siblings (or other family members) may also need space to process their emotions, such as feelings of losing a brother or sister (Zamboni, 2006). When parents' and families' level of attunement has increased to better support the child's gender identity and expression, conjoint sessions with parents and youth can begin to explore options for gender expression and transition.

Exploring Options for Gender Expression/Transition

When working with youth, it is often very important to youth to be allowed to express their affirmed gender. Depending on the age of the youth and the level of safety in their environment, gender expression and transition may take various forms and should be negotiated delicately. For example, for a 7-year-old assigned boy, living in a conservative rural area, who is already being bullied at school, it may be most comfortable to first explore

---

BOX 14.1 Interventions for Increasing Attunement

- Beginning with separate sessions for parents and child
- Processing parents' fear and loss
- Providing accurate gender education
- Addressing differences in level of support between parents
- Including siblings or other family members

female gender expression at home. The child should be asked about a preference for name and pronouns and the child's wishes should be respected. So, for this 7-year-old, perhaps she prefers female pronouns and a chosen name, but wants them used only at home for now, since others do not yet know about the transgender identity. Clinicians can explore with families how/when/if they want to come out to others, such as extended family, friends, and people at school or in their religious communities. Again, the child's wishes should be respected regarding who knows and when and how they are told.

For another family, it may make sense to move immediately to affirmed gender expression outside the home, to use chosen name and pronouns in all settings, and pursue pubertal blockers or hormone therapy. Often, youth who are approaching or experiencing puberty feel distress about their bodies changing in ways that are not congruent with their affirmed gender and feel urgency about beginning hormones. In this case, clinicians should begin the readiness process for medical gender transition as previously discussed.

Interventions With Transgender Adults in Families/Couples

Even though many transgender people begin experiencing gender dysphoria in childhood, sometimes they do not disclose or address this experience until adulthood. For others, it is not until adulthood that gender dysphoria manifests or becomes clear. This section discusses some of the unique experiences of people who come out as transgender and seek help in adulthood. Specific challenges and interventions for couples are discussed followed by those for transgender parents and their children.

Coming Out and Seeking Help in Adulthood

Many transgender people do not disclose their transgender identity to their families until adulthood due to the stigmatization and discrimination they face in society and in their families of origin. Sometimes a shift in their lives, such as retirement, or a loss, such as of a parent or spouse, prompts coming out to families and friends. Other times, transgender individuals may be in extreme distress because of their hidden identity (Zamboni, 2006). It is common for people to spend many years attempting to fulfill assigned gender roles, which often includes getting married and having children. When hiding a transgender identity finally becomes unbearable and the person comes out, it is understandably difficult for families to adjust to the new information. Historically, it has been assumed that disclosing a transgender identity in adulthood would automatically mean losing a spouse and children (Lev, 2004), and sometimes that does happen, though many times, families find ways to stay connected and integrate the new understanding of the family member.

Raj (2008) proposed a Transformative Therapeutic Model for working with the loved ones of transgender people. According to this model, it is vital to listen to every member of the family system's narratives about pertinent themes and patterns as they relate to the transition. Then the clinician can begin validating the array of concerns, feelings, and thoughts family members have as well as challenging them about assumptions and myths regarding gender. Sometimes situations that exist in a partnership or family system may be initially seen by the family as detrimental, but can be deconstructed and reframed into also being an opportunity. Families can then experience transformation, which occurs through *resolving* or *dissolving*. Resolving happens when the clinician is able to support the family's developmental process to evolve and transform, thus resolving conflicts over time. Since resolution is not every couple's or family's reality, dissolving takes place in an instance of divorce or loss of the transgender family member. Clinicians can help families dissolve in ways that are respectful and as constructive as possible, maintaining some level of contact between family members. Clinicians then help families strategize about changing roles and identities and future identity management/disclosure (Raj, 2008).

Couples

When a transgender partner decides to pursue gender transition, the reaction of the cisgender partner can vary widely and often depends on the way in which the disclosure happens. For a couple who has been in a heterosexual marriage for many years with no discussion of gender variance, the cisgender partner may feel shocked, betrayed, and devastated after finding out his or her spouse is transgender. On the other hand, for couples who have previously discussed gender variance, or who already perform roles outside of gender norms, the decision to pursue gender transition may not come as such a surprise. In either instance though, gender transition raises challenges in the couple requiring adaptation and change.

Gender transition can be an all-consuming process for the transgender person, being preoccupied with all of the important changes they are experiencing. This can sometimes cause cisgender partners to feel left out or that their needs are not being considered. Clinicians can help couples balance the needs of both partners, validating that gender transition is a very exciting and meaningful process and, at the same time, the cisgender partner's needs are also important. Cisgender partners may feel that their sense of comfort, normalcy, or stability is lost and constantly thinking about gender transition can be overwhelming. It may be helpful for couples to agree to have some time together where gender transition is not discussed, such as a gender-free date night, to provide a break for the cisgender partner.

Through gender transition, couples may experience shifts in gender roles and/or sexual orientation and partners sometimes need to examine or redefine their sexual orientation (Raj, 2008). For instance, if a transgender man previously identified as a lesbian and had a cisgender female partner, they may identify as heterosexual after gender transition; at the same time, the lesbian-identified partner must also reconsider her identity in terms of sexual orientation, now being partnered with a man (Lev, 2004). Clinicians should allow space for discussion of identities and roles and how they may shift and be impacted by the transitioning partner. Additionally, couples may experience a change in their social identities. Couples who were previously identified as heterosexual may face new experiences of marginalization as a queer couple (Lev, 2004). Conversely, couples previously identified as queer now appear heterosexual and may feel loss around their identification with the queer community (Coolhart et al., 2008).

Transgender Parents and Their Children

When a parent pursues gender transition, children may feel the loss of a mother or father figure and struggle to adjust to their parent's new role (Zamboni, 2006). It can be stressful for children to figure out what to call their parent and to alter how they view their parent (Veldorale-Griffin, 2014). Thus, clinicians should facilitate family discussions, allowing space for children to express sadness, grief, and frustration. Sometimes it is difficult for transgender parents to hear their children's struggles with transition as they may feel guilty, selfish, or responsible for these feelings. However, clinicians should coach parents to tolerate this discomfort and really listen to their children. It is important that children feel that their parents can hear their experiences and take care of them through this change. As previously discussed, transition can be an all-consuming experience, and transgender parents should be conscious of maintaining their role as a parent. Sometimes children feel like their relationship with the transgender parent no longer feels like a parent–child relationship (Veldorale-Griffin, 2014), which can leave them feeling alone in having to adjust through transition.

The developmental stage of children may have an impact on how they react and adjust to gender transition of a parent. Preschool-age children seem to have the easiest time adapting to a parent's transition, whereas adolescents often struggle the most (White & Ettner,

2004). This may be due to the level of influence peers have during adolescence and teens may worry about disclosing their parent's gender transition to friends. Children may experience stress around bullying (Veldorale-Griffin, 2014); thus a close eye should be kept on peer experiences so that children can be protected. It may be important to consider a child's developmental stage when choosing to disclose a parent's transgender identity. In general, disclosure should happen because withholding the information may actually be more difficult for children; however, for a child in later adolescence, it may be better to wait until the child is in early adulthood (White & Ettner, 2004).

In order to support children's adjustment through gender transition, clinicians should help parents maintain collaborative, constructive coparenting practices. When there are high levels of conflict between parents, children surely struggle more. In fact, factors within the parental relationship may impact children more than the gender transition itself, such as being separated from either parent, the cisgender spouse opposing the transition, and parental conflict about the transition (White & Ettner, 2004). When parents are able to build healthier relationships with each other, they are also able to build healthier relationships with their children (White & Ettner, 2007). High levels of conflict can lead to children feeling like they are being put in the middle of their parents' relationship, which can be very stressful (Veldorale-Griffin, 2014). So once again, parents need to remain conscious of maintaining their roles as parents, which can be challenging during times of high stress. Clinicians can coach parents in this process and inform them that parent–child relationships have the potential of improving through the course of gender transition, where the transgender parent is able to be who they really are, leading to more comfortable, authentic relationships (Veldorale-Griffin, 2014).

ETHICAL AND LEGAL IMPLICATIONS

To work effectively with transgender clients and their families, clinicians should understand the ethical and legal implications related to working with this population. First, according to the American Counseling Association's (ACA) *Code of Ethics* (2014), it is necessary to honor diversity, embrace a multicultural approach, and promote social justice. Further, the code of ethics for both the ACA (2014) and the American Association for Marriage and Family Therapy (AAMFT, 2015) prohibits discrimination based on gender identity. Thus, clinicians are responsible ethically to gain the cultural sensitivity necessary to work with issues of gender identity. This section discusses two particularly important ethical and legal issues: informed consent for medical gender transition and gender transition in childhood and adolescence.

Moving Toward Informed Consent for Medical Gender Transition Treatments

Many physicians require letters of support from mental health professionals in order to initiate hormone treatment or perform gender-affirming surgeries. This puts clinicians in a power position, serving as a gatekeeper, which can be damaging to the clinician–client relationship (Rachlin, 2002). Ethically, therapists do not abuse their power in relationships with clients (AAMFT, 2015); thus clinicians should be cognizant of this potential dynamic. Clients may feel like they need to say the right things, prove their gender identity is legitimate and true, and jump through hoops, which can prevent the readiness process from being an opportunity for determining a plan of action (Bockting et al., 2006). Additionally, many clients feel it is unfair, as cisgender people do not have to meet the same standard in order to access medical treatments and body-altering surgeries. This requirement has largely been based on the standards of care provided by the World Professional Association for Transgender Health (Coleman et al., 2012). Based on these standards, many medical providers do still require letters from mental health professionals. However, there is a shift happening in the field in response to the unfairness inherent in this system.

Some medical providers are moving toward an informed consent model, particularly for prescribing hormones. The Informed Consent Model is based on the idea that transgender people should not be required to attend therapy to access transaffirmative medical care and that they should be able to give consent for medical treatments after being informed of the benefits, risks, and impacts of the treatment. This idea is similar to clinicians' use of informed consent in counseling and marriage and family therapy, where clients choose to engage in treatment after being informed of significant information regarding the nature of all treatment processes and procedures (AAMFT, 2015; ACA, 2014). Under this model, therapy is optional for transgender people on their journey to medical gender transition.

So that transgender clients do not feel forced to engage in therapy, it is ethical for clinicians to explore these different options with transgender clients and their families to determine whether informed consent is both available locally and most appropriate for the family. Having these conversations with clients honors ACA's ethical principles of autonomy and veracity (ACA, 2104). Informed consent is typically available only for transgender people 18 years of age and older, as minors are unable to give voluntary consent (ACA, 2014), and may fit best for transgender people who are very clear about their medical needs for transition and have supportive family systems, or other systems of support in place. Going through the readiness process with a clinician may be most appropriate when transgender clients have concerns or questions about their gender, uncertainty about how or when to move forward with transition, have limited support, or are in the beginning stages of coming out.

Gender Transition in Childhood and Adolescence

Many parents and perhaps clinicians have concerns about the ethics of allowing children and adolescents to undergo gender transition. They may wonder: Should young people really be making life-altering decisions about their gender at such a young age? The answer is complicated. After all, at the center of ethical principles lies the notion of avoiding harm to clients (ACA, 2014). Many transgender people know about their identities from very early in life, with early childhood being the most common time for it to emerge and adolescence being the second most common time (Brill & Pepper, 2008). However, what we know about gender variance in childhood and adolescence is that it does not always lead to a transgender identity in adulthood. Gender variant children may grow up to be cisgender, transgender, gay, lesbian, bisexual, and heterosexual (Lev, 2004; Malpas, 2011). Experts in the field have called children *persisters* when they develop into transgender adults and *desisters* when their gender identities eventually align with their assigned gender (e.g., Drescher, 2013; Hidalgo et al., 2013). The likelihood of gender dysphoria persisting into adulthood is more likely for adolescents than it is for children (Coleman et al., 2012), but the truth is, we cannot be 100% sure about the permanency of any particular gender identity.

Because of this, the consideration of gender transition for children and adolescents should be explored with delicacy and complexity. For many young people, there is a significant amount of distress accompanying the pressure to perform in their assigned gender role. This distress and its associated symptomatology should be assessed thoroughly and considered heavily. If it seems likely that young people's mental health could improve if they are able to express their gender identity, this relief may outweigh the risk of a later shift in gender identity/expression. In this case, a clinician would be acting ethically to remedy or minimize unavoidable harm (ACA, 2014). Regardless of children's long-term gender identities, the children's beliefs about their own gender should be heard, respected, and normalized, shifting the focus from the future outcome to valuing the child in the moment (Coolhart, in press). For younger children in particular, transition may be approached as an exploration of life as another gender rather than a permanent choice that cannot be altered (Coleman et al., 2012). There is no reason that gender exploration and transition have to be seen through a pathologizing lens. Rather, the ability to explore gender could be seen as a gift (Coolhart, in press) that is a journey, not a destination.

When young people are exploring new gender expressions and considering gender transition, decisions are made about what steps to take. For prepubescent children, gender transition can be achieved without medical interventions since their bodies have not yet begun to develop secondary sex characteristics. Thus, the social steps of wearing clothing and hairstyles and using a name and pronouns that express their gender identity is all that is necessary. As children approach puberty, they may also be considering the hormonal suppression of puberty, where their body's natural puberty gets delayed. The World Professional Association for Transgender Health standards of care (Coleman et al., 2012) recommend that children reach Tanner Stage 2 before inducing pubertal suppression. While in some cases, this may be most appropriate in order for the child to begin to experience some of the physical changes of puberty to be sure that they do not feel congruent. In other cases, this may not be the most ethical treatment if the child is experiencing extreme distress about the anticipated changes. Hormonal delay can allow a youth more time to solidify gender identity (Bernal & Coolhart, 2013), stop physical changes that may be causing distress, and allow a family more time to increase attunement to the youth's gender.

As children progress into puberty, they may desire hormone treatment that is congruent with their affirmed gender. In other words, a young person who identifies as a girl may want to begin estrogen so that she can go through a puberty resembling her female peers. These decisions should be considered carefully, taking into account the youth's stability and persistence in their gender identity, their understanding of the impacts of hormones, including the potential for lifelong infertility, and their family's level of attunement and readiness. *AAMFT Code of Ethics* (2015) suggests that clinicians strive to find balance between conflicting goals within families, as can occur in families, as can happen when youth want transition and parents struggle with their own readiness for this step. For many youth, gender identity is quite solid in adolescence, transition is something they have wanted for some time, they are emotionally distressed by the current state of their bodies because it does not match their internal sense of self, and they have family support. For these youth, in order to avoid harm (ACA, 2014), it is often the most ethical choice to initiate hormonal treatment. Refusing medical intervention for adolescents could prolong gender dysphoria and lead to physical changes that provoke mistreatment and discrimination (Coleman et al., 2012). Also, earlier medical intervention may prevent changes that are irreversible and/or require further medical or surgical interventions for the youth later in life (i.e., chest reconstruction, tracheal shave, facial hair removal). When youth receive medical treatments, legally, at least one parent needs to provide consent. Thus, working with families on attunement allows youth to legally obtain necessary medical treatments.

CASE CONCEPTUALIZATION

In order to conceptualize further, a case is presented that highlights some of the key components learned in this chapter. This case introduces an adolescent meeting criteria for gender dysphoria with a family who is struggling to achieve attunement. This family also is dealing with concurrent problems as specified in the *DSM-5*. We discuss how these challenges can be addressed clinically.

Presenting Concerns

Ana is a 15-year-old transgender young woman. Her parents emigrated from Mexico to the United States before she was born. Ana's parents worked very hard to move to the

United States and then had four children after settling in to their new residence. Ana has an older brother, Marco, who is 17, a younger sister, Clara, who is 12, and her youngest brother, Juan, is 9. She describes herself as having a strong sense of Latina pride, which was instilled in her at a young age by her parents.

Ana is experiencing severe psychological distress because puberty is affecting her body in ways that are not congruent with her internal sense of gender. For instance, her body is masculinizing by the deepening of her voice and the development of facial hair. For these reasons, Ana wants to begin hormone treatment immediately.

Concurrent Problems

Ana's brother Marco strongly opposes Ana's gender identity, regularly calling her derogatory names, expressing embarrassment around his friends, and picking fights with her almost daily. This conflict meets criteria for a sibling relationship problem. This conflict negatively affects Ana's mood and she feels the loss of a relationship with Marco, to whom she has always been close. Ana has always looked up to Marco and relied on him for support and now, when she needs it most, she is feeling alone.

Ana is also struggling significantly in the school environment and her situation qualifies as an Academic or Educational Problem. Ana has been skipping school and therefore has seen a drastic decline in her grades. Once a very strong student, Ana's current level of achievement is far below her potential. She is also experiencing conflict with her teachers, which is a new dynamic since coming out as transgender. In Ana's younger years, teachers treated Ana with respect and she was generally well liked.

Finally, Ana is also a target of (perceived) Adverse Discrimination or Persecution because of her female gender expression. People at school victimize Ana and discriminate against her due to her being a part of a marginalized and underserved population.

Background History and Stressors

Ana's parents wanted to immigrate to the United States in order for their children to have access to quality education. After coming out as a transgender young woman, her parents feel as though she is not taking full advantage of her educational opportunities. Ana has been skipping class due to bullying and victimization by other students and even teachers. She attends a public high school that is primarily composed of White teenagers and faculty. Ana feels as though she is an outsider not only in terms of her Latina heritage but also her identity as a transgender woman. She has been told multiple times by her teacher that she should wait to socially transition until she becomes an adult. In a recent parent–teacher conference, her parents agreed with the opinion of the teacher and no longer want Ana to present as a female. Prior to that, Ana's parents were allowing Ana to express her gender in any way that felt comfortable for her. Because Ana's parents have limited knowledge of the English language, Ana feels as though her teacher took advantage of the situation.

Strengths

Among Ana's protective factors is her ability to advocate for herself. Since entering high school, she has been an active member of her school's Gay/Straight Alliance. The Gay/Straight Alliance provided Ana with tips to talk to her family about her identity as a transgender woman of color, which she used in conversations with her brother Marco. Although the Gay/Straight Alliance is relatively small and has only a few youth of color, Ana feels as though she has found a space in the lesbian, gay, bisexual, transgender, and queer community.

Another sign of Ana's resilience is her ability to access transgender-affirmative social media websites on her cell phone and her computer at home. These websites provide her with the opportunity to connect online with other transgender youth of color. She was able to see other Latina transgender women who were successfully navigating their transition and related experiences. This served as inspiration and hope for Ana, since she was not able to see this in her immediate social contexts. She also received advice from other transgender women of color on these social media sites about combating racism and transphobia.

DSM-5 Impressions and Implications

Ana has felt that her assigned sex at birth has been incongruent with her internal sense of gender since she was 4 years old. She would beg her mom for dresses and bows when she was growing up. As she began maturing, she hid her transgender identity and stole her younger sister's clothing at any chance she could. She has been particularly distressed since the onset of puberty due to the physical changes in her body, which she wants to stop and reverse as soon as possible. This distress, in addition to her experienced gender incongruence, meets the first criteria for Gender Dysphoria (APA, 2013). Ana wants to develop as a typical girl, gaining the curves she sees happening to her female classmates, meeting the third criteria for Gender Dysphoria (APA, 2013). She wants everyone to know that she is a girl, that she feels like other girls do, and she wants to be treated accordingly, meeting the fifth criteria for Gender Dysphoria (APA, 2013). After being in so much distress, she came out to her family a year ago, began presenting as female 6 months ago, and feels better about her gender since being able to express it outwardly. Based on Ana's description of her experience, she meets *DSM-5* criteria for Gender Dysphoria, given that she meets at least two criteria in addition to experiencing distress due to the gender incongruence (APA, 2013).

Relational Problems

Ana's older brother Marco is having the most difficult time with her gender transition. He has never used the proper pronouns or name for his sister, which frustrates Ana. Her frustration then leads her to argue with her brother. Marco frequently makes fun of Ana's gender expression and does not seem to understand that this is not just a "phase." He also talks negatively about Ana's gender identity to his friends, which is contributing to the problems with her peers at school. Before coming out, Ana reports that she and her brother Marco were extremely close and spent much time together. Currently, all they do is fight or avoid each other around the house and at school.

Although Ana's parents allowed her to dress in feminine clothing before meeting with her teachers, they were not able to fully understand Ana's transgender identity. There was not much open dialogue between Ana and her parents when she came out as transgender. Ana felt relieved when her parents initially did not have much of a reaction to her coming out, but now she is very upset because, since talking with her teachers, her parents are making a big deal about restricting her feminine expression.

Assessments

In order to therapeutically treat Ana and her family system as well as prepare the family system for Ana's eventual medical gender transition, a clinician could effectively use the readiness process designed for youth and their families (Coolhart et al., 2013). Assessing the youth's family support is the most important part of the process because Ana is still very much dependent on her family. This means that she is dependent on her parents to sign waivers for any type of medical treatment she receives during transition. The first goal is increasing attunement, understanding, and support in Ana's family, particularly her parental subsystem and with her brother Marco. In doing this, it will be vital to have different members of the family system attend sessions, and even conduct sessions solely with Ana and some solely with her parents.

As part of the readiness process, clinicians would assess a variety of domains, including early awareness of gender and family context, parental/family attunement to youth's affirmed gender, current gender expression, school context, sexual/relationship development, current intimate relationships, physical and mental health, support, and future plans/expectations. This process should serve as a guide to the clinician when collaboratively helping the family decide what their best option is for Ana's transition. Additionally, this process provides information about how to best support not only Ana, but also the rest of her family system, as Ana moves forward with gender transition.

Interventions

One of the main interventions for working with Ana and her family is to validate and empathize with each family member's opinions, thoughts, and feelings throughout the process. This may be difficult for the clinician because Ana's parents want her to present as a male in school, which drastically differs from Ana's desires. Recognizing that the parents may be going through a grieving process of losing a son while gaining a daughter may be crucial for the system. The clinician also needs to be culturally sensitive in that the family's Mexican heritage may influence how they think about and emotionally process Ana's transgender identity. Additionally, the clinician should be aware of how racism and transphobia intersect in Ana's experience and how she understands these forms of oppression.

It would also be helpful for the clinician to facilitate some sibling sessions with Ana and Marco, since they appear to have the most conflict within the family unit. It is vital for the whole system to support Ana in furthering her transition, especially because she experiences much discrimination and victimization in the school context. By building up her familial support, this may combat against negative interactions while in her school setting. Additionally, the clinician may need to assist in advocacy in the school setting, particularly because of Ana's parents' limited knowledge of the English language.

Ethical and Legal Implications

Ethically, Ana's situation presents a few concerns. For example, the fact that Ana is 15 years old and is desperate to start hormones is difficult for not only her family system, but could be for the clinician treating the family as well. Changing a youth's body at such a young age could be scary and worrisome for Ana's family, which is why carefully going through the readiness process is so vital. The clinician may also feel hesitant to write a letter of support for the youth to begin hormones at the age of 15. However, one must consider that if the clinician does not introduce hormones, Ana may experience even more psychological distress as her body continues to masculinize. These further changes in Ana's body may cause irreversible effects and/or the need for additional avoidable surgeries. Her long-term ability to be visibly perceived as female may also be impacted since the more her body masculinizes, the harder it will be for her to blend in. Thus, living without hormone treatment and not medically transitioning could be unethical for Ana's treatment.

Legally, since Ana is younger than the age of 18, she needs her parents' consent for any medical treatments such as starting hormones. Therefore, if her parents were not supportive of Ana furthering her gender transition, she legally would not be able to obtain hormones without their consent. This could create even more problematic dynamics within Ana's family system.

DISCUSSION

As you continue to reflect on the case study and the overall approach, contemplate these questions:

- What would be important to consider when assessing the family's emotional process?
- What questions could be asked to explore Ana's early awareness of gender in her family context? How might this impact her current gender expression and family relationships?
- What are some of your personal biases about or experiences with cultural intersectionality? How might that impact your therapeutic work with this family?
- How do you understand the system dynamics between Ana's parents and her other siblings, particularly Marco? Whom would you invite into family therapy sessions?
- How would you use interventions that are gender affirmative but also validating to family members that may not be accepting of Ana's transgender identity?

SUMMARY

Clearly, gender dysphoria affects not only transgender individuals, but also their partners, parents, children, and siblings. During gender transition, loved ones go through their own emotional process, where they must reconceptualize their transgender family members and make adjustments in how they relate to the new gender presentation. Families' experiences can further be complicated by systemic factors larger than the family, including whether the person is transitioning to female or male, and the person's race, socioeconomic status, and age. All of these systemic factors should be considered when assessing and intervening in families, as well as keeping in mind the ethical and legal implications of gender transition. Because family support is the greatest protective factor for transgender individuals' physical and mental health, it is imperative to use a family systems approach in the treatment of gender dysphoria.

REFERENCES

American Association for Marriage and Family Therapy. (2015). *AAMFT code of ethics*. Alexandria, VA: Author.

American Counseling Association. (2014). *ACA code of ethics*. Alexandria, VA: Author.

American Psychiatric Association. (2013). *Diagnostic and statistical manual of mental disorders* (5th ed.). Arlington, VA: American Psychiatric Publishing.

Badgett, M. V., Lau, H., Sears, B., & Ho, D. (2007). *Bias in the workplace: Consistent evidence of sexual orientation and gender identity discrimination*. Los Angeles, CA: The Williams Institute.

Balsam, K. F., Molina, Y., Beadnell, B., Simoni, J., & Walters, K. (2011). Measuring multiple minority stress: The LGBT People of Color Microaggressions Scale. *Cultural Diversity and Ethnic Minority Psychology*, 17(2), 163–174. doi:10.1037/a0023244

Bernal, A. T., & Coolhart, D. (2013). Learning from sexual minorities: Adolescents and the coming out process. *Guidance and Counselling*, 20(3/4), 128–138.

Bockting, W. O., Knudson, G., & Goldberg, J. M. (2006). Counseling and mental health care for transgender adults and loved ones. *International Journal of Transgenderism, 9*(3–4), 35–82. doi:10.1300/J485v09n03_03

Boss, P. G. (1999). *Ambiguous loss: Learning to live with unresolved grief.* Cambridge, MA: Harvard University Press.

Bradford, J., Reisner, S. L., & Xavier, J. (2013). Experiences of transgender-related discrimination and implications for health: Results from the Virginia Transgender Health Initiative Study. *American Journal of Public Health, 103*(10), 1820–1829. doi:10.2105/AJPH.2012.300796

Brill, S., & Pepper, R. (2008). *The transgender child: A handbook for families and professionals.* San Francisco, CA: Cleis Press.

Budge, S. L., Adelson, J. L., & Howard, K. A. (2013). Anxiety and depression in transgender individuals: The roles of transition status, loss, social support, and coping. *Journal of Consulting and Clinical Psychology, 81*(3), 545–557. doi:10.1037/a0031774

Carroll, L., Gilroy, P. J., & Ryan, J. (2002). Counseling transgendered, transsexual, and gender-variant clients. *Journal of Counseling and Development, 80*(2), 131–139.

Coleman, E., Bockting, W., Botzer, M., Cohen-Kettenis, P., DeCuypere, G., Feldman, J., . . . Zucher, K. (2012). Standards of care for the health of transsexual, transgender, and gender-nonconforming people, version 7. *International Journal of Transgenderism, 13*(4), 165–232.

Cook-Daniels, L., & Munson, M. (2010). Sexual violence, elder abuse, and sexuality of transgender adults, age 50+: Results of three surveys. *Journal of Gay, Lesbian, Bisexual, and Transgender Family Studies, 6*(2), 142–177. doi:10.1080/15504281003705238

Coolhart, D. (2012). Supporting transgender youth and their families in therapy: Facing challenges and harnessing strengths. In J. Bigner & J. Wetchler (Eds.), *Handbook of LGBT-affirmative couple and family therapy.* New York, NY: Routledge Press.

Coolhart, D. (in press). Helping families move from distress to attunement. In C. Meier & D. Ehrendaft (Eds.), *The gender affirmative model: A new approach to supporting gender non-conforming and transgender children.*

Coolhart, D., Baker, A., Farmer, S., Melhaney, M., & Shipman, D. (2013). Therapy with transsexual youth and their families: A clinical tool for assessing youth's readiness for gender transition. *Journal of Marital and Family Therapy, 39*(2), 223–243.

Coolhart, D., Provancher, N., Hager, A., & Wang, M. (2008). Recommending transsexual clients for gender transition: A therapeutic tool for assessing readiness. *Journal of Gay, Lesbian, Bisexual, and Transgender Family Studies, 4*(3), 301–324.

Coolhart, D., Ritenour, K., & Grodzinski, A. (2017). *Experiences of loss and ambiguous loss for parents of transgender male youth: A phenomenological exploration.* Manuscript in preparation.

Drescher, J. (2013, June 25). Invitation to a dialogue: Gender identity. *The New York Times.* Retrieved from http://www.nytimes.com/2013/06/26/opinion/invitation-to-a-dialogue-gender-identity.html?_r=0

Ehrensaft, D. (2011). *Gender born, gender made: Raising healthy gender-nonconforming* children. New York, NY: The Experiment.

Ellis, K. M., & Eriksen, K. (2002). Transsexual and transgenderist experiences and treatment options. *The Family Journal, 10*(3), 289–299. doi:10.1177/10680702010003005

Emerson, S. (1996). Stages of adjustment in family members of transgender individuals. *Journal of Family Psychotherapy, 7*(3), 1–12. doi:10.1300/J085V07N03_01

Goldblum, P., Testa, R. J., Pflum, S., Hendricks, M. L., Bradford, J., & Bongar, B. (2012). The relationship between gender-based victimization and suicide attempts in transgender people. *Professional Psychology: Research and Practice, 43*(5), 468–475. doi:10.1037/a0029605

Grant, J. M., Motett, L. A., Tanis, J., Harrison, J., Herman, J. L., & Keisling, M. (2011). *Injustice at every turn: A report of the national transgender discrimination survey.* Washington, DC: National Center for Transgender Equality and National Gay and Lesbian Task Force.

Hidalgo, M. A., Ehrensaft, D., Tishelman, A. C., Clark, L. F., Garofalo, R., Resenthal, S. M., . . . Olsen, J. (2013). The gender affirmative model: What we know and what we aim to learn. *Human Development, 56,* 285–290. doi:10.1159/000355235

Kenagy, G. P. (2005). The health and social service needs of transgender people in Philadelphia. *International Journal of Transgenderism, 8*(2/3), 49–56. doi:10.1300/J485v08n02_05

Kübler-Ross, E. (1969). *On death and dying: What the dying have to teach doctors, nurses, clergy, and their own families.* New York, NY: Scribner.

Kuvalanka, K. A., Weiner, J. L., & Mahan, D. (2014). Child, family, and community transformations: Findings from interviews with mothers of transgender girls. *Journal of Gay, Lesbian, Bisexual, and Transgender Family Studies, 10*(4), 354–379. doi:10.1080/1550428X.2013.834529

Lev, A. I. (2004). *Transgender emergence: Therapeutic guidelines for working with gender variant people and their families*. Binghamton, NY: The Haworth Press.

Malpas, J. (2011). Between pink and blue: A multi-dimensional family approach to gender nonconforming children and their families. *Family Process, 50*(4), 453–470. doi:10.1111/j.1545-5300.2011.01371.x

Meyer, I. H. (1995). Minority stress and mental health in gay men. *Journal of Health and Social Behavior, 36*(1), 38–56.

Meyer, I. H. (2003). Prejudice, social stress, and mental health in lesbian, gay, and bisexual populations: Conceptual issues and research evidence. *Psychological Bulletin, 129*(5), 674–697. doi:10.1037/0033 -2909.129.5.674

Meyer, I. H. (2015). Resilience in the study of minority stress and health of sexual and gender minorities. *Psychology of Sexual Orientation and Gender Diversity, 2*(3), 209–213. doi:10.1037/sgd0000132

Newfield, E., Hart, S., Dibble, S., & Kohler, L. (2006). Female-to-male transgender quality of life. *Quality of Life Research, 15*, 1447–1457. doi:10.1007/s11136-006-0002-3

Norwood, K. (2013). Grieving gender: Trans-identities, transition, and ambiguous loss. *Communication Monographs, 80*, 24–45. doi:10.1080/03637751.2012.739705

Nuttbrock, L., Hwahng, S., Bockting, W., Rosenblum, A., Mason, M., & Becker, J. (2010). Psychiatric impact of gender-related abuse across the life course of male-to-female transgender persons. *Journal of Sex Research, 47*(1), 12–23. doi:10.1080/00224490903062258

Rachlin, K. (2002). Transgender individuals' experiences of psychotherapy. *The International Journal of Transgenderism, 6*(1), 97–103.

Raj, R. (2008). Transforming couples and families: A trans-formative therapeutic model for working with the loved-ones of gender-divergent youth and trans-identified adults. *Journal of Gay, Lesbian, Bisexual, and Transgender Family Studies, 4*(2), 133–163. doi:10.1080/15504280802096765

Ryan, C., Huebner, D., Diaz, R. M., & Sanchez, J. (2009). Family rejection as a predictor of negative health outcomes in White and Latino lesbian, gay, and bisexual young adults. *Pediatrics, 123*(1), 346–352.

Ryan, C., Russell, S. T., Huebner, D., Diaz, R., & Sanchez, J. (2010). Family acceptance in adolescence and the health of LGBT young adults. *Journal of Child and Adolescent Psychiatric Nursing, 23*(4), 205–213. doi:10.1111/j.1744-6171.2010.00246.x

Sevelius, J. M. (2013). Gender affirmation: A framework for conceptualizing risk behavior among transgender women of color. *Sex Roles, 68*(11–12), 675–689. doi:10.1007/s11199-012-0216-5

Stone Fish, L., & Harvey, R. G. (2005). *Nurturing queer youth: Family therapy transformed*. New York, NY: W. W. Norton.

Travers, R., Bauer, G., Pyne, J., Bradley, K., Gale, L., & Papadimitriou, M. (2012). *Impacts of strong parental support for trans youth: A report prepared for Children's Aid Society of Toronto and Delisle Youth Services*. Retrieved from http://transpulseproject.ca/wp-content/uploads/2012/10/Impacts-of-Strong-Parental -Support-for-Trans-Youth-vFINAL.pdf

Veldorale-Griffin, A. (2014). Transgender parents and their adult children's experiences of disclosure and transition. *Journal of Gay, Lesbian, Bisexual, and Transgender Family Studies, 10*, 475–501. doi:10.1080/ 1550428X.2013.866063

Wahlig, J. L. (2015). Losing the child they thought they had: Therapeutic suggestions for an ambiguous loss perspective with parents of a transgender child. *Journal of Gay, Lesbian, Bisexual, and Transgender Family Studies, 11*(4), 305–326. doi:10.1080/1550428X.2014.945676

Watson, R. J., Barnett, M. A., & Russell, S. T. (2016). Parental support matters for the educational success of sexual minorities. *Journal of Gay, Lesbian, Bisexual, and Transgender Family Studies, 12*(2), 188–202. doi:10.1080/1550428X.2015.1028694

White, T., & Ettner, R. (2004). Disclosure, risks and protective factors for children whose parents are undergoing a gender transition. *Journal of Gay and Lesbian Psychotherapy, 8*(1/2), 129–146. doi:10.1300/ J236v08n01_10

White, T., & Ettner, R. I. (2007). Adaptation and adjustment in children of transsexual parents. *European Child and Adolescent Psychiatry, 16*(4), 215–221. doi:10.1007/s00787-006-0591-y

Zamboni, B. D. (2006). Therapeutic considerations in working with the family, friends, and partners of transgendered individuals. *The Family Journal, 14*(2), 174–179. doi:10.1177/1066480705285251

15

DISRUPTIVE, IMPULSE-CONTROL, AND CONDUCT DISORDERS: GENERAL SYSTEMIC PROPERTIES

Aaron Hugh Jackson

*T*his chapter focuses specifically on the assessment and treatment of Disruptive, Impulse-Control, and Conduct Disorders from a family systems perspective. Addressing these disorders from a family systems perspective is quite a bit different than approaching them from an intrapsychic or individual counseling perspective. Rather than focusing on any one particular individual in a family as the source of the problem, we see presenting problems as a function of the family system. We may ask the question, "What function does this behavior serve?" or "How is the family supporting or maintaining the presenting problem?" We may have to render a *Diagnostic and Statistical Manual of Mental Disorders* (5th ed.; *DSM-5;* American Psychiatric Association [APA], 2013) diagnosis, but we will also establish a systemic diagnosis. This systemic diagnosis considers relational aspects, such as rules, roles, patterns, and processes. This systemic diagnosis helps us tailor interventions aimed at improving the entire family system. A systemic treatment plan keeps the focus on the family system, rather than just one member of the family. In many cases, the symptom bearer or identified client is the reason for a referral or office visit. A systemically based assessment and treatment plan places emphasis on the systemic factors that support symptomatic behaviors and encourages the counselor to address issues from a systemic perspective.

In the course of this chapter, we briefly explore the six specific diagnoses frequently encountered in our work with families. The chapter also directs us to study relational and cultural features of these diagnostic categories and gain insight into the process of assessing family systems as well. We discuss interventions and any ethical and legal considerations are also covered. The chapter concludes with a case conceptualization. In the process of this case conceptualization, the knowledge we have presented here is applied in a way that is practical and useful for the systemic clinician.

DSM-5 AND FAMILY SYSTEMS

The *DSM-5* began its journey to our offices in 2000. Work groups were formed and an emphasis was placed on garnering a research basis for its diagnostic categories. Time and space prevent a thorough presentation of the history and development of the *DSM-5*. Interested readers may investigate these developments at the following web address www.psychiatry.org/psychiatrists/practice/dsm. In 2007, the *DSM* task force and various work groups set about the task of refining the document for publication. In 2013, the *DSM-5* was published and its information disseminated to the behavioral health care field for consumption and application. There were a few changes made to the *DSM*, a few chapters were modified, new terminology was established, and a new chapter or two arose. One of the most astounding changes in the *DSM-5* was the removal of the multiaxial system of evaluation. (For a summary of those changes in the *DSM-5*, please visit www.psychiatry.org/psychiatrists/practice/dsm/educational-resources/dsm-5-fact-sheets).

The language in the *DSM-5* alludes to mental disorders being something that occur "in an individual's cognition, emotion regulation, or behaviors. . . ." (APA, 2013, p. 20), thereby giving limited regard or limited consideration for processes external to the individual (Denton & Bell, 2013, p. 152). The definition of a mental disorder mentions "distress or disability in social, occupational, or other important activities" (APA, 2013, p. 20) but still no significant position on consideration of systemic or family-based assessment and diagnosis. The Global Assessment of Relational Functioning (GARF) was particularly useful to the family systems clinician. The GARF, similar to the Global Assessment of Functioning, was an instrument intended to assess the family or relational unit along the axes of problem solving, organization, and emotional climate, on a scale of 1 to 100 for each scale (Gladding, 2011). This scale is absent from the newest version of the *DSM*. Even though this scale was seemingly underused by family practitioners, it was considered a reliable and valid instrument (Denton & Bell, 2013). The GARF is not published in the *DSM-5*. There are, however, some useful aspects of the *DSM-5* that are indeed helpful to the family counselor. For example, the *DSM-5* includes an assessment tool called the World Health Organization Disability Assessment Schedule which is a general assessment of daily functioning in which the client rates ease or difficulty of basic life tasks, such as bathing, self-care, and taking care of household duties and responsibilities (APA, 2013, p. 745). This tool may be helpful in family treatment planning in several ways. For example, should a client identify challenges in "Getting along with people who are close to you" (Item D4.3), the family counselor may target that as one area in need of systemic intervention.

The *DSM-5* retains the chapter titled "Other Conditions That May Be a Focus of Clinical Attention." It is clearly noted that the "conditions or problems listed in this chapter are not mental disorders" (APA, 2013). This chapter includes Z code designations that allow some recognition of family or systemic issues that present themselves during the assessment process. These designations allow for the assessment of external issues that directly impact the diagnostic process, and thus have an impact on systemic treatment planning. As indicated in the *DSM-5*, these conditions are not mental disorders, but they should be considered as being influential in the diagnostic and treatment process (APA, 2013, p. 715). Examples include:

> Parent–Child Relational Problems
> Relationship Distress With Spouse or Intimate Partner
> Disruption of Family by Separation or Divorce
> Child Affected by Parental Relationship Distress

Many other designations are included in the aforementioned *DSM* chapter. These other designations allow the diagnostician to indicate conditions or problems such as sexual abuse, child abuse, and issues with housing or occupational problems. As guidelines prevent publication of diagnostic criteria or other descriptions of conditions or problems, it is recommended that the reader read and review the *DSM-5* chapter, and become familiar with its information. The Z code categories discussed in this chapter are not considered mental disorders; therefore, reimbursement by third-party payors and insurance companies is highly unlikely (Gladding, 2011).

Despite the absence of the GARF Scale in the *DSM-5*, other instruments have been included, some of which may be useful for the family counselor systemic clinician. For example, the *DSM-5* includes Cross-Cutting Symptom Measures (CCSM), which help systemic clinicians gain a deeper understanding of the presenting issue by looking at the additional factors that play a role in its manifestation. Additionally, these tools can be helpful not only during the initial assessment phase, but they may also be used to assess growth and progress over time.

These CCSMs are available in two forms: patient–informant and parent–guardian versions. Both forms may be useful to the family counselor systemic clinician for obvious reasons. The adult version of the CCSM assesses 13 various psychiatric domains, including anger, mania, suicidal ideation, and substance abuse, among others. The parent–guardian version of the CCSM assesses 12 various psychiatric domains, including, but not limited to, depression, sleep disturbance, repetitive thoughts, substance abuse, and inattention. (These instruments are available online at www.psychiatry.org/dsm5.) General guidelines for their use include using these tools at various intervals to track changes. It is also suggested that the same person conduct the assessment over time, using the same informant, parent, or guardian as the source of information, as familiarity with the individual may add to the validity of the assessment. Higher scores in any specific domain indicate the need for further investigation and intervention. The use of clinical judgment in decision making, guided by ethical and professional standards, is encouraged in the use and application of these and all assessment processes (APA, 2013).

The Cultural Formulation Interview (CFI) will be of particular interest to the family counselor. Structurally, the CFI assesses four domains of the client experience: (a) Cultural Definition of the Problem, (b) Cultural Perceptions of Cause, Context, and Support, (c) Cultural Factors Affecting Self-Coping and Past Help Seeking, and (d) Cultural Factors Affecting Current Help Seeking. The CFI is a 16-question interview, available in self-report and informant versions, conducted to "obtain information during a mental health assessment about the impact of culture of key aspects of an individual's clinical presentation and care" (APA, 2013, p. 750). The CFI assesses various aspects of the client's culture, such as "aspects of an individual's background . . . and current social contexts that may affect his or her perspective . . .; the influence of family, friends, and other community members on the individual's experience and other areas of concern" (APA, 2013, p. 750).

The CFI appears to be a systemically grounded instrument. It asks questions related to family background, relational factors, and other systemic issues that might have a significant impact on behavior, cognition, or emotions. While not purely a method for family assessment, it can clearly yield helpful information for the family counselor's use during the treatment planning process. The CFI can be found at www.psychiatry.org/psychiatrists/practice/dsm/dsm-5/online-assessment-measures.

As these things are included in the *DSM-5*, it is practical to make use of them. The Z codes as they relate to family and relational functioning should be indicated on any systemic assessment and summary of diagnostic findings. These instruments—the cross-cutting measures and the CFI—should be a part of the family assessment process. More discussion on the use and application of these items occurs later in the chapter.

Diagnostic Features of Disruptive, Impulse-Control, and Conduct Disorders

The *DSM-5* describes Disruptive, Impulse-Control, and Conduct Disorders as those disorders related to problems with self-control in the domains of emotions and behaviors

(APA, 2013; Zuddas, 2014). Other diagnostic categories in the *DSM-5* include such concerns; however, the diagnoses covered in this chapter are specific in that they relate to behaviors that violate the rights of other individuals or they cause a conflicting relationship with social norms or those in positions of authority (APA, 2013). Symptoms displayed by the client may appear to satisfy criteria for several different diagnoses and systemic clinicians should carefully evaluate presenting behaviors. For example, the *DSM-5* discusses (p. 475) how adjustment disorders may sometimes be difficult to distinguish from conduct disorders. Upon closer examination, we are reminded of the importance of the significance of differential diagnosis. As such, the systemic clinician should be very much aware of the various differentiating criteria, and should become very familiar with the criteria for each and every diagnostic possibility in the *DSM-5*.

The specific diagnoses that fall under the category of Disruptive, Impulse-Control, and Conduct Disorders are summarized in the following sections. In all of these diagnostic categories, some generalities bear mentioning. At the core of these diagnoses, we contend with the notions of behaviors and emotions. Some diagnoses are more closely related to "behavioral" issues, and some are more closely related to "emotional" issues. Upon closer examination, we see that the diagnosis of pyromania more closely resembles a behavioral issue, while the diagnosis of intermittent explosive disorder seems to contain more emotional elements. Oppositional defiant disorder bridges the gap between the two in terms of emotional and behavioral factors, in that it contains considerable elements of each of the aforementioned domains (APA, 2013).

These diagnoses tend to show up earlier in life and it is rare that clinical presentations become evident later in adulthood. As these symptoms show up in the early years of life, we must consider these behaviors in the appropriate developmental context. Some behaviors seen in early childhood and adolescence can be considered quite normal. Behaviors should be considered in terms of what is considered normal for one's age, culture, and gender prior to determining pathology. As that is the case, we are encouraged to attend to the "frequency, persistence, and pervasiveness, and impairment associated with these behaviors" throughout the diagnostic process (APA, 2013, p. 462).

Oppositional Defiant Disorder

This disorder is generally defined as being represented by a period of moodiness, insolent, and vindictive behavior over the past 6 months (APA, 2013, p. 462). Four of eight symptoms are required for diagnosis. Symptoms of oppositional defiant disorder are related to such behaviors as intentionally disturbing or aggravating others, noncompliance with rules, displacing blame, and argumentative, among others. In order for the diagnosis to be applicable, a certain set of behaviors has to have been present for the past 6 months. An additional diagnostic concern is noted in that these behaviors must be "exhibited during interaction with at least one individual who is not a sibling" (APA, 2013, p. 462). In essence, this means that the behaviors happen outside of the family dynamic. The diagnostician would want to assess interactions between and among friends and family, school peers, teachers, and people in positions of authority outside of the family.

Intermittent Explosive Disorder

This diagnosis is generally applicable in situations where the individual lacks the ability to control anger and aggression. This inability to control anger and aggression may be expressed in various ways, and the *DSM-5* includes two separate criteria for these expressions. Criterion A1 covers verbal aggression or physical aggression directed toward people, property, or animals (APA, 2013). These signs of aggression should be evident twice per week on average, over a period of 90 days, and injury to property, animals, or individuals is not noted. A Criterion A2 diagnosis requires three behavioral outbursts over a period of

12 months in which injury or damage occurs to people, property, or animals (APA, 2013). The behavioral reaction to certain events may be over and above what would be expected for any given situation. For example, a child might respond to being told to go to bed by breaking a window. One key element is that the outbursts are spontaneous, meaning that the explosive behaviors have not been planned, and there is no sense of reward for the outburst. In other words, the behaviors happen "in the moment," and often with negative effects. In order for this diagnosis to apply, the client must be at least 6-years-old in terms of age or developmental level.

Conduct Disorder

Conduct Disorder is generally defined as consistent behaviors that violate the rights of others and the generally accepted standards of behavior for any given age group. These behaviors may involve hurting people or animals, significant rule breaking, and the destruction of property. The individual may engage in the act of stealing. Overall, there are 15 distinct criteria covering the domains of (a) aggression toward people or animals, (b) destruction of property, (c) deceitfulness or theft, and (d) serious violations of rules. Of those specific criteria delineated in the *DSM-5*, the individual must exhibit at least three of those behaviors over the past 12 months, with at least one of the criteria being displayed in the past 6 months.

In regard to Conduct Disorder and age of onset, the clinician should include an age specifier when making the diagnosis:

- *Childhood Onset*—appropriate when at least one of the behaviors occurred prior to age 10.
- *Adolescent Onset*—used when the individual did not exhibit any of the specified behaviors prior to age 10.
- *Unspecified Onset*—typically used when the clinician cannot determine the presence or absence of specified behaviors prior to or after the age of 10.

Awareness of the various systemic, environmental, and family factors associated with the age of onset is important here. As systemic clinicians, we are mindful of the idea that behaviors of any type rarely occur in a vacuum. As that is the case, systemic clinicians may consider the impact of various influential factors in determining age of onset. For example, the *DSM-5* notes that such things as "large family size, inconsistent child-raising practices, and parental criminality" (p. 473) among others play a role in the course and development of conduct disorder. Environmental factors, such as "exposure to violence, peer rejection, and delinquent peer groups" (p. 473) may also play a role in the course and development of conduct disorder (APA, 2013). As that is the case, systemic clinicians are to attend to such factors and to make treatment plans focused on addressing the family and environmental factors.

The reader notes the age of 10 being of importance when discussing and determining the aforementioned subtypes. This information is usually gathered from parents, guardians, or other caregivers. Children themselves may be able to reliably report such information, but a discussion between the counselor and parents or caregivers is necessary in order to corroborate any information received from the child.

Other diagnostic specifiers include lack of remorse or guilt, lack of empathy, lack of concern about performance in school or other related activities, and affect. These specifiers are added to the initial diagnosis in an effort to add depth and awareness to the general diagnosis. In addition, the diagnostician may add a severity measure to the diagnosis. The severity can be assessed mild, moderate, or severe, and adds additional depth and meaning to the diagnosis. (APA, 2013, pp. 471–472).

Pyromania

A diagnosis of Pyromania is applicable when the individual frequently engages in the act of fire-setting. This fire-setting is often accompanied by a degree of tension and arousal prior to the act itself. During and after the act, the individual experiences pleasure and gratification. Individuals with this disorder find themselves fascinated by fire—spending time watching a fire, or watching things burn. The individual does not engage in the act of fire-setting for the purpose of reward or recognition. Rather, the fire-setting is simply done for the pleasure and purpose of watching things burn. There are no age restrictions. The *DSM-5* specifies six distinct criteria for this disorder, and each must be met fully.

Kleptomania

Kleptomania describes a constant and persistent failure to avoid the act of stealing things that are not really needed. The stealing seems to be done for the mere act itself. As with pyromania, the act of planning and participating in the act of stealing is accompanied by tension, pleasure, and relief. There are no age limits or restrictions, and each of the five distinct diagnostic criteria must be met prior to making a diagnosis of kleptomania.

In cases of pyromania, kleptomania, or any of these disorders, the systemic counselor wants to consider, as was discussed earlier in the chapter, the functionality of behaviors related to these disorders. For example, if we view the behaviors from an individual perspective, we may miss the systemic importance of such behaviors. On the individual level, the symptoms and behaviors are seen as something the individual is doing as a result of internal impulses. If we look at the behaviors from a systemic perspective, we may see something different. We may see that the child engages in fire-setting or stealing because he or she receives attention as a result of doing so, attention being what he or she is desperately trying to obtain. Consider what happens in the following case example:

> Casey is in the fourth grade. He has two brothers and is the youngest member of the family. Casey often feels like his older siblings get all of the attention because they both exceed in school and are both really good athletes. Casey has tried to get the attention of his parents by asking them for help with his homework, seeking praise for doing well in school, and asking to help his parents do things around the house. These attempts to gain attention from his parents were unmet. As a result, he decided to set fire to a trash can in the lunchroom at school in an effort to gain attention. His plan worked perfectly. After he set fire to the trash can, the principal called his parents and his parents rushed to the school. Thus he earned the undivided attention of his parents, the school, and his friends.

A systemic counselor assesses the functionality of Casey's behavior and likely determines that Casey wants attention from his parents. Thus, the systemic counselor suggests ways in which his parents can share more time with Casey. The counselor may also assist the family in ways to increase warmth and nurturing behaviors as a whole. If Casey receives the attention he wants in a healthy and responsive manner, the behaviors associated with pyromania should theoretically disappear.

Other Specified Disruptive, Impulse-Control, and Conduct Disorder

This diagnostic category can be used by the systemic clinician when some type of disordered behavior is present, and similar to, other disruptive, impulse control, or conduct disorder, but the full criteria for that disorder have not been met. When this is used, the clinician must also set forth the reasons why this diagnosis is rendered, and why the specific reason that the more specific diagnosis was not given. This diagnosis should be considered when behaviors or symptoms cause "clinically significant impairment" (APA, 2013,

p. 479), but the behaviors do not fulfill the diagnostic requirements of the proscribed disorders in this chapter. Rather, the diagnostician might indicate this diagnosis in cases where the identified client engages in stealing, but fails to fulfill one or all of the required criteria. For example, the identified client may meet all of the criteria for Kleptomania with the exception that the client steals for the purpose of exacting revenge on someone.

Unspecified Disruptive, Impulse-Control, and Conduct Disorder

The systemic clinician would use this diagnosis in the event that an individual demonstrates behaviors related to a disruptive, impulse control, or conduct disorder are present, but those symptoms do not meet the full criteria for any of the disorders specified under the heading of Disruptive, Impulse-Control, and Conduct Disorder. For example, the diagnostician indicates this disorder when full criteria of a specified disorder are not met, but the client experiences clinically significant impairment. In these cases, the clinician chooses not to describe the reasons for the unspecified diagnosis. This sometimes results due to the lack of adequate or reliable information upon which to base the specific diagnosis.

These diagnoses may be present in individuals within the family units with whom you work. As a systemic clinician, you must be intimately familiar with the *DSM-5* and its contents. You must have an in-depth understanding of all the information contained within its pages, and it is good practice to keep the *DSM* close at hand and consult its pages with regularity. The *DSM* contains a wealth of information, even though as several authors have noted (Denton & Bell, 2013; Hill & Crews, 2005, as cited in Gladding, 2011; Lebow, 2014; Strong and Busch, 2013), the current state of the *DSM* marginalizes those clinicians with a family systems orientation. The *DSM-5*, for all practical purposes, disregards a relational diagnostic process. The "medical model" of mental illness prevails, and as noted earlier, mental illness occurs "within an individual." The question may arise at this point: "How do we as systemic clinicians make use of the *DSM-5* diagnostic categories for Disruptive, Impulse-Control and Conduct Disorders?"

An extra burden is laid upon us. In essence, we will engage in the multilevel assessment process. While more difficult and burdensome, it is not impossible to do. Generally speaking, the family counselor will diagnose the individual client with the appropriate disorder and then, the family counselor will assess the entire family system. In essence, we will have conducted two separate assessments with two diagnoses. Due to the nature of systemic counselor and clinical practicality, the systemic counselor engages in a two-tier diagnostic process. One diagnosis will categorize the individual having a specific diagnosis or diagnoses. The other assessment—the systemic assessment—will provide insight into the functional processes of the family, and give us insight as to how family dynamics have played a role in the development and maintenance of the diagnosis of the individual client. As noted earlier, third-party payers typically do not reimburse for Z codes. Reimbursements for the other diagnoses, such as the diagnostic categories we examine in this chapter, are determined by those third-party payers and insurance companies. As space and time prevent an exhaustive discussion of the role of the rules and guidelines of insurance companies and third-party payers, clinicians should take time to learn about those important guidelines on their own. This information can often be obtained via the insurance company's website, or via a conversation with an insurance company representative.

RELATIONAL AND CULTURAL FEATURES

Relational and cultural features related to conduct and behavioral disorders are examined in this section. For the purpose of clarity, *relational features* are defined as those features allied with familial or community connections. Examples of these familial or community connections to be considered are intergenerational relationships, parental relationships, sibling relationships, and community relationships or factors. Cultural features to be considered are related to gender, age, ethnicity, and socioeconomic factors, among others. As systemically oriented counselors, we recognize that all of these things are inextricably connected, and should be considered as such. Systemic clinicians fully recognize the importance of culture and context as a whole. Relational and cultural factors impact the family, and the family exists and functions within the context. Each family must be appreciated for its own unique culture and the contributions that it makes to itself, extended family, and the community as a whole. The "whole" is made up of several parts, which must be examined on their own, in an effort to understand the contributions that each specific domain makes to the way the entire system functions. In an effort to further understand the impact of these cultural and relational factors on family systems, we study the smaller domains so that we may understand the "whole" system more fully.

"Mental disorders are defined by cultural, social, and familial norms" (APA, 2013, p. 14). When we assess behavior, we must view that behavior in the context of culture. Behavioral reactions to the same event vary greatly across cultures. Likewise, normative behaviors vary across cultures and family systems. Different families have different rules and expectations for behavior. Community and cultural expectations may also dictate standards by which some behaviors or actions are judged or tolerated. For example, consider the cultural responses to death across various cultures. Goodwin (2015) examined various cross-cultural responses to grief and bereavement. Although he noted several commonalities, specific rituals for dealing with grief, loss, and death varied widely across cultures. Cassim, Stolte, and Hodgetts (2015) discuss the use of "metanyms" or material objects that are used in Bhuddist practices to maintain a daily connection with the dead. This is vastly different from other cultures (e.g., Judeo-Christian) views of the finality of death. As systemic clinicians we can expect to see a wide range of grief responses in the families with whom we serve. Systemic clinicians can expect to see variations in verbal and nonverbal reactions, belief systems, and spiritual expressions. Some of the expressions of grief we see may be very different or similar to those methods of mourning that we practice in our own culture.

In an effort to be culturally insightful of these things, systemic clinicians should focus more on the degree to which the behaviors or actions become problematic for the family (APA, 2013). The *DSM-5* notes that "impairment associated with the behaviors indicative of the diagnosis be considered in relation to the what is normative for a person's age, gender, and culture when determining if they are symptomatic of the disorder" (p. 462). Also of note, the diagnostic criteria for any given diagnostic category indicate that the behaviors must cause "distress" or "negative impact" on the client before the diagnosis can be rendered (APA, 2013, p. 14). Problems with friends, colleagues, teachers, and family members might indicate distress. Being arrested, expelled from school, or fired from a job might indicate a negative impact for the client, for example. A degree of clinical judgment, and cultural awareness, are necessary when considering the rendition of any mental health diagnosis.

Generally speaking, there are several cultural and relational commonalities across the diagnoses discussed in this chapter. Across all of these diagnostic categories, the prevalence rate is higher in males than in females, with the exception of Kleptomania (APA, 2013). In the case of kleptomania, the prevalence among females is much higher. Females exhibit kleptomania at a rate of three times that of males. Age is a factor in this diagnostic category as well. Most behaviors can be seen early in the developmental process, with fewer showing signs and symptoms of these disorders later in life (APA, 2013). Christophersen and VanScoyoc (2013) note that disruptive behavior disorders typically reveal themselves in the child's early- to middle-grade years. These disorders may reveal themselves in school settings. Referrals may be brought about due to disruptive behaviors in the classroom or in other childcare settings, such as after school care. Christophersen and VanScoyoc (2013) also indicate that these behavioral manifestations may also be related to other serious issues, such as substance use and depression (p. 15).

These behaviors can also be influenced by other aspects of culture and relationships. Many authors point to factors relating to parenting style, community characteristics, environmental factors, and family dynamics as playing a role in the development and maintenance of conduct and conduct-related disorders. Additional risk factors include low socioeconomic status, teenage pregnancy, lack of social networks, marital instability, and mood disorders (Christophersen & VanScoyoc, 2013). As it relates to parenting styles, Freeze, Burke, and Vorster (2014) revealed that parenting styles that are described as "authoritative" tend to be more associated with healthy and positive child trajectories. Those family parenting styles in which an "authoritarian" or "neglecting" parenting style resulted in less prosocial outcomes over time. Less helpful parenting characteristics are described as being harsh, rigid, and punitive. Lack of clear rules and the inconsistent application of those rules tend to contribute to conduct issues as well. Freeze et al. (2014) also noted that families in which permissive mothers and overly controlling fathers were present were indicated in cases where boys demonstrated conduct-disordered behaviors. Lack of parental school involvement and lack of cognitive stimulation from parents is related to the development of conduct disorders (Christophersen & VanScoyoc, 2013).

Raudino, Fergusson, Woodward, and Horwood (2013) examined the process through which conduct problems were passed from generation to generation. Looking across generations, these researchers found links between the behaviors of grandparents, parents, and children, which are indicative of a process whereby conduct-disordered behaviors were passed down from grandparent, to parent, to child through the process of modeling and social learning. Their research further indicated a link between conduct-related issues in parents and conduct-related problems in their children. It can be deducted that the family environment may support and encourage antisocial/conduct-disordered behaviors in children and grandchildren, thus perpetuating the problem at hand. During early developmental stages of life, parents serve as the primary agents of socialization, and thus, what is taught to children in the early years influences behavior in later years (Vandervelt-Adriance et al., 2015).

Approaching the issue of conduct disorders from a different perspective, Vandervelt-Adriance et al. (2015) explored factors that served as protective factors to the development of conduct-disordered behavior. Protective factors were examined on child, family, and community levels. The authors speak of the child-related factors of temperament and inhibitory control. *Temperament* is related to self-regulate and manage behavioral and emotional responses to situations. *Inhibitory control* is defined as "the capacity to plan and suppress inappropriate actions" (Rothbart, Ahadi, & Evans, 2000, as cited in Vandervelt-Adriance et al., 2015, p. 126). This trait is related to the ability to control and manage appropriate and inappropriate behaviors. Inhibitory control is also related to lesser rates of aggression and the development of prosocial behavior.

From the family, the child needs to receive clear expectations and guidelines for behavior. Skills should be modeled, taught, and developed. Additionally, parents need to be warm, responsive, and have the ability to anticipate the needs of the child, and be prepared to satisfy those needs effectively. Lower levels of conduct problems are related to warm, nurturing parents, and a consistent supply of warm, nurturing behaviors. Maternal social support is also indicated in the literature as being conducive to lower levels of conduct problems in children (Vandervelt-Adriance et al., 2015).

Environmental quality is also related to behavior. Many studies have examined the quality of neighborhood and its relation to conduct in general (Henggeler & Sheidow, 2012; Raudino et al., 2013; Vandervelt-Adriance et al., 2015). High neighborhood quality is seen as a protective factor against conduct problems. High-quality neighborhoods are described as those neighborhoods characterized by "high social cohesion, control, and low crime" (Jafee et al., 2007, as cited in Vandervelt-Adriance et al., 2015, p. 67).

With all of this in mind, we must be mindful, once again, of the impact and influence of culture and context on the way that we view, or most importantly, assess and diagnose conduct-disordered behaviors. Mizock and Harkins (2011) bring to light the issue of diagnostic bias and its impact on the way clinicians view the diagnosis of conduct disorder.

The authors point out that Conduct Disorder is overdiagnosed in populations of color. They go on to describe the impact of overdiagnosis in people of color on academic performance, treatment in the criminal justice system, and mental health care. In terms of the impact on mental health care, Mizock and Harkins (2011) describe how conduct-disordered behaviors are often comorbid with depression, separation anxiety, and adjustment disorders. It could be that the exhibition of conduct-disordered behaviors is symptomatic of underlying disorders that go untreated due to what they define as "diagnostic bias." To overcome this diagnostic bias, Mizock and Harkins (2011) suggest clinicians engage in a culturally sensitive diagnostic process in which they are fully informed of how socioeconomic status, violence, and racial discrimination all play a role in behavioral presentations.

Many factors play a role in human behavior. In this section we have reviewed some of the relational and cultural factors that we must consider when we are categorizing disruptive, impulse control, and conduct disorders. The reader has an understanding of the significant role of culture and context, and the importance of considering culture and context in the assessment and diagnosis of these or any other disorders, and these complex features will be present in each and every family with whom the family counselor works. Treatment and intervention must be tailored to the unique needs of each family, and the first step in effective treatment planning lies in a thorough, professional, and culturally insightful assessment of the family before us.

FAMILY SYSTEMS ASSESSMENTS

Assessment is the process through which the family counselor is able to gain insight into the family, their presenting problems, and their context. Through the assessment process, the family counselor learns as much as possible about the family. He or she may use formal and informal methods of assessment in an effort to establish this clear picture of the family. At this point, it is necessary to emphasize the fact that as family counselors, we must go beyond assessing the individual. We may have an identified patient with a diagnosis of Intermittent Explosive Disorder, but what does that mean to the systemic clinician, with his or her own set of theories, interventions, and treatment goals? What do we assess once an individual has a diagnosis and presents with his or her family in our office?

As systemic clinicians, we look at things systemically. We have a certain set of assumptions as we move forward with our assessment process. Rather than focus on the behaviors of the identified patient, we look deeper into the family processes behind that behavior. We look at relationship patterns within the family and we focus our attentions on the systemic processes that support, maintain, or encourage any dysfunctional behavior. Thomlinson (2007) sets forth five distinct concepts that allow the family counselor to see things systemically:

1. The family as a system is greater than the sum of its individual systems.
2. The family system performs functions.
3. The family system develops systems and subsystems.
4. The family system is constantly evolving, attempting to strike a balance between change and stability.
5. Family behaviors are best understood as being a product of circular causality, rather than a linear progression of behaviors.

Once the systemic clinician views behavior as a function of a family system, we can look at any given behavior much differently and treat accordingly. There are a few different methods and guidelines through which we may assess the family from a systemic perspective. The first is through an informal process of assessment. Informal assessments allow us to gather information about the family through the use of observations, interviews, or self-report methods (Flamez, Hicks, & Clark, as cited in Capuzzi & Stauffer,

2015). Informal assessments allow the family counselor to gather a large amount of useful information in a rather unstructured or semistructured manner. Informal assessments allow the family counselor to gather rich, detailed information that more formal methods of assessment may miss or disregard.

Despite the absence of the GARF Scale in the *DSM-5*, other instruments have been included, some of which may be useful for the systemic clinician. For example, as mentioned earlier, the *DSM-5* includes Cross-Cutting Symptom Measures (CCSMs). CCSMs can be very useful to the systemic clinician. They provide the systemic clinician with additional insight into the various influential factors in the presentation of symptoms. They may be used to enhance the initial diagnostic process in general, and they may also be used to track improvement or decompensation of the client's presenting symptoms over time (APA, 2013).

These CCSMs are available in two forms: (a) patient–informant and (b) parent–guardian forms. Both of these may be useful to the family counselor for obvious reasons. The adult version of the CCSM assesses 13 various psychiatric domains, including anger, mania, suicidal ideation, and substance abuse, among others. The parent–guardian version of the CCSM assesses 12 various psychiatric domains, including but not limited to depression, sleep disturbance, repetitive thoughts, substance abuse, and inattention. (These instruments are available online at www.psychiatry.org/dsm5). General guidelines for their use include using these tools at various intervals to track changes. It is also suggested that the same person conduct the assessment over time, using the same informant, parent, or guardian as the source of information, as familiarity with the individual may add to the validity of the assessment. Higher scores in any specific domain indicate the need for further investigation and intervention. The use of clinical judgment in decision making, guided by ethical and professional standards, is encouraged in the use and application of these and all assessment processes (APA, 2013).

The Cultural Formulation Interview (CFI) is of particular interest to the family counselor. Structurally, the CFI assesses four domains of the client experience: (a) Cultural Definition of the Problem, (b) Cultural Perceptions of Cause, Context, and Support, (c) Cultural Factors Affecting Self-Coping and Past Help Seeking, and (d) Cultural Factors Affecting Current Help Seeking. The CFI is a 16-question interview, available in self-report and informant versions, conducted to "obtain information during a mental health assessment about the impact of culture on key aspects of an individual's clinical presentation and care."(APA, 2013). The CFI assesses various aspects of the client's culture, such as "aspects of an individual's background . . . and current social contexts that may affect his or her perspective . . .; the influence of family, friends, and other community members on the individual's experience and other areas of concern" (APA, 2013).

The CFI appears to be a systemically grounded instrument. It asks questions related to family background, relational factors, and other systemic issues that might have a significant impact on behavior, cognition, or emotions. While not purely a method for family assessment, it can clearly yield helpful information for the systemic clinician's use during the treatment planning process. The CFI can be found at www.psychiatry.org/psychiatrists/practice/dsm/dsm-5/online-assessment-measures.

As these things are included in the *DSM-5*, it is practical to make use of them. The V-Z codes as they relate to family and relational functioning should be indicated on any systemic assessment and summary of diagnostic findings. These instruments—the Cross-cutting measures and the CFI—should be a part of the family assessment process. More discussion on the use and application of these items occurs later in the chapter.

When a family or couple first arrives in your office, a general systemic assessment is necessary. A structured or semistructured interview is suggested. Christophersen and VanScoyoc (2013) point out the value of the clinical interview as a tool in identifying disruptive behaviors in children. At a minimum, this general assessment should address each of the following domains of family functioning (Gehart & Tuttle, 2003; Gladding, 2011; Thomlinson, 2007):

The presenting issue

- This is the primary reason the family is seeking services. The family counselor/systemic clinician should make an extended effort to ask the family, "What brings you to family counseling?" or some other question that allows the family to explain their reasons for being there. In some cases, especially those cases that are referred to us, we might tend to let the referring agency/clinician influence our ideas about the families need for services. This is especially true when a family has been referred due to a behavioral concern with a child.

Composition and organization of the family

- Here, the family is essentially defined. Of whom the family consists and how the family is organized are made clear. Because families are so diverse, we should not let our own ideas about family cloud getting a clear picture of the client family. We work with nuclear families, single parent families, same sex families, and extended families, among others. In many cases, the family may be defined as including members of the community, such as faith leaders and nonblood "kin." We also seek answers to questions like, "Who makes the rules?" and "What are the subsystems in this family?"

Family processes

- In general, we look for insight into how the family operates. Communication patterns, behavioral patterns, and daily functioning are areas we could investigate. A straight-forward approach in this area might be asking the family to describe a typical day, or to describe what it looks like in the family when they are arguing. We are looking for information related to how the family system might be contributing to, or addressing the presenting problem.

Emotional atmosphere

- In this section, the family counselor seeks to get an overall understanding of warmth, emotional availability, and responsiveness of the family. We seek to get a glimpse into things like the tone and range of feelings expressed in the family. Empathy is considered as well. Here we might note how parents and children express emotions, and when they do express these emotions, how does the family system respond? Are children allowed to express emotions and do parents respond accordingly, without shutting down the emotional expression of another family member? Parental responsiveness has been associated with social competence, moral development, and self-regulated behavior (Wilson & Durbin, 2013).

Strengths, resources, and connections

- In this area, we seek information about the many things the family is doing right. We want to know how the family is meeting its needs and what it has been doing in order to make it to this point in time. We want to know the resources on which the family depends for survival or maintenance. Connections to school systems, medical care, family support, and community connections/activity may be considered areas for assessment at this point.

Crises and safety concerns

- It is paramount that we assess safety and risk concerns during the family assessment. We need to be concerned with physical safety, as well as the possibility of abuse and neglect. Specifically, the family counselor is concerned about any type of physical (including sexual) and psychological abuse, domestic violence, or any suicidal/homicidal ideations, threats, or attempts (Petridis & Hannan, 2011). The systemic clinician must be able to contact the appropriate agencies and community resources in an effort to ensure the safety of the family and the necessary supports it needs to move past concerns of safety and risk. Communities vary widely in terms of the resources available. Additionally, access to these various resources varies widely from place to place. Systemic clinicians should network with the various agencies and resources in any given area in order to facilitate a quick and effective referral and response process in the event of any critical concern, such as suicidal ideation or domestic violence.

Substance use

- The systemic clinician should assess for the presence of substance use in the family. Its effects are often felt on the nuclear family and in the extended family, often reaching into other parts of the family's life, such as work and school. Family members experience the range of emotions, from guilt to embarrassment. Diagnosticians might ask questions directly about substance use. Questions such as: "Does anyone in the family have a problem with alcohol or drugs?" "Is there a family history of substance use?" "Has anyone ever been in trouble at school or at work because of substance use?"

Intimacy

- Intimacy can be defined broadly and is not necessarily defined by sexuality, although sexuality can certainly be considered an aspect of intimacy. Hook, Gerstein, Detterich, and Gridley (2003) define intimacy as being a "multidimensional concept" inclusive of (a) love and affection—the awareness that they are cared for by another person or persons, (b) personal validation—knowing that you are loved and appreciated. There is a general sense of feeling accepted and appreciated when this is present, (c) trust—made evident by having a sense of safety, privacy, and confidentiality, and (d) self-disclosure, or having a feeling that it is safe to render oneself vulnerable and being comfortable with revealing secrets, facts, and intimate details of their lives to their partner.

Culture and context

- The importance of understanding the culture and context of your client family was explained earlier. Specific areas to assess and consider include the following (Canfield, 2015; Corey, 2009; Thomlinson, 2007): immigrant status vis-à-vis the dominant culture; socioeconomic status; education; ethnicity; religion; gender; age; race, discrimination, and oppression; minority or majority status; demographic background.

Collateral information

- The systemic clinician should gather information from multiple sources throughout the assessment process. A consideration should be given to teachers, other care providers, school counselors, and especially parents and other family members. Many of the behaviors shown by those with conduct-disordered behaviors are subtle, and only reveal themselves in restricted environments. As that is the case, multiple perspectives on the behaviors and sources of information are necessary (Buitelaar et al, 2013).

Comorbidity

- The family, as a whole and individually, should be assessed for comorbid disorders. The diagnostician looks for complicating issues as they relate to mood disorders, anxiety disorders, and substance use disorders. Past experiences with the recovery process need to be explored as well. The systemic clinician should also gather information related to the presence of learning disorders (Buitelaar et al., 2013).

Systemic clinicians note that the *DSM-5* contains both a Clinician-Rated Severity of Oppositional Defiant Disorder Scale and a Clinician-Rated Severity of Conduct Disorder Scale. (available at www.psychiatry.org/psychiatrists/practice/dsm/dsm-5/online-assessment-measures).

These rating scales can give the systemic clinician more insight into the presenting diagnosis. In addition, they provide the systemic clinician with a framework through which to gauge symptom severity. For example, the Clinician-Rated Severity of Oppositional Defiant Disorder scale focuses on the number of presenting symptoms in various settings, and rates severity on a scale from Level 0—None to Level 3—Severe. The Clinician-Rated Severity of Conduct Disorder focuses on risk of harm or injury to others. This scale also rates severity on a scale from Level 0—None, to Level 3—Severe.

Cross-cutting measures provide additional insight into the presenting issues that may be evident during the assessment process. These CCSMs are available on the adult self-report version and the parent–guardian-rated version. Systemic counselors can use the information gained from these instruments to further refine the assessment findings, and tailor interventions accordingly. "The adult version consists of 23 questions that assess 13 psychiatric domains. Areas assessed include depression, anger, suicidal ideation, sleep problems, and substance use among others" (APA, 2013, p. 734). The parent–guardian-rated version seeks information from adult parents and caregivers and is intended for children ages 6 to 17. On the parent–guardian version, 25 questions assess 12 psychiatric domains, including "depression, anger, mania, inattention, substance use, and irritability (p. 734)," among others (APA, 2013). A child-rated version, for children ages 11 to 17, is available online at www.psychiatry.org/dsm5.

Clinician-Rated Severity Rating Scales

Two clinician-rated severity scales pertain to the topic of this chapter. The Clinician-Rated Severity of Oppositional Defiant Disorder and the Clinician-Rated Severity of Conduct Disorder are available at www.psychiatry.org/psychiatrists/practice/dsm/dsm-5/online-assessment-measures.

The Clinician-Rated Severity of Oppositional Defiant Disorder Scale asks clinicians to rate the severity of the clinical presentation, particularly in relation to the number of symptoms and number of settings in which the behaviors take place. This scale is intended to provide the clinician with additional insight into the behavioral manifestation of symptoms over the past 7 days. It is suggested that the scale be completed initially and at ongoing intervals throughout the treatment process. Severity is rated on a 4-point scale, ranging from 0, meaning no symptoms are present, to 4, meaning that the clinical presentation is "severe."

The Clinician-Rated Severity of Conduct Disorder Scale invites the clinician to rate severity of conduct disorder in terms of the degree or severity of harm to others based on the clinician's clinical judgment. Severity is rated on a 4-point scale, and in similar fashion to the aforementioned rating scale, it is intended to rate the severity of behaviors in the past 7 days. Again, it is suggested that the systemic clinician complete the scale in an ongoing manner.

The Cultural Formulation Interview

- The CFI was discussed earlier in this chapter. For further direction and guidance, consult the *DSM-5*, or find the document at www.psychiatry.org/psychiatrists/practice/dsm/dsm-5/online-assessment-measures.

Theory-Based Assessment

Theory provides us with a framework through which we view the client problem. Theory provides us with a way to encase problems, and it gives us insight into how we need to address the given problem. For example, a structural family therapist can relate any given family concern, issue, or problem to challenges in the family system—namely with the family's boundaries, alignments, and power structure. For example, during an assessment, the counselor notes that the younger children often overrule parental instructions. This would indicate an unhealthy power structure in the family. Theoretically, the parental hierarchy needs to hold the most power in the family. Thus, the structural family therapists make an effort to further assess the pattern and intervene as appropriate. As structural family therapy views the presenting problem through those lenses, the counselor also views the solution to the problem. Just as the counselor formulates a theoretical hypothesis about the presenting problem, he or she formulates a consistent theoretical hypothesis about the solution to the problem. This theoretical hypothesis about the solution includes the same theoretical language used to describe the problem. The following section goes into greater detail about how theory is applied to presenting problems, as well as to the solution.

Standardized Assessment Instruments

In addition to the general, or informal, clinical interview, several formal and specific instruments are identified in the literature as helping assess and diagnose disruptive behavior disorders. Buitelaar et al., 2013; Christophersen and VanScoyoc, 2013; and Barry, Golmaryami, Rivera-Hudson, & Frick, 2013 discuss the use of several different structured psychiatric interview guides applicable to the assessment of conduct-disordered behaviors. The structured interview guides include the Diagnostic Interview Schedule for Children (Shaffer, Fisher, Lucas, Dulcan, & Schwab-Stone, 2000), the Schedule for Affective Disorders and Schizophrenia for School Age Children—Present and Lifetime (Ambrosini, 2000, as cited in Barry et al., 2013), the Child Attachment and Play Assessment (Farnfield, 2015), the Diagnostic Interview for Children and Adolescents (Herjanic & Campbell, 1977), and the Development and Well-Being Assessment (Goodman, Ford, Richards, Gatward, & Meltzer, 2000). The family counselor should consider the use of these in any comprehensive approach to the assessment of conduct problems. Practical considerations such as cost, applicability, time, normative factors, and appropriateness should guide the clinician in the choice and use of any standardized interview tool. These assessments place a great deal of emphasis on individual assessment. The systemic clinician can make use of them in many ways. The information gained from these instruments should be shared with the parent–guardian in the family in an open and honest way. Parents and caregivers should be given the information in such a way that it makes sense and promotes collaboration and understanding. Furthermore, the counselor could use the results of the instrument to guide treatment planning. For example, if it were to be revealed through an assessment tool, such as the Development and Well-Being Assessment, that the child has a behavioral disorder, that particular disorder should be directly addressed in the treatment plan.

Common assessment tools for the assessment of conduct problems are discussed by Barry et al. (2013); Buitelaar et al. (2013); and Christophersen and VanScoyoc (2013). The assessment tools are considered under the categories of broad band rating scales and narrow band rating scales. *Broad band rating scales* assess behaviors on a broader scale, and consider issues that impact behaviors from a wider perspective. *Narrow band rating scales* assess behaviors in the context of specific diagnostic categories. Broad band rating scales generally may not specifically or directly assess the presence of a conduct disorder. Rather, these broad band scales offer a more complex picture of the behaviors in context of other comorbid behaviors. Even though these assessment tools may not be completely congruent with specific diagnostic criteria, they may point out other behaviors or concerns that may be addressed in the treatment-planning process (Barry et al., 2013). Examples of broad band rating scales include the Behavior Assessment System for Children—2 (Reynolds &

Kamphaus, 2004), the Child Behavior Checklist (Achenbach & Rescorla, 2001), and the Strengths and Difficulties Questionnaire (Goodman, 1997).

The assessment of callous–unemotional traits is recommended by Barry et al. (2013). To assess these specific traits, the use of the antisocial process screening device and the inventory of callous–unemotional traits is discussed. The antisocial process screening device (Frick & Hare, 2001) gathers information from multiple informants on a 20-item questionnaire to assess the presence and impact of callous–unemotional traits. Callous–unemotional traits are exemplified by fearlessness, the lack of empathy or remorse, and deficient emotional expression (Barry et al., 2013, p. 58). The inventory of callous–unemotional traits (Frick & White, 2008) is suggested for the presence of callous–unemotional traits (Barry et al., 2013; Buitelaar et al., 2013). Findings of callous–unemotional traits can and should be considered an area of systemic intervention. Hawes and Dadds (2005, as cited in Barry et al., 2013) discuss how interventions are aimed at teaching parents the use of positive reinforcement and encouraging prosocial behavior as possible strategies in clinical settings.

In addition to the specific assessment of conduct-related disorders and behaviors, the clinician should consider the use of standardized family assessment instruments. The use of these instruments helps provide the clinician with detailed knowledge as it relates to strengths, characteristics, and family functioning (Flamez et al., as cited in Capuzzi & Stauffer, 2015). The trend among family counselors is to rely more heavily on informal assessment measures and clinical interviews, yet the many standardized assessment tools could greatly assist the gathering of the complex, complicated information needed to thoroughly assess the families with whom we work (Flamez et al., as cited in Capuzzi & Stauffer, 2015; Gladding, 2011).

Gladding (2011) discusses the availability of over 1,000 assessment instruments that may be useful for the systemic clinician. When selecting assessments for clinical evaluation, systemic clinicians should exercise a practical approach to their implementation. Consult reference works, such as the *Mental Measurements Yearbook,* or Tests in Print; review scholarly journals and abstracts, reviews of the test, and test manuals for information that would help guide selection of these instruments. A review of normative information, reliability, and validity should always be a part of your test selection process. The tools that are chosen should be culturally appropriate and free from gender bias (Thomlinson, 2007). A few of these instruments are reviewed in the next sections.

The family assessment device by Epstein, Baldwin, and Bishop (1983) can be used for several different purposes: as an initial screening instrument to detect the presence of problems within a family system; to identify the specific areas in which families are experiencing problems; and to monitor progress and change over time.

Marital Satisfaction Inventory

The *Marital Satisfaction Inventory, Revised* is used to measure "the nature and extent of conflict within a marriage or relationship." (Snyder, 1997, p. 1). The test consists of 150 True/False questions (fewer if there are no children in the family) in a 25-minute time frame. The instrument measures such things as affective communication, aggression, child-rearing practices, sexual dissatisfaction, and global distress. The instrument provides a nice way to initiate the process of family counseling, and it also offers suggestions for treatment and intervention.

Conflict Tactics Scales and Conflict Tactics Scales 2

The Conflict Tactics Scales and the Conflict Tactics Scales 2 by Straus (1979, 1995) are tools used to assess violence in families and intimate relationships. Each is available in an updated version. The Conflict Tactics Scales 2 can be administered in 10 minutes or less, and it contains 78 items. The questions inquire about the behaviors in the partner and in the respondent. The Conflict Tactics Scales is widely used in cases to gain data as it relates to physical assaults against a partner. New scales have been included in the newer versions that assess sexual coercion and an injury scale.

The instruments reviewed previously are a sampling of the many tools available to the systemic clinician. As noted earlier, there are many reliable and valid tools available to the family counselor. The systemic clinician should consider the use of these instruments in an effort to provide a thorough, complex, and comprehensive picture of the family. The remainder of the counseling process depends heavily on gathering reliable data about the family. Accurate diagnosis and assessment lead to an accurate treatment plan, and ultimately to the well-being of the families we serve. As that is the case, any assessment should include numerous and varied sources of information.

Systemic clinicians may also make use of behavioral observation methods to collect assessment data. These observational techniques can be conducted in a structured or unstructured manner. Structured observational techniques involve the counselor assigning a task to the family, and then observing the family's approach to the task. For example, the counselor may suggest that the family negotiate a mutually agreeable time for the children to be in bed each night. After assigning the task, the counselor attends to communication patterns, power differentials, family alignment, and coalitions. Unstructured observational techniques involve the counselor simply paying attention to family interaction patterns during the assessment. For example, during the first family session, the counselor notes that the children respond more respectfully to one parent as opposed to the other parent. The systemic clinician may make a clinical hypothesis about this interaction and note it for future assessment and possible intervention.

In this section, we have discussed the assessment process and its importance to the process of family counseling. At this point, the family counselor is aware of formal and informal methods of discovering the richness that each family brings to the session. Structured interview techniques and standardized instruments are available to us. The importance of the assessment process cannot be emphasized enough. The information gathered during this assessment process should be as thorough and accurate as possible, using multiple sources of information. The assessment process informs the way that we intervene with our families. Now that we have a sound awareness of the assessment process, let us move to a discussion of how we might intervene with our families.

FAMILY SYSTEMS INTERVENTIONS

The interventions should be targeted to the issues revealed throughout the assessment process. In general, the intervention should be geared toward empowering the family. The interventions should be systemically oriented and should address the issue from different levels. The systemic clinician should consider involving other parts of the system. For example, many families and children are referred to us by school counselors, faith leaders, or medical providers. As that is the case, those other parts of the system—those who refer clients to us—should be considered a vital part of the treatment process in some way (Buitelaar et al., 2013). In an effort to address the needs of families faced with the challenges associated with disruptive, impulse control, and conduct disorders, we discuss evidence-based practices (EBPs) and common factors approaches.

Evidence-Based Practices

The recent movement toward the integration of EBP has resulted in the emergence of many different models intended to address the issue of conduct disorders and antisocial behavior. Henggeler and Sheidow (2012) discuss the standards for determination if an intervention can be considered "evidence based." Those standards are that "1) the intervention had to demonstrate favorable decreases in antisocial behavior in randomized clinical trials among conduct disordered or delinquent adolescents, 2) demonstrate replicability across two different research teams, 3) demonstrate sustained effects for at least 12 months." (pp. 33–34). Many authors have suggested the use of these evidence-based interventions (Buitelaar et al., 2013; Christophersen & VanScoyoc, 2013; Henggeler & Sheidow, 2012; Kaslow, Broth, Smith, & Collins, 2012; Scudder, Herschell, & McNeil, 2016). Time and space allow for only a summary of a few of these interventions. Systemic clinicians should be aware of the many different EBPs, and engage in a process of discovery so as to determine the correct models for their unique families, practice settings, and community needs.

Parent–Child Interaction Therapy

Christophersen and VonSocyoc (2013), Funderburk and Eyburg (2011), and Kaslow et al. (2012) describe parent–child interaction therapy as an evidence-based intervention designed with the intention of application to families with children diagnosed with disruptive behavioral disorders. The intervention is intended for children ages 2.5 to 7 years and their parents. The *DSM-5* notes that these symptoms can emerge during the preschool years, middle childhood, and early adolescence (APA, 2013). Children and parents attend between 12 and 20 sessions, which are 1 hour in length. Parent–child interaction therapy (PCIT) targets parent–child interaction processes, especially targeting the skills of praise and reflection. The intervention also teaches parents to avoid certain things, such as critical responses, questions, and commands (Christophersen & VanScoyoc, 2013). Parents are encouraged to be more nurturing and positive over the course of the intervention. Particular attention is given in helping parents use appropriate reactions and consistent disciplinary practices. Outcome studies have shown many benefits, among which are decreased parental stress, decreased child behavioral problems, and increased parenting skills. Of note are the findings that the effects of the intervention often extend to those parts of the system that are not directly engaged in the process of therapy, such as school and home settings. Effects are also noted in children and siblings not directly involved in counseling (Scudder et al., 2016).

For training guidelines, further research, and other resources about PCIT consult the voluminous information available to the clinician through PCIT International (www.pcit. org). Training involves a classroom element and ongoing consultation with PCIT trainers.

Multisystemic Therapy

Multisystemic therapy (MST) is "an intensive family and community based treatment that addresses the multiple determinants of serious anti-social behavior in juvenile offenders" (MST White Paper—available at www.mstservices.com). MST approaches problem behaviors with the understanding that a juvenile's behavior can be influenced by many relational, social, and environmental factors. The website for the MST organization, www.mstserv ices.com, lists several significant accomplishments of this approach. MST has shown effectiveness in:

- Reduction of out-of-home placements of up to 50%
- Improved school attendance
- Reduction of rearrest rates of up to 70%
- Improved family relationships and family functioning
- Decreased psychiatric symptoms in adolescents
- Decreased substance use in adolescents

Gladding (2011) and Haley (as cited in Capuzzi & Stauffer, 2015; Buitelaar et al., 2013; Hengeller & Sheidow 2012) have examined multisystem therapy and summarized the characteristics of that intervention. Hengeller and Sheidow (2012) describe MST as "one of the most extensively validated and widely transported evidence-based psychological treatments." (p. 34). MST is provided for 60 hours over the course of 3 to 5 months. The approach is grounded in general systems theory, behavioral parent training, and cognitive behavioral therapy. MST is also grounded firmly in Bronfrenbrenner's theory of social ecology (1979, as cited in Hengeller & Sheidow (2012). Bronfrenbrenner's theory posits that human behavior should be considered in the context of other influential aspects of the environment in which we live. Each layer of our ecological system influences, and is influenced by, behavior. As individuals, we are influenced by many things, such as the school environment, the world of work, our family system, and other larger institutions. As all of these parts of the ecosystem influence us, these parts of the system should be considered during the assessment process. They should also be accessed as an aid to change during the treatment process. Other theoretical influences are structural family therapy, Haley's strategic formulations, and social learning theory. This approach not only recognizes the internal functions of a family that influence behavior; it also recognizes the impact of schools, communities, and families as having an impact on adolescent behavior. For example, as children enter the school system, they may be exposed to behaviors that are very different than those behaviors expected or tolerated in the home. Should that be the case, the family system may experience additional stress as it relates to communication, discipline, and interaction with other parts of the ecosystem. In cases such as this, it is within the realm of possibilities that the clinician may encourage the family to engage in communication with the school in an effort to address behavioral concerns. Simultaneously, the clinician may work with the family in an effort to develop additional strategies for behavioral management in the home.

MST is provided in a team format, including a mix of junior- and senior-level clinicians, and doctoral-level practitioners. The MST team typically works with only four to six families at one time due to the intense nature of the intervention. Team members rotate being on-call. MST is responsible for the implementation and program development of MST in the community. Contact MST Services for further assistance and information, or visit their website at mstservices.com.

Functional Family Therapy

Functional family therapy (FFT) is an evidence-based treatment approach that was developed for the purpose of addressing severe behavioral problems in adolescents (Gladding, 2011; Graham, Carr, Rooney, Sexton, & Wilson Satterfield, 2014; Hengeller & Sheidow, 2012; Oliver & Castillo, as cited in Capuzzi & Stauffer, 2015; Sexton & Tumer, 2010). FFT has a long and extensive research history, beginning with the first study published over 40 years ago. Goals of the intervention are to replace dysfunctional family functioning with healthier and more productive activities. FFT integrates several theoretical perspectives inclusive of behavioral and cognitive behavioral in the context of a relational or systemic focus. From the perspective of the clinician who practices FFT, all behavior serves a function in the context of the family, and avoids placing blame on any singular individual. The approach is broken down into several stages with distinct goals for each stage. The three-stage process is summarized in the following sections:

Stage 1—Assessment

The family is assessed in terms of behaviors and the functions they serve. A great deal of emphasis is placed on engagement and rapport building. Clinicians avoid confrontation and focus on gaining a thorough understanding of the behavior in context of family functioning. During this stage, counselors halt negative family reactions and reframe the interactions in an effort to give the family a different perspective on their actions. For example, during the assessment, a clinician notices that one family member consistently speaks over another family member. In that case, the clinician may raise awareness of the process, discuss possible strategies, and practice the new learned behavior in an attempt to improve communication and prevent the instance from happening again.

Stage 2—Behavioral Change
New behaviors replace the negative behaviors of old. A focus is placed on helping the family learn more adaptive and effective behaviors. Various interventions can be used here and they can be drawn from other approaches such as cognitive behavioral therapy and general systems theory in an effort to promote healthier family functioning. For example, enactments, a tool taken from structural family therapy, are often used for this purpose. During an enactment, the counselor may suggest different strategies for addressing any given problem. The counselor, along with the family, may develop strategies for implementation. During the enactment, the counselor serves as a coach and guide as the family learns to integrate the new behavior. As the family experiments with the new behavior, the counselor provides feedback and support while growth is taking place.

Stage 3—Maintenance
During this stage, the counselor focuses on moving the new behaviors out into the family's real world. The skills learned in counseling are put to the test at home, at school, and in the community. The process of termination becomes a reality during this stage when the family can demonstrate the "motivation, skills, and resources needed to maintain a positive clinical trajectory" (Waldron & Brody, 2010, as cited in Hengeller & Sheidow, 2012, p. 43). As families adopt newer, more effective strategies, and are able to demonstrate the ability to come up with strategies on their own, the clinician can anticipate the day when termination from services becomes a reality. The clinician looks for a new sense of power and autonomy in the family systems as demonstrated by the family's ability to solve its own problems, come up with its own solutions, and rely less and less on the counselor for feedback and guidance. At this time, the prospect of termination should be introduced into the conversation.

FFT Incorporated (www.fftllc.com) manages the implementation and development of FFT. A three-phase process for the implementation of FFT involves counselor training, site self-sufficiency and on-site supervisor development, and program maintenance, which includes ongoing consultation, supervision, and maintenance in order to ensure fidelity to the model.

Medical/Pharmacotherapy

Pottick, Warner, Vander Stoep, and Knight (2014) summarize resources that describe the prevalence of psychotropic medication use among children and adolescents. As that is the case, the family counselor can expect to interact with medical professionals. They should also expect to see the use of psychotropic medications by children in the families with whom they provide services. Consequently, a familiarity with these medications is necessary. Counselors should seek information about commonly prescribed medicines, their uses, side effects, and routes of administration (Christophersen & VanScoyoc, 2013).

Systemic clinicians are urged to be mindful of scope of practice and competence issues. Licensed medical professionals should lead the way in terms of concerns related to medication use. Even though counselors may be familiar with the common medications, they must ensure that they do not suggest, recommend, or otherwise provide medical information about psychotropic medications. Medical professionals are trained and competent in the prescription of medicines. Counselors, as part of a systemic approach, can be helpful in this process, though, while still operating within their scope of practice. Counselors might inquire about medication adherence, side effects, and benefits. As the counselor learns about this information, the systemic clinician would be in a position to relay any concerns about medication, and he or she could encourage and/or facilitate conversations with medical professionals about medication concerns.

Sources of information about prescription medications include PDR.net (www.pdr.net), the U.S. Food and Drug Administration (www.fda.gov/Drugs), and through the web-based resources for the prescription drug itself. Drug information can be useful for the family in several different ways. For example, a child may be prescribed a certain drug with warnings that a possible side effect is depression or sadness. Having this type of information might empower parents to make a more informed decision on the taking of the drug for their child. Likewise, should parents decide the medication is appropriate for their child, they would be alerted to any significant changes in their child's behavior. This could make the parents more attentive to their child, thus empowering them as parents, and helping them to be better advocates for their child's well-being.

For all of the benefits that evidence-based practices (EBPs) bring to the field, practitioners express concern that these "manualized" treatments detract from the flexibility that is needed in working with families. Other clinicians fear that these treatment approaches encroach upon the creativity needed in professional practice. Many of these EBPs are costly and require consultation or employment of specifically trained personnel (Haley, as cited in Capuzzi & Stauffer, 2015). As with anything else in the clinical world, costs and benefits must be weighed, and clinical decisions must be made. Additionally, EBPs and other standardized approaches to intervention and treatment should be evaluated for cultural appropriateness. Systemic clinicians should consult cross-cultural variables, normative data, and other scholarly resources when determining the culturally appropriate use of any intervention.

The Common Factors Approach

An ongoing discussion in the field of counseling, and in the field of family counseling specifically, revolves around the use of evidence practices and common factors in therapy. While EBPs show many promises, there is also concern in the profession that these EBPs are limited in their application to real world issues presented in family therapy. Several authors (Karam, Blow, Sprinkle, and Davis, 2015; Kaslow et al., 2012; Lebow, 2014) have argued for the inclusion, consideration, and integration of "common factors" in practice in an effort to bring some degree of balance to the rigid application of EBPs.

The term *common factors* refers to those things that are responsible for change and growth in families that are not specified in distinct models of intervention. Specific common factors include a consideration of the following (Karam et al., 2015; Lebow, 2014):

Client Factors

Families and their individual members bring strengths and resources to the therapeutic process. In many cases, the family is unaware of those strengths and resources, and some of those positive aspects may be elusive for the family counselor. The family counselor needs to appreciate the contributions made by the individual and family. At some level, the family has done something to survive. They have engaged in their own process of staying afloat through negotiation, change, communication, and bargaining in most cases. At a minimum, the survival instinct in the family needs to be appreciated. For example, we often see families who are challenged in many ways: substance use, aggression, criminal activity, and so forth. Despite all of these negative attributes, the family has somehow managed to survive over the years. They have survived because they have adapted to social and environmental conditions that many would consider unlivable. Even though these adaptations may be unhealthy of dysfunctional, they *are* adaptations nonetheless, and these show evidence that the family does have flexibility and that it does have the ability to adapt to stressful conditions in the environment. Those survival traits need to be recognized and the family made aware of them. Possibilities for more healthy and functional adaptive behaviors can be hoped for.

The Therapeutic Alliance

Several factors contribute to the therapeutic alliance. We must consider the strength of the relationship between the family and the counselor as one of utmost importance. The relationship must be built on trust, openness, and impartiality. Other traits of successful therapeutic alliances include respect, acknowledgement of validation, and a willingness to work with the family on goals. The counselor must be relatable and easy to approach with challenges, fears, and contributions to the process (Shaw & Murray, 2014). Wampold (2001, as cited in Karam et al., 2015) alludes to the idea that the contributions made by the therapist are greater than those changes that come about as a result of any treatment that the family may receive.

Hope

Families often come to family counseling as a final step toward problem resolution. They have tried to solve the problem by themselves (often over a long period of time), through friends and extended family, and through the intervention of a faith leader. A state of hopelessness is pervasive. The counselor needs to provide some degree of hope for family members and the future they will share together. Show the family members in some ethical way that change is possible and that you have a deep belief in their ability to heal.

Interventions, from a common factors approach, offer a broader approach than those interventions provided in EBPs. The interventions provided from a common factors approach come from the broader theoretical perspectives that provide the foundation for systemic intervention. Structural family therapy, strategic family therapy, and cognitive behavioral therapy, among others, provide insight into how the change process works. These interventions help families grow, learn new family processes, and learn to solve their own problems.

Families need to hear how things are going. Research has pointed out the benefits of an ongoing feedback loop in the counseling process (Halford et al., 2012, as cited in Karam et al., 2015). Feedback needs to come at regular intervals. Progress toward goals, acknowledgement of change, validation of struggles, and appreciation for hard work needs to be provided to the family in an ongoing manner. The family should also be given the chance to provide feedback to the systemic clinician. Families should be invited to provide feedback about the process of counseling, their ideas about progress, and the overall satisfaction with services. For further information about the process of obtaining client feedback, and the many benefits thereof, consult Shaw and Murray (2014).

In addition to these general common factors, the practice of systemic counseling and therapy has a unique set of its own common factors (Karam et al., 2015; Lebow, 2014). They are summarized as follows:

A Systemic and Relational Conceptualization of Presenting Problems

Presenting problems are viewed through a systemic lens, rather than through the lens of individual blame or responsibility. In any given clinical situation, the problematic behavior is seen as both (a) being a function of the family and (b) serving a purpose or function in the family. As presenting problems are systemic in nature, the solution to those problems is through systemic change.

Changing Dysfunctional Family Processes

Families maintain dysfunctional behaviors for a number of reasons. First, it may be easier to maintain dysfunctional behavior than it is to change. Second, families may not be aware that they are maintaining the dysfunctional behavior. Third, families may not know how to change dysfunctional behavior. The family counselor seeks to alter the entire process around dysfunctional behavior, not through altering the behavior of one person, but by altering the behavior of the entire family. The counselor focuses on transactional patterns and interactional sequences and makes positive changes.

Recognition and Involvement of External Systems

As families both influence and are influenced by other people, families, and institutions, the systemic clinician should consider involving those other parts of the family's ecosystem. Family counselors might involve people who are not a part of the immediate family. For example, during a family assessment, this author recognized the important relationship between a school custodian and the identified patient. Following all ethical and professional protocols, the family agreed to have the school custodian come to a family session. The school custodian was able to offer the counselor and the family a great deal of insight into the child's experience at the school and the process of counseling was significantly improved as a result.

Logistical Factors

Family counseling is quite different than individual counseling in many ways. It is obvious that family counseling involves more than one person at a time, with several family members being present in a family counseling session. Managing the session effectively requires skill and systemic insight. Family counseling might be shorter in duration (2001), but in this counselor's experience, the opposite can be and is true quite often. Sessions may be longer in duration, and they may occur more or less frequently. Mixing couple, family, subsystem, and individual sessions may be considered as well, as long as the appropriate ethical and professional guidelines are followed, and the practice is pragmatic (Lebow, 2014).

This section has examined various interventions that may be used in cases involving disruptive, impulse control, and conduct disorders. EBPs contribute greatly to the body of knowledge as it relates to effective treatment and intervention. These EBPs have demonstrated positive outcomes in numerous studies and their use is rather expansive, for many influential reasons. Common factors in therapy have been discussed as well. Common factors are those things that are present in the therapeutic process, regardless of any specific model that may be applied. The systemic clinician is encouraged, once again, to explore these and all methods of intervention and to make decisions based on the needs of the family, practicality, and counselor competence.

ETHICAL AND LEGAL IMPLICATIONS

Ethical and legal concerns play a role in each and every case in which the systemic clinician is involved. In the context of disruptive, impulse control, and conduct disorders, we attend to all of the general ethical and legal issues—confidentiality, privacy, cultural sensitivity, for example. Additional ethical and legal concerns arise when disruptive, impulse control, and conduct disorders are present. This is especially true when multiple parts of the system are engaged. Parents, schools, and other caregivers all add a layer of complexity to the ethical and legal dilemmas that may present themselves over the course of treatment. Systemic clinicians find guidance in consulting the various ethical codes available through their professional organizations. Systemic clinicians will specifically attend to those guidelines offered by the American Counseling Association and the American Association for Marriage and Family Therapists (ACA, 2014; AAMFT, 2015).

Disruptive, impulse control, and conduct disorders all contain factors that may contribute to heightened risk and safety concerns for the client, family, and others. Diagnoses in this category include such behaviors and actions that may impinge upon the lives of others and bring the client and family into contact with authority figures. Specific risk factors include suicidal ideation, personal injury, damage to property, aggression, substance use, and harm to animals (Barry et al., 2013; Buitelaar et al., 2013; Corey, Corey, and McCallanan, 2011; Hengeller and Sheidow, 2012; Vander Stoep et al., 2011). As such, the systemic clinician attends to such matters through appropriate risk and safety screening.

Systemic clinicians are especially mindful of issues related to custody and guardianship in cases involving minors. A complicating factor in this issue is that the rules and regulations in relating to guardianship status may vary from state to state (Adams & Boyd, 2010). In some cases, the family that presents to counseling may be clearly constructed in terms of parental rights and responsibilities. However, in other cases, families may present with unclear boundaries relating to legal rights and responsibilities. Families who present for services may be constructed of friends, allies, nonblood kin, aunt, uncles, and/or other second- or third-order relatives. These caregivers and guardians may have assumed legal status, but they may have never obtained such status legally (Dewey & Gottlieb, 2011). As rules and regulations regarding guardianship vary across state lines, the systemic clinician must takes steps to become familiar with those various rules and regulations and practices accordingly. Custody arrangements, when present, vary from family to family. Custody arrangements delineate relationships between children and parents/caregivers in terms of parental duties and responsibilities. Systemic clinicians often encounter custody arrangements when working with families that include divorced families. Due to the unique nature of families and custody arrangements in general, systemic clinicians are encouraged to inquire about the presence of such custody arrangements, become familiar with the provisions within those arrangements, and conduct their therapeutic interactions appropriately. Guardianship status and custodial status have significant implications for the systemic clinician and attention to these issues is imperative. Such therapeutic functions as confidentiality, informed consent, privacy, and billing, among others, are impacted by custodial arrangements and guardianship status (Fridhandler & Lehmer, 2014).

Disruptive, impulse control, and conduct disorders usually present during childhood and likely involve referral from other agencies and institutions. Malmberg and Field (2013) note that childhood behavior problems are the reason behind most referrals for mental health care. These referrals come from schools, medical practices, and pastoral care facilities, among others. In general, pediatric medical service providers usually are the first to screen and refer a child for mental health or behavioral health concerns (Wong & Talmi, 2015). As the systemic clinician works with multiple care providers from various institutions, we must attend to the notion of collaboration and coordinated care. Systemic clinicians should strive to follow ethical guidelines as related to coordination and collaboration of services with other care providers. Actions such as sharing treatment plans, the frequent sharing of treatment summaries, and the active involvement of other care providers in the treatment-planning process are among the many ways systemic clinicians may engage in collaborative care.

Systemic clinicians who work with clients exhibiting symptoms of disruptive, impulse control, and conduct disorders may find themselves involved with the court system. As the behavioral manifestations may include such things as aggression, property damage, fire-setting, or stealing, clients may likely, in the past or future, find themselves involved with the judicial system, thus exposing the family system to another level of concern and involvement. This involvement may include such things as court-ordered or involuntary treatment and the rendering of expert opinions. Mental health treatment is seen as an important part of the juvenile justice process, most of this treatment being court ordered. With an emphasis on least restrictive environments, juvenile offenders and their families are seeking this court-ordered treatment from behavioral health care providers in the community (Dewey & Gottlieb, 2011). Dewey and Gottlieb (2011) also note the importance of the family system in the context of court-ordered treatment for juvenile offenders. Children and juveniles are dependent on their families and caregivers for transportation and monitoring of progress in counseling. Thus, parents, guardians, and caregivers should be willing, able, and motivated to assist the juvenile throughout the process of court-ordered treatment and court proceedings. Systemic clinicians should also seek consent from parents and caregivers of minors and juveniles. Ethical guidelines also suggest that clinicians seek the "assent" of minor children prior to the rendering of services. Minors are not legally capable of consenting to treatment in the eye of the law, but in the interest of autonomy, the systemic clinician seeks the minors' permission prior to the provision of services. The AAMFT *Code of Ethics* suggests that systemic clinicians seek permission for treatment from those persons who are legally authorized or permitted to provide that permission for those who do not possess such legal status (AAMFT, 2015; Dewey & Gottleib, 2011).

CASE CONCEPTUALIZATION

In order to enhance your knowledge of the information provided in the chapter, a case study has been provided in this section. In this case study, Ben has been referred for assessment and counseling by his school counselor. The case example takes us through the process of assessment, treatment planning, and intervention. It demonstrates the importance of systemic intervention.

Presenting Concerns

Ben (11) and his family were referred for family counseling by Ben's school counselor. The family consists of Ben (11), his father, Abel (33), and his aunt, Cheryl (30). The family lives in a poor, rural community with very few professional services. Ben is estranged from his mother. Ben has exhibited behavioral concerns for the past 2 years. Examples of his behavior include disrespect toward teachers, constant fighting, and poor performance in school. In the past, Ben has spoken disrespectfully toward his teachers, and at times, shown aggression as well. In the beginning of the school year, Ben was sent to In School Suspension for slapping a bus monitor after she directed him to step onto the sidewalk. Serious infractions occur on an irregular basis, but there seem to be daily infractions of a smaller scale—making inappropriate remarks to teachers and other students, spitting on the floor, disrupting class. Most recently, Ben began stealing clothing from other students, and intentionally damaging the personal belongings of other students, especially small electronic devices such as phones and tablet devices.

Concurrent Problems

School counselors have been seeing Ben for the past 16 months with little to no change in behavior. Additionally, Ben has weekly appointments with the school social psychologist and the school social worker. His aggressive acts have continued, as have his destructive tendencies. Despite the lack of change in Ben's behavior, he is consistent in his attendance at appointments with his school counselor, and he is quiet and respectful during those meetings. The school counselor's interventions generally revolve around problem-solving, decision-making, and communication skills. The school counselor reports Ben's compliance during their brief visits, but he does not change his behavior in his daily interactions with others. The family has never been seen together. The referral was made for family counseling as a last resort. If Ben's behavior problems persist, the school will pursue a legal remedy for the situation. He also is at risk for expulsion from school.

Background History and Stressors

The family consists of Ben, Abel (father), and Cheryl (aunt). His mother has not been seen for 4 years. Current concepts of her whereabouts place her either "in jail or dead." Ben expresses little concern for his mother's whereabouts. Abel states, "We just don't talk about her . . . that's a rule in our house." Abel and Cheryl seem to be united as a subsystem, taking turns with different parental duties, such as monitoring school work, getting Ben to bed, taking care of medical concerns, and attending to household responsibilities. Both are employed and share household costs. Cheryl moved in with Abel and Ben following discharge from an inpatient substance abuse treatment facility. She has been living with Abel and Ben for 2 years. Cheryl moved in out of a sense of duty to her only remaining family. Abel and Cheryl deny any romantic interest or involvement. Ben is receptive to being parented by Abel and Cheryl. He seems to be compliant and respectful toward them. The family is somewhat isolated.

Strengths

A few areas of strength are noted. Ben does seem to be connected to the resources at his school, namely, the school counselor and school psychologist whom he sees with some regularity. Ben and Cheryl seem to present as a "united front" to some degree and Ben responds to their parenting measures. There is some discipline in the house and there is no indication of severe or harsh punishment practices. It appears that the family is able to meet its basic needs such as food, clothing, shelter, and safety. No immediate safety or risk issues are noted. Cheryl has shown a remarkable degree of strength and resiliency in the maintenance of her sobriety. Both adults are employed with limited benefits in that Abel has health insurance coverage through his employer. Some social engagement is noted, primarily through church activities, but the family remains somewhat isolated. It should be noted that the family as a whole has presented for help in this case, which needs to be recognized, and the family has shown appreciation for its strength, resilience, and willingness to engage in the process of counseling.

DSM-5 Impressions and Implications

Ben clearly meets diagnostic criteria for Conduct Disorder. The diagnosis is consistent with the diagnostic impressions gathered from the school psychologist, school counselor, and school social worker. As a result, the following diagnoses were established:

Conduct Disorder—Childhood Onset Type, With Limited Prosocial Emotions, Lack of
      Remorse or Guilt, Moderate
Parent–Child Relational Problem
Academic or Educational Problem

Relational Problems

The family seems to be limited in terms of emotional responsiveness, nurturance, or warmth. Ben cannot recall any time in which he was hugged, praised, or otherwise commended for any achievement. Abel and Cheryl do not recognize the importance of support and encouragement in terms of Ben's development. Cheryl makes the statement, "Why should we praise him for doing what he is supposed to do anyway?"

The family is isolated and is limited to Ben, Abel, and Cheryl. They are unaware of any living relatives or relatives who are not incarcerated. Little or no interaction with the larger ecological system takes place. The family does attend church on special occasions. Abel and Cheryl identify as Methodists, and say they enjoy going to church, but they cannot describe any specific ways in which the church influences the family. Both Abel and Cheryl are employed. Abel has worked at a local grocery store for 11 years and Cheryl is employed at a denim manufacturing plant. Abel has health insurance for himself and Ben through his employer. Cheryl is uninsured.

Assessments

In looking at the family as a whole, a structural diagnosis was made, through the lens of structural family therapy (Minuchin, 1974). Structural family therapy places emphasis on, obviously, family structure, organization, and how the family attempts to solve the problem (Gehart & Tuttle, 2003; Heckler & Wetchler, 2003). It appears that this family, although somewhat organized in terms of its hierarchy, is somewhat ineffective in the way that it addresses presenting problems, specifically Ben's behavior at school. The family is organized in that Abel and Cheryl seem to take some responsibility as adults in making sure the basic needs of the family are met—food, clothing, medical care, shelter, safety. However, the family system seems rather ineffective in addressing Ben's problematic behavior. The approach to discipline and behavior can be described effectively as "nonexistent." In terms of boundaries, it appears that there is a clear delineation between the parental hierarchy (Abel and Cheryl) and the child (Ben). Within the parental hierarchy, Abel and Cheryl seem to have worked out some sort of agreement in terms of responsibilities and roles.

During the assessment process, the family was asked to participate in an enactment (Parmanand & Benoit; as cited in Capuzzi & Stauffer, 2015). During the enactment, Abel and Cheryl were asked to establish a time for Ben to be in bed every night, and to communicate this to Ben. Abel and Cheryl were notably uncomfortable with the process, and did not seem to recognize the need to have a set bed time for Ben. Chery stated, "He goes to bed when he wants to. He usually passes out on the couch watching television." The counselor had to provide sentence stems to the parental subsystem in an effort to start the conversation. Both Cheryl and Abel were prompted to begin the conversation by saying, "I think Ben should go to bed at _____." Abel and Cheryl eventually set a bed time at 9:30 p.m. They communicated this new rule to Ben, who responded by saying, "Okay . . . works for me."

The CFI was completed during the assessment process (APA, 2013, p. 752). Throughout the process of the interview, the family was able to provide additional details and insight about the cultural implications of the presenting problem. Abel and Cheryl had a good idea as to why they were referred for counseling. They knew that Ben had been acting inappropriately at school, but they had little insight into why the problem seemed too "big" to the school counselor. As a family, little insight was expressed as to the reasons for the presenting problem. There was a tendency to blame others at the school, such as the principal or the school counselor, for Ben's troubles. The family saw stealing as a way of survival from a cultural perspective. It was placed in the context of a historical precedent that it was "okay to take from others if the other person had plenty to begin with." A family history of legal issues was made evident over the course of completing the CFI. In regard to seeking help for the problem, the family indicated that they really did not know help was available for something related to stealing.

The Clinician Rate Severity of Conduct Disorder was completed. The presenting problem was given a rating of "moderate" due to the fact that Ben had displayed several of the behaviors listed in the diagnostic criteria. No aggression or confrontation toward others was noted within the last 7 days, which aided in the decision to rate the behavior as "moderate" and not "severe".

Interventions

Based on the presenting problems, the systemic clinician chose to intervene from the "common factors" approach, using structural family therapy (Wechtler, 2003) as the primary theoretical foundation. After reviewing the results of the assessment with the family, a collaborative treatment plan was established. The treatment plan generally addresses these things:

Parental Subsystem
The parental subsystem (Abel and Cheryl) will be strengthened as evidenced by:

- Demonstrating the ability to conduct "family check ins" in their own home, at least once per week, by the end of Week 12.
- Demonstrating the ability to communicate their expectations to Ben about his behavior at school, by the end of Week 4.

Emotional Responsiveness
The family will enhance emotional responsiveness as evidenced by:

- Demonstrating the ability to accurately reflect feelings elicited by Ben, at least twice during each session, throughout the course of counseling.
- The appropriate use of physical touch (hugs, holding hands, placing arm around shoulders) at least twice during each session, beginning with Week 6.

Behavioral Issues
Behavioral disruptions at school will decrease, as evidenced by:

- The presence of conduct grades at or above "good" on Ben's next report card, which is scheduled to be released during Week 8.
- The absence of reported behavioral issues, as indicated by Ben's teacher, during weekly phone/live conferences with Abel or Cheryl, beginning during Week 2.

Ecosystemic Growth and Expansion
The family will expand its social support network, as evidenced by:

- Enrolling Ben in a recreational sport of his choice, by the end of Week 12.
- Abel and Cheryl will attend the Adult Sunday School class at their church at least twice during the first month of counseling.

The common factors approach was chosen for a few different reasons. First, there is a lack of clinicians who are properly trained and supervised in EBPs in the rural area in which this family lives. In addition, there are very few clinicians of any sort available in the community. Second, the case presented involved a heightened degree of risk, and the family was in need of immediate assistance. The family does not present in crisis, but the behaviors, if not immediately addressed, run the risk of escalating to a critical level, and thus delaying treatment may have added to that escalated risk.

The family comes to counseling with a number of strengths. Those strengths should be noted and emphasized—made clear to the family. The counselor should appreciate those strengths as well. Among those strengths, we can note the following: there is some degree of organization in the home; Abel and Cheryl do make an attempt at parenting, supporting Ben and each other; and it appears that basic needs are met as far as nutrition, medical care, housing, and safety are concerned. Abel and Cheryl are employed. Cheryl has a history of substance abuse, but she also is in recovery and is living a drug-free life at present. While Ben does have challenges with his behavior, he seems to relate well to school counselors, Abel, and Cheryl.

During the assessment, the family seems to be rather comfortable with the process. No reluctance was noted. The family seemed to engage in conversations and seemed untroubled with the questions asked by the counselor. After the assessment, the counselor will focus on strengthening the therapeutic relationship, establishing trust, and building rapport. Structural family therapists refer to this as the process of "joining" with the family (Gehart & Tuttle, 2003). The family needs to be comfortable with the process. The active, directive nature of structural family therapy requires that trust and comfort be present. The counselor will follow the treatment plan, and focus first on empowering and strengthening the parental hierarchy. In an effort to do this, a few specific interventions will be used. Enactments (Parmanand & Benoit, as cited in Capuzzi & Stauffer, 2015), an established intervention in structural family therapy, will be used to get the parental hierarchy involved in Ben's life. For example, the counselor will use a "family check in" during each session. During this exercise, the parents will be asked to talk about the school day with Ben, specifically asking about his school work, performance on tests, and behavior. The counselor will monitor the conversation for positive communication and will offer support and coaching when necessary. As there is a lack of emotional responsiveness in the family, the counselor will encourage praise and recognition of Ben whenever possible.

The counselor will also encourage "parent conferences" during the sessions. During these sessions, Abel and Cheryl will be asked to have a conversation about how things are going in the home, thoughts about Ben's performance at school, or any other pressing topic that might be present in the family. These conversations will take place with Ben in the room. This will accomplish a few different things. First, it will give Abel and Cheryl a chance to talk with each other about what is going on in the home, thus promoting active engagement and enhanced communication. Secondly, it will give Ben the chance to see Abel and Cheryl working together as a team, hopefully as a strong, united entity, thus empowering the parental hierarchy. As with the "family check in," the counselor will monitor the "parental conferences" for healthy and effective communication, and will provide support and coaching when needed. For example, the counselor may have to offer coaching around active listening, reflection skills, and feedback processes.

The main reason for referral was Ben's problematic behavior in school, notably physical aggression, stealing, disrespect, fighting, and disruptive behavior. The counselor makes the hypothesis that Abel and Cheryl have not set limits on those behaviors in any direct manner. As part of the initial steps at growth, the "family check in" will focus on those problematic behaviors. The counselor will encourage conversation around those problematic behaviors in which the parental hierarchy will discuss behavioral expectations for Ben in school and at home. Abel and Cheryl will discuss consequences of behavioral infractions and will settle on disciplinary actions as a team. The importance of clear expectations and the consistent use of praise and discipline will be emphasized. The counselor will lead a discussion on healthy disciplinary processes with the family, and they will be encouraged to establish their own disciplinary guidelines, which will emphasize safety and growth. Other topics will be discussed in these "family check ins." Abel and Cheryl will engage Ben in strategies that will help his grades improve as well. The family will be encouraged to implement strategies that will help in this area: family study sessions, school work review sessions, homework sessions are examples.

As the family continues in counseling, and as they demonstrate growth in session, the counselor will encourage the family to make the "parent conferences" and "family check in" a part of their regular life, outside of the counseling session.

As there are many different parts of the family's ecosystem involved in this case, it is important to get the family involved with these different parts of the system. As the referral emerged from the school system, it is necessary to involve that institution in the process of counseling. Ben spends time with the school counselor, school psychologist, and school social worker. The school-based interventions are more individually focused and will continue throughout the course of family counseling. In the spirit of collaborative care and systemic intervention, these professionals will be a part of the counseling process. The counselor will remain in contact with these professionals, sharing monthly progress reports (at a minimum) in an effort to remain consistent in terms of goals and objectives. The counselor will suggest a medical exam for everyone, and a collaborative relationship will be established with medical professionals as well. As the counseling process continues, the family may wish to get involved with some sort of recreational activity, and they may wish to look further into their spiritual lives as well. The counselor will be mindful of those things and will support those endeavors as needed. Structural perspectives see families as being embedded in the larger social structure, and thus, parts of the larger social structure should be considered as integral to family growth and development.

As part of the common factors approach, the counselor will schedule regular feedback sessions. During these feedback sessions, the counselor will emphasize the growth the family has made, and will share areas that need more energy. The family will be able to provide feedback to the counselor as well. The family will be able to share concerns or offer ideas about changing the direction of counseling. The feedback session also provides a time for reflection for the family. They are given a chance to think about the changes that have occurred, and they are given the opportunity to relish in their success. The feedback session can also serve as a break from process of counseling, a time to relax and take a break from the rigors of growth, so to speak.

Ethical and Legal Implications

As the family will be seen by a systemic clinician, it will be necessary to identify the entire family as the client. In doing so, the counselor will be clear in setting expectations related to participation from everyone at each and every session. As all family members will be seen at the same time, expectations of privacy and confidentiality should be made clear and taken in the context of everyone working together at the same time. The clinician will also need to be mindful of the need to work collaboratively with other care providers and to ensure that information is shared according to all applicable ethical and legal guidelines.

There is little or no concern for immediate safety or risk issues. Some behaviors, if they continue, may result in legal involvement for Ben. In this case, the counselor explained limitations of confidentiality and made sure the family understood those limitations. Even though safety is a minimal issue at this time, the counselor will conduct ongoing risk and safety assessments and respond accordingly. At some point concerns may arise as to Cheryl's legal status as a guardian for Ben. Cheryl plays a significant role in the structure of this family and it may be beneficial to solidify her position in the family system for ease of communication with schools, medical providers, and other parts of the system.

DISCUSSION

The case example demonstrates how a systemic clinician working from a common factors approach might have intervened with this family. As you continue to reflect on the case study and the overall approach, contemplate these questions:

- What are your thoughts about Cheryl and her role in the family? Cheryl is Ben's aunt and she lives with Ben and his father, Abel. Are there additional concerns that need to be addressed because of the way in which this family has constructed itself?
- What were your assumptions about the culture of this family? As you read about the family, did you assume that the family belonged to any particular racial or ethnic group? Did you make any assumptions based on their living arrangements or the choices they made as parents? Reflect on the answers to these questions.
- How might the use of EBPs impact this family? What benefits or challenges might this family experience if the clinician were to have implemented something like MST, or PCIT?
- Can you identify any individual as needing individual counseling? If so, why would that be necessary? How would you work collaboratively with other care providers in this situation?
- What is the impact of generational issues on this family? Is there a connection between Ben's behavior and the behavior of those who belonged to prior generations? Would these generational issues present additional challenges for this family or for the clinician?

SUMMARY

Disruptive, impulse control, and conduct disorders present unique challenges to families. Behaviors associated with this diagnostic category typically present themselves during childhood and adolescence. As that is the case, these behaviors impact many aspects of the family ecosystem such as the school and the criminal justice system. As these behaviors impact so many parts of the family system, the counselor is encouraged to address the issue through the lens of family systems theory. A thorough assessment is required prior to addressing the problem. A family systems assessment can include clinical interviews, standardized instruments, and observational elements, all of which were covered in this chapter. This chapter also covered a wide range of interventions, which include the "common factors" approach, as well as a description of many EBPs. A case example was presented in an effort to demonstrate, in the limited space available, a realistic approach to working with a family that is struggling with problematic behaviors in an adolescent child.

Throughout the process of family counseling, the counselor must make many decisions. Interventions and approaches must be practical and effective, and they must be focused on strengths, wellness, and culturally appropriate techniques. The many valuable characteristics the family brings into counseling must be used to further family development. Collaboration is a key element among all parts of the family's ecosystem and the counselor must strive to work closely with all involved; the family counselor should expect other caregivers to do the same with them. Above all else, be mindful of the ethical guidelines that direct professional activities. The ethical codes put forth by the American Counseling Association and the AAMFT should serve as a guide in your work with the families who seek your services.

REFERENCES

Achenbach, T. M., & Rescorla, L. A. (2001). *Manual for the ASEBA school-age forms and profiles.* Burlington: University of Vermont Research Center for Children, Youth, and Families.

Adams, Z., & Boyd, S. (2010). Ethical challenges in the treatment of individuals with developmental disabilities. *Ethics and Behavior, 20*(6), 407–418.

American Association for Marriage and Family Therapy. (2015). *AAMFT code of ethics.* Alexandria, VA: Author. Retrieved from http://www.aamft.org/iMIS15/AAMFT/Content/Legal_Ethics/Code_of_Ethics.aspx

American Counseling Association. (2014). *ACA code of ethics.* Alexandria, VA: Author. Retrieved from http://www.counseling.org/docs/ethics/2014-aca-code-of-ethics.pdf?sfvrsn=4

American Psychiatric Association. (2013). *Diagnostic and statistical manual of mental disorders* (5th ed.). Arlington, VA: American Psychiatric Publishing.

Barry, C. T., Golmaryami, F. N., Rivera-Hudson, N., & Frick, P. J. (2013). Evidence-based assessment of conduct disorder: Current considerations and preparation for DSM-5. *Professional Psychology: Research and Practice, 44*(1), 56–63.

Buitelaar, J., Smeets, K., Herpers, P., Scheepers, F., Glennon, J., & Rommelse, N. (2013). Conduct disorders. *European Child and Adolescent Psychiatry, 22,* S49–S54. doi:10.1007/s00787-012-0361-y

Canfield, B. (2015). Diversity and intercultural work in family counseling. In D. Capuzzi & M. Stauffer (Eds.), *Foundations of marriage, couples, and family counseling* (pp. 53–70). Hoboken, NJ: Wiley.

Cassim, S, Stolte, O., & Hodgetts, D. (2015). Metonymic objects, cultural practices, and narrative repair: Sri Lankan responses to the Indian Ocean tsunami. *Journal of Health Psychology, 20*(7), 974–983.

Christophersen, E., & VanScoyoc, S. (2013). Diagnosis and management of disruptive behavior disorders. In E. Christophersen & S. VanScoyoc (Eds.), *Treatments that work with children: Empirically supported strategies for managing childhood problems* (2nd ed.). Washington, DC: American Psychological Association. doi:10.1037/14137-002

Corey, G. (2009). *Theory and practice of counseling and psychotherapy.* Belmont, CA: Thomson Brooks/Cole.

Corey, G., Corey, M., & Callanan, P. (2011). *Issues and ethics in the helping professions* (8th ed.). Belmont, CA: Brooks/Cole.

Denton, W. H., & Bell, C. (2013). DSM-5 and the family therapist: First-order change in a new millennium. *Australian and New Zealand Journal of Family Therapy, 34*(2), 147–155.

Dewey, L., & Gottlieb, M. (2011). Ethical guidelines for providing court ordered outpatient psychotherapy to juvenile offenders. *Journal of Forensic Psychology Practice, 11,* 1–20.

Epstein, N. B., Baldwin, L. M., & Bishop, D. S. (1983). The McMaster family assessment device. *Journal of Marital and Family Therapy, 9*(2), 171–180.

Farnfield, S. (2015). The child attachment and play assessment (CAPA): Validation of a new approach to coding narrative stems with children ages 3–11 years. *International Journal of Play Therapy.* Advance online publication. doi:10.1037/a0038726

Flamez, B., Hicks, J., & Clark, A. (2015) Effectively using research and assessment in couples and family therapy. In D. Capuzzi & M. Stauffer (Eds.), *Foundations of marriage, couples, and family counseling* (pp. 71–96). Hoboken, NJ: Wiley.

Freeze, M. K., Burke, A., & Vorster, A. C. (2014). The role of parental style in the conduct disorders: A comparison between adolescent boys with and without conduct disorder. *Journal of Child and Adolescent Mental Health, 26*(1), 63–73.

Frick, P. J., & Hare, R. D. (2001). *Antisocial process screening device: APSD.* Toronto, ON, Canada: Multi-Health Systems.

Frick, P. J., & White, S. F. (2008), Research review: The importance of callous-unemotional traits for developmental models of aggressive and antisocial behavior. *Journal of Child Psychology and Psychiatry, 49,* 359–375. doi:10.1111/j.1469-7610.2007.01862.x

Fridhandler, B., & Lehmer, M. (2014). Ethical issues in coparent counseling. *Journal of Child Custody, 11,* 139–158.

Funderburk, B. W., & Eyberg, S. (2011). Parent–child interaction therapy. In John C. Norcross, Gary R. VandenBos, & Donald K. Freedheim (Eds.), *History of psychotherapy: Continuity and change* (2nd ed., pp. 415–420). Washington, DC: American Psychological Association.

Gehart, D., & Tuttle, A. (2003). *Theory based treatment planning for marriage and family therapists*. Belmont, CA: Brooks/Cole.

Gladding, S. (2011). *Family therapy: History, theory, and practice* (5th ed.). Boston, MA: Pearson.

Goodman, R. (1997). The Strengths and Difficulties Questionnaire: A research note. *Journal of Child Psychology and Psychiatry, 38*(5), 581–586.

Goodman, R., Ford, T., Richards, H., Gatward, R. and Meltzer, H. (2000). The development and well-being assessment: Description and initial validation of an integrated assessment of child and adolescent psychopathology. *Journal of Child Psychology and Psychiatry, 41*, 645–655. doi:10.1111/j.1469-7610.2000 .tb02345.x

Goodwin, E. K. (2015). The end of all tears: A dynamic interdisciplinary analysis of mourning and complicated grief with suggested applications for clinicians. *Journal of Spirituality and Mental Health, 17*, 239–266.

Graham, C., Carr, A., Rooney, B., Sexton, T., & Wilson Satterfield, L. R. (2014). Evaluation of functional family therapy in an Irish context. *Journal of Family Therapy, 36*(1), 20–38.

Haley, M. (2015). Legal, ethical, and professional issues. In D. Capuzzi & M. Stauffer (Eds.), *Foundations of marriage, couples, and family counseling* (pp. 101–122). Hoboken, NJ: Wiley.

Henggeler, S. W., & Sheidow, A. J. (2012). Empirically supported family-based treatments for conduct disorder and delinquency in adolescents. *Journal of Marital and Family Therapy, 38*(1), 30–58.

Herjanic, B., & Campbell, W. (1977). Differentiating psychiatrically disturbed children on the basis of a structured interview. *Journal of Abnormal Child Psychology, 5*, 127–1345.

Hook, M., Gerstein, L., Detterich, L., & Gridley, B. (2003). How close are we? Measuring intimacy and examining gender differences. *Journal of Counseling and Development, 81*, 462–472.

Karam, E. A., Blow, A. J., Sprenkle, D. H., & Davis, S. D. (2015). Strengthening the systemic ties that bind: Integrating common factors into marriage and family therapy curricula. *Journal of Marital and Family Therapy, 41*(2), 136–149.

Kaslow, N. J., Broth, M. R., Smith, C. O., & Collins, M. H. (2012). Family-based interventions for child and adolescent disorders. *Journal of Marital and Family Therapy, 38*(1), 82–100.

Lebow, J. (2014). Common factors. In J. Lebow (Ed.), *Couple and family therapy: An integrative map of the territory* (pp. 113–128). Washington, DC: American Psychological Association. doi:10.1037/14255–005

Malmberg, J., & Field, C. (2013). Preventative behavioral parent training: A preliminary investigation of strategies for preventing at risk children from developing later conduct problems. *Child and Behavior Family Therapy, 35*(3), 212–227.

Minuchin, S. (1974). *Families and family therapy*. Cambridge, MA: Harvard University Press.

Mizock, L., & Harkins, D. (2011). Diagnostic bias and conduct disorder: Improving culturally sensitive diagnosis. *Child and Youth Services, 32*(3), 243–253.

Parmanand, S. & Benoit, E. (2015). Structural theory: Approaches and applications. In D. Capuzzi & M. Stauffer (Eds.), *Foundations of marriage, couples, and family counseling* (pp. 215–236). Hoboken, NJ: Wiley.

Petridis, T., & Hannan, J. (2011). Innovations in practice: A safety approach to child inclusive family dispute resolution. *Journal of Family Studies, 17*, 36–43.

Pottick, K. J., Warner, L. A., Vander Stoep, A., & Knight, N. M. (2014). Clinical characteristics and outpatient mental health service use of transition-age youth in the USA. *The Journal of Behavioral Health Services and Research, 41*(2), 230–243.

Raudino, A., Fergusson, D. M., Woodward, L. J., & Horwood, L. J. (2013). The intergenerational transmission of conduct problems. *Social Psychiatry and Psychiatric Epidemiology, 48*(3), 465–476.

Reynolds, C. R., & Kamphaus, R. W. (2004). BASC-2: *Behavior assessment system for children*. Upper Saddle River, NJ: Pearson.

Scudder, A., Herschell, A., & McNeil, C. (2016). Parent-child interaction therapy for children with disruptive behavior disorders. In L. Reddy, T. Files-Hall, & C. Schaefer (Eds.), *Empirically based play interventions for children* (2nd ed., pp. 159–179). doi:10.1037/14730-009

Sexton, T., & Turner, C. W. (2010). The effectiveness of functional family therapy for youth with behavioral problems in a community practice setting. *Journal of Family Psychology, 24*(3), 339–348.

Shaffer, D., Fisher, P., Lucas, C. P., Dulcan, L. K. , & Schwab-Stone, M. E. (2000). NIMH diagnostic interview schedule for children version IV (NIMH DISC-IV): Description, differences from previous versions, and reliability of some common diagnoses. *Psychological Medicine: A Journal of Research in Psychiatry and the Allied Sciences, 39,* 28–38.

Shaw, S. L., & Murray, K. W. (2014). Monitoring alliance and outcome with client feedback measures. *Journal of Mental Health Counseling, 36*(1), 43–57.

Snyder, D. K. (1997). *Marital satisfaction inventory—revised* (MSI-R) manual. Los Angeles, CA: Western Psychological Services.

Straus, M. A. (1979). Measuring intrafamily conflict and violence: The conflict tactics (CT) scales. *Journal of Marriage and Family, 41*(1), 75–88. doi:10.2307/351733

Straus, M. A. (1995). *Manual for the conflict tactics scales.* Durham: Family Research Laboratory, University of New Hampshire.

Strong, T. and Busch, R. (2013). *DSM-5* and evidence-based family therapy? *Australian and New Zealand Journal of Family Therapy, 34,* 90–103. doi:10.1002/anzf.1009

Thomlinson, B. (2007). *Family assessment handbook: An introduction and practical guide to family assessment* (2nd ed.). Belmont, CA: Thompson.

Vandervelt-Adriance, E., Shaw, D., Brennan, L., Dishion, T., Gardner, F., & Wilson, M. (2015). Child, family, and community protective factors in the development of children's early conduct problems. *Family Relations, 64,* 64–79. doi:10.1111/fare.12105

Vander Stoep, A., Adrian, M., Mc Cauley, E., Crowell, S. E., Stone, A., & Flynn, C. (2011). Risk for suicidal ideation and suicide attempts associated with co-occurring depression and conduct problems in early adolescence. *Suicide and Life-Threatening Behavior, 41*(3), 316–329.

Wetchler, J. (2003). Structural family therapy. In L. Hecker & J. Wetchler (Eds.), *An introduction to marriage and family therapy* (pp. 63–91). New York, NY: Routledge.

Wilson, S., & Durbin, C. (2013). Mother-child and father-child dyadic interaction: Parental and child bids and responsiveness to each other during early childhood. *Merrill-Palmer Quarterly, 59*(3), 249–279.

Wong, S., & Talmi, A. (2015). Open communication: Recommendations for enhancing communication among primary care and mental health providers, services, and systems. *Families, Systems, and Health, 33*(2), 160–162.

Zuddas, A. (2014). The poor outcome of conduct disorders: A need for innovative, more effective therapeutic interventions. *European Child and Adolescent Psychiatry, 23,* 515–517. doi:10.1007/s00787-014-0579-y

16

FAMILY SYSTEMS AND SUBSTANCE-RELATED AND ADDICTIVE DISORDERS

Amber Lange, Amanda Rovnak, Carrie VanMeter, and Trevon Clow

*A*mericans' pervasive use of alcohol and drugs poses significant challenges to clinicians practicing from a systemic perspective. Currently, over 14.7 million Americans report alcohol use disorders, 4.3 million Americans report drug use disorders, and 2.6 million Americans report combined alcohol and drug use disorders (Substance Abuse and Mental Health Services Administration [SAMHSA], 2014). While these numbers are alarming, even more alarming is the fact that the vast majority of these individuals are untreated. The National Institute on Drug Abuse (NIDA) reports that in 2013, 22.7 million Americans needed treatment for a substance-related disorder, yet only 2.5 million Americans reported receiving treatment at a substance facility (NIDA, 2015). Thus, substance-related problems pose significant biological, mental, physical, and spiritual problems in American society. These problems are extremely challenging to prevent, diagnose, treat, and overcome. To combat some of these challenges, the American Psychiatric Association (APA) offers the Substance-Related and Addictive Disorders chapter within the *Diagnostic and Statistical Manual of Mental Disorders* (5th ed.; *DSM-5*; APA, 2013). This chapter provides a road map for describing criteria necessary for identifying and diagnosing substance-related and addictive disorders as well as a systemic lens to view this road map. Traditionally, substance use disorders (SUDs) have been viewed as a problem within an individual, yet viewing these disorders as problems between members of a system can change one's perspective away from the addicted person toward the entire system. This perspective shift may reduce blame and finger pointing at the addicted person while also providing new knowledge about the systems role in substance-related and addictive disorders.

DSM-5 AND FAMILY SYSTEMS

The *DSM-5* identifies 10 classes of substance- and one class of nonsubstance-related disorders including alcohol; caffeine; cannabis; hallucinogens; inhalants; opioids; sedatives, hypnotics, or anxiolytics; stimulants; tobacco; and other or unknown substances. Gambling is the only nonsubstance-related disorder. Each of these disorders has a direct impact on psychological and biological functioning with activation of the reward pathways in the brain. Substances may be legal (alcohol), prescription (controlled), or illicit (cocaine)—with defining features of a substance-related problem including increased use over time in extent and frequency; significant emotional, physical, and relational problems; and failure to abstain from use despite problems caused by the use.

Symptoms associated with use are classified as either SUDs or substance-induced disorders (SIDs). A SUD is defined as "a cluster of cognitive, behavioral, and physiological symptoms indicating that the individual continues using the substance despite significant substance-related problems" (APA, 2013, p. 483). SIDs are syndromes that manifest after ingestion of a substance (intoxication) or that manifest shortly after cessation of, or reduction in, excessive and chronic use of a substance.

There is little room within the *DSM-5* definitions of SUDs or SIDs to encompass a family or systemic perspective on substance use, meaning that these disorders are reserved for individual diagnosis. At this time, there is no diagnosis for a substance-disordered system or family. Counselors who are making a diagnosis of SUD or SID need to keep in mind the individual nature of the diagnosis and use the specific codes only for clients meeting criteria for a SID or SUD. Family members need diagnosis codes based on their specific presenting problems with a clinician taking into account the symptoms of the family member and the level of distress caused by the SID or SUD.

Substance Use Disorder

Diagnosis of an SUD requires confirmation of two to three of 11 established criteria to qualify for a *mild* SUD, confirmation of four to five criteria to qualify for a *moderate* SUD, and confirmation of six to 11 criteria to qualify for a *severe* SUD. Criteria 1 to 4 are related to impaired control, criteria 5 to 7 are related to social impairment, criteria 8 to 9 are related to risky use, and criteria 10 to 11 are related to pharmacological symptoms. Specifiers that may be used to describe further the substance use disorders include *in early remission, in sustained remission, on maintenance therapy*, and *in a controlled environment. In early remission* is used when none of the 11 diagnostic criteria for the substance (craving is an exception) have been met for the past 3 months but fewer than 12 months and full criteria were met in the past. *In sustained remission* is used when none of the 11 diagnostic criteria have been met for the past 12 months or longer (craving is an exception) and full criteria had been met in the past. *On maintenance therapy* has limited application and is used when an agonist, a partial agonist, an agonist/antagonist, or a full antagonist medication is prescribed and none of the criteria for an *opioid* use disorder or a *tobacco* use disorder are met (except tolerance to, or withdrawal from, the replacement medication). *In a controlled environment* is used when there is limited access to the substance due to the client being in a restricted environment (i.e., jail, hospital).

Substance-Induced Disorders

SIDs require either recent ingestion or discontinued use of alcohol, drugs, or unknown toxins as well as experiencing problems related to the ingestion or discontinued use. SIDs tend to be temporary with a defining feature being a negative impact on mental and/or biological functioning. Disorders within this category include intoxication, withdrawal, or a substance/medication-induced disorder. Intoxication requires the recent use of a substance, resulting in symptoms such as incoordination or slurred speech. Withdrawal requires cessation of a substance that was used for a prolonged period and resulting in negative physical and mental symptoms such as insomnia, vomiting, anxiety, or tremors. A substance/medication-induced mental disorder is identified as a mental disorder such as depression or anxiety that develops after or due to ingestion of a substance.

Substance-Related Disorders—Other (or Unknown) Categories

Substance-related other (or unknown) categories exist to facilitate diagnosis primarily when the substances are not one of the 10 identified substances within the *DSM-5,* are unknown substances, or when the symptoms do not fully fit the currently established criteria. *Other (or Unknown) Substance Intoxication* and *Other (or Unknown) Substance Withdrawal* are utilized when the client presentation involves intoxication or withdrawal but the substance is not listed elsewhere or is unknown to the clinician. *Unspecified [substance name] Related Disorder* is utilized when the client presentation does not meet full criteria for the specific substance yet does cause distress or impairment for the client. *Unspecified Other (or Unknown) Substance Use Disorder* is utilized when the client presentation does not meet full criteria for any substance-related disorder or any specific other (or unknown) substance, yet does cause distress or impairment for the client.

Nonsubstance-Related Disorders

In addition to the Substance-Related Disorders, the *DSM-5* also addresses Non-Substance-Related Disorders. The salient features of nonsubstance-related disorders are recurrent behaviors that lead to clinical impairment or distress. Individuals must exhibit four to five criteria to qualify for a *mild* diagnosis, exhibit six to seven criteria to qualify for a *moderate* diagnosis, and exhibit eight or nine of the total criteria to qualify for a *severe* diagnosis.

Gambling Disorder

Currently, Gambling Disorder is the only nonsubstance-related disorder within the *DSM-5.* There was much debate as to whether or not behavior-based disorders, such as gambling, could withstand the rigorous neurobiological criteria necessary to be classified within the substance-related and addictive disorder category in the *DSM-5.* Before the fifth edition, gambling was diagnosed primarily as an impulse control disorder. By 2013, research was compelling enough to support gambling as an addictive-related disorder due to the physiological and neurobiological brain processes associated with gambling behaviors mimicking brains similar to drug-addicted individuals (Potenza, 2008; Potenza et al., 2013; Zack & Poulos, 2009). Criteria for gambling disorder surround repeated gambling behaviors (chasing the win), money and finances, ruined relationships, anxiety, restlessness, and dishonesty.

Changes to the Substance-Related and Addictive Disorders Chapter

The transition from the *Diagnostic and Statistical Manual of Mental Disorders* (4th ed., text rev.; *DSM-IV-TR;* APA, 2000) to the *DSM-5* established a number of critical changes. Most importantly, the *DSM-5* moved to a dimensional understanding of substance-related disorders. Substance use and substance dependence were removed as separate disorders, as these diagnoses implied a distinct difference between the two disorders and/or implied a hierarchy with dependence being a more severe disorder than abuse. Neither of these cases was completely accurate, as some clients would exhibit severe abuse symptoms without qualifying for dependence while others, adolescents in particular, qualified with one or two symptoms of dependence without meeting full criteria for the diagnosis. Since these individuals did not meet criteria for dependence or abuse, they were left as "diagnostic orphans" and often were classified as "not otherwise specified."

A growing body of literature identifies that SUDs are better organized on a continuum. Per the *DSM-5,* individuals need to exhibit at least two of 11 criteria to qualify for a substance-related diagnosis. This continuum is in contrast to the prior edition where individuals need to meet at least one criterion for a substance *abuse* diagnosis or three different criteria for a substance *dependence* diagnosis. In the *DSM-5,* abuse and dependence criteria from *Diagnostic and Statistical Manual of Mental Disorders* (4th ed.; *DSM-IV;* APA, 1994) are combined into one unified list with the exception of the deletion of the criteria of legal problems and the addition of the criteria craving.

Legal Problems

Legal problems were removed as a criterion for several reasons including some clinicians' overuse of recurrent legal problems as the sine qua non symptom necessary to diagnose abuse. The criteria also were prone to social justice issues due to some populations encountering higher rates of arrests due to their age, race, gender, or socioeconomic status. Additionally, since all states are not consistent in enforcing substance use laws, use of the criteria created reliability challenges across the nation. Finally, the recurrent legal problem criteria may be a valid criminal justice marker, but is not a valid clinical marker.

Craving

Craving, defined as an intense desire to use alcohol or drugs, was added as a criterion due to evidence that reward pathways in the brain were activated upon cessation or withdrawal from alcohol and drug use. Strong evidence exists that intense cravings are related to high relapse rates and extinction of cravings is related to successful treatment outcomes (Wilson, 2015). The phenomenon of craving occurs, in part, due to classical conditioning and is known to be experienced by most individuals with severe substance-related disorders as well as by those who experience withdrawal (Murphy, Stojek, Few, Rothbaum, & MacKillop, 2014; Pickens et al., 2011). Those attempting to refrain from gambling also report a similar craving phenomenon (Cunningham-Williams, Gattis, Dore, Shi, & Spitznagel, 2009). Additionally, although not listed as a criterion item, the *DSM-IV-TR* identified most (if not all) individuals with substance dependence as likely to experience cravings.

Additional Changes

Several additional changes occurred within the fifth edition. Here is an abbreviated version of several of these changes.

- The word *addiction* has been removed from the diagnostic terminology due to the uncertainty of the definition and negative connotations of the word.
- New recording procedures whereby the counselor uses the code that applies to the class of substance but records the name of the specific substance. For example, the counselor would record moderate *alprazolam* use disorder (rather than moderate sedative, hypnotic, or anxiolytic use disorder).
- Option to use the *Level 2—Substance Use Adult, Parent/Guardian of Child Age 6–17, or Child Age 11–17* Cross-Cutting Symptom Measures (available at www.psychiatry.org/practice/dsm/dsm5/online-assessment-measures).

- Consolidation of remission specifiers early full remission, early partial remission, sustained full remission, sustained partial remission, to *early remission* (none of the criteria, except for craving, have been met for at least 3 months but for less than 12 months) and *sustained remission* (none of the criteria, except for craving, have been met at any time during a period of 12 months or longer).
- Removal of the specifier for a physiological subtype (i.e., with physiological dependence) because withdrawal and tolerance are normal and expected processes during some medical treatments and were erroneously diagnosed as addiction.
- Renaming *on agonist therapy* to *on maintenance therapy* for application to individuals being maintained on a partial agonist, an agonist/antagonist, or a full antagonist.
- Renaming of other (or unknown) substance-related disorder to Other (or Unknown) Substance Use Disorder.
- *Cannabis Withdrawal* and *Cannabis Withdrawal Syndrome* have been added. *Amotivational Syndrome* also has been added.
- Phencyclidine (or phencyclidine-like)-related disorders has been consolidated into the *Hallucinogen-Related Disorders*.
- Cocaine-related disorders and amphetamine (or amphetamine-like)-related disorders have been classified into a new category titled *Stimulant-Related Disorder* to align better with the *International Statistical Classification of Disease (ICD)*.
- Polysubstance-related disorder has been removed with all SUDs being diagnosed separately.
  - In situations where only one substance-related criterion is met, a provisional diagnosis may be used.
- Addition of *Caffeine Withdrawal* with two new criteria: headache and difficulty concentrating.
- Renaming of nicotine-related disorders to *Tobacco-Related Disorders*.

Diagnosing Substance-Related and Addictive Disorders

Mental health professionals who utilize a systemic approach have traditionally been opposed to the medicalization of individuals. This opposition is philosophically based and grounded in the belief that medically based problems identified within the *DSM-5* are more accurately conceptualized as relational concerns co-occurring *between* individuals and not necessarily *within* individuals. Mental health clinicians utilizing a systemic approach argue that language within the *DSM-5* does not offer a broad enough lens for talking about alcohol and drug-related problems due to the targeted focus on individual behaviors as opposed to a broader focus on relational interactions. This narrower behavior-based focus is necessary for diagnosis, yet has the potential of limiting a mental health clinician's understanding of an alcohol or drug-related disorder. As a result, many clinicians find themselves on the horns of a dilemma emerging from the discrepancy between making a diagnosis and the theoretical treatment orientation toward relational-based problem identification. Denton and Bell (2013) stated this dilemma succinctly when they said: "Many family systemic clinicians will have to continue to use one lens (systemic) for treatment and a different lens (*DSM-5*) for diagnosis" (p.147).

Systemic Lens

The need for a systemic lens is critically important when considering the role of a mental health professional who utilizes a systemic approach in the treatment of substance-related and addictive disorders. The systemic lens offers a comprehensive and distinctly unique perspective that includes an understanding that addiction is a system problem with an addicted individual serving one of the several roles. When an addicted individual leaves the system for treatment, he or she may return to the system with a new role (sobriety). If other family members continue to behave in their old and familiar roles, they may not be prepared or ready fully to accept the addicted individual's new sober role. As these family members continue to behave in a way consistent with their previously established roles, the newly sober individual, who is unfamiliar with the sober role, finds himself or herself easily drawn back to the familiarity of the addict role. This understanding is predicated on the idea that each member intuitively knows and follows his or her role within the system; when this happens the system is said to be balanced. When any one individual within the system tries to change his or her role, the whole system needs to change so balance can be maintained; otherwise it is not uncommon for the newly sober individual to revert to the old and familiar addict role. The system continues to break down or change until each member in the system is once again able to know or follow his or her (old or new) role.

For example, dad attends a 21-day inpatient treatment program to address his drinking and when dad returns home everyone is excited that dad is no longer drinking. This excitement lasts for a few weeks and then subsides. Dad, in his new sober role, is now more alert and attentive. Suddenly, both high school-aged kids seem to be getting in more trouble because dad notices they are staying out late, sleeping in, and missing the bus at least twice a week. Dad and mom argue over the kids missing the bus and dad determines that a new rule needs to be created whereby the kids need to be home on school nights by 9:00 p.m. Neither of the kids agrees with this rule and mom agrees that the kids need time to be social, have fun, and be with their friends. Mom and the kids agree that it has been that way for a long time and everything has been fine. One Tuesday night, neither of the kids comes home and instead, they text mom and dad to say they are staying the night at friends. Mom and dad argue with mom deciding to sleep on the couch. Dad is anxious and annoyed. He feels isolated, disrespected, and alone, and decides to drink. In the following weeks, the kids are back to staying out late and occasionally missing the bus. Dad is drunk and mom is mad at dad for drinking, but no one is yelling at the kids for staying out on weekdays.

Diagnostic Lens

The systemic lens described previously may be one helpful way of understanding the development, maintenance, relapse, or recovery of addicted individuals and systems, but a diagnostic lens remains necessary for all mental health professionals, including systemic clinicians to receive reimbursement for therapy. The Substance-Related and Addictive Disorders chapter of the *DSM-5* provides diagnoses only of individuals who exhibit an actual alcohol or drug problem. Thus, no diagnostic codes are provided within this chapter to diagnose relational interactions between family members. This lack of codes may leave the systemic clinician in a quandary as how best to proceed with family members and/or loved ones who are experiencing distress from the member using alcohol or drugs. Since family members may present with symptoms such as anger, worry, sadness, or fear, it is recommended that the reader review the Depressive Disorder chapter, the Anxiety Disorder chapter, and Trauma-Related and Stressor-Related Disorders chapter of the *DSM-5* to assist in diagnoses for family and loved ones.

RELATIONAL AND CULTURAL FEATURES

Relational and cultural features provide significant context for understanding the etiology, progression, and recovery from substance-related and addictive disorders. Relational features are those that describe the ways in which the family or system is connected. These features can be positive or negative, with the defining feature being the holding together of the system. Cultural features can be described as the groupings by which the family or system identify. These features may be aspects such as age, gender, race, religion, or ethnicity. Relational and cultural features may be subtle or obvious, but in both cases are relevant to the assessment, treatment, and recovery of the substance-using person and system.

Relational Features

Achieving an understanding of the overarching family system concepts relevant to both family systems and addiction work may enable the systemic clinician better to conceptualize both the problems and potential solutions for sober living. When considering family systems approaches to substance-related and addictive disorders, the underlying assumption is that treating the family, as opposed to the individual, results in comprehensive change. This assumption is well supported by research indicating that the family system is vital to treatment success for addicted individuals (Benishek, Kirby, & Dugosh, 2011; Fischer & Wiersma, 2012; Heinz, Wu, Witkiewitz, Epstein, & Preston, 2009; Crane, Moore, and Eggett, 2013). These studies identify family systems treatment as successful for many different populations such as female substance-abusing partners, gay and heterosexual substance-abusing couples, families with addicted teens, and for individuals with addicted partners who refuse to attend therapy. Additionally, behavioral couples therapy (BCT) is consistently considered the treatment of choice when one partner is sober and one partner is suffering from addiction, as well as for addicted couples.

Achieving the previously mentioned successes with families and individuals dealing with addiction issues requires systemic clinicians to have an intricate understanding of family system principles and knowledge of how these principles are related to substance-related and addictive disorders. Although a comprehensive review of all systems principles is not possible, the following salient concepts are addressed: circular causality, nonsummativity, homeostasis, family roles, boundaries, and equifinality. These six concepts are addressed to help systemic clinicians understand how relational problems in addicted systems may develop, how they are maintained, and how they can be changed.

Circular Causality

Circular causality is defined as the change that happens in the family system due to a change taking place for one family member, producing reactionary changes for other family members, which in turn informs change in the family member who initially changed (See Figure 16.1.). This principle serves to explain why it may not be necessary for change to *begin with* the addicted individual. It may be the case that change with a partner or another family member is the critical change needed to allow the addicted individual to seek sobriety. Figure 16.1 depicts an example of how a husband diagnosed with an alcohol use disorder is not the first person to change within his family, yet he still experiences change as a result of his wife's attendance at Al Anon. The wife's attendance eventually leads to a host of systemic changes across the entire family, eventually resulting in a better environment for all.

Nonsummativity

Nonsummativity is a way of expressing that the family system is not only greater than, but also different from, the sum of its parts. This means that accepting only one family member's experience of substance use is insufficient for developing a comprehensive understanding of the problem. This concept can be illustrated through the popular Indian parable of the blind men and the elephant. In this scenario, each blind man is allowed to

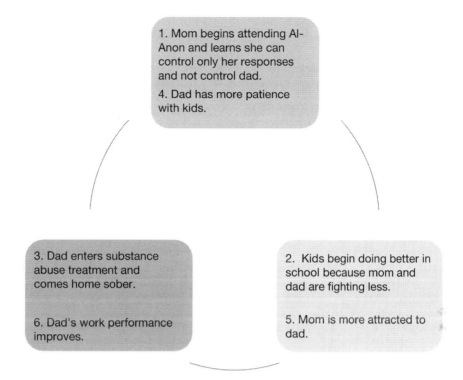

FIGURE 16.1 Circular causality. Mom's change informs the family's change. In turn, the family's change informs dad's change.

inspect only a particular feature of the elephant: one examines the tusk, one examines the foot, one examines the tail, and one examines the head. Each blind man then provides a description of the elephant, which is rooted in his perception. Soon, the blind men are arguing and fighting about the appearance of the elephant. Upon witnessing the bickering, the Raja proclaims that the men are unseeing and unable to conceive the whole. In the same way, understanding any one member of an addicted system leaves the systemic clinician with an incomplete description of that system.

For example, Anthony, a 35-year-old African American male attended four sessions of therapy. As part of his initial assessment, he was diagnosed with an Adjustment Disorder with anxiety and depression due to his wife filing for a divorce and experiencing a high level of daily stress. As part of the assessment, he stated that he had been a good husband over the past 6 years and supportive of his wife's choices. He reported no medical problems, no legal problems, and no alcohol or drug problems. During three sessions, the counselor and Anthony focused on various ways he could adjust to the impending divorce and cope with the dysregulation he was experiencing. At the fourth session, Anthony's wife attended the session and stated that Anthony had been using heroin for the past 4 years. She reported that he lost his job 1 year ago after failing to complete a treatment program and she could no longer handle his addiction. She stated he spent their savings on drugs and steadily refused help. When the counselor asked Anthony about the discrepancy between his and his wife's report, he stated that he did not think his drug use was relevant information and that his wife was "just out to get him."

This example highlights how one perspective on a problem is often insufficient for understanding the scope of that problem. Nonsummativity highlights how important it may be to hold client reports somewhat loosely with the remembrance that each can provide one perspective on a problem. In this example, it likely will take a system perspective to fully understand the heroin use disorder as well as the divorce.

Homeostasis

Homeostasis is the property of a system in which individual parts of the system are regulated in a way that maintains balance and stability within the system. In the same way that a natural system seeks homeostasis, so does the family system. All families strive to maintain balance by regulating behaviors to accommodate the optimal function of the family system. For healthy families, the behaviors are brought about in an attempt to achieve homeostasis to promote the success and betterment of individual members. Sometimes, however, family systems, to maintain homeostasis, fall into patterns of behavior that are not productive for the individual members. In the case of addicted families, the patterns of behavior that emerge simply to maintain the mere functioning of the family system can have detrimental effects on individual members.

For example, about a year ago, 17-year-old Carrie bought a prescription of attention-deficit/hyperactivity disorder medicine from a friend to help her lose weight and focus more. She found the medicine somewhat helpful and began buying more over time. Her grades improved and she lost a little weight. Her mother noticed the change and praised her for her better grades and focus on self-care. At a party a few months ago, Erik asked her if she wanted to try cocaine. Being curious, she said yes and loved the experience. Over the past 3 months, she has steadily been using more and more cocaine. She finds she has more energy, no appetite, and feels good whenever she uses. Fighting has started to transpire between Carrie and her mom. Carrie yells and screams and insists that her mom leave her alone and that nothing is wrong. Her mother keeps pushing that something does not seem right. Several hours after each argument, Carrie's mom approaches Carrie and apologizes for the fight and tells Carrie that she loves her and is concerned for her well-being. Carrie says "fine." Carrie's use continues as does her mother's concern.

In this example, Carrie's behavior has changed with her mother noticing more irregular patterns in her functioning. The mother's apology creates homeostasis for their system and allows Carrie and her mom to continue their relationship as if nothing is wrong. Negative effects of this homeostasis include nondisclosure of Carrie's problem, denial of the mother's instinct, and eventual rupture of the relationship between Carrie and her mother.

Family Roles

Wegscheider-Cruse (1981) originally proposed six roles of addicted family members. The roles he identified are intended to offer systemic clinicians a means of organizing the family, giving them a road map of sorts to the family structure. Having this road map offers the systemic clinician an adequate understanding of the ways in which each member is dealing with the stress and chaos associated with addiction. These roles include the dependent, the enabler, the family hero, the family mascot, the scapegoat, and the lost child.

Dependent Role

The *dependent* is identified as the addicted family member. The dependent member may be ruled by guilt and shame and may use alcohol and/or drugs to help numb pain as a reaction to current or past family dysfunctional interactions (familial sexual abuse, divorce, controlling parents, generational alcohol or drug use). The dependent individual may be using alcohol or drugs to distract himself or herself from problems in the family (low income, sibling rivalry, problems in school, parental discord), placate boredom, to have a good time, to improve mood, for distraction, or for concentration and focus. There are unlimited reasons why an individual may begin and maintain use. For purposes of family roles, the dependent is the individual in the family abusing alcohol or drugs.

Enabler Role
The *enabler,* typically the partner of the dependent, protects the addicted member by not allowing him or her the opportunity to take responsibility for behaviors. For example, behaviors include calling off work for the dependent when he or she is too drunk to work, paying bills when the dependent forgets, or picking up children from school because the dependent is too high to drive. The enabler is considered to be *codependent* on the alcohol- or drug-using family member, meaning that the enabler relies on the behaviors of the alcohol- or drug-using family member to keep the family functioning. In the example, the enabler's behavior of calling off work for the drunk partner serves the function of protecting the partner's employment and the family's income base, yet at the same time also serves the function of protecting the partner's continued drinking and failure to take responsibility for choices.

Family Hero Role
The *family hero,* typically the oldest child, is the family star and is distinguished among the family by his or her successes. The successes of the hero help the family to be distracted from the addicted member and the family's dysfunction. The family hero tends to have a proclivity for caretaking and behaving in a parental manner and in this way, the hero is said to be *parentified.* For example, the family hero may get siblings ready for school, make dinner, help siblings with homework, participate in several activities at school, and be president or leader of a club or organization. He or she is typically a well-behaved child and is responsible and dependable.

Family Mascot Role
The *family mascot,* typically the youngest child, is the family jokester. He or she is a master at distracting the family away from family troubles, typically through a quick-witted sense of humor. For example, behaviors include being the class clown at school, laughing, singing, and jumping around when parents are fighting, or being silly at the dinner table to distract the family from the fact that mom is drunk.

Scapegoat Role
The *scapegoat,* often identified as the angry child, is typically in trouble at home and school. For example, behaviors include combativeness between self and parents and teachers, skipping school, getting into fights with peers, disrupting a quiet evening at home by throwing temper tantrums, or sneaking out late at night. Much attention is placed on the scapegoat via discipline and punishment. The scapegoat tends to have behaviors that are opposite to those of the family hero although both the hero's and the scapegoat's behaviors are ways to help distract attention away from the addicted member. Even if siblings are the cause of a disruption, it is common that blame falls to the scapegoat. This blame is an additional way that anger and frustration build for the scapegoat and eventually lead to rebellion, which may foster the use of alcohol and drugs.

Lost Child Role
The *lost child,* identified as the quiet one, forgoes his or her needs so that other members of the family can use their energy to focus on the addicted parent. The lost child is characterized as withdrawn. For example, behavior includes playing video games alone in his or her room all day, passively engaging in family activities, and lacking a strong opinion about what happens in the family.

This list of family roles is one way to help understand how family members are organized within addicted systems. Although these roles were defined over 35 years ago, literature continues to identify family roles as important concepts in addiction work (Juhnke & Hagedorn, 2006; Reiter, 2014). It also is important to note that others have written on additional roles family members may fulfill (Black, 2001; Johnson, 1986), while others believe that no differences exist between family roles of addicted and nonaddicted families.

Boundaries

Boundaries within the family system are invisible lines that help define with whom, when, and how information is shared. Boundaries also exist between family members and between the family and outside influences. In healthy families the flow of information between family members and between the family and the outside world is neither completely closed nor completely open. When boundaries between family members are healthy, there is a balance between what to share and what to keep private. Among substance-abusing families, boundaries often are either too rigid or too enmeshed, with either extreme considered unhealthy.

Rigid Boundaries

Rigid boundaries do not allow information to flow from one individual in the family to others, or from inside the family to outside the family. This lack of information leaves individuals cut off from each other and unable to share thoughts and feelings and to be isolated from outside help. The term *cutoff* means that an individual separates himself or herself emotionally and is alone in dealing with family conflict. Addicted families with rigid boundaries may spend large amounts of effort and time trying to keep their family intact with an unspoken rule that what happens in the home stays in the home and is not to be shared with others.

For example, Ian is a 45-year-old Caucasian male who has drunk heavily for the past 20 years. He has been married 19 years and has two children, ages 14 and 18. Neither child can remember a time when friends were allowed to spend the night because of their dad's drinking nor do they recall their dad attending school-related evening or weekend events. Mom's response to dad's drinking has always been "That's just your dad" and she specifically tells the kids "Do not talk bad about your father."

Enmeshed Boundaries

Enmeshed boundaries allow too much information to flow from one individual in the family to another, or from inside the family to outside the family. This exposure to information leaves individuals too close to each other due to oversharing of thoughts and feelings and leaves family members without a sense of privacy from each other and the outside world. Addicted families with enmeshed boundaries spend large amounts of effort and time oversharing and triangulating children and family members against one another. Triangulation is the concept of involving a third person within a dyad's problem to create an alliance with one of the two people in the dyad.

For example, Ki-Ann is a 34-year-old Asian American woman with a methamphetamine use disorder. She is in the process of getting a divorce and her soon-to-be ex-husband Allen has custody of their 8-year-old daughter, Amiee. Allen repeatedly talks with Amiee about her mom and how Amiee's mom has abandoned their family. Allen tells Amiee about how terrible Ki-Ann is and that Ki-Ann is a bad mom and rotten wife. He tells Amiee how upset he is about his divorce and about how hard he worked to save his marriage. Amiee just listens.

These two boundary examples highlight under- and overdisclosure in family systems. It is important to note that although neither example is considered healthy, both rigid and enmeshed boundaries serve the function of protection. It may be that the addicted person is being protected, children are being protected, or partners are protecting themselves; in some way, someone in the system utilizes under- or overdisclosure to protect.

Equifinality

One final concept that aids in a fuller understanding of family systems and substance-related and addictive disorders is equifinality. *Equifinality* is the concept that any desired end point can be achieved through a multitude of means. In addiction work, systemic clinicians want to begin with the most efficient and effective treatment to help reorganize the family around sober living, yet families may not always take this most efficient or effective route toward sobriety. If this happens, the systemic clinician moves toward other treatments and interventions, utilizing patience while watching the family work through the process in the way that is best for them. While there appears to be wasted energy as the family is encumbered by trials, errors, and relapse, it is important for the systemic clinician to be aware of the fact that these trials may be necessary for some families. Although the process may seem disorganized, time-consuming, or slow, it is important to keep the end point of sobriety in mind.

For example, Jose is a 54-year-old Hispanic married male. He is devoutly Catholic. He entered treatment due to alcohol and heroin. He spent 3 days in a detoxification clinic, and 21 days in an inpatient setting. Upon completion of the 21 days, Jose reported that he was going home to his family. The counselor recommended that Jose complete 6 weeks of intensive outpatient treatment and 16 weeks of outpatient treatment but Jose declined. The counselor attempted to provide a rationale for the additional treatment including (a) less relapse potential, (b) increased knowledge and insight on use, (c) additional support for himself and his family, (d) free family counseling, and (e) better results with medical management of the heroin addiction. Even still, Jose declined. The counselor expressed worry and concern. Jose still declined. Jose went home to his family and church. He struggled, he lapsed, he called his priest for help. He went to confession and began attending mass regularly. He struggled more. His family and his church supported him through his recovery. The treatment center counselor called Jose on occasion to support him in his recovery efforts. In the example, Jose is navigating his recovery. His choice of treatment and support are inconsistent with the counselor's preferred protocols. Indeed, the counselor draws her opinion from evidence-based research and clinical experience, yet she chooses to support Jose and believes in his ability to find and maintain a sober life even if he falters or takes longer than she feels necessary. This counselor believes in the concept of equifinality.

Cultural Features

Cultural features are conceptualized in an unlimited amount of ways in addiction work (W. R. Miller & Carrol, 2014), yet tend to cluster around scientifically collected data due to the amount of research in the field of addiction. Three primary ways data is collected include the type of substance, participant age, and ethnicity. Benefits of data collection procedures include the ability to capture individual reports of use and to correlate these reports with factors such as age, socioeconomic status, level of education, ethnicity, or employment. Substance use data collection creates a story that typically begins in youth and stretches across the life span. Unfortunately, for youth whose use continues beyond exploration, their story can be riddled with emotional, behavioral, familial, social, and spiritual problems.

Adolescent Alcohol and Drug Use

In the United States, the earlier the age at which an individual begins the use of any drug, regardless of gender or cultural affiliation, the poorer the prognosis for that individual.

Persistent alcohol and drug use in adolescents disrupts biological and cognitive maturation and places an individual at risk for lifelong chronic addiction-related problems.

Many adolescents' first experimentations with drug use include alcohol, tobacco, marijuana, or some combination of these three substances. In fact, these three drugs account for the majority of adolescent drug use, with marijuana being the most frequently used among this age group. When examining the question of why drug use is persistent among adolescents, it is instructive to recognize that many adolescents hold faulty perceptions regarding the dangers associated with their drug use. A recent study found that 68% of high school students agreed that it was safe to smoke marijuana. (Johnston, O'Malley, Miech, Bachman, & Schulenberg, 2015).

Adolescents use alcohol and drugs for a variety of reasons that range from simply enhancing their social image to attempting to regulate their mental and emotional health. For those teens who do develop an affinity for alcohol and drugs, a peer culture is created whereby delinquency and deviance are fostered with increased use, resulting in declined physical and mental health and declined family- and school-related activities and communication.

Cigarette use among adolescents is a pervasive problem and has been shown to have a statistical correlation with other forms of drug use. Adolescents who smoke cigarettes report the use of illicit drugs at nine times the rate of adolescents who do not smoke cigarettes (SAMHSA, 2014). Currently, 4.9% of all adolescents report cigarette use, with the highest level of use reported by Caucasians, followed by Hispanic or Latinos, African Americans. Asian Americans reported the lowest use. Although cigarette smoking is at an all-time low compared to the past 20 years, the use of electronic cigarettes surpassed the use of traditional tobacco cigarettes with over 16% of 12th graders reporting vaporizing as opposed to just over 11% reporting smoking tobacco cigarettes (Johnston et al., 2015).

Beyond alcohol and tobacco use, illicit drugs are also a substance of use for some adolescents; 27.2% of high schoolers report some form of illicit drug use. Among these individuals, Hispanic or Latino adolescents report the highest rate of illicit drug use, followed by African Americans, and then Caucasians. Asian American adolescents report the least amount of illicit drug use (SAMHSA, 2015).

While illicit drug use is a problem among adolescents, there is some support to indicate that interventions from family and the legal system may be effective in preventing the problems' persistence into adulthood. The majority of adolescents who experiment with either alcohol or drugs do not go on to develop a lifelong substance use problem. Factors important in mitigating the lifelong persistence of adolescent substance use include limited time of using, restricted access to the substance, forced treatment, and strong parental support.

An emergent issue among adolescents is the use and abuse of prescription medications including stimulants, benzodiazepines, and pain killers. Because prescription medications can be obtained through legitimate means, they are often more accessible than other drugs to teens looking to experiment. Adolescents come to abuse prescription medications for many of the same reasons that they do illicit drugs. Adolescents perceive stimulants to have academic performance–enhancing properties, but research indicates these perceptions are fallacious. No additional value beyond the treatment of the condition for which a stimulant is prescribed can be gained from its use (Ilieva, Boland, & Farah, 2013). Adolescents use benzodiazepines and pain killers due to their euphoric and pain-killing effects, but these drugs can be very expensive and adolescents who become addicted to such substances often transition to heroin, a cheaper, yet much more addictive, alternative.

Binge drinking and alcohol use can be significant problems for adolescents. The highest binge drinking rate (five or more drinks at one time within a 2-week period) have been reported by Caucasian youth followed by Hispanic and African American youth. Asian American youth report the least amount of binge drinking episodes (SAMHSA, 2015). Studies have shown that among adolescents who begin drinking by age 15, 14.2% will go on to have an alcohol-related disorder (SAMHSA, 2013). This statistic is significant and highlights the need for the application of early intervention and prevention techniques among seventh, eighth, and ninth graders.

As with any other client, systemic clinicians must be cognizant of the adolescent's cultural needs to offer the best course of treatment. Understanding challenges such as language barriers, varying levels of *acculturation* (adoption of cultural traits and characteristics where one is currently residing versus their values from their homeland), socio-economic status, religious beliefs (such as drunkenness is a sin), and perceived and actual parental and social support all play a role in achieving optimal treatment. Adolescents have unique treatment needs when compared with adults. Adolescents are not always able to give an accurate and objective account of their behavior or behavior patterns. They are also not likely to see themselves as needing or wanting adult help. One positive feature of adolescents who do enter treatment is that youth has been using alcohol or drugs for far less time than adults and tend to stop their use when forced into treatment or forced to obey legal sanctions. Thus, it is important to consider the level of oversight and follow-up care necessary by systemic clinicians for adolescents who do enter the treatment system.

Adult Alcohol and Drug Use

Screening for alcohol and drug use in adults, regardless of the presenting problem, is always necessary by a systemic clinician because adults may not associate their alcohol and drug use with their presenting problems. Like adolescents, adult use is predicated on social, familial, environmental, and biological stressors, as well as use for purposes of a good time. Like adolescents, adults also report alcohol and marijuana as the two most frequently used drugs. Of those who are using, adults ages 18 to 25 report 2.5 times more illicit drug use than adults older than age 25. This understanding about age is significant in conceptualizing substance-related problems as the most common trajectory for alcohol and drug use begins in one's teens and peaks in one's early adult life. This trajectory is the case regardless of culture with Caucasian Americans reporting the highest level of use followed by African Americans and Hispanic or Latino Americans. Asian Americans report the least amount of heavy use (NIDA, 2015). These cultural reports of use are consistent with adolescent statistics as well.

Cultural Implications of Alcohol and Drug Use

When considering the implications of alcohol and drug data, it is crucial for systemic clinicians to remember that numbers are generalizations and clients have just as many unique features as they have culturally identified ones. Therefore, it is more important to rely on a client's personal narrative before making assumptions based on generalized data-informed treatment. It is also important to note that researchers collect data primarily on individual use as opposed to family accounts of use and many times substance use data do not take into account familial interactions related to substance use. Thus, the caution for the systemic clinician is to reflect on the concept of nonsummativity and recognize that the data alone, although specific, is not robust in conceptualizing a complete understanding of the individual.

FAMILY SYSTEMS ASSESSMENTS

Screens and assessments are used to identify and estimate the extent, duration, frequency, and impact of substance use on individuals, families, and systems. Screens, instruments that indicate the need for further assessment, are utilized in a myriad of health care environments including emergency rooms, primary care offices, other doctor offices, health fairs, treatment centers, and counseling offices. Assessments, instruments for gathering information related to diagnosis and treatment planning, are utilized by clinicians as part of the intake process and for creating a biopsychosocial understanding of the client and family system. Most substance-related screening and assessment instruments are specific to an individual, but a few exist to help in family system circumstances.

Alcohol, Drug, and Gambling Screens

The Substance-Related Disorders chapter of the *DSM-5* specifically identifies diagnoses of alcohol and drug use in individual terms. To help in the diagnosing process, the APA makes available proposed Level 1 Cross-Cutting Symptom Measures and Level 2 Cross-Cutting Symptom Measures (APA, 2013, pp. 733–748; www.psychiatry.org/psy chiatrists/practice/dsm/*DSM-5*/online-assessment-measures). If a client responds that he or she had been bothered to a "slight" or greater degree by his or her substance use on the Level 1 Cross-Cutting Measure, then the systemic clinician is prompted to administer the Level 2 Cross-Cutting Symptom Measure for substances. The Level 2 Substance Use Measure covers nine drugs (caffeine omitted) and seeks to identify how often the client has used. Separate measures have been developed for adults and youth and all are available for download from the link provided. For those willing to disclose use, an advantage of the Level 2 Substance Use Measure is that it provides a quick snapshot of current use as well as serving as a follow-up screening tool. The Level 2 Substance Use measure is repeatable so that it can be used several times to monitor progress throughout the course of treatment.

Screening for Alcohol Use

Alcohol screening is designed to gather information about the drinking habits of individuals. An individual's answers to three simple questions can be predictive of risky drinking behavior. These questions are: Do you drink? Have you had four or more drinks per day (three if you are a woman) or 14 or more per week (seven if you are a woman)? (Moyer, 2013). Unfortunately, for many Americans, accurately answering these questions can prove difficult because most are not familiar with the amount of alcohol that constitutes "one drink." For example, some people are surprised to learn that a 750 ml bottle of wine contains five drinks and a shot (1.5 ounces) of liquor is the equivalent of one drink. Overestimating how much alcohol is actually in a pour is a commonly made mistake, with most individuals erring on the side of too much alcohol (National Institute on Alcohol Abuse and Alcoholism, 2010). The question with the most predictive force in alcohol screening may be "How many times in the past year have you had X or more drinks in a day?" where X is five for men and four for women, and a response of greater than or equal to 1 is considered positive (Smith, Schmidt, Allensworth-Davies, & Saitz, 2009, p. 783).

Screening for Drug Use

The most accurate drug screening measure available is in-office and laboratory-based drug testing. These types of screens require basic training in collecting and handling specimens as well as the actual testing and reporting of results. Drug testing is used if it is critical to know *that* a client is using drugs and/or it is critical to know *which* drugs are being used. Drug screening tends to be legally mandated (court- or work-ordered), but families may also stipulate that testing of an addicted family member be conducted as part of treatment. Drug screening is more commonly utilized in substance use centers and community mental health agencies than it is in private practice. When drug screening is not an option, simple straightforward questioning about drug use is favored. Screening for drug use follows a similar model as screening for alcohol use in that a series of questions is used to assess the client's current level of use. A common combination of questions is: Do you use drugs? Which ones and how often? A wealth of knowledge about the client can be elicited with these simple questions but the systemic clinician must remember that getting quality information is predicated upon honest reporting from the client. If the systemic clinician is unlikely to receive accurate responses from the client and drug screening is not an option, then the utilization of resources such as probation officers, police reports, and/or family members may be required to gather reliable information.

Screening Family Members

In addition to screening the individual, the systemic clinician is also able to illicit quality information about the substance issues within a family by talking with other family members. Alcohol and drug use often cause marriage difficulties, financial troubles, domestic violence, anxiety, depression, and distress for both the addicted member as well as loved ones. Data show that these types of troubles tend to be present even when other variables, such as gender, age, ethnicity, marital status, socioeconomic status, employment status, family history of alcohol problems, and minimum drinking amounts are held constant (Greenfield, Karriker-Jaffe, Kaplan, Kerr, & Wilsnack, 2015). Family members experiencing these consequences of substance-related disorders are often eager to share their knowledge about the problem. In fact, after individual self-report, family members may be the next best source of information regarding the extent, duration, frequency, amount, and costs affiliated with the substance use.

Alcohol, Drug, and Gambling Assessments

Screening instruments tend to be quick and brief. To achieve a more comprehensive understanding of an individual or family, it may be necessary to complete an addiction-related assessment. Four types of assessments commonly utilized for substance-related disorders include the biopsychosocial assessment, the American Society of Addiction Medicine (ASAM) criteria, genograms, and ecomaps. A biopsychosocial assessment is a comprehensive holistic interview focusing on the biological, psychological, and sociological domains of an individual's life. The ASAM criteria are specific domains to be used as part of an interview process for the purpose of establishing treatment recommendations. Both the genogram and the ecomap are pictorial diagrams created for the purpose of displaying patterns and themes within the client's life.

Biopsychosocial Assessment

Clinical interviewing utilizing biopsychosocial assessment tools such as the Addiction Severity Index (McLellan, Luborsky, O'Brien, & Woody, 1980) or the Global Appraisal of Individual Needs (Dennis, Titus, White, Unsicker, & Hodkgins, 2002) help systemic clinicians obtain a more comprehensive understanding of individuals who are referred for substance use treatment. Biopsychosocial assessments cover broad domains and assess the past and current levels of functioning. Although there is not one single biopsychosocial assessment in use, many of the available assessments contain questions regarding a range of similar topics including presenting problems and symptoms; socioeconomic background; religious preferences; disabilities, if present; gender and sexual preferences; prior mental and/or substance use treatment; medical problems; alcohol/drug use (the past and current); legal problems; education and employment status; client-identified strengths; and a diagnosis based on the prior information provided. Both the Addiction Severity Index and the Global Appraisal of Individual Needs have additional questions covering alcohol and drug use and are available in adult and adolescent versions.

Biopsychosocial assessments can be time consuming and are further complicated when clients present with multiple alcohol, drug, and legal histories. Alcohol and drug histories can be problematic for assessment due to the client's age and proclivity for various drugs over the course of his or her lifetime. Take, for instance, the following example: A client presents to treatment stating that he wants his wife "off his back" because he is no longer using heroin. The client reports recent use of alcohol, marijuana, and Suboxone. Upon screening, it is discovered that the client has a long and complicated history of drug use. The client used marijuana and ecstasy in his 20s; used marijuana, alcohol, and opioids in his 30s; used alcohol and heroin in his early 40s, for which he entered treatment. Assessments such as these are time consuming, to be sure, but acquiring an understanding of this complex history is necessary for the systemic clinician to make an accurate diagnosis. For the client, this process may be confusing and frustrating because he or she is unaware of how prior history informs the current problem and diagnosis. Following screenings such as these, the systemic clinician is then left with the dilemma of determining whether to focus on the immediate issues being presented or develop a more systematic treatment approach to address the underlying cause of these lifelong patterns of addiction.

American Society of Addiction Medicine Criteria

To further reduce difficulty in assessing diagnosing and treatment planning, the ASAM developed ASAM criteria comprising six dimensions. These dimensions are meant to represent a holistic biopsychosocial assessment with results utilized for treatment placement (Mee-Lee, 2013). The six domains are: (a) acute intoxication and/or withdrawal potential; (b) biomedical conditions and complications; (c) emotional, behavioral, or cognitive conditions and complications; (d) readiness to change; (e) relapse, continued use, or continued problem potential; and (f) recovery/living environment (ASAM, 2016). Answers from all of these domains are tallied with a recommendation for care. Clients are recommended to treatment based on the severity of their problems within each of the domains with *early intervention* being the lowest level of care and *medically managed intensive inpatient services* being the highest level of care (ASAM, 2016).

Genogram

Another assessment tool that may be a better fit for assessing families is a genogram. A *genogram* is a generational pictorial diagram identifying events such as marriage, birth, divorce, remarriage, illness, and death. Each event is identified by a particular symbol with family members identified by other symbols. Genograms can be constructed using family of origin members and/or family of choice members—sometimes genograms even include pets. In a substance use assessment, genograms help the systemic clinician and the client detect patterns and relationships within the immediate family and between generations of family members. Thus, a genogram can quickly highlight that dad, grandpa, and myself all have an alcohol problem and all three of us are divorced. Although genograms are used typically for assessment purposes, it should be noted that they can be revised during treatment to reflect changes in the client and/or the family.

Ecomap

Similar to the genogram is an ecomap. An *ecomap* is a pictorial diagram identifying the ecological system of an individual. Both personal and social interactions are depicted as well as the strength and quality of these interactions. Since a genogram specifically identifies interactions between familial generations, it may be helpful for a systemic clinician also to consider using an ecomap as part of his or her assessment since the ecomap may visually represent how an individual is interacting with his or her environment, where weak and strong systems exist, and what potential resources may be within the systems.

When it comes to screening and assessment, perhaps the greatest tools available to the systemic clinician are his or her senses. A successful assessment of the individual or family dynamic requires that the systemic clinician not only listens to what is being said verbally, but also be attuned to the meta-communication of the client and family members. *Meta-communication* is the set of implied meanings surrounding the actual verbal communication. In many cases, a client or family member says one thing to a systemic clinician while simultaneously giving less explicit clues as to the layers of meaning behind what is being said through his or her behavior. It is the systemic clinician's responsibility to be mindful of these less explicit forms of communication and utilize the information gained from them to inform treatment. Additionally, learning to detect how altered clients appear and smell may help the systemic clinician as well. Being able to identify a client in an altered state due to substance use enables the systemic clinician to service them better by developing a plan of action for dealing with safety issues associated with working with an altered client.

Minimization and Denial in Screening and Assessment

During the screening process, clients and their families may use minimization and denial when questioned about the amount, frequency, or extent of the substance-related problem. To *minimize* is to provide answers that are less than the full truth or answers that appear to make the situation look better than the facts. *Denial* is a psychological process by which one does not fully accept the facts of a situation as truth. It is not difficult to see why many may use minimization and denial as part of the screening process. Clients fear that an affirmative answer to questions about use may leave them in a situation where partners leave, systemic clinicians tattle, bosses fire, and parents shame. Additionally, for some, there is an ever-present threat of legal trouble if information is reported to probation officers or family members. Thus, systemic clinicians need to be prepared for clients and family members to present potentially with minimization or denial and have a plan for how to handle such information.

Screening and assessment within the alcohol and drug domain take education, practice, and more practice. Systemic clinicians need to have intimate knowledge about alcohol and drugs as well as knowledge about minimization and denial. Systemic clinicians also need to remain current in their knowledge because of new illicit drugs, as well as medication to treat alcohol and drug use continuing to change. Hundreds of screens and assessments are available to help with diagnosing and treatment planning. For further information and comprehensive reviews of alcohol- and drug-screening tools, see G. A. Miller (2014) and Juhnke and Hagedorn (2006). These resources can greatly help the systemic clinician choose instruments that fit within the systemic clinician's setting.

FAMILY SYSTEMS INTERVENTIONS

Family-based therapies have proven to be appropriate and effective interventions for individuals with SUD and their families (Fletcher, 2013; O'Farrell & Clements, 2012; Rowe, 2012). While a variety of specific therapies and approaches exist within the realm of family addictions therapy, common among them is the aim of utilizing the family in reducing the individual's substance use and promoting long-term recovery (Fals-Stewart, Lam, & Kelly, 2009). The following is a representative sampling of common family-based therapy approaches.

Family Systems Therapy

The *family systems therapy* approach to addictions counseling is rooted in the principles of general systems theory (Rohrbaugh, Shoham, Spungen, & Steinglass, 1995; Steinglass, Bennett, Wolin, & Reiss, 1987). According to the family systems approach, the family, as a system, seeks to maintain a balance between the substance use of the addicted member and the maintenance of family functioning (homeostasis). As a result, addictive behaviors are often unwittingly reinforced and bolstered by the interactional and behavioral norms established within the family. Accordingly, no one person is to blame for the cycle of addictive behavior, and to overcome the problem the family, as a whole, must seek to identify and alter the interactional sequences and associated meanings that perpetuate the cycle of addiction (Walsh, 2006).

A practitioner utilizing family systems therapy seeks to address the issue of addiction indirectly, by targeting the interactional sequences present within the family that contributes to the addictive behavior. Treatment involves the interruption of the established family interactional sequences, allowing the family system to reorganize itself around new information and modes of behavior. This process of reorganization forces family members to reevaluate their behaviors and relationships with one another, fostering a greater sense of responsibility to themselves and the family system. Following initial interventions, outcomes are evaluated and new interventions are formulated, again with the aim of interrupting the behavioral norms and interactional sequences of the family. This process is repeated until the problem is resolved (Walsh, 2006). Specific interventions associated with the family systems approach include the clinical relationship, the genogram, detriangulation, increasing insight, education, working with the individual subsets, and process questions (Walsh, 2006).

Behavioral Couples Therapy

A second family-based approach is *behavioral couples therapy (BCT)*. The critical tenet of this view is the belief that the behaviors of those closely associated with an individual suffering from addiction tend to perpetuate and reinforce addictive behaviors within the individual (Fals-Stewart et al., 2009). As such, this therapy seeks to not only treat the addictive behavior of the individual suffering from SUD, but also to strengthen the relationship between the addicted member and his or her partner. It is believed that the maintenance of a healthy, functional relationship is pivotal in eliminating SUD.

Historically, BCT has been used as a supplement to more traditional SUD treatment; however, there is research to support the use of BCT as a stand-alone intervention for couples struggling with SUD (Bischoff, 2008; O'Farrell & Schein, 2011; Vedel, Emmelkamp, & Schippers, 2008). The standard BCT course of treatment ranges between 12 and 20 weeks, but can be administered in a 12- or 6-session format with either an individual couple or in a small group format with multiple sets of couples (Fals-Stewart, Klostermann, Yates, O'Farrell, & Birchler, 2005).

Before the commencement of treatment, practitioners of BCT often require that the partners have demonstrated a significant level of commitment to each other, requiring that they be married or have maintained at least 1 year's cohabitation. Treatment begins with an intake procedure consisting of interviews with each partner, both together, and separately, a paper-and-pencil assessment to measure the level of substance use and quality of the relationship, and an observation of the couple's pretreatment communication and problem-solving skills (Birchler, Fals-Stewart, & O'Farrell, 2008).

Once begun, the therapy proceeds with two distinct types of intervention. First, the practitioner seeks to address the achievement and maintenance of abstinence by:

- Assisting the couple in anticipating and mitigating substance exposure
- Guiding the couple in the creation of behavioral contracts
- Encouraging the couple to attend relevant self-help meetings
- Encouraging the couple to monitor and report as part of its behavioral contract compliance with relevant medication regiments, that is, Disulfiram, Naltrexone, Methadone, etc. (Birchler et al., 2008).

As the couple moves through treatment, the focus shifts from recovery and abstinence to strengthening the relationship. To this end the practitioner seeks to strengthen the couple's relationship by:

- Establishing interventions that increase positive exchanges within the relationship
- Assisting the couple in finding activities it can enjoy as a couple/family
- Providing communication skills training
- Providing problem-solving skills training (Birchler et al., 2008)

Behavior couples therapy has been manualized, which makes the sessions quite structured, and it is recommended that systemic clinicians receive proper training before attempting to utilize this approach with couples (McCrady & Epstein, 2008; O'Farrell & Fals-Stewart, 2006). It is important to note that there have been several variations of BCT developed but discussion on all of the differences between these variations is beyond the scope of this chapter. For a more exhaustive list of literature on these variations please see Fletcher's (2013) review of couple treatment.

Multidimensional Family Therapy

A common treatment for families of adolescents suffering from SUD is *multidimensional family therapy (MDFT)*. MDFT views the relationships between the adolescent, the parents, the broader family, and their community as inextricably intermingled. As such, the therapy seeks to affect change in the adolescent by promoting change in each of these four key domains. MDFT is an eclectic treatment system that focuses on the relationships among cognition, affect, behavior, and environmental input to address the substance use and the family (Liddle, Rodriguez, Dakof, Kanzki, & Marvel 2005). While the therapy has evolved to treat multiple problems faced by adolescents, such as truancy, poor performance in school, and criminal behaviors, the therapy was originally developed to treat adolescents struggling with drug addiction (MDFT, 2016).

MDFT is a proven manualized treatment approach (Liddle, 2009). Treatment is designed to progress in three stages and can range between 16 and 25 sessions, typically taking place over a 4- to 6-month period. These sessions can be delivered in multiple settings including outpatient, in-home, intensive outpatient, day treatment, and residential settings, making MDFT a very flexible approach (MDFT, 2016). The primary goal of MDFT is to improve adolescent, parental, and overall family functioning to treat the SUD and other problematic behaviors (Liddle & Hogue, 2001).

During treatment, practitioners seek first to create an environment among family members that is conducive to change by enabling them to identify the problem(s) facing the family and provide motivation for change and adherence to treatment. Once the problem areas have been identified, practitioners assist the family in creating goals to address each of the four key domains. Goals for the adolescent are typically focused on promoting prosocial behaviors and communication strategies. Parental goals focus on enhancing parenting practices including teamwork, independence, and rebuilding bonds with the adolescent. More broadly, family and community goals are established which target the day-to-day functioning of the family and the relationship between the family and social institutions. During the final phases of treatment, the practitioner provides an overview of the progress made by the family and helps them create plans of action to implement as they encounter the future, posttreatment (MDFT, 2016).

MDFT has shown consistent results in reducing adolescent drug use (Berker & Curry, 2008; Vaugh & Howard, 2004; Waldron & Turner, 2008). MDFT has also been shown to have high retention rates for treatment when compared to individual treatment (Liddle, Dakof, Henderson, & Rowe, 2011). When compared to individual-based cognitive behavioral therapy, adolescents receiving MDFT have shown a greater decrease in drug use and better abstinence rates (Liddle, Dakof, Turner, Henderson, & Greenbaum, 2008; Liddle, Rowe, Dakof, Henderson, & Greenbaum, 2009).

ETHICAL AND LEGAL IMPLICATIONS

Practitioners of mental health have spent more than a century considering ethical issues and evolving codes of ethical behavior to assist in complicated situations. Perhaps the most valuable function of these codes is to alert mental health professionals of situations that may become ethically complex. Families, seen from a systemic perspective and involving multiple members, can add several dimensions to this process. Substance disorders also dramatically complicate how we anticipate and think about acting ethically for the benefit of the client(s). With a goal of helping our clients (and avoiding harmful outcomes), it is essential to understand the codes and apply them effectively.

The language and functional structure of the *DSM-5*, regarding substance-related disorders, provides systemic clinicians some strategies for avoiding ethical dilemmas. While the purposes of the American Association for Marriage and Family Therapy (AAMFT) *Code of Ethics* (2015), the American Counseling Association (ACA) *Code of Ethics* (2014), and the *DSM-5* do not specifically relate, they do inform each other. The *DSM-5* provides 11 diagnostic criteria for substance use disorders and four criteria for SIDs. While all of these criteria are valuable in diagnosing, discussing, and educating, the diagnostic criteria 5 to 8 for the substance use disorder (evaluating family, social, and personal obligations and behaviors) are particularly valuable for systemic clinicians. When working with families experiencing SIDs, Criterion B (evaluating problematic behaviors or psychological changes) is also helpful. We explore these relationships in further detail as they relate to the ethical codes.

Four themes from the AAMFT Code (2015) and from the ACA Code (2014) which can be utilized by systemic clinicians to anticipate ethical conflicts that apply to substance-related disorder cases include ensuring beneficial relationships, avoiding countertransference and discrimination, providing informed consent, and practicing within professional competence. This section explores these four areas and considers ways to apply the *DSM-5* in concert with the AAMFT Code and the ACA Code for better practice.

Ensuring Beneficial Therapeutic Relationships

The primary goal of offering any form of therapy service is to improve the lives of clients. The AAMFT *Code of Ethics* 1.9 (2015) and the ACA *Code of Ethics* A.1.a (2014) maintain that it is the clinician's obligation to ensure that the relationship is beneficial to the client.

Similarly, to ensure that the lives of the clients are improving, the systemic clinician must utilize metrics to measure client progress. Measuring progress in the context of family therapy for substance use, however, can be challenging due to the unpredictable and often immeasurable nature of the associated disorders. For the marriage and family systemic clinicians struggling with this issue, the *DSM-5* provides structure and language to aid in measuring the benefits of therapy.

Practitioners must be aware that the metrics used to assess progress in marriage and family therapy will often seem less measurable than those used in individual addictions work. For instance, the concept of codependence, which is embedded in addictions work, is consistent with and is informed by a family systems perspective, but is not specifically measurable. Codependence occurs when the client who struggles with substance issues is dependent on the behaviors of the other members of the family for the maintenance of his or her addictive behaviors. A systemic clinician should consider changes in the family system (i.e., a decrease in codependent behaviors such as enabling) as therapeutic progress, even if it may not directly impact individual substance-related problematic behaviors. The idea of therapeutic progress is particularly important for family systems systemic clinicians because these shifts can be of great benefit to the nonaddicted family members.

When treatment planning, goal setting, and measuring family progress, the *DSM-5* criteria can be used to create specific numerical goals. An example being: if there is an individual diagnosis of a SUD, Criterion 5 measures the failure to fulfill major role obligations. Beyond providing a useful topic for family discussions, this is a behavior that is measurable and relates to the functioning of the family system. Criterion 6 (social or interpersonal problems exacerbated by the alcohol use) and Criterion 7 (giving up important activities) can be measured similarly within a systemic perspective. If the problem is with substance intoxication, Criterion B (which focuses on problematic behaviors resulting from intoxication) serves the same discussion and measurement purposes.

Avoiding Discrimination

A specific standard highlighted in the *AAMFT Code of Ethics* can be noted in code 1.1 of the AAMFT Code that instructs systemic clinicians to avoid discrimination. While this code explicitly addresses discrimination by race, age, ethnicity, and so forth, it can also be expanded to include forms of discrimination commonly encountered by those struggling with addiction. *The ACA Code of Ethics* discusses this issue in A.4.b by asking counselors to avoid imposing the counselor's beliefs or values onto the client (2014). There are many preconceived beliefs about individuals struggling with substance-related issues. The comedian, Mitch Hedberg, who unfortunately passed away from substance-related causes, quipped, "Alcoholism is a disease, but it's the only disease you can get yelled at for having." Since addiction has a behavioral component, it can be easy to judge and discriminate against substance users. Recognizing that this discrimination exists will enable the systemic clinician to be more mindful of the client's situation and avoid engaging in unintentional discrimination.

Historically, the language used to communicate about substance-related issues, even within the helping professions, has served only to reinforce this tacit discrimination toward users. Consider the weight of some terms utilized in American culture regarding substance-related issues: addict, alcoholic, junkie, pill head, and so forth. Acknowledging this history, the *DSM-5* provides language and foundational concepts that allow practitioners to shift focus away from potentially discriminatory language, preferring to focus instead on the identification of specific behaviors. Whereas the *DSM-IV-TR* used the terms *abuse* and *dependence* to classify pathological users, the *DSM-5* uses the terms *use* and *induced*. The *DSM-5*, therefore, encourages practitioners to understand the client and the family relationships with substances as behavioral issues as opposed to the issues being solely personal. This delineation not only enables the practitioner to engage with the client in a nondiscriminatory way, it also empowers professionals a less bias-laden language with which to discuss these issues with colleagues. In short, the *DSM-5* encourages discussing the behaviors involved rather than labeling the individual, therefore decreasing stigma.

Informed Consent and Confidentiality

In thinking about ethics for systemic clinicians who are counseling individuals and families with substance-related problems, perhaps the most valuable item addressed in the AAMFT and ACA code involves informed consent. A well-thought-out informed consent process, using the *DSM-5*, is a systemic clinician's best tool for avoiding situations involving deception, communication with third parties, and potentially harmful situations.

The rules for how a systemic clinician communicates with other professionals and handles ethical dilemmas can be understood by all parties through informed consent before the therapeutic relationship begins by providing the specifics in writing (AAMFT, 2015, 2.2). Systemic clinicians can give forethought to potential issues, provide a written and verbal framework for dealing with them, and have a signature from all parties noting the acceptance of the agreed upon structure.

The AAMFT Code 1.2 describes *informed consent* as an opening task where the systemic clinician ensures the client can understand the process of therapy and the risks involved. ACA Code A.2. complements this understanding noting that the informed consent process is ongoing, and outlines the rights and responsibilities of both the counselor and the client. ACA code B.4.b also notes that, when working with couples and families, counselors clearly define who is the "client" and asks counselors to assume that, unless there is an agreement otherwise, the couple or family is to be considered the client. Additionally, The Code of Federal Regulations' Confidentiality of Alcohol and Drug Abuse Patient Records (2016) outlines the required elements of informed consent to be disclosed under subpart C for alcohol and drug abuse patient records. These elements include the names of the therapist, patient, person to whom the disclosure is to be made, the purpose of the disclosure, and the specific information to be disclosed. The document should include a signature of the client (and parent if a minor), and the date, and it also suggests an expiration date and conditions for appropriate revocation of consent. Current Health Insurance Portability and Accountability Act of 1996 laws require systemic clinicians to define clearly what specific information can be disclosed to which individuals under what circumstances. The rules concerning minors and informed consent may vary from state to state, so it is important for systemic clinicians to be aware of applicable local regulations when working with minors.

Two instances in which it may be permissible for a systemic clinician to disclose client information are in the case of medical emergency and when the systemic clinician is served with a court order requesting the release of records. It is important to keep in mind that if a court order is issued, the systemic clinician is advised to seek legal counsel to proceed in a manner most consistent with both legal matters and professional ethical standards. The fine for the first offense of disclosing information in a manner not consistent with Health Insurance Portability and Accountability Act of 1996 regulations is up to $500, and up to $5,000 for each subsequent offense.

When developing an informed consent procedure, the systemic clinician is given the discretion to produce an agreement outlining the circumstances in which information may be disclosed to other family members. The *DSM-5* can help the systemic clinician in creating an informed consent procedure specifically for families with substance-related issues, thus allowing the systemic clinician to anticipate and prevent some of the most common ethical issues. For example, an issue that commonly creates a conflict for the systemic clinician when working with those struggling with substance issues is deception. If a systemic clinician becomes aware of unspoken or untrue information offered by an individual client that may be harmful, the systemic clinician finds himself or herself in an ethical dilemma. In this situation, the systemic clinician has information that may be harmful to the client (the family), but he or she is also bound by the rules of confidentiality. AAMFT Code 2.1 states that, since marriage and family therapy may involve more than one person, systemic clinicians are to disclose the circumstances where confidentiality is limited in the informed consent process. A prescient informed consent structure can prevent this ethical dilemma.

Another confidentiality dilemma can arise when working with other professionals. AAMFT Code 1.13 and ACA code B.1d. similarly direct clinicians to disclose, upon agreeing to provide services, the limits of confidentiality. The refusal of a family member to accept the terms of the informed consent, including third-party professional communication, is valuable information for the systemic clinician regarding the expectations and motives of the clients. For instance, a client may not want communication with his or her substance use specialist to prevent the family systemic clinician from having access to the results of mandatory random drug tests. Consent to communicate with other treating professionals can decrease the chances of ethical conflict as therapy progresses.

Further, through physical or emotional abuse, driving under the influence (sometimes with children in the car), or contracting sexually transmitted diseases, people who are intoxicated can be at an increased risk of causing harm to others. In discovering this information, a systemic clinician can easily find himself or herself in an ethical dilemma between safety and confidentiality, which can also lead to legal complications.

The systemic clinician is legally responsible for the information collected within the therapeutic relationship(s). Ethical codes offer direction and structure to clinicians in this legal obligation to protect clients. ACA code B.2.a offers direction stating that confidentiality requirements do not apply when foreseeable harm is evident and the clinician can serve in a protective role. ACA code B.2.e. balances the risk of breaching confidentiality for the sake of protection by noting that only essential information be given and that clients be informed prior.

A systemic clinician can utilize the *DSM-5* and the informed consent process to prevent these ethical and legal dilemmas with a family by using a "no-secrets contract." In the informed consent process, the systemic clinician discloses in detail what will be done in cases in which the systemic clinician becomes aware of a secret, or a deception. The no-secrets contract informs all members that the systemic clinician will consult with the individual who is withholding information, or being untruthful, to determine the best way to disclose this information to the other family members with an understanding that a secret will not be held confidential.

If a clinician chooses to use a no-secrets contract, creating the contract should be a considered process. The *DSM-5* diagnostic criteria can provide the framework for creating some of the elements of the no-secrets contract. It offers measurable and specific language that is functional for the purpose of outlining how everyone in this therapeutic relationship is going to behave on issues of truthfulness. In the case of a SUD, the systemic clinician can use *DSM-5* criteria 1 to 4 to offer detail to the no-secrets contact. An example of this is:

- *The systemic clinician can expect honesty from all parties regarding the use of substances, including amounts, duration, efforts to refrain from using alcohol—both successful and unsuccessful.* (*DSM-5* Criteria 1 and 2)
- *The systemic clinician can expect honesty regarding all activities related to obtaining and using alcohol.* (*DSM-5* Criterion 3)
- *The systemic clinician can expect honesty regarding cravings or a strong desire or urge to use alcohol* (*DSM-5* Criterion 4).

Competence

AAMFT Code 3.10 and ACA Code C2. address the issue of competence, directing marriage and family systemic clinicians not to diagnose, treat, and advise outside of the recognized boundaries of their competence. Similar to a marriage and family therapy education, there are certifications that require education and experience for addictions specialties in both the mental health and the medical fields. Substance addiction is unique insofar as substance issues are a factor in every aspect of health care, not just mental and emotional health. It is, therefore, sometimes difficult to find a demarcation of competence in addictions work. The *DSM-5* offers some direction in this regard such as a common vocabulary for all of the health care professionals, the accessibility to diagnostic criteria by all trained health care professionals, and the use of the criteria as the basis for appropriate referrals, education, and treatment planning.

Systemic clinicians are in a position to work with addictions specialists and complement their work. The family systems perspective on familial relations and how they impact presenting issues of addiction can help everyone involved to create a shift in the social structure, enhancing the work of the other specialists.

The *DSM-5* can help systemic clinicians achieve their primary goal of bettering the lives of their clients while staying within the competence of the systemic clinician profession. The diagnostic criteria for each disorder can be used as a template for determining which issues are family related. As discussed previously, items 5 to 7 of the substance use criteria are directly related to social and family life: role obligations, interpersonal problems, and reduction of important activities. Reports from family members can help the client presenting with substance-related issues to understand how his or her behavior is impacting others. For substance intoxication and withdrawal, the client with the presenting problem may not be in a state of mind to accurately recall how he or she was impacted by substance use or the effect it had on his or her environment. All involved professionals would benefit from the information gathered in a family session in assessing criteria B (problematic behavior) and C (signs and symptoms). The information gained from a systemic clinician would be helpful to other professionals in making an appropriate diagnosis and determining therapeutic progress. Often, much of this information can be obtained only through directed discussions with the family. This treatment and reporting, particularly if structured to reflect the *DSM-5* criteria, is within the competence of a marriage and family systemic clinician and complements other areas of substance-related health care.

A working knowledge of the *DSM-5*, the AAMFT Code, and the *ACA Code of Ethics* can help marriage and family systemic clinicians to practice more effectively when working with substance-related clients and families. The *DSM-5* can provide language and structure to help the systemic clinician treat families ethically, particularly when it comes to common substance-related issues such as deception, confidentiality, harmful situations, and third-party communication. The *DSM-5* helps systemic clinicians anticipate and approach ethical dilemmas with criteria that can be used to provide informed consent effectively, measure therapeutic progress, avoid discrimination, and work within the bounds of their competence.

CASE CONCEPTUALIZATION

Presenting Concerns

Mike and Judy Jones were a married, Caucasian couple in their early 60s. They presented for treatment after Mike was caught stealing prescription opiates from his elderly father.

At that time, the family did not press charges but required that Mike obtains an assessment and follow recommendations. The previous year, Mike had retired from a job in the city government office and had been working side jobs and volunteering with his time since retirement. Judy still needed to work 3 years before she was eligible for retirement. This time frame had become somewhat of a stressor as Judy was no longer enjoying her job due to administrative changes. Mike began using opiates, specifically Vicodin, 3 years ago following back surgery. At first, his use was as prescribed, but over time, he found himself taking more than prescribed. He reported that he was able to reduce his use for months at a time, but the free time during retirement seemed to contribute to an increase in his use. He denied residual pain from his back surgery. The problematic use of medications was a surprise to his family. Mike and Judy described their marriage as close, and the secret of Mike's addiction had greatly impacted their trust. The couple had raised two adult children and was looking forward to having time to travel and visit family once they were both retired. The couple reported that they were comfortable financially and Mike maintained his side jobs primarily to keep him busy and because he enjoyed them.

Concurrent Problems

The couple had never attended counseling in the past. Mike received medical treatment for his back pain but was no longer involved in medication or pain management therapy. Judy was concerned about Mike's substance use and their marriage, but was reluctant to attend treatment, as she feared what others might think. Mike, remorseful about his behaviors, was willing to attend treatment. He had some reservations about past coworkers finding out about his substance use. Both Judy and Mike expressed frustrations and concerns with retirement and the expectations for their lives after work.

Background History and Stressors

Both Mike and Judy were raised in intact, religious households. Mike and Judy attended Catholic Mass weekly and most weeks they also had Sunday family dinners. There was no family history of mental health issues or substance use. The only reported medical issue was Mike's history of back pain and treatment. He denied residual pain or issues with his back since surgery. The stigma of addiction was one of their largest stressors; the couple expressed shame in sharing this information with their families and friends. The couple lived in the same house where they raised their children, the one they built together when they first married. They lived near where they were raised by their parents, with family nearby.

Strengths

Mike and Judy reported having a strong, close relationship. They enjoyed spending time together and also with extended family and close friends. In addition to shared friends, they each maintained their circles of friends from work and other activities. Mike and Judy attended church together weekly. Mike was involved with mission trips and volunteer work since he retired. Mike played basketball with friends from work once a week. Both considered themselves to be caretakers, jumping in when friends or family needed help. Judy liked to cook and bake. Both were well liked by others and committed to their paid work, volunteer work, friends, and family.

DSM-5 Impressions and Implications

Mike was the primary focus of clinical concern in this scenario. The initial diagnostic impression for Mike was Moderate Vicodin Use Disorder (APA, 2013). To meet the criteria for moderate opioid use disorder, clients must meet four to five of the DSM-5 diagnostic criteria. Mike reported experiencing substance use symptoms sporadically since his back surgery 3 years ago. He identified an increase in symptoms since his retirement, 1 year ago, with peak use over the past 3 months. Mike reported that he began taking more than the prescribed amount of opiates for his back pain. Once his prescription ran out and he was no longer able to obtain opiates from his primary care physician, he started taking them from his father who also had a past surgery. He identified cravings that varied in intensity level, increased tolerance to pain medications, and some mild withdrawal symptoms when he was unable to obtain opiates. Mike went days at a time without pain medication if it could not be obtained, but despite his best efforts, he would begin using again within a few days. Mike's use of opiates did not impact his family, work, or social obligations. He denied using when it would have been dangerous, for example when driving or using machinery in his side jobs.

Mike denied that he continued using opiates due to pain and reported that the back surgery relieved any medical issues he was having. Both Mike and his wife denied any family conflict until Mike was caught taking his father's medication and Judy realized that he had been using and had been dishonest with her.

Relational Problems

When Mike was caught taking prescription medications from his father, his parents were forgiving but insisted that he get treatment. Judy was less forgiving and hurt by the situation. Due to her self-reported lack of understanding about addiction, she vacillated between withdrawal from the situation and overinvolvement, which caused tension and conflict. The lack of trust that developed related to the addiction caused Judy to question everything Mike did after she became aware of his use. She doubted herself as she had not noticed the change in Mike and moved back and forth between feelings of sadness, anger, and shame toward Mike. Based on these symptoms, it would be important to consider Relational Distress With Spouse as an area for clinical focus. To consider Mike and Judy from a systemic perspective, their needs as a couple were considered and referrals were made to family educational groups, family self-help groups (Al-Anon), and couple's counseling. From this perspective the best way to help Mike is to work with the entire system. Additionally, Mike identified his recent retirement as a trigger to his increased substance use. Judy reported struggling with her current work situation, the fact that she was unable to retire but Mike has, and that her need to attend work and provide their health insurance to pay for Mike's treatment had prevented her from being more involved in his recovery. The couple's expectation for what retirement was going to look like for them had drastically changed. Phase of Life Problem is another area of treatment that might warrant consideration (APA, 2013).

Assessments

A general starting place for treatment might be obtained via the use of a clinical interview/biopsychosocial assessment. While Mike would provide the majority of the information for the assessment, related to drug history, it would be ideal if Judy would supplement with collateral information. Mike denied an extensive drug and alcohol history, which made his drug history an easier process than most. While Judy was unaware of most of his use after surgery, she could help fill in pieces related to behavioral issues and also medical history. A family genogram is an additional layer of assessment to examine the systemic score of the problem. While both Judy and Mike denied a family history of substance use, the genogram helped them look at family relationships, areas of support, and also help put their views about substance use and recovery into perspective. Mike was open about his substance use and admitted to using opiates. Urine drug screens or blood monitoring would be appropriate during early recovery to monitor abstinence.

Interventions

An empirically supported marital approach to substance use is behavioral couples therapy (BCT; O'Farrell & Clements, 2012). Judy and Mike were married without co-occurring mental health diagnoses, which made them good candidates for BCT. Behavioral techniques are used along with written contracts to address the substance use as well as potential emotional distress related to the elimination of substance use. Judy and Mike worked with the systemic clinician to anticipate and mitigate substance exposure. They also attended 12-step support groups (for Mike, Alcoholics Anonymous or Narcotics Anonymous; Judy would be referred to AL-Anon) and Mike was referred to a physician to be evaluated for pharmacotherapy (e.g., Suboxone). If the medication were recommended, the couple would work with the systemic clinician to contract for compliance and monitoring (Birchler et al., 2008). As Judy and Mike moved forward in recovery, the focus moved to strengthening the relationship. As the couple reported that they enjoyed activities together, the focus was on communication-skills training and problem-solving–skills training. Through their 12-step meeting attendance and relationship focus, they addressed issues related to mistrust and communication about Mike's substance use. They were also able to get on the same page regarding retirement and expectations. Judy had an opportunity to learn more about addiction and recovery, and both better understood the family dynamics of substance use.

Ethical and Legal Implications

Considering the *ACA Code of Ethics*, one of the first considerations was informed consent. The basic premise of the counseling relationship was explained, procedures for communication with other professionals (i.e., if a medical evaluation is made) and other specifics of the therapeutic relationship were explored. Both Judy and Mike signed the informed consent form, indicating their agreement and understanding. They were informed of the potential benefits and risks of counseling. A key ethical area to be addressed when working with couples or families is that of confidentiality. During the informed consent process, it is important to explain the limitations of confidentiality to clients should an ethical dilemma arise. Deception is a common issue in substance use counseling. Systemic clinicians may be better prepared to address deception by using a "no-secrets contract." The no-secrets contract informs all members that the systemic clinician will consult with the individual who is withholding information or being untruthful to determine how to reveal the secret. Both parties were informed that secrets would not be kept.

DISCUSSION

As you continue to reflect on the case study and the overall approach, contemplate these questions:

- What other information might you need or want to make an accurate clinical diagnosis?

- What is the *DSM-5* diagnosis, including Z codes?

- What more would you like to know about this family (psychosocial, behavioral, cognitive, relational, etc.) to encapsulate the larger systemic impact?

- Joining with the couple/family is a critical step in counseling. How would you engage both Mike and Judy to promote change as a couple and make them feel comfortable with the counseling process?

- Other than reduced substance use or abstinence, how would you assess that change has occurred in Mike and Judy's relationship and that interaction and communication have improved?

SUMMARY

This chapter has provided important information for systemic clinicians utilizing a family systems approach for the treatment of substance-related and addictive disorders. Significant changes were made to the *DSM-5* diagnosis of substances, including a shift in terminology. The evaluation of presenting symptoms, diagnosis criteria, assessment considerations, cultural issues, and relational factors are intertwined during diagnosis. While working with SUDs, it is the role of the systemic clinician to consider relational and cultural factors, appropriate assessment measures and interventions, as well as all ethical and legal implications that will have an impact on improving the inner workings of the family system.

Before assessment, the systemic clinician needs to have a thorough grasp of the *DSM-5* criteria to accurately diagnose SUDs, SIDs, and Other Addictive Disorders. Significant changes to the *DSM-5* provide a continuum for substance use diagnosis with specifiers of mild, moderate, and severe. Cravings have been added as criteria, and legal issues have been eliminated. Gambling has been added under Other Addictive Disorders based on supporting research. A challenge for systemic clinicians is the use of a systemic lens and a shift from medicalization, which is inherent in the *DSM-5* and addictions treatment. From a systemic perspective, the individual with an addictive disorder has a role in the family, as do other family members. This individual typically receives a diagnosis for treatment reimbursement, while other family members may meet criteria for reimbursement under Other Conditions That May Be a Focus of Clinical Attention (APA, 2013).

Part of the assessment is considering the cultural framework of families and the relational interactions of members. The case of Mike and Judy demonstrated this framework while considering the biological, psychological, and sociocultural factors that influence the makeup of individual members of the family and how these factors transpire within the system. Important family systems principles to consider are circular causality, nonsummativity, homeostasis, family roles, boundaries, and equifinality. The role of the systemic clinician is to consider how relationships develop, are maintained, and change while considering these principles. Most instruments to assess addiction are individually focused, looking at the symptoms of the addicted individual. To make similar assessments within a family systems approach, a systemic clinician will often use biopsychosocial assessment with collateral information from family members, genograms, and the systemic clinician's tools of observation including an awareness of meta-communication.

After assessment and diagnosis, there are several approaches that may be used to provide systemic treatment for addicted couples of families. Research shows that the inclusion of families in substance use treatment is more successful than treating the individual alone. Family systems therapy and MDFT are used in working with family systems; BCT is considered the treatment of choice for couples with an addicted member. Mike and Judy were ideal candidates for BCT based on their biopsychosocial composition.

As with all counseling, ethical and legal considerations are important. The *ACA Code of Ethics* provides guidelines for ethical decision making. There are four areas that stand out about addiction-related cases: ensuring beneficial therapeutic relationships, avoiding discrimination, informed consent, and practicing within professional competence. In cases of addiction, it is important to define therapeutic progress that may be seen in behavioral manifestations other than actual substance use (i.e., codependency behaviors). Systemic clinicians need to focus on behaviors and not labels. Deception and secrets are common themes in couples and family counseling, leading systemic clinicians to consider "no-secrets" policies in confidentiality practices. Systemic clinicians working in the area of substance use need to be sure they are practicing within their professional scope; consultation with medical professionals and addiction specialists may be considered.

REFERENCES

American Association for Marriage and Family Therapy. (2015). *AAMFT code of ethics.* Alexandria, VA: Author. Retrieved from http://www.aamft.org/iMIS15/AAMFT/Content/Legal_Ethics/Code_of_Ethics.aspx

American Counseling Association. (2014). *ACA code of ethics.* Alexandria, VA: Author.

American Psychiatric Association. (2000). *Diagnostic and statistical manual of mental disorders* (4th ed., text rev.). Washington, DC: Author.

American Psychiatric Association. (2013). *Diagnostic and statistical manual of mental disorders* (5th ed.). Arlington, VA: American Psychiatric Publishing.

American Society of Addiction Medicine. (2016). What is the ASAM criteria? Retrieved from http://www.asam.org/quality-practice/guidelines-and-consensus-documents/the-asam-criteria/about

Becker, S. & Curry, J. (2008). Outpatient interventions for adolescent substance abuse: A quality of evidence review. *Journal of Consulting and Clinical Psychology, 76*(4), 531–543.

Benishek, L. A., Kirby, K. C., & Dugosh, K. L. (2011). Prevalence and frequency of problems of concerned family members with a substance-using loved one. *The American Journal of Drug and Alcohol Abuse, 37*(2), 82–88. doi:10.3109/00952990.2010.540276

Birchler, G. R., Fals-Stewart, W., & O'Farrell, T. J. (2008). Couple therapy for alcoholism and drug abuse. In A. S. Gurman (Ed.), *Clinical handbook of couple therapy* (4th ed.). New York, NY: Guilford Press.

Bischoff, R. J. (2008). Couple therapy for substance abuse. *Journal of Couple and Relationship Therapy, 7,* 175–179. doi:10.1080/15332690802107255

Black, C. (2001). *It will never happen to me: Children of alcoholics as youngsters, adolescents, adults.* Center City, MN: Hazelden.

Confidentiality of Alcohol and Drug Abuse Patient Records, (42 C.F.R. § 2.31(a); 45 C.F.R. § 164.508(c)) (2016).

Cunningham-Williams, R. M., Gattis, M. N., Dore, P. M., Shi, P., & Spitznagel, E. L., Jr. (2009). Towards DSM-V: considering other withdrawal-like symptoms of pathological gambling disorder. *International Journal of Methods in Psychiatric Research, 18*(1), 13–22.

Dennis, M., Titus, J., White, M., Unsicker, J., & Hodgkins, D. (2002). *Global appraisal of individual needs (GAIN): Administration guide for the GAIN and related measures.* Bloomington, IL: Chestnut Health Systems. Retrieved from http://www.chestnut.org

Denton, W. H., & Bell, C. (2013). DSM-V and the family systemic clinician: First-order change in a new millennium. *Australian and New Zealand Journal of Family Therapy, 34*(2), 147–155.

Fals-Stewart, W., Klostermann, K., Yates, B. T., O'Farrell, T. J., & Birchler, (2005). Brief relationship therapy for alcoholism: A randomized clinical trial examining clinical efficacy and cost-effectiveness. *Psychology of Addiction Behaviors, 19,* 363–371.

Fals-Stewart, W., Lam, W., & Kelly, M. (2009). Learning sobriety tougher: Behavioral couples therapy for alcoholism and drug abuse. *Journal of Family Therapy, 31,* 115–125.

Fischer, J. L., & Wiersma, J. D. (2012). Romantic relationships and alcohol use. *Current Drug Abuse Reviews, 5,* 98–116.

Fletcher, K. (2013). Couple therapy treatments for substance use disorders: A systematic review. *Journal of Social Work Practice in the Addictions, 13,* 327–352. doi:10.1080/1533256x.2013.840213

Greenfield, T. K., Karriker-Jaffe, K. J., Kaplan, L. M., Kerr, W. C., & Wilsnack, S. C. (2015). Trends in alcohol's harms to others (AHTO) and co-occurrence of family-related AHTO: The four US National Alcohol Surveys, 2000–2015. *Substance Abuse: Research and Treatment, 9*(Suppl. 2), 23–31. Retrieved from doi:10.4137/SART.S23505

Heinz, A. J., Wu, J., Witkiewitz, K., Epstein, D. H., & Preston, K. L. (2009). Marriage and relationship closeness as predictors of cocaine and heroin use. *Addictive Behaviors, 34*, 258–263. doi:10.1016/j.addbeh.2008.10.020

Ilieva, I., Boland, J., & Farah, M. J. (2013) Objective and subjective cognitive enhancing effects of mixed amphetamine salts in healthy people. *Neuropharmacology, 64*, 496–505.

Johnson, V. E. (1986). *Intervention: How to help someone who doesn't want help.* Minneapolis, MN: Johnson Institute Books.

Juhnke, G. A., & Hagedorn, W. B. (2006). *Counseling addicted families: An integrated assessment and treatment model.* Florence, KY: Brunner-Routledge.

Liddle, H. A. (2009). *Multidimensional family therapy for adolescent drug abuse: Clinician's manual.* Center City, MN: Hazelden Publishing.

Liddle, H. A., Dakof, G. A., Henderson, C. E., & Rowe, C. L. (2011). Implementation outcomes of multidimensional family therapy-detention to the community (DTC): A reintegration program for drug-using juvenile detainees. *International Journal of Offender Therapy and Comparative Criminology, 55*(4), 587–604.

Liddle, H. A., Dakof, G. A., Turner, R. M., Henderson, C. E., & Greenbaum, P. E. (2008). Treating adolescent drug abuse: A randomized trail comparing multidimensional family therapy and cognitive behavior therapy. *Addiction, 103*(10), 1660–1670.

Liddle, H. A., & Hogue, A. (2001). Multidimensional family therapy for adolescent substance abuse. In E. F. Wagner & H. B. Waldon (Eds.), *Innovations in adolescent substance abuse interventions* (pp. 229–261). New York, NY: Pergamon.

Liddle, H. A., Rodriguez, R. A., Dakof, G. A., Kanzki, E., & Marvel, F. A. (2005). Multidimensional family therapy: A science-based treatment for adolescent drug abuse. In J. Lebow (Ed.), *Handbook of clinical family therapy* (pp. 128–163). New York, NY: Wiley.

Liddle, H. A., Rowe, C., Dakof, G., Henderson, C., & Greenbaum, P. (2009). Multidimensional family therapy for early adolescent substance abusers: Twelve-month outcomes of a randomized controlled trial. *Journal of Consulting and Clinical Psychology, 77*(1), 12–25.

McCrady, B. S., & Epstein, E. E. (2008) *Overcoming alcohol problems: A couples-focused program therapist guide.* New York, NY: Oxford University Press.

McLellan, A. T., Luborsky, L., O' Brien, C. P., & Woody, G. E. (1980). An improved evaluation instrument for substance abuse patients: The Addiction Severity Index. *Journal of Nervous and Mental Diseases, 168*, 26–33.

Mee-Lee, D. (Ed.). (2013). *The ASAM criteria: Treatment for addictive, substance-related, and co-occurring conditions.* Chevy Chase, MD: American Society of Addiction Medicine.

Miller, G. A., (2014). *Learning the language of addiction counseling.* Hoboken, NJ: Wiley.

Miller, W. R., & Carroll, K. M. (2014). *Rethinking substance abuse.* New York, NY: Guilford Press.

Morgan, T. B., Crane, D. R., Moore, A. M., & Eggett, D. L. (2013). The cost of treating substance use disorders: Individual versus family therapy. *Journal of Family Therapy, 35*(1), 2–23.

Moyer V. A., on behalf of the U.S. Preventive Services Task Force. (2013). Screening and behavioral counseling interventions in primary care to reduce alcohol misuse. *Annals of Internal Medicine, 159,* 210–218. doi:10.7326/0003-4819-159-3-201308060-00652

Multidimensional Family Therapy. (2016). About MDFT. Retrieved from http://www.mdft.org/

Murphy, C. M., Stojek, M. K., Few, L. R., Rothbaum, A. O., & MacKillop, J. (2014). Craving as an alcohol use disorder symptom in *DSM-5*: An empirical examination in a treatment-seeking sample. *Experimental and Clinical Psychopharmacology, 22*(1), 43–49. doi:10.1037/a0034535

National Institute on Alcohol Abuse and Alcoholism. (2010). *Rethinking drinking: Alcohol and your health.* (NIH Publication No. 15-3770) Washington, DC: U.S. Department of Health and Human Services. Retrieved from https://pubs.niaaa.nih.gov/publications/RethinkingDrinking/Rethinking_Drinking.pdf

National Institute on Drug Abuse. (2015). Drug facts: Nationwide trends. Retrieved from https://www.drugabuse.gov/publications/drugfacts/nationwide-trends

O'Farrell, T., J., & Clements, K. (2012). Review of outcome research on marital and family therapy in treatment for alcoholism. *Journal of Marital and Family Therapy, 38*(1), 122–144.

O'Farrell, T. J., & Fals-Stewart, W. (2006). *Behavioral couples therapy for alcoholism and drug abuse.* New York, NY: Guilford Press.

O'Farrell, T. J., & Schein, A. Z. (2011). Behavioral couples therapy for alcoholism and drug abuse. *Journal of Family Psychotherapy, 22,* 193–219.

Pickens, C. L., Airavaara, M., Theberge, F., Fanous, S., Hope, B. T., & Shaham, Y. (2011). Neurobiology of the incubation of drug craving. *Trends in Neurosciences, 34*(8), 411–420. doi:10.1016/j.tins.2011.06.001

Potenza, M. N. (2008). The neurobiology of pathological gambling and drug addiction: An overview and new findings. *Philosophical Transactions of the Royal Society B: Biological Sciences, 363*(1507), 3181–3189. Retrieved from doi:10.1098/rstb.2008.0100

Potenza, M. N., Balodis, I. M., Franco, C. A., Bullock, S., Xu, J., Chung, T., & Grant, J. E. (2013). Neurobiological considerations in understanding behavioral treatments for pathological gambling. *Psychology of Addictive Behaviors, 27*(2), 380–392. doi:10.1037/a0032389

Reiter, M. D. (2014). *Substance abuse and the family.* New York, NY: Routledge.

Rohrbaugh, M., Shoham, V., Spungen, C., & Steinglass, P. (1995). Family systems therapy in practice: A systematic couples therapy for problem drinking. In B. M. Bongar & L. E. Beutler (Eds.), *Comprehensive textbook of psychotherapy: Theory and practice* (pp. 228–253). New York, NY: Oxford University Press.

Rowe, C. L. (2012). Family therapy for drug abuse: Review and updated 2003-2010. *Journal of Marital and Family Therapy, 38*(1), 59–81.

Smith, P. C., Schmidt, S. M., Allensworth-Davies, D., & Saitz, R. (2009). Primary care validation of a single-question alcohol screening test. *Journal of General Internal Medicine, 24*(7), 783–788. Retrieved from doi:10.1007/s11606-009-0928-6

Steinglass, P., Bennett, L., Wolin, S., & Reiss, D. (1987). *The alcoholic family.* New York, NY: Basic Books.

Substance Abuse and Mental Health Services Administration. (2013). *Results from the 2012 national survey on drug use and health: Summary of national findings.* NSDUH Series H-46, HHS Publication No. (SMA) 13-4795. Rockville, MD: Author.

Substance Abuse and Mental Health Services Administration. (2014). *Results from the 2013 national survey on drug use and health: Summary of national findings.* NSDUH Series H-48, HHS Publication No. (SMA) 14-4863. Rockville, MD: Author.

Substance Abuse and Mental Health Services Administration. (2015). *Behavioral health barometer: United States, 2015* (HHS Publication No. SMA–16–Baro–2015). Rockville, MD: Author.

Vaugh, M. G., & Howard, M. O. (2004). Adolescent substance abuse treatment: A synthesis of controlled evaluations. *Research on Social Work Practice, 14,* 325–335.

Vedel, E., Emmelkamp, P. M. G., & Schippers, G. M. (2008). Individual cognitive-behavioral therapy and behavioral couples therapy in alcohol use disorder: A comparative evaluation in a community-based addictions treatment centers. *Psychotherapy and Psychosomatics, 77,* 280–288.

Waldron, H. B., & Turner, C. W. (2008). Evidence-based psychosocial treatments for adolescent substance abuse. *Journal of Clinical Child and Adolescent Psychology, 37*(1), 238–261.

Walsh, J. (2006). Family systems theory. In A. C. Kilpatrick & T. P. Holland (Eds.), *Working with families: An integrative model by level of need* (4th ed.; pp. 167–192). Boston, MA: Pearson.

Wegscheider, S. (1981). *Another chance: Hope and health for the alcoholic family.* Palo Alto, CA: Science and Behavior Books.

Wilson, S. (2015). *Wiley handbook on the cognitive neuroscience of addiction.* New York, NY: Wiley-Blackwell.

Zack, M., & Poulos, C. (2009). Parallel roles for dopamine in pathological gambling and psychostimulant addiction. *Current Drug Abuse Reviews, 2*(1), 11–25.

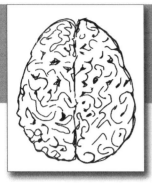

NEUROCOGNITIVE DISORDERS: SYSTEMIC FUNCTIONALITY

Carol Podgorski

Neurocognitive disorders refer to the class of disorders most often associated with Alzheimer's disease and other dementias. According to the Centers for Disease Control and Prevention (2011), there are approximately 16 million Americans currently living with some form of cognitive impairment. With few exceptions such as traumatic brain injury and HIV-related dementia, age is the greatest risk factor for the majority of neurocognitive disorders. With Americans older than 85 constituting the fastest growing segment of our population, the incidence of these illnesses is increasing exponentially. Cognitive impairment is increasing globally as well. In 2012, the World Health Organization (2012) estimated that 35.6 million people were living with dementia worldwide and projected that the number will nearly double every 20 years, reaching 115.4 million in 2050, with the majority living in developing countries.

For every person with a neurocognitive disorder, there is usually at least one family caregiver assisting with activities of daily living and other medical tasks. In 2015, the Alzheimer's Association reported that there were 15.7 million nonprofessionals, most of whom were families, providing care to others with dementia (Alzheimer's Association, 2015). It is not uncommon for family caregivers to serve in this role for between 3 and 10 years. The effects of many neurocognitive disorders extend far beyond cognitive and physical impairment of the person with the illness. These disorders often interrupt the normal trajectory of the family life cycle with ripple effects across all generations of the family in domains including family function, interpersonal relationships, caregiver health and well-being, and financial stability, Thus, it is imperative for medical, behavioral health, and social service providers to acquire a broader understanding of the far-reaching impact that a neurocognitive disorder can have not only on the person with the diagnosis, but also on the family, community, and health and social service systems that may both support and hinder the family's illness and caregiving experiences.

DSM-5 AND FAMILY SYSTEMS

Medical sociologists use the term *illness experience* to refer to the ways in which people define and adjust to perceived interruptions to their health (Ritzer, 2007). There are many factors that contribute to the illness experience as perceived by the person with the diagnosis or symptoms and by the family as well. Oftentimes, one's illness experience can be a more potent predictor of health care outcomes than the clinical manifestations of the illness itself. Behavioral health professionals are often well positioned to assist patients and family members by challenging and modifying their perceptions of the illness experience in an effort to create a more useful illness frame or constructive coping strategy. This next section provides disorder-specific information and related constructs to enhance the mental health practitioner's understanding of neurocognitive disorders, diagnostic criteria and clinical manifestations, and how the disease entity can impact the person with the diagnosis and the family. Understanding of the disease entity is critical to the development of effective behavioral health and family interventions.

Overview of Neurocognitive Disorders

Neurocognitive Disorders (NCDs), according to the *Diagnostic and Statistical Manual of Mental Disorders* (5th ed.; *DSM-5*; American Psychiatric Association [APA], 2013), refer to a group of disorders characterized by three key features. First, the primary clinical deficit associated with an NCD is cognitive function (i.e., complex attention, executive function, learning and memory, language, perceptual-motor, or social cognition). Second, symptoms associated with NCDs must represent an acquired decline from one's previously attained level of cognitive function and therefore are not developmentally related. Third, patient or family report of a cognitive deficit is insufficient to meet criteria for an NCD. In other words, the deficit must also be observable by objective evidence such as history, physical examination, or laboratory findings, with preference for standardized neuropsychological testing.

The *DSM-5* chapter titled Neurocognitive Disorders replaces the *Diagnostic and Statistical Manual of Mental Disorders* (4th ed., text rev.; *DSM-IV-TR*; APA, 2000) chapter titled Delirium, Dementia, and Amnestic and Other Cognitive Disorders. The major changes reflect the directives issued by the APA's *DSM-5* Task Force to the subject matter experts who comprised the various content-specific work groups. First, the Task Force recommended that the work groups propose changes based on "advances in scientific knowledge and in current views and clinical practices" (Ganguli et al., 2011 p. 206). According to Ganguli et al. (2011), a major departure from *DSM-IV-TR* was recognition of neurocognitive impairment as a focus for diagnosis even if it does not rise to the threshold of affecting everyday functioning. The *DSM-IV-TR* had required that the deficit significantly interfered with functioning or relationships with others (Sachdev, Perminder, Mohan, Taylor, & Jeste, 2015). Second, the work group more specifically defined the domains of brain functioning that would be involved in the diagnoses of the NCDs. As Ganguli et al. (2011) explained, the term *neurocognitive* rather than *cognitive* was applied to the NCDs to emphasize that in these disorders, neural substrates are disrupted. A neural substrate is one of the parts of the central nervous system that regulates a specific behavior. Examples of neural substrates include language acquisition, memory, and human empathy. In accordance with APA's focus on clinically observable symptoms, the Work Group noted that such disruptions are generally recognizable from history, examination, or investigations, and that they result in a decline in cognitive function from a previous level of performance. The third departure from *DSM-IV-TR* is increased specificity in the identification of neurocognitive symptoms. In *DSM-5,* a neurocognitive disturbance can occur in one or more of the following six cognitive domains: complex attention, executive function, learning and memory, language, perceptual-motor, and social cognition (Sachdev et al., 2015). The next change also reflects increased specificity in that function along each cognitive domain is now classified as *major* or *mild*, and working definitions for each level of impairment are provided (APA, 2013). In addition, *DSM-5* also provides working definitions of the neurocognitive domains and the corresponding impairments in everyday functions that the clinician would be likely to produce or observe in a clinical setting (Ganguli et al., 2011).

Categories of Neurocognitive Disorders in the *DSM-5*

There are three categories of NCDs in *DSM-5*, including Delirium, Mild Neurocognitive Disorder, and Major Neurocognitive Disorder. Each NCD category is analogous to that of a clinical syndrome or a group of symptoms that occur together and commonly constitute a specific type of abnormality.

Delirium

Delirium is a mental disturbance characterized by disturbance in attention, cognition, and awareness. Symptoms of delirium typically develop abruptly in a matter of hours or over a few days. Delirium is uncommon in community-dwelling older adults (1%–2%), but the prevalence increases in emergency departments (10%–30%), as delirium often co-occurs with medical illness (Inouye, 2006). Although most individuals with delirium experience a full recovery either with or without treatment, early recognition and intervention usually shortens the duration (Solai, 2009). If the underlying cause of delirium goes untreated, symptoms may rise to the level of a more serious condition such as coma, seizures, or even death (Inouye, 2006).

The *DSM-5* (APA, 2013) defines diagnostic criteria for delirium and for a number of etiological subtypes. Specific types of delirium include substance withdrawal delirium, specified by type (e.g., alcohol, sedative, opioid); medication-induced delirium, specified by class of medication taken (e.g., sedative, anxiolytic, stimulant); delirium due to another medical condition, specified by medical condition; and delirium due to multiple etiologies, specifying other medical conditions and circumstances contributing to the disturbance of cognition.

Mild Neurocognitive Disorder

The distinction between *major* and *mild* NCDs is the extent to which impairments interfere with capacity for independent function in everyday activities (Ganguli et al., 2011). In contrast to major NCD, a diagnosis of mild NCD requires evidence of "modest" decline from a previous level of function in one or more of the cognitive domains, and the deficits do not interfere with the person's capacity to function independently in daily activities although the tasks may require greater effort (APA, 2013, p. 605). Although individuals with minor NCD commonly show signs of limited impairment, they also demonstrate a capacity to overcome those deficits using compensatory strategies such as practice and use of assistive devices. Mild NCDs may be coded with two specifiers, including etiology (e.g., Alzheimer's disease, traumatic brain injury) and presence or absence of behavioral disturbance (APA, 2013, p. 605). Prevalence estimates of mild NCDs, more commonly known as mild cognitive impairment, vary among older adults from 2% to 10% at age 65, and from 5% to 25% by age 85 (Ward, Arrighi, Michels, & Cedarbaum, 2012). Apathy and depression are two of the most commonly observed behavioral manifestations among individuals with mild NCD (Gitlin, Kales, & Lyketsos, 2012).

Major Neurocognitive Disorder

A diagnosis of major NCD requires evidence of "significant" decline from a previous level of performance in at least one domain of cognitive function; and the cognitive impairment interferes with the person's capacity to carry out everyday activities to the extent that assistance is required (APA, 2013, pp. 602–604). Major NCDs are coded first by the etiology of the disorder when it is known (e.g., Alzheimer's disease, Lewy Body disease). When etiology is unknown, it is coded as dementia in other diseases classified elsewhere with behavioral disturbance. Two additional specifiers are applied when assigning NCD diagnoses. Those include presence or absence of behavioral disturbance (e.g., psychotic symptoms, mood disturbance, agitation), and severity based on capacity to function independently (e.g., mild, moderate, or severe). "Mild" is defined as having difficulties with activities such as housework or managing household finances. "Moderate" reflects difficulties with basic activities of daily living such as feeding or dressing. "Severe" is used when the person is fully dependent for all activities of daily living.

The *DSM-5* criteria for major NCD differ from criteria for "dementia" as described in *DSM-IV-TR* in a few substantive ways. First, major NCD requires significant decline in only one cognitive domain. Second, impairment in memory, formerly a hallmark feature of dementia, is not essential for a diagnosis of major NCD. Third, the functional threshold for diagnosing major NCD is that cognitive deficits "interfere with independence in everyday activities," in contrast to the *DSM-IV-TR* requirement of "significantly interferes with work or social activities or relationships with others." The determination of "significant" cognitive decline is based on both the subjective concern of an individual, knowledgeable informant, or clinician, and the objective demonstration, via an objective measure, of substantial impairment in cognitive performance (Sachdev et al., 2015). The major NCD definition is somewhat broader than the term *dementia*, in that individuals with substantial decline in a single domain can receive this diagnosis.

Etiological Subtypes of Major and Mild Neurocognitive Disorders

In addition to the broad categories of neurocognitive disorders that include delirium, mild NCD, and major NCD, the mild and major NCDs are also characterized by etiological subtypes. The extensive neurobiological and clinical research efforts that have taken place over the past 30 years have yielded significant advancements in the knowledge base about NCDs and variants thereof. As a result, NCDs can now be distinguished by factors including etiology or cause of the disorder, as well as biomarkers, genetic markers, and other clinical features such as those that can be observed through imaging. Thus, the *DSM-5* provides independent diagnostic criteria for the following major or mild NCD due to Alzheimer's disease; vascular dementia; with Lewy bodies; Parkinson's disease; frontotemporal dementia; traumatic brain injury; HIV infection; substance/medication-induced; Huntington's disease; prion disease; another medical condition; multiple etiologies; and unspecified NCD. Diagnostic criteria across these NCD subtypes vary by features that include subtle or sudden onset, rate of progression, evidence of memory or learning deficits, evidence of genetic mutations, behavioral or language variants, evidence of brain abnormalities on neuroimaging by region of the brain, presence of hallucinations, diagnosis of Parkinson's disease or parkinsonian features, presence of cardiovascular disease or risk factors, history of posttraumatic amnesia, changes in substance or medication usage, presence of infection with HIV, presence of motor features of prion disease, and history or presence of other medical or mental disorders.

The prevalence rates of these NCD subtypes across the population range from negligible to significant, and the subtypes often vary by age at onset, course of progression, and degree of functional impairment. The most prevalent NCD subtype is Alzheimer's disease. In 2015 there were an estimated 46.8 million people worldwide living with dementia and an estimated 9.9 million new cases each year (Alzheimer's Disease International, 2015). Based on data from the 2010 U.S. Census and a population-based study of chronic health diseases of older people conducted by the Chicago Health and Aging Project, the Alzheimer's Association reported that approximately 5.3 million Americans of all ages have Alzheimer's disease (Alzheimer's Association, 2015). Of these, 5.1 million are 65 years of age and older and almost two-thirds are women. Dementia prevalence increases with age, from 5.0% of those aged 71–79 years to 37.4% of those over age 90 (Plassman et al., 2007).

Vascular NCD is the second most common cause of NCD and accounts for approximately 20% of dementia diagnoses. Vascular dementia refers to a group of disorders caused by cerebrovascular insufficiency or restricted blood flow to the brain. Stroke is a primary cause of vascular dementia. Unlike Alzheimer's disease, risk factors for stroke and, hence, vascular dementia can be reduced through control of root causes including high blood pressure, high cholesterol, and diabetes.

The DSM-5 and "Dementia"

The *DSM-5* states that the term *dementia* will continue to be used but more commonly in reference to older adults with NCDs (APA, 2013, p. 591). In addition to the term *dementia*, other terms often used to refer to NCDs include Alzheimer's disease, mild cognitive impairment, and the broad category of Alzheimer's Disease and Related Disorders.

Diagnosis of Neurocognitive Disorders

NCDs are most often diagnosed by primary care physicians, geriatricians, neurologists, and psychiatrists. Nurse practitioners, physician assistants, and psychologists are also permitted to diagnose NCDs. The scope of practice is defined by state licensing bodies, by professions, and by the practice setting that credentials medical providers. By definition, neurocognitive disorders are those in which there is disruption to a neural pathway. Although cognitive dysfunction is the primary criterion for an NCD, it is not the only domain assessed in establishing a diagnosis. The differential diagnosis process includes ruling out illnesses that can mimic dementia or cause confusion. Examples of such illnesses include urinary tract infections, vitamin B_{12} deficiency, thyroid conditions, and depression. In addition to administration of neuropsychological tests, medical providers routinely order laboratory tests of blood and urine. Medical providers perform physical and neurological exams and in some medical settings biomarker tests are also conducted to determine genetic contributions to symptom presentation (American Academy of Neurology, 2011).

Chronic Illness Typologies and Neurocognitive Disorders

There is considerable variation across the NCD subtypes in terms of how they manifest as chronic illnesses. Features of chronic illnesses greatly influence patient and family responses to both diagnosis and the illness itself. The chronic illness typology developed by Rolland (2012) provides a useful framework for understanding the range of reactions that families have to NCDs. In his model, he describes how chronic illnesses vary by onset and course. According to Rolland (2012), illness onset can be divided into acute or gradual. Alzheimer's disease is an example of an NCD with a gradual onset, whereas delirium, traumatic brain injury, and vascular dementia due to stroke have more of an acute onset. Acute-onset illnesses generally require an immediate response by families akin to crisis management. For example, older adults with delirium typically present with a sudden onset of confusion, which mobilizes families to seek medical attention immediately, often through emergency departments. On the contrary, families respond to NCDs with gradual onset in a variety of ways, generally increasing responsivity as the symptoms increase or as function declines. Thus, for NCDs with a slow, subtle onset, individuals experiencing symptoms and their family members are often more likely to adopt a watchful waiting approach before seeking an evaluation or medical intervention. For example, older adults who began to notice symptoms of cognitive decline that did not significantly interfere with their life-styles or capacity to function often report at the time of diagnosis that they did not pursue diagnosis earlier because they could usually find other explanations for their memory lapses. Similarly, adult children of parents with cognitive impairment often report that they put off seeking diagnosis until they could no longer ignore the symptoms as they began to interfere with health status or safety.

The other construct in Rolland's typology is the course of illness. Rolland (2012) describes the course of chronic diseases as taking three general forms: progressive, con-stant, or relapsing/episodic. With respect to a progressive illness such as NCD due to Alzheimer's disease, the illness does not remit and so the family member is "perpetually symptomatic" and the disability worsens in a gradual way. Thus, the family is required to continually organize and reorganize itself to adapt to losses and other manifestations of the disease. In contrast, a constant course illness is characterized by the occurrence of an initial event such as an acute medical event or injury, followed by a stable biological course. NCDs that can present with constant course include traumatic brain injury and vascular NCD. In these illnesses, families respond at the time of sudden onset or crisis, and then develop coping mechanisms and plans of care once the family member's condition stabi-lizes. The third type of illness is relapsing- or episodic-course illnesses, such as asthma or autoimmune illnesses. This type of illness is characterized by fluctuation between stable periods with little to no symptomatology and periods of active symptoms. Rolland con-tends that when confronted by this type of illness, families are typically strained by both the frequency of transition between crisis and low-symptom periods, and the ever present uncertainty of when a recurrence will take place. For example, people with rheumatoid arthritis often report that they can be pain free one day and wake up the next with severe fatigue, joint swelling, and an inability to get out of bed. Such flares can last for weeks. The unpredictable nature of flares creates uncertainty not only for the person with rheuma-toid arthritis but also for partners, children, coworkers, and others who rely on this per-son to carry out specific responsibilities. Although NCDs are progressive in nature, thus precluding the potential for relapse, the episodic nature of illness more aptly captures the sporadic and less stable presentation of behavioral symptoms commonly associated with NCDs. Such symptoms are a source of frequent distress for families of individuals with NCDs.

The third characteristic associated with chronic illness is the extent to which a chronic ill-ness leads to death or shortens one's life expectancy. Rolland (2012) identified the chronic illness feature with the most profound psychosocial impact on families to be the expecta-tion of whether a disease is likely to cause death. With life-limiting illnesses, Rolland states that the family's experience is often characterized by anticipatory losses and pervasive effects on family life. Anticipatory loss is the experience of grief that a person or family feels in anticipation of someone's death. This type of loss can also be experienced by the person with a life-limiting illness and is especially prevalent in those with dementia. Per-vasive or widespread effects of illness on family life are commonly disease specific. For fami-lies providing 24/7 care to someone in late stages of dementia, for example, family members may grow accustomed to adhering to a schedule whereby one family member must always be at home providing care, which, in turn, precludes family participation in activities or events outside of the home (e.g., attending a child's concert or sporting event; going out to dinner together as a family). Another pervasive effect is often financial. The out-of-pocket costs of providing care to someone with dementia are high, which for many families forces them to make difficult decisions about how to prioritize their resources (e.g., a second car, college tuition, retirement savings plan, and family vacation).

NCDs pose challenges for those with symptoms, their families, and health care pro-fessionals alike. According to the Alzheimer's Association, Alzheimer's disease is the only disease among the top 10 leading causes of death that cannot be prevented, cured, or even slowed (Alzheimer's Association, 2016). For this reason, many people with symptoms of cognitive impairment do not seek diagnosis; many physicians do not diagnose it; and families fail to accept it, organize around it, or cope with losses associated with it. Thus, many do not seek treatment or services. Another challenge with NCDs, particularly NCD due to Alzheimer's disease, is that it is often associated with the primary symptom of "memory loss." Because so many adults experience age-associated memory changes as early as age 40, symptoms of NCDs are often not assigned the status of an "illness" or "disease." Because Alzheimer's disease is commonly misperceived solely as memory loss rather than as a brain disease, families of members with Alzheimer's disease are often surprised to learn that it is a fatal illness in that its progression eventually affects organ function.

RELATIONAL AND CULTURAL FEATURES

The *DSM-5* (APA, 2013) states that individuals' and families' level of awareness and concern about neurocognitive symptoms may vary across ethnic and occupational groups. One of the goals of the *DSM-5* was to move toward becoming more globally relevant. Toward this end, the *DSM-5* contains increased focus on cultural and social contexts in the descriptions of each set of diagnostic criteria. Sachdev et al. (2015) explained that the increased emphasis on sociocultural factors in the *DSM-5* was intended to remind the clinician of the impact that these factors have on illness manifestations, course, and patterns of help-seeking behaviors.

Culture, Ethnicity, and Neurocognitive Disorders

According to the Alzheimer's Association (2013), older African Americans in the United States are about two times more likely than older Whites to have Alzheimer's disease and other dementias. Older Hispanics are about one and one-half times more likely than older Whites to have these conditions. The first study to examine dementia risk in a population representing the six most representative racial and ethnic groups in the United States found that the incidence of dementia was highest in African Americans and lowest in Asian Americans (Mayeda, Glymour, Quesenberry, & Whitmer, 2016). The investigators compared dementia incidence in more than 274,000 Kaiser Permanente members across six racial and ethnic groups, including Whites, Asian Americans, Latinos, African Americans, American Indians/Alaskan Natives, and Pacific Islanders. They reviewed 14 years of medical visits in electronic health records tracking data on race, ethnicity, and dementia diagnoses, including Alzheimer's disease, vascular dementia, and nonspecific dementia. They found that the rate of occurrence in African Americans was 65% higher than in Asian Americans based on the following annual rates of cases per 1,000 population that their data yielded: 26.6 for African Americans; 22.2 for American Indians/Alaskan Natives; 19.6 for Latinos and Pacific Islanders; 19.3 for Whites; and 15.2 for Asian Americans.

The higher prevalence of dementia among African Americans has been explained more often in terms of risk factors than causal factors. Although studies suggesting a genetic link have yet to be confirmed, conditions such as hypertension, diabetes, stroke, and obesity, all risk factors for dementia, as well as health behaviors such as high fat intake and smoking, are more common in African Americans and Latinos than in Whites. In addition to health-related risk factors, socioeconomic factors including lower levels of education and lower income among older racial and ethnic minorities may also contribute to increased risk.

Along with increased risk for dementia, racial and ethnic groups also experience disparities in health care experiences. For example, Medicare data show that African Americans are less likely than Whites to be diagnosed with dementia and, when African Americans and Latinos are diagnosed, the diagnosis is often made in later stages of the disease, which results in higher use of health care services and higher costs (Alzheimer's Association, 2013). A comprehensive review of studies published prior to 2014 found consistent and adverse disparities among Blacks and Hispanics compared to non-Hispanic Whites in the prevalence and incidence of Alzheimer's disease, mortality, participation in clinical trials, use of medications and other interventions, use of long-term services and supports, health care expenditures, quality of care, and caregiving (Lines, Sherif, & Wiener, 2014).

Neurocognitive Disorders and Family Systems

The identification, assessment, diagnosis, course, and treatment of neurocognitive disorders are all influenced, if not determined, by the relationships and systems in which those with symptoms are embedded. Public health sciences have incorporated the interrelatedness of health and social factors in approaches toward understanding health behaviors since the 1950s.

Health Belief Model

The Health Belief Model (HBM) offers a conceptual way of thinking about how a person's, family's or group's beliefs about an illness or a health behavior influence the likelihood that a person will take a health action (see Figure 17.1). The HBM was developed in the 1950s by psychologists at the Public Health Service (Rosenstock, 1974) in an effort to better understand why screening programs for tuberculosis were not effective. The HBM has been applied to understanding health behavior change related to diseases, including diabetes, sexually transmitted diseases, HIV, eating disorders, and dementia, and has also been applied to preventive health behaviors such as smoking cessation and physical activity; sick role behaviors such as medication compliance; and health care utilization. The major tenets of the HBM (Rosenstock, 1974) are as follows:

- Individuals who perceive a given health problem as serious are more likely to engage in behaviors to prevent the health problem from occurring or to reduce its severity;
- Individuals who perceive that they are susceptible to a particular health problem will engage in behaviors to reduce their risk of developing the health problem;
- Individuals who believe that a particular action will reduce susceptibility to a health problem or decrease its seriousness will take action;
- An individual's assessment of barriers or obstacles to behavioral change will influence health behavior;
- An individual's sense of self-efficacy regarding competence to successfully engage in a health behavior also influences action;
- A cue or trigger is necessary to prompt a health behavior; and
- Modifying characteristics, such as demographics, psychosocial and sociocultural factors, as well as structural variables, often affect all of these perceptions regarding health-related behaviors.

The HBM and its core elements have been applied to NCD due to Alzheimer's disease in a number of studies that yielded similar findings regarding barriers to diagnosis. The first study by Werner (2003) examined factors that influenced intention to seek a cognitive evaluation for memory problems. Data from this study indicated that *barriers* to seeking an examination, rather than *perceived benefits*, constituted the most significant predictor of behavior. The barriers they identified included participants' lack of knowledge and misconceptions regarding the usefulness of an examination and treatment options for

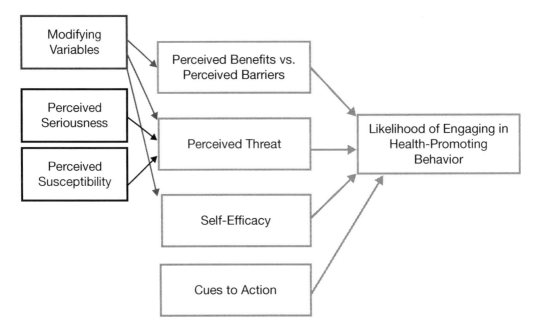

FIGURE 17.1 The Health Belief Model.

Source: www.en.wikipedia.org/wiki/File:The_Health_Belief_Model.pdf

memory concerns, and the psychological costs involved in participating in a cognitive assess-ment and receiving a diagnosis. The investigators also found that *cues to action* played a role in predicting intentions to seek a cognitive examination.

In an effort to further culturally informed research and service planning related to dementia care seeking, Sayegh and Knight (2013) conducted a literature review on the effects of barriers on diagnostic delays and impairment levels at initial evaluation. They found that there was consistent evidence that minority ethnic older adults with dementia tended to have greater diagnostic delays and higher levels of cognitive impairment and behavioral and psychological symptoms of dementia at initial evaluation than their non-Hispanic White counterparts. They also found several barriers to seeking care for demen-tia among minority ethnic groups, including lower levels of acculturation and accurate knowledge about dementia, more culturally associated beliefs about dementia, such as the perception of memory loss as normal aging and stigma associated with dementia, and health system barriers.

The third application of the HBM involved a study of South Asian older adults with memory impairment. The investigators, Giebel et al. (2015), reported that South Asians and health professionals highlighted several difficulties that deterred seeking help and access to care, including a lack of knowledge of dementia, mental illness, and local services; stigma; culturally preferred coping strategies; and linguistic and cultural barriers in communica-tion and decision making.

A study by Sun, Gao, and Coon (2013) found that Chinese Americans between the ages of 55 and 64 were more likely than those 85 and older to develop concerns about Alzheimer's disease. The investigators attributed this finding to increased literacy about dementia, to the younger generation's attentiveness to dementia symptoms because of their caregiving experience, and to their likely increased perceptions of susceptibility to demen-tia due to their knowledge of genetic risk.

McCleary et al. (2013) conducted an investigation of pathways to dementia diagnosis among South Asian Canadians in an effort to better understand their early perceptions of dementia-related changes and their responses to those changes. Respondents reported that they attributed early signs of dementia to aging or personality, and some regarded the symptoms as "normal." Before seeking medical attention, family members modified physical or social environments to accommodate symptoms. Investigators reported that South Asian families delayed seeking help up to 4 years, and that safety concerns and need for other medical treatment were often the triggers to seek a dementia diagnosis.

A comparison across the findings from these studies suggests that the HBM provides a useful framework for understanding how families across various cultures and ethnic groups shape their illness experiences relative to cognitive impairment. The findings further suggest the need for the systemic therapist to take time to listen and understand the client's knowledge and beliefs about memory loss and dementia as a starting point for intervention. Through a better understanding of the client's perceptions of health and illness, health concerns, and concerns about treatment, the skilled therapist may become better equipped to identify cues to action that may, in turn, lead to diagnosis or use of appropriate services.

The Influence of Family Dynamics on the Experience of NCDs

It is well established that family conflict diminishes the health and quality of life for persons with NCDs and their family caregivers. Dementia negatively affects family relationships and often triggers or reignites conflict in families (Cantegreil-Kallen & Rigaud, 2009). Research suggests that the quality of family relationships prior to dementia often predict outcomes later in the disease process (Steadman, Tremont, & Davis, 2007). Family conflict is prevalent in families with dementia and most often surfaces in mild to moderate stages of NCDs due to Alzheimer's disease (Peisah, Brodaty, & Quadrio, 2006). Numerous publications indicate that the costliest manifestations of family conflict emerge at the end of life. One such paper reported that family conflict was present in 55% of 120 deaths examined in the study, and that interdisciplinary teams rated conflict as "extremely important" in 44% of those deaths (Kramer, Boelz, & Auer, 2006). Back and Arnold (2005) reported that physicians viewed family conflict regarding treatment options as a major barrier to discussing preferences and providing quality end-of-life care. Family discord often contributes to nursing home admissions, hospitalizations and treatments that are costly, both financially and emotionally, and do not reflect the wishes of the person with NCD. Kramer et al. (2006) summarized causes of conflict from the end-of-life care literature as including a family member's perception that others are providing insufficient help; lack of agreement regarding care coordination, patient needs, and the nature of the illness; and spillover from longstanding family issues. There is a recursive relationship between family conflict and family dysfunction, which typically involves communication, problem solving, and role performance. Whether spouse or child, family caregivers with high levels of burden report greater family dysfunction in terms of communication and role performance (Tremont, Davis, & Bishop, 2006). Caregivers considering nursing home admission for the person with NCD were found to have higher burden, more family dysfunction, and fewer social supports than those not considering placement (Spitznagel, Tremont, Davis, & Foster, 2006).

The high prevalence of discord in families with NCDs, along with the considerable emotional and financial costs related to conflict, indicates that treatment planning in this population calls for assessing families for what the *DSM-5* refers to as Other Conditions That May Be a Focus of Clinical Attention (APA, 2013, pp. 715–727). These constitute conditions that may be the presenting problem or cause of distress but the family member's symptoms do not meet criteria for a defined mental disorder. The domains most relevant to family issues in these later stages of the life cycle include Relational Problems (e.g., parent–child relational problem, sibling relational problem); relationship distress with spouse or intimate partner; and adult maltreatment and neglect problems.

Family relationships have been found to contribute to the tremendous variability in diagnosis, caregiving, medical decision making, and end-of-life care. Conflict arises from the point when family members differ in their perceptions of symptoms in a loved one, whether they should pursue a diagnostic evaluation, whether a loved one should remain at home independently, whether it is time for professional caregiving or long-term care placement, and end-of-life decisions. Family members often disagree about what is best for the person with the NCD, what is best or easiest for the family members or caregivers, what is "fair," what is "right," what the consequences are for taking an action or taking no action. Many siblings experience hurt feelings when they discover that they were not selected to make health care, financial, or legal decisions on behalf of the parent with the NCD.

Families also disagree about things such as when, how, and to whom to disclose a diagnosis of an NCD. Hellstrom and Torres (2013) studied couples living with dementia and their preferences about disclosing the diagnosis to others. The investigators explored disclosure preferences and focused on what couples living with dementia want to know and tell about the disease. Their analysis revealed five preference patterns regarding what the couples wanted to know and how they felt about sharing information about the disease with others. They labeled the patterns as follows: want to know and tell (no reservations about it); want to know and tell (some reservations about it); want to know but do not want to tell; want to know but cannot decide if we want to tell; and cannot agree on either knowing or telling. The findings showed that it is usually the preferences of the person with the diagnosis that guide the couple's approach to disclosure.

FAMILY SYSTEMS ASSESSMENTS

The fundamental assumption of medical family therapy, as described by McDaniel, Doherty, and Hepworth (2014), is that all health and relationship problems are biological, psychological, and social in nature. The illness experiences described, endured, and reported by patients with NCDs, their families, and those who provide their health care embody this claim. Because contextual factors are so important to each health behavior from symptom recognition to how a family copes throughout the course of the disease, a comprehensive assessment of the individual with NCD symptoms, the family, and the systems in which they are embedded is essential to the development of appropriate and effective plans of care. Relevant domains of assessment, as well as suggested approaches and measures, are described here.

Family Composition, Structure, Relationships, and Function

An assessment that begins with a focus on the whole family conveys the message that the symptoms or illness that the identified patient may be experiencing affects not only that individual but every member of the family. This information-gathering approach, partially a therapeutic intervention in and of itself, also serves to reinforce the notion that the family is a system with its own unique history, strengths, values, beliefs, and patterns of functioning. This approach to assessment also allows the clinician to capture the essence of the index patient's personhood as a way to punctuate that the person is more than a constellation of symptoms. Use of a genogram, as described by Gerson, McGoldrick, and Petry (2008), provides an effective approach and tool for this purpose. Essential pieces of information include family composition, preferably with two to three generations of family members including those who are deceased and their cause of death; marriages and divorces; ages and gender of each family member; level of education and/or occupation for each; details about the family's physical and mental health history to the extent they are comfortable sharing; race and/or ethnicity; and religious or spiritual beliefs, to name a few. This interview also assists the clinician in understanding the family life cycle stages and associated tasks with which the family is occupied. For instance, a person who develops an early-onset NCD at the age of 50 has a different impact on a family than someone who begins showing symptoms at age 80. During this interview, it is helpful to ascertain information about the family's experience with health and illness as well as their beliefs about health, illness, their health care practitioners, if any, and openness to medical care. It is also useful to identify if there are other people, resources, or community organizations that provide support or add stress to the family.

A genogram interview also provides the clinician with opportunities to observe and gather information about family structure, quality of relationships among family members, family functioning, and family strengths. Measures such as the Family Assessment Device and the Dyadic Adjustment Scale are useful tools to help characterize how a family or couple is organized and functions. The Family Assessment Device, a questionnaire designed to evaluate families according to the McMaster Model of Family Functioning (Epstein, Baldwin, & Bishop, 1983), comprises 53 items that constitute seven scales, which measure problem solving, communication, roles, affective responsiveness, affective involvement, behavior control, and general functioning. The Dyadic Adjustment Scale (Spanier, 1976) is a 32-item questionnaire, completed by couples, that yields scores on four subscales, including dyadic consensus, dyadic satisfaction, dyadic cohesion, and affectional expression. This instrument continues to be widely used to measure couples' adjustments to illnesses and other adversities families experience. The backdrop of information provided by the genogram interview provides the clinician with the contextual information needed to shape the approach for eliciting information from the family about the presenting problem. Because NCDs so often trigger reactions including denial and family conflict, it is often useful for the clinician to ask each family member to address a question such as, "How can I be helpful?" or "What would you like to have happen as a result of our work together?"

Assessment of Symptoms Related to the Neurocognitive Disorder

Clinical judgment dictates when it would be most appropriate to gather details about the type, onset, and progression of NCD symptoms that the index person is experiencing as well as who the most appropriate informant would be. It is important to identify and acknowledge validations and discrepancies across reports. In cases in which the identified patient has received an NCD diagnosis, it is essential for the mental health clinician to know the diagnosis and subtype as well as the stage of illness, and to obtain copies of any medical reports that could inform behavioral health treatment. For example, reports of the patient's performance on neuropsychological tests such as the Mini-Mental State Exam (Folstein, Folstein, & McHugh, 1975) or the Montreal Cognitive Assessment (MoCA; Nasreddine et al., 2005) provide the clinician with valuable information about both the strengths and deficits of the patient's cognitive function which, in turn, inform the development of appropriate clinical interventions.

Assessing Symptoms of Distress

Behavioral symptoms including depressed mood, apathy, irritability, anger, anxiety, and agitation often develop as manifestations of both mild and major NCDs. The Neuropsychiatric Inventory (Cummings, 1997) is a tool commonly used to assess the presence and severity of behavioral symptoms associated with an NCD. Depression, anxiety, and caregiver burden are also prevalent in family members caring for someone with an NCD. Since depression and anxiety can exacerbate cognitive function, it is important to assess and treat these disorders. Similarly, outcomes for those with NCDs and their caregivers who experience depression and burden are less favorable especially when considering the added stress attributable to the high prevalence of relational problems in this population. Screening tools commonly used to assess for these behavioral symptoms include the Patient Health Questionnaire-9 (PHQ-9; Kroenke, Spitzer, & Williams, 2001) and the Geriatric Depression Scale (Yesavage et al., 1982–1983) for depression; the Generalized Anxiety Disorder 7-Item Scale (Spitzer, Kroenke, Williams, & Löwe, 2006); and the Zarit Burden Interview (Bédard et al., 2001) for caregiver burden.

Although administration of these instruments reflects an individual orientation to treatment, the context in which they are administered can transform the assessment into a relational intervention. For example, administration of a depression or anxiety screen to one partner in the presence of another punctuates the clinician's level of concern, thus validating the partner's stress and calling the other partner's attention to the need for intervention. In addition, the presence of a partner in the room while administering a PHQ-9 or any other screening tool may elicit one partner to challenge the accuracy of his or her responses, thus contributing to increased validity of the screen.

Assessing Coping Styles

Those living with cognitive impairment and family members inevitably adopt strategies to cope with the effects of the NCD on the family. In broad strokes, there are essentially two styles of coping, one characterized by emotion-focused strategies, the other by a problem-focused orientation. People who use emotion-focused coping strategies tend to express and process the emotions associated with the stressor, whereas those who use problem-focused coping techniques aim to eliminate the stressor. Although coping strategies can vary among members of a family, a family's response to illness often reflects a shared family of origin experience or beliefs that have been passed down from previous generations. For instance, a family's coping strategy is sometimes tied to the family's narrative (e.g., "If something can go wrong, it will"; "Life isn't fair"; "We are truly blessed"). Evidence suggests that problem-focused coping strategies in family caregivers of those with NCDs yield more favorable outcomes (Tschanz et al., 2013). The Ways of Coping Questionnaire developed by Folkman and Lazarus (1988) is a 66-item tool that identifies the processes that people use to cope in stressful situations. The scores reflect the extent to which the participant used each of the following eight coping styles to deal with an identified stressful situation: confrontative, distancing, self-controlling, seeking social support, accepting responsibility, escape avoidance, planful problem solving, and positive reappraisal. This instrument is intended for completion by an individual, yet the tool can be used as a relational intervention as well. For example, if administered to a group of siblings with caregiving responsibilities for a parent, a systemic professional could facilitate a discussion of each sibling's coping style to help him or her collectively identify which style is best suited for the caregiving tasks that are needed in the family. Those with a problem-focused orientation may be better suited to tend to tasks that they can check off their to-do lists (e.g., scheduling appointments, preparing meals, legal/financial management, coordinating services), whereas those who are emotion-focused may be more comfortable comforting the parent about the diagnosis, taking the parent to a support group or a church service, or providing support to the siblings who are struggling most with the situation.

FAMILY SYSTEMS INTERVENTIONS

Families contend with a wide range of emotions, stressors, and responsibilities across the course of an NCD. Rolland's paradigm for understanding "time phases of illness" provides a suitable framework for organizing this discussion of family system interventions. Rolland (2012) asserts that illness is not a static state and suggests that illness processes develop over time. Reflective of this notion, many chronic illnesses, including Alzheimer's disease, Parkinson's disease, and cancer, are commonly described in terms of "stages." The concept of time phases, as conceptualized by Rolland, provides a way for clinicians and families to better understand and anticipate the chronic illness as an ongoing process with stage-specific hallmark features, foreseeable transitions, and changing demands. Each phase is characterized by its own psychosocial challenges and developmental tasks that may require a family to alter both attitudes and behaviors in order to adapt. The three major phases of a chronic disease include crisis, chronic, and terminal (Rolland, 2012). Applying these phases to an NCD due to Alzheimer's disease, the *crisis phase* includes the period when signs of cognitive decline or dysfunction begin to appear and they are noticed by self or others; the decision-making process regarding whether and when to seek a diagnosis; and the initial period of adjustment to the diagnosis. This phase may span 1 to 5 years.

The *chronic phase* of Alzheimer's disease occurs once the family adjusts to accommodate the illness following diagnosis. Rolland (2012) refers to this period as "the day-to-day living with chronic illness" phase and in the case of dementia, this phase is likely to span a number of years. In the beginning of this phase, many families will have accepted the illness and defined "a new normal" for family life. Also during this phase, families come to acknowledge the prospect of, and later experience, increasingly common occurrences of episodes that underscore deterioration in the person's cognition and capacity for independent functioning. For families, the process of accommodating the illness involves tasks including seeking information about the disease, treatment options, and strategies to cope with illness manifestations; establishing rapport with health care providers and teams; and developing a base of support to promote well-being, minimize caregiver burden, and increase capacity to attend to the other myriad family and life cycle–specific responsibilities.

The *terminal phase* of an illness is typically characterized by the inevitability of death and attention to the ill family member's quality of life (Rolland, 2012). Families in the end stages of Alzheimer's disease often grapple with their understanding of the dying person's wishes. At the same time family members function as advocates to ensure that the person's care needs are being met appropriately with attention toward maximizing the patient's comfort while minimizing pain and discomfort. In contrast to other chronic illnesses in which the terminal phase is characterized by "letting go" and imagining a return to life following the loved one's passing, in the case of dementia, most family members have already grieved the loss of their loved one many times over as they endured what Nancy Reagan termed "the long goodbye."

Medical Family Therapy Interventions

The 10 clinical strategies for medical family therapy developed by McDaniel et al. (2014) provide a useful blueprint from which to conceptualize systemic treatment plans tailored to the particular challenges families with NCDs encounter.

Recognize the Biological Dimension

Although the etiologies of many NCDs remain at the forefront of international research agendas, recent scientific advances and technological developments in imaging (National Institute on Aging, 2015) have identified genes, biomarkers, and neuroanatomical brain changes that promote understanding of the disease process. These scientific advances underscore the fact that despite the neuropsychiatric and behavioral symptoms associated with dementia, NCDs are *medical* and not mental disorders. People with NCDs and their families frequently refrain from obtaining or sharing a dementia diagnosis due to fear of stigma and ostracism. It is often useful for clinicians to ascertain the family members' understanding of the illness and to reframe their interpretation in a way that might better serve the family. Families that harbor this secret often become socially isolated, which can exacerbate symptoms and accelerate the rate of decline by reducing stimulation for the person with the NCD.

Similarly, it is useful for family members to understand that behavioral changes that they may observe in someone with an NCD are behavioral symptoms of the disorder more often than intentional disruptive actions. Families often benefit from receiving information that explains the root causes of NCDs, manifestations of the disorder, and strategies for intervention.

Elicit the Family Illness History and Meaning

A family's previous illness experience often shapes how family members will respond to the emergence of illness symptoms or to a diagnosis. Family responses to illness are often passed down from previous generations and serve to shape a family's narrative of illness. Prior illness experiences often contribute to responses that span a continuum from fear and distrust of physicians or hospitals to belief in miracles, science, and the "power of prayer." Interventions including cognitive behavioral therapy as well as narrative approaches are useful in helping family members to shift cognitions and beliefs that interfere with effective coping strategies.

Respect Defenses, Remove Blame, and Accept Unacceptable Feelings

The first step in this clinical strategy involves interpreting and clarifying information that was gathered through the genogram development process. This includes observing and understanding the relationship dynamics in the family, particularly with respect to the person with the NCD; eliciting each family member's understanding of the diagnosis or illness; and drawing out each member's perceptions of what effects this illness may have on the family going forward. When working with contentious families, those with propensity toward violence, and those at risk for exacerbation of mood disorders, it is important for the clinician to judiciously decide when to meet with the family as a whole and when to meet with individuals or subsets of family members.

Denial is a common response to many chronic illnesses, but it is especially prevalent in families with NCDs. This, in part, reflects that fact that NCD symptoms, with the exception of delirium, commonly have an insidious onset and do not interfere significantly with function in early phases of the illness. In addition, the stigma associated with dementia often prevents families from sharing the diagnosis with others out of fear of embarrassment, ostracism, or becoming isolated from others. Although this response may be comforting to families at the outset of an NCD, it can become more problematic when it interferes with the family's willingness to accept the disease, plan for the disease, and seek treatment and services to ameliorate the distress that the disease eventually causes for family members. Clinicians can assist families in at least two ways. First, the clinician can help family members move toward accepting the diagnosis or presence of illness. It is often useful to focus on using the words that the family uses to describe the illness rather than using diagnostic terms that the family is not yet ready to accept. Another intervention to assist family members toward acceptance is to help them identify all of the ways in which the family has not changed since the NCD symptoms appeared.

Second, the clinician can help families to coconstruct a message about the diagnosis that is acceptable to all, along with a plan for sharing the diagnosis. The plan may include making a list of the people with whom they would like to share the information, identifying the person who will share the message, and deciding the timetable and method of dissemination.

The risk factors for many NCDs include health behaviors over which family members have some degree of control. They include lack of exercise, poor diet, and drug addiction that contribute to cardiovascular disease, the risk of stroke and vascular dementia; prolonged, excessive use of alcohol, which can lead to Korsakoff's syndrome; reckless driving and affinity for adventure, which may lead to motor vehicle and recreational accidents that often result in traumatic brain injury; and unsafe sexual behaviors that are associated with HIV infection and HIV-related dementia. When confronted with manifestations of an NCD, families sometimes grapple with beliefs that this illness could have been prevented if the person with the illness had made better choices or had lived a healthier lifestyle. Similarly, the person with the diagnosis also may assume personal responsibility and, hence, guilt about having placed this illness burden on the family. In these circumstances, it is often useful for the clinician to find an appropriate way to assuage feelings of guilt and blame. A clinician who is well versed in the science and etiology of NCDs can assist family members by reviewing the myriad factors that contribute to the incidence of NCDs. For families who have limited affinity for data and science, other strategies that are often effective in shifting perceptions include existential and mindfulness approaches that focus on the here and now, as well as the use of spirituality.

In advanced stages of NCDs, family caregivers often struggle to care for family members who no longer resemble their former selves in terms of appearance, personality, or behaviors. It is common for caregivers to share that while they may love and have compassion for the person with the NCD, they no longer like him or her. Similarly, family members often express feelings of guilt upon sharing that they often wish that the person with dementia would die. Clinicians can help by providing a safe, nonjudgmental space for family members to share their innermost feelings while also validating the caregivers' emotions.

Facilitate Communication

Many couples and families struggle with communication under the best of circumstances, but when a family member develops an NCD, communication issues become more challenging. Aside from family dynamics that interfere with effective communication, cognitive impairment adds an additional layer of complexity. An important and useful intervention toward improving communication involves teaching family members about the cognitive strengths and deficits of the loved one. This is where collaboration with the diagnosing provider becomes important. One-size-fits-all communication interventions are seldom effective. When a clinician has access to the patient's medical records and cognitive testing, these records provide information not only about the patient's cognitive deficits, but also about the components of the patient's memory and function that remain intact. Thus, as the systemic clinician works with family members, these records hold valuable information that allow for tailored approaches to communication. For example, if the family is learning to communicate with someone with frontotemporal dementia often characterized by executive dysfunction, the clinician can explain the importance of using simple, one-step commands. When the dementia impairs short-term memory, as is most often the case, clinicians can assist family members to use and practice giving single commands such as, "Put on your coat now." When family members alter the words in a request such as, "Okay. We need to leave now. Time to get your coat." this requires the person with cognitive impairment to process and make sense of new words, which often contributes to increased confusion.

In addition to facilitating communication with the person with cognitive impairment, clinicians can also play a valuable role in assisting patients and family members to communicate more effectively with members of the health care team. Systemic clinicians can assist by helping families develop a list of questions about the illness, about medications, and about treatment options, and can also help to interpret information that a medical provider has given to the family. For example, medical providers often share the patient's score on a cognitive test with the family and indicate if the score represents a change from prior performance. Although family members often appreciate the report, without knowledge of which cognitive domains the testing assessed and what that means in terms of everyday function, it is difficult for families to make a connection between the patient's performance in the office and what they observe in the home. A mental health clinician can bridge this gap by describing the instrument and by providing examples of how the patient's scores might predict his or her capacity to function at home. In addition to developing content for communications with health care providers, it is also useful for clinicians to help families learn how to package that information to maximize effective communication. Packaging involves securing an appropriate time to speak with the medical provider; prioritizing requests or questions to make sure that the most important issues get addressed; and using a respectful tone. Similarly, clinicians can also provide useful interventions to assist health care providers in communicating information in ways that families can understand. Clinicians often have greater awareness of considerations such as cultural beliefs or health literacy issues that may affect how families process medical information.

Attend to Developmental Issues

NCDs can arise for individuals at various times throughout the life span and, hence, affect family members at various times throughout the family life cycle. For instance, diagnoses of early-onset Alzheimer's disease occur as early as age 40. Hence, the diagnosis may interrupt the person's capacity to remain gainfully employed, may transform the person's high school–age children into caregivers, and may often cause financial hardship for families as care needs become increasingly complex. Another important factor for clinicians to consider is that the course of many NCDs can last for 10 to 20 years. This means that families cannot develop one caregiving plan and expect it to remain intact throughout the course of the illness. This necessitates that families develop comfort with seeking, asking for, and accepting support from multiple sources. In addition to helping clients accept this as reality, clinicians can also intervene by helping families negotiate plans of care that consider the strengths, resources, geographic parameters, and coping styles of each support person in an effort to minimize family stress and conflict.

Reinforce the Family's Nonillness Identity

When families are confronted with a chronic illness such as an NCD, one of the most beneficial interventions a clinician can provide is to help the family come to accept the diagnosis, develop plans to manage it over time, and then help the family restore its sense of normalcy. A useful narrative approach is to help the family "externalize the illness" by enabling them to separate the illness from the family member with the diagnosis. This intervention involves helping the person with the disease and family members come to perceive the illness as an "uninvited guest" while, at the same time, embracing the person's strengths, interests, and personality that remain intact. This intervention serves to rebalance the family and helps them focus on the here and now rather than on what the future may bring.

Provide Psychoeducation and Support

There is a growing base of evidence that supports the benefit of psychoeducation and support for those with NCDs and their families. Milne, Guss, and Russ (2014) evaluated the efficacy of a time-limited, professional-facilitated psychoeducation program, Course for Carers, developed in the United Kingdom. Their findings indicated that this course provided psychological support, offered advice, enhanced coping skills, boosted confidence, increased knowledge, and prepared the caregiver for the future. Similarly, Ducharme, Lachance, Levesque, Zarit, and Kergoat (2015) evaluated the efficacy of providing a booster session of the Canadian-based program Learning to Become a Family Caregiver. The study subjects were caregivers who had participated in this program 6 months earlier at the time their loved ones received a dementia diagnosis. The findings indicated that booster session participants completed the session "prepared to provide care." In addition, the program had a positive effect on psychological distress and enhanced a caregiver's self-efficacy in dealing with caregiving situations.

Many opportunities for psychoeducational interventions arise when working with those affected by NCDs. Family members frequently seek interventions to help manage behavioral symptoms, such as apathy, depression, anxiety, and anger. Good working knowledge of behavioral as well as cognitive behavioral treatment approaches is essential.

Battle between fostering independence and accepting that person can no longer function in a certain way.

Increase the Family's Sense of Agency

McDaniel et al. define *agency* as "the activation of the individuals and families to meet their needs related to health, illness and the health care system, and to contribute to their community" (2014, p. 13). The task for the behavioral health professional is to assist families in determining how much control they are willing to allow the NCD to have in their lives. This is an intervention most appropriately carried out toward the end of the crisis phase and at the beginning of the chronic disease phase. Given the prolonged course of dementia, however, it is not uncommon to revisit this goal periodically as function declines in the person with the NCD and caregiving responsibilities among family members become more demanding. Through this intervention, the clinician assists family members with rank-ordering competing priorities and identifying availability of resources. A key feature often involved in the goal of increasing agency is enhancing the acceptability and capacity of family members to seek and ask for help.

Enhance the Family's Sense of Communion

Communion is defined as "the sense of being cared for, loved, and supported by family members, friends, and professionals" (McDaniel et al., 2014, p. 14). The high prevalence of family conflict in families with NCDs indicates that family members may not perceive a consistently present sense of communion. Those experiencing cognitive impairment often feel betrayed by family members who call attention to their memory lapses or insist on a diagnostic evaluation. As suggested in the family conflict literature, some family members often perceive having a disproportionately larger share of caregiving responsibilities or financial burden. In addition to perceiving a lack of support from family, those with NCDs and their family members often report that they become socially isolated after revealing a diagnosis of dementia to their friends. Another factor that contributes to the perceived diminution of support is the prolonged course of many NCDs. It is common for family and friends to come forward during the crisis phase of illness; it is less common for this level of support to be sustained throughout the disease. In addition, family caregivers often do not wish to be perceived as burdensome by others.

An effective intervention to enhance a client's sense of communion is referral to a support group. Disease-specific support groups are available for Alzheimer's disease, Parkinson's disease, and Lewy Body disease, for instance, and many communities also have organizations and faith communities that provide groups for caregivers as well as others focused on chronic illness or more specifically on grief and loss. The Alzheimer's

Association provides a variety of support groups, including ongoing support for caregivers, and time-limited early stage support groups for those with dementia and family members. Support services also exist in the form of telephone hotlines with 24/7 availability, social media, blogs, and Internet chat rooms.

For more than two decades, the New York University Caregiver Initiative has developed an evidence base of support for the efficacy of caregiver support interventions, including support groups. The mission of this program is to reduce burden and distress in dementia caregivers and to improve quality of care for those with dementia. The intervention strategy combines six sessions of individual and family counseling, support group participation, and additional on-call telephone consultations in a flexible counseling approach that is tailored to each caregiving family. Published reports of more than 20 years of randomized clinical trials testing this intervention indicate that, compared with control groups, spousal caregivers who participated in this intervention reported fewer symptoms of depression and stress, better physical health, increased satisfaction with the emotional and practical support they received, as well as increased closeness to their families. In addition, many caregivers were able to postpone or avoid placing their spouses in residential care (Mittelman, Ferris, Shulman, Steinberg, & Levin, 1996; Mittelman, Haley, Clay, & Roth, 2006). This intervention is currently available using telehealth technology (www.ttdc.hcinter active.com/content/program-overview).

Maintain an Empathic Presence With the Family

Families living with NCDs typically do not require behavioral health services throughout the course of the disease. Families often seek support at the time of diagnosis, as the disease progresses affecting the person's cognitive or physical function or behavioral symptoms, as caregiver burden increases, and as quality-of-life or end-of-life considerations come into play. Providing families with permission to return for services as needs arise often gives them a sense of comfort as well as a secure and consistent base of support.

ETHICAL AND LEGAL IMPLICATIONS

There is probably no greater domain of systemic influence on patients and families coping with NCDs than that regarding ethical and legal implications. Whenever a person is vulnerable in terms of losing capacity to make his or her own medical and legal decisions, such decisions become the responsibility of others including family members, physicians, or court-appointed guardians. Although health care providers and public health messages strongly encourage those with NCDs or symptoms of NCDs to pursue early diagnosis so that they can be involved with making decisions and ensuring that their preferences are honored, many systemic factors, including family relationship dynamics, health beliefs, culture, age, personality and financial considerations, prevent those with NCDs from having or exercising a voice in such matters. Evidence suggests that proxies and surrogates seldom represent the wishes of the person with NCD.

In addition, well-intentioned health care providers may introduce their own personal biases as situations arise such as health care decision making; strong identification with the circumstances, thoughts, or feelings of a patient or family member; when organizational policies conflict with principles of patient- and family-centered care; or when cultural or religious beliefs do not align with those of the family. The ethical codes of both the American Association for Marriage and Family Therapy (AAMFT, 2015) and the American Counseling Association (ACA, 2014) address standards for conduct, which are relevant to practice with this clinical population. For example, the AAMFT *Code of Ethics* addresses the principle of nondiscrimination (Standard 1.1); informed consent for those incapable of providing consent (Standard 1.2); multiple relationships that could impair professional judgment (Standard 1.3); abuse of power in the therapeutic relationship (Standard 1.7); and client autonomy in decision making (Standard 1.8). Similarly, the ACA *Code of Ethics* includes standards that speak to the following: client welfare as the primary responsibility (Section A.1.a); informed consent including sensitivity to developmental and cultural considerations (Section A.2.c); informed consent with clients who lack ability to provide consent (Section A.2.d); avoiding harm and refraining from imposing one's values on others (Sections A.4.a and A.4.b); and standards for conduct when working with multiple clients such as a patient and family member (Sections A.8 and B.4.b).

There are numerous ethical and legal dilemmas that arise throughout the course of an NCD, especially a major NCD such as dementia. In the early stages of an illness, as symptoms become more pronounced, families are confronted with decisions regarding safety. Driving, cooking, and management of finances are three safety issues that often arise earlier in the course of a major NCD. Families struggle with finding a balance between, on the one hand, honoring autonomy and promoting the independence of the person with the NCD, and, on the other hand, considering the burdens of taking on additional caregiving responsibilities, absorbing added expenses by purchasing services, and carrying responsibility for the safety of a loved one or others in the family or community who may be at risk of harm if no action is taken. A recent study by Brown and Ott (2004) examined the relationship between on-road driving score and ratings of driving ability made by a dementia patient, an informant/caregiver, and an experienced neurologist. Findings indicated that only the neurologist's ratings were significantly related to on-road driving score, although the informant's ratings were more valid than those of the dementia patient.

In middle stages of dementia (as the person with the NCD begins to struggle with decision making; carrying out activities of daily living without prompts or assistance; and the increased isolation and depression that co-occurs with word-finding difficulty, remembering names of friends and family members, and loss of capacity to engage in activities previously enjoyed), families assume increased responsibility for issues related to quality of life. During this phase, family members often consider whether it is safe and/or beneficial for their loved one to remain living alone or in the present living situation. They often find themselves in conflict with the person with the NCD as well as with each other as they try to take control of another's quality of life. Intervention at this phase often involves taking control of another's finances and medical decisions, including medication management, and forcing a loved one to attend a day program or other socialization activity against his or her will based on the premise that "it is for the best."

For caregivers in intimate relationships with a person with a major NCD, the middle stage may also introduce ethical considerations around intimacy and sexual behavior. The caring.com website (www.caring.com), a leading online destination for caregivers seeking information and support as they care for aging parents, spouses, and other loved ones, posted an article on "Dementia and Sex: How Your Sex Life May Change When a Partner Has Dementia" by Paula Spencer Scott. The article's subheadings aptly capture the essence of the issues that couples face when accommodating an NCD: the ethicality of sexual relations in a cognitively impaired partner; how to address sexual dysfunction in a partner with dementia; how to cope when a partner with dementia has paranoia and accuses a partner of having an affair; how to respond to a partner with dementia who requests sex frequently; and how to address issues regarding sex and intimacy in residential care settings.

In the last phase of a major NCD, families generally assume responsibility for their loved one's medical decision making. A report by Reamy, Kim, Zarit, and Whitlatch (2011) highlights the ethical issues inherent in this task. In this study, the investigators interviewed 266 dyads consisting of an individual with mild to moderate dementia (IWD) and his or her family caregiver to determine the individual's beliefs for five values related to care—autonomy, burden, control, family, and safety. The authors set out to determine if there were discrepancies within the IWD-caregiver dyads. They found that caregivers consistently underestimated the individual's values for all five values and yet caregivers will become the surrogate decision makers for their loved ones as dementia progresses. These study findings suggested the need for assessments of values and preferences in care and to develop programs that assess values, consider the caregiver's beliefs about care, and improve communication within the dyad in the early stages of dementia.

Another example of an ethical dilemma is antipsychotic medication use for residents with dementia in long-term care facilities. A published report by Bonner et al. (2015) described the rationales that providers and family members cite for the use of antipsychotic medications in people with dementia living in nursing homes. The study was conducted in 26 medium- and large-sized facilities in five Centers for Medicare and Medicaid Services regions. Data on individuals diagnosed with dementia who received an antipsychotic medication were collected from medical record abstraction and interviews with prescribers, administrators, direct care providers, and family members. Investigators coded reasons for antipsychotic prescribing. Major reasons cited for using antipsychotic medications in the study sample of 204 nursing home residents were: behavioral (84%), psychiatric (78%), emotional states (51%), and cognitive diagnoses or symptoms (56%). The most common behavioral reasons identified were verbal (45%) and physical aggression (42%). Psychosis (46%) was the most frequently described psychiatric reason. Anger (46%) and sadness (10%) were the most common emotional states cited. The authors concluded by affirming that antipsychotic drug therapy is frequently used in circumstances for which these drugs are not approved and for which evidence of efficacy is lacking.

End-of-life care is another issue with great ethical and legal implications. Families often grapple with deciding if and when it is time to pursue options including home care services, residential care facilities, palliative care, and hospice care. Each option is associated with choices that balance the person's dignity, autonomy, quality of life, and care preferences with the family's readiness, willingness, treatment preferences, and financial resources to make and implement such decisions.

The knowledge base of information about NCDs is considerable and growing. New developments from research on dementia, in the cognitive sciences, and in behavioral health interventions for patients and caregivers continue to shape best practices for treatment. Thus, it is imperative that systemic professionals who choose to work with this vulnerable and complex population of patients and families commit to pursuing continuing professional education as called for by the AAMFT ethical standard on professional competence and integrity (Standard III) as well as the ACA codes that address standards for professional responsibility (Section C).

CASE CONCEPTUALIZATION

Rooted in concepts presented and discussed throughout this chapter, the following case study describes examples of ways in which a diagnosis of early-onset Alzheimer's disease can affect the person with the diagnosis as well as the other family members along multiple dimensions. The case highlights the value that a thorough, multisystemic assessment brings to enhancing the therapist's awareness of key elements of individual and family history, the family's previous illness experience, and relationship patterns, and concludes with examples of care plan goals and interventions that reflect a systemic approach to treatment.

Presenting Concerns

Doug Spencer is a 57-year-old Caucasian male who was diagnosed at age 55 with early-onset Alzheimer's disease. He is married to Kate (56) and they have two children, Michael (27) whom they adopted from China at 3 months of age, and Lindsey (22), their biological child. Michael is married to Anna and they have three children aged 5, 3, and 2. Since the onset of Doug's symptoms over 2 years ago, this family has encountered many stressors, including the loss of his job due to his inability to function as required, applying for long-term disability, Kate's new job, and the recent loss of Kate's mother to cancer. Doug's neurologist referred him and his wife for counseling to help reduce their stress and to improve Doug's mood.

Concurrent Problems

Doug has had a lifelong history of depression, which began when he was around 14 years old when he learned that he had a painful, musculoskeletal condition that would preclude him from participating in high school sports. He began self-medicating with alcohol and pain medication by the age of 16, and did not seek treatment for his mood until his first year in college. He reported that psychotherapy was "a little helpful" but that he found "a couple of pills and a few beers to be even more helpful." Doug reduced his alcohol consumption substantially after college but grew dependent on opiates originally prescribed for pain control. At age 45, Doug entered treatment for his opiate addiction and has remained in remission for the past 10 years. Other than some occasional gastrointestinal issues and residual back pain, Doug has no other health issues. He is taking Donepezil (10 mg/day) for Alzheimer's disease and Citalopram (10 mg twice/day) for depression. In addition, he and his wife attend the monthly Early Stage Support Group at their local Alzheimer's Association chapter, and he occasionally attends meetings at Narcotics Anonymous. After he stopped working he lost touch with his social network which, in turn, exacerbated his depressive symptoms.

Kate was diagnosed with ulcerative colitis several years ago and tries to stay focused on living a healthy lifestyle. She is well aware that stress exacerbates her colitis symptoms and feels "tremendous pressure" to stay well for the sake of her family. She goes to a "spiritual enlightenment" group at her church each week and also takes weekly yoga classes.

Background History and Stressors

Doug and Kate met in college and married shortly after graduation. Doug completed his master's degree in education and worked for 30 years as a high school music teacher. He had a natural affinity for connecting with students and, as a result, won several teaching awards. In addition to teaching, he dabbled in song writing and performing around the region, and also had a job as a music critic for the local newspaper. Two years ago he recognized that he was beginning to have problems organizing his lectures. He and Kate dismissed this as "stress-related" because at that time they were providing in-home end-of-life care for Kate's mother who was receiving hospice care. In addition, they were excited and exhausted by their roles as grandparents and were coming to realize that toddlers required a lot more energy than infants. Yet they welcomed this kind of stress because, not only were they caring for Kate's mother, but for the previous 5 years they had been struggling with their daughter's eating disorder (anorexia nervosa) and depression. Over the next 6 months, Doug realized that he could no longer ignore his cognitive symptoms. He struggled to focus when teaching, he could not find words that used to come to him so easily, and he could no longer stay organized at school, let alone as a musician and columnist. He scheduled an appointment with a neurologist at a memory disorders clinic who confirmed his greatest fear: that he was suffering with early-onset Alzheimer's disease. His neurologist suggested that he apply for long-term disability because the stress of work was contributing to his depression, which further impaired his cognitive function.

Kate had not been employed since before she became a parent. She had some previous work experience as a teacher for English as a Second Language, but when she and Doug moved from a large metropolitan area to a smaller, less culturally diverse region, there was less demand for her skills. Nonetheless she realized that she had to find a job because the family would not be able to meet its expenses on Doug's monthly Social Security Disability check. She reached out to a few friends and, through word of mouth, learned about a receptionist/clerk job in a large cardiology practice and was hired. This was a big adjustment for the entire family as Kate had always been available to help with whatever needs would arise.

At age 21, Lindsey had just graduated from a 2-year program at the local community college. It had taken her almost 4 years to complete the program because of interruptions caused by her eating disorder and related hospitalizations. She had been doing better physically and emotionally, and had mustered the energy to apply to a 4-year college to complete her bachelor's degree. She was a strong student and was granted a scholarship to pursue her dream of attending a prestigious college to study music composition. When she learned of her father's diagnosis, despite her parents' insistence that she go, she declined the offer and decided to stay close to home. She reasoned that the years she would be away at school would undoubtedly be her father's "best years" and that she did not want to miss them. Although her parents appreciated Lindsey's sensitivity to her father's situation, they feared that proximity to her father's progressive disease might trigger a recurrence of her eating disorder. In addition, they also feared that she would once again try to reposition herself and her needs to reestablish herself as the family's "center of attention."

Michael's lived experience of the family's struggles with addiction, depression, colitis, cancer, eating disorders, and now dementia contributed to changes in perspectives about medicine. He had seen his family become "medicalized" over the years and he believed that this came to overshadow the essence of who they were as people and as a family. In response to this growing perception, he began to study Eastern medicine in college, which also provided him with an opportunity to become more familiar with his native Chinese culture. As a result of his studies, he came to adopt strong beliefs in homeopathic medicine and his views on Western allopathic medicine were often at odds with those of his family.

Strengths

The Spencer family has many strengths. Doug and Kate have a strong marriage, one that had been strengthened by the struggles they endured together over the years—fertility issues, stressors with adoption, child's eating and mood disorders, Doug's substance use, and a parent with terminal cancer. Although they have not always agreed and often argued about the best way to do things, their commitment to their marriage had never wavered. With the exception of Michael, they trust their physicians and believe in the science of medicine. They are willing to seek and use services. They have strong relationships with their children, although their relationship with Lindsey has "had its ups and downs over the years." Kate and Michael and Anna belong to a large nondenominational church, one that they find welcoming and comforting. They have a close relationship with the pastor there. The family members have shown resilience throughout their lives. Doug and Kate have two dogs, which Doug finds most comforting. Their three grandchildren are a source of joy and laughter for all of them.

DSM-5 Impressions and Implications

Before the first counseling session, Doug had signed a release for his physicians to send copies of his medical records. The counselor had an opportunity to review the records before meeting Doug and Kate. Doug's records indicated the following:

Current medical diagnoses:

Mild neurocognitive disorder due to Alzheimer's Disease, with behavioral disturbance, mild
Major depressive disorder, recurrent, moderate
Opioid use disorder in remission
Back pain
Relationship distress with spouse or intimate partner
Highly emotional expression level within family
Phase of life problem

Current prescriptions:

Donepezil (10 mg/day) for NCD due to Alzheimer's disease
Citalopram (100 mg/day) for depression
Meloxicam (7.5 mg/day) for back pain

The neurologist's report indicated that Doug's MRI showed brain atrophy and other changes consistent with Alzheimer's disease, and that he scored a 23 on the MoCA, with the greatest deficits in short-term memory and word retrieval. He was oriented to person, place, and time, and performed well on tasks assessing attention and visual spatial abilities. His MoCA score was consistent with norms for "mild cognitive impairment."

Relational Problems

Through the family assessment, several relational problems were identified:

1. Doug reported that he feels "angry" about his dementia diagnosis, and feels "useless and guilty" as a husband who can no longer support his family. He also reported that "everyone walks on eggshells around him" and that "they hover over him waiting to jump in to help him even before he needs help." He "resents" that he had to leave the workforce 10 years before he expected to do so.
2. Kate reported that she is adjusting to reentry into the workforce. She shared that her new job is "stressful" and that she feels "emotionally exhausted from being around sick, scared cardiac patients all day long." She shared that she believes that this is depleting the emotional energy she would like to have available for Doug, the grandchildren, and herself at the end of the day.
3. Doug and Kate reported that they had begun seeing signs of Lindsey's eating disorder and depression returning. She was displaying "anger outbursts" on a regular basis, and had been interjecting comments, such as "it's all about Dad all the time now." They explained to the counselor that the family had been organized around Lindsey's illness for so long, and then briefly around Kate's mother's illness. They had resolved to work on putting their marriage "front and center" once Kate's mother passed because they both believed that it had "taken a backseat" to Lindsey's needs.
4. Doug and Kate experienced slight but growing tension with Michael as he expressed his strong beliefs that they were wasting their time and money on medical care for an untreatable condition such as Alzheimer's disease.

Assessments

The counselor administered the following assessments:

Patient Health Questionnaire-9 (PHQ-9): Doug scored 17 (moderate depression); Kate scored 8 (mild depression)

Generalized Anxiety Disorder: Doug scored 12 (moderate anxiety); Kate scored 16 (severe anxiety)

Zarit Caregiver Burden Scale (Screen): Kate scored 8, which indicates a high level of burden and signals recommendation for intervention. Kate endorsed that she "nearly always" feels that she does not have enough time for herself, feels stressed, feels strained, and feels uncertain about how to care for Doug.

Family Assessment Device: Information from Doug and Kate indicated that they scored lowest in communication and problem solving. With respect to *communication*, they often missed the emotions that the other was trying to convey. They scored low on *problem solving* because, while they recognized problems in need of resolution, they were unable to decide on a course of action.

Counselor's diagnosis of Kate:

Adjustment Disorder With Mixed Anxiety and Depressed Mood
Relationship Distress With Spouse or Intimate Partner

Interventions

The counselor integrated information from reports by Doug and Kate, observations of Doug and Kate as well as the process and content of their interactions, the family assessment and measures, and information from the medical records. Together these sources of information provided a snapshot of the biological, psychological, relational, social, and medical domains of function for this family. Thus, the counselor identified the following treatment plan goals:

1. Reduce symptoms of depression and anxiety to maximize Doug's cognitive function
   a. Using techniques from narrative therapy, externalize "dementia" to reinforce the message that "Doug ≠ Dementia"—e.g., that dementia is "an unwanted guest."
   b. Review with family the cognitive domains on the MoCA where Doug performed well. Call attention to Doug's cognitive strengths and provide psychoeducation about how these translate into activities and responsibilities Doug can do to contribute to household function. Similarly, in an effort to increase the probability of his success, point out tasks that Doug may not be able to do and make an effort to help him avoid them.
   c. Provide Doug with reminders and other cues that could allow him to have some control over his day, thereby reducing his anxiety.
2. Reduce family conflict to reduce symptoms of depression
   a. Improve communication between Doug and Kate by observing communication patterns in terms of Doug's cognitive deficits (inability to multitask; distracted by noisy environment; word-finding difficulty; reduced capacity to hold onto a thought while waiting for his turn to speak). Cocreate ground rules for communication to

accommodate Doug's strengths and deficits and to emphasize that Doug is not allowed to treat Kate disrespectfully. Practice observing and interpreting nonverbal messages.

b. Allow each family member to reflect on the other's perspective of how dementia has affected his or her life to demonstrate that everyone is suffering from this illness.

c. Rebalance power in Doug and Kate's relationship by ensuring that Doug participates in decision making and household responsibilities to the extent he is able.

3. Reduce caregiver burden

a. Encourage Kate to identify a period of "me time" each week to use as she chooses.

b. Expand the system of support by reconnecting Lindsey with her psychotherapist to reduce her dependence on her parents for emotional support.

c. Explain to the family, particularly Michael, the value of nonmedical interventions that have been found to reduce manifestations of dementia, including a heart healthy diet, exercise, social connectedness, and mindfulness, and make a plan to integrate these into family life for Doug's benefit.

Ethical and Legal Implications

Because Doug maintains capacity for legal and medical decision making, the counselor encouraged Doug and Kate to see an attorney to get Doug's wishes in place. This involved designating a Health Care Proxy and stating wishes regarding Advance Directives. The counselor assured Doug that a form such as the Medical Orders for Life Sustaining Treatment form is a living document in that it was designed to accommodate changes in preferences that accompany manifestations of changes in illness and/or function. This would also be a time for Kate to consider whether her legal documents were in need of revision in light of Doug's cognitive decline. The counselor invited them to have this discussion in a future session as it may be easier to have in the safe presence of a facilitator.

Although it was still safe for Doug to drive at this point in his illness, the counselor facilitated a discussion with Doug, Kate, and their children about the process he would like to have in place for deciding when he should no longer drive. The options included but were not limited to: seek a recommendation from the neurologist or primary care physician, take a simulated driving test, and periodically review Doug's comfort with driving while monitoring whether he gets lost more frequently, changes in reaction time, and distractions while driving.

DISCUSSION

As you continue to reflect on the case study and the overall approach, contemplate these questions:

- How would you prioritize the goals for treatment in this case?

- In what ways are Doug and Kate likely to benefit more from the proposed family systems approach to therapy as opposed to an individual approach to therapy? When would an individual approach be more appropriate?

- What systemic interventions might be effective toward reducing Kate's feelings of caregiver burden?

- Based on your profession's code of ethics, what specific ethical codes might you apply?

- What would likely be the advantages and disadvantages of family therapy sessions with Michael and Lindsey?

SUMMARY

Neurocognitive disorders are a heterogeneous group of illnesses that differ from one another in a variety of significant ways. They differ by etiology, prevalence rates, age at onset, constellation of symptoms, illness course, rate of progression, and availability of treatment options. They also differ in terms of the degree to which there is public awareness of the disorders and the ways in sociocultural factors influence perceptions of and responses to the disorders. Family characteristics and other sociocultural factors largely influence the family's experience of life with an NCD as well as health outcomes for the person with the illness and others in the family. The illness experience is shaped by the time interval between symptom onset and diagnosis; willingness to seek medical intervention; access to adequate and appropriate health care; capacity to accept an NCD diagnosis; and access to support services. Similarly, the illness experience is influenced by how the family functions in terms of relationship quality, communication, problem solving, and coping styles, as well as by previous experiences with illness. Treatment for NCDs requires intervention approaches that address far more than the biomedical aspects of the disorder. Mental health providers trained in systemic treatment approaches can serve an important adjunctive role by improving the illness experience for families throughout the often long disease course, and by serving as an interface with medical providers in the roles of advocate, interpreter, and collaborator. The growing body of knowledge on collaborative care practices, as well as the demand for team-based approaches to care, are creating more opportunities for systemically trained mental health professionals to serve in these greatly needed roles.

REFERENCES

Alzheimer's Association. (2013). *Race, ethnicity and Alzheimer's disease* (Alzheimer's and Public Health Spotlight). https://www.alz.org/documents_custom/public-health/spotlight-race-ethnicity.pdf

Alzheimer's Association. (2015). 2015 Alzheimer's disease facts and figures. *Alzheimer's and Dementia, 11*(3), 332–384.

Alzheimer's Association. (2016). 2016 Alzheimer's disease facts and figures. *Alzheimer's and Dementia, 12*(4), 459–509.

Alzheimer's Disease International. (2015). The prevalence of dementia worldwide. Retrieved from http://www.alz.co.uk/adi/pdf/prevalence.pdf

American Academy of Neurology. (2011). *Clinical practice guideline process manual.* St. Paul, MN: Author.

American Association for Marriage and Family Therapy. (2015). *AAMFT code of ethics.* Alexandria, VA: Author.

American Counseling Association. (2014). *ACA code of ethics.* Alexandria, VA: Author.

American Psychiatric Association. (2000). *Diagnostic and statistical manual of mental disorders* (4th ed., text rev.). Washington, DC: Author.

American Psychiatric Association. (2013). *Diagnostic and statistical manual of mental disorders* (5th ed.). Arlington, VA: American Psychiatric Publishing.

Back, A. L., & Arnold, R. M. (2005) Dealing with conflict in caring for the seriously ill. *Journal of the American Medical Association, 293*(11), 1374–1381.

Bédard, M., Molloy, D. W., Squire, L., Dubois, S., Lever, J. A., & O'Donnell, M. (2001). The Zarit Burden Interview: A new short version and screening version. *Gerontologist, 41*(5), 652–657.

Bonner, A. F., Field, T. S., Lemay, C. A., Mazor, K. M., Andersen, D. A., Compher, C. J., . . . Gurwitz, J. H. (2015). Rationales the providers and family members cited for the use of antipsychotic medications in nursing home residents with dementia. *Journal of the American Geriatrics Society, 63*, 302–208. doi:10.1111/jgs.13230

Brown, L. B., & Ott, B. R. (2004). Driving and dementia: A review of the literature. *Journal of Geriatric Psychiatry and Neurology, 17*, 232–240.

Cantegreil-Kallen, I., & Rigaud, A. S. (2009). Systemic family therapy in the context of Alzheimer's disease: A theoretical and practical approach. *Psychologie et Neuropsychiatrie du Vieillissement, 7*(4), 253–263.

Centers for Disease Control and Prevention. (2011). Cognitive impairment: A call for action, now! https://www.cdc.gov/aging/pdf/cognitive_impairment/cogimp_poilicy_final.pdf

Cummings, J. L. (1997). The Neuropsychiatric Inventory: Assessing psychopathology in dementia patients. *Neurology, 48,* S10–S16.

Ducharme, F., Lachance, L., Levesque, L., Zarit, S. H., & Kergoat, M. J. (2015). Maintaining the potential of a psycho-educational program: Efficacy of a booster session after an intervention offered family caregivers at disclosure of a relative's dementia diagnosis. *Aging and Mental Health, 19*(3), 207–216. doi:10.1080/13607863.2014.922527

Epstein, N. B., Baldwin, L. M., & Bishop, D. S. (1983). The McMaster Family Assessment Device. *Journal of Marital and Family Therapy, 9*(2), 171–180. doi:10.1111/j.1752-0606.1983.tb01497.x

Folkman S., & Lazarus R. S. (1988). *Manual for the ways of coping questionnaire: Research edition.* Palo Alto, CA: Consulting Psychologists Press.

Folstein, M. F., Folstein, S. E., & McHugh, P. R. (1975). Mini-mental state: A practical method for grading the cognitive state of patients for the clinician. *Journal of Psychiatric Research, 12*(3), 189–198.

Ganguli, M., Blacker, D., Blazer, D. G., Grant, I., Jeste, D. V., Paulsen, J. S., . . . Sachdev, P. S. (2011). Classification of neurocognitive disorders in DSM-5: A work in progress. *American Journal of Geriatric Psychiatry, 19*(3), 205–210. doi:10.1097/JGP.0b013e3182051ab4

Gerson, R., McGoldrick, M., & Petry, S. (2008) *Genograms: Assessment and intervention* (3rd ed.). New York, NY: W. W. Norton.

Giebel, C. M., Zubair, M., Jolley, D., Bhui, K. S., Purandare, N., Worden, A., & Challis, D. (2015). South Asian older adults with memory impairment: Improving assessment and access to dementia care. *International Journal of Geriatric Psychiatry, 30*(4), 345–356. doi:10.1002/gps.4242

Gitlin, L., Kales, H., & Lyketsos, C., (2012). Nonpharmacologic management of behavioral symptoms in dementia. *Journal of the American Medical Association, 308*(19), 2020–2029. doi:10.1001/jama.2012.36918

Hellstrom, I., & Torres, S. (2013). A wish to know but not always tell: Couples living with dementia talk about disclosure preferences. *Aging and Mental Health, 17*(2), 157–167.

Inouye, S. K. (2006). Delirium in older persons. *New England Journal of Medicine, 354*(11), 1157–1165.

Kramer, B. J., Boelz, A. Z., & Auer, C. (2006). Family conflict at the end of life: Lessons learned in a model program for vulnerable older adults. *Journal of Palliative Medicine, 9*(3), 791–801.

Kroenke, K., Spitzer, R. L., & Williams, J. B. (2001). The PHQ-9: Validity of a brief depression severity measure. *Journal of General Internal Medicine, 16*(9), 606–613.

Lines, L. M., Sherif, N. A., & Wiener, J. M. (2014). *Racial and ethnic disparities among individuals with Alzheimer's disease in the United States: A literature review.* RTI Press. Retrieved from http://www.rti.org/publications/rtipress.cfm?pubid=23763

Mayeda, E. R., Glymour, M. M., Quesenberry, C. P., & Whitmer, R. A. (2016). Inequalities in dementia incidence between six racial and ethnic groups over 14 years. *Alzheimer's and Dementia: The Journal of the Alzheimer's Association, 12*(3), 216–224. doi:10.1016/j.jalz.2015.12.007

McCleary, L., Persaud, M., Hum, S., & Pimlott, J. G., Cohen, C. A., Koehn, S., . . . Garcia, L. (2013). Pathways to dementia diagnosis among South Asian Canadians. *Dementia, 12*(6), 769–789. doi:10.1177/1471301212444806

McDaniel, S. H., Doherty, W. J., & Hepworth, J. (2014). *Medical family therapy and integrated care* (2nd ed.). Washington, DC: American Psychological Association.

Milne, A., Guss, R., & Russ, A. (2014). Psycho-educational support for relatives of people with a recent diagnosis of mild to moderate dementia: An evaluation of a "Course for Carers." *Dementia, 13*(6), 768–787. doi:10.1177/1471301213485233

Mittelman, M. S., Ferris, S. H., Shulman, E., Steinberg, G., & Levin, B. (1996). A family intervention to delay nursing home placement of patients with Alzheimer's disease: A randomized controlled trial. *Journal of the American Medical Association, 276*(21), 1725–1731.

Mittelman, M. S., Haley, W. E., Clay, O. J., & Roth, D. L. (2006). Improving caregiver well-being delays nursing home placement of patients with Alzheimer disease. *Neurology, 67*(9), 1592–1599.

Nasreddine, Z. S., Phillips, N. A., Bédirian, V., Charbonneau, S., Whitehead, V., Collin, I., . . . Chertkow, H. (2005). The Montreal Cognitive Assessment, MoCA: A brief screening tool for mild cognitive impairment. *Journal of the American Geriatrics Society, 53*(4), 695–699.

National Institute on Aging, National Institutes of Health, & U.S. Department of Health and Human Services. (2015). *2014–2015 Alzheimer's disease progress report: Advancing research toward a cure.* Retrieved from https://d2cauhfh6h4x0p.cloudfront.net/s3fs-public/2014-2015_alzheimers-disease-progress-report.pdf?maJSMEv2CY5HS8MnjFt2RTujfgTu1a1e

Peisah, C., Brodaty, H., & Quadrio, C. (2006). Family conflict in dementia: Prodigal sons and black sheep. *International Journal Geriatric Psychiatry, 21*(5), 485–492.

Plassman, B. L., Langa, K. M., Fisher, G. G., Heeringa, S. G., Weir, D. R., Ofstedal, M. B., . . . Wallace, R. B. (2007). Prevalence of dementia in the United States: The aging, demographics, and memory study. *Neuroepidemiology, 29*, 125–132, doi:10.1159/000109998

Reamy, A. M., Kim, K., Zarit, S. H., & Whitlatch, C. J. (2011). Understanding discrepancy in perceptions of values: Individuals with mild to moderate dementia and their family caregivers. *Gerontologist, 51*(4), 473–483.

Ritzer, G. (2007). Blackwell encyclopedia of sociology. Retrieved from http://www.blackwellreference .com/public/tocnode?id=g9781405124331_chunk_g978140512433115_ss1-16#citation

Rolland, J. (2012). Mastering challenges in serious illness and disability. In F. Walsh (Ed.), *Normal family processes* (4th ed., pp. 452–482). New York, NY: Guilford Press.

Rosenstock, I. (1974). Historical origins of the Health Belief Model. *Health Education Monographs, 2*(4), 328–335.

Sachdev, P., Perminder, S., Mohan, A., Taylor, L., & Jeste, D. V. (2015). DSM-5 and mental disorders in older individuals: An overview. *Harvard Review of Psychiatry, 23*(5), 320–328. doi:10.1097/HRP.0000000000 000090

Sayegh, P., & Knight, B. G. (2013). Cross-cultural differences in dementia: The sociocultural Health Belief Model. *International Psychogeriatrics, 25*(4), 517–530. doi:10.1017/S104161021200213X

Scott, P. S. (2017). Dementia and sex: How your sex life may change when a partner has dementia. Retrieved from https://www.caring.com/articles/dementia-changes-sex-life

Solai, L. K. K. (2009). Delirium. In B. J. Sadock (Ed.), *Kaplan and Sadock's comprehensive textbook of psychiatry* (9th ed., pp. 1153–1167). Philadelphia, PA: Lippincott Williams & Wilkins.

Spanier, G. B. (1976). Measuring dyadic adjustment: New scales for assessing the quality of marriage and similar dyads. *Journal of Marriage and the Family, 38*, 15–28.

Spitzer, R. L., Kroenke, K., Williams, J. B., & Löwe, B. (2006). A brief measure for assessing generalized anxiety disorder: The GAD-7. *Archives of Internal Medicine, 166*(10), 1092–1097.

Spitznagel, M. B., Tremont, G., Davis, J. D., & Foster, S. M. (2006). Psychosocial predictors of dementia caregiver desire to institutionalize: Caregiver, care recipient, and family relationship factors. *Journal of Geriatric Psychiatry and Neurology, 19*(1), 16–20.

Steadman, P. L., Tremont, G., & Davis, J. D. (2007). Premorbid relationship satisfaction and caregiver burden in dementia caregivers. *Journal of Geriatric Psychiatry and Neurology, 20*(2), 115–119.

Sun, F., Gao, X., & Coon, D. W. (2013). Perceived threat of Alzheimer's disease among Chinese American older adults: The role of Alzheimer's disease literacy. *Journals of Gerontology, Series B: Psychological Sciences and Social Sciences, 70*(2), 247–257. doi:10.1093/geronb/gbt095

Tremont, G., Davis, J. D., & Bishop, D. S. (2006). Unique contribution of family functioning in caregivers of patients with mild to moderate dementia. *Dementia and Geriatric Cognitive Disorders, 21*(3), 170–174.

Tschanz, J. T., Piercy, K., Corcoran, C. D., Fauth, E., Norton, M. C., Rabins, P. V., . . . Lyketsos, C. G. (2013). Caregiver coping strategies predict cognitive and functional decline in dementia: The Cache County Dementia Progression Study. *The American Journal of Geriatric Psychiatry, 21*(1), 57–66. doi:10.1016/j .jagp.2012.10.005

Ward, A., Arrighi, H. M., Michels, S., & Cedarbaum, J. M. (2012). Mild cognitive impairment: Disparity of incidence and prevalence estimates. *Alzheimer's Dementia, 8*(1), 14–21. doi:10.1016/j.jalz.2011.01.002

Werner, P. (2003). Factors influencing intentions to seek a cognitive status examination: A study based on the Health Belief Model. *International Journal of Geriatric Psychiatry, 18*(18), 787–794.

World Health Organization. (2012). *Dementia: A public health priority.* Geneva: Author.

Yesavage, J. A., Brink, T. L., Rose, T. L., Lum, O., Huang, V., Adey, M., & Leirer, V. O. (1982–1983). Development and validation of a geriatric depression screening scale: A preliminary report. *Journal of Psychiatric Research, 17*(1), 3.

PERSONALITY DISORDERS AND SYSTEMS

Marilyn Haight and Esther Benoit

*P*ersonality Disorders (PDs) constitute a significant public health problem, with respect to associated functional impairment, extensive treatment utilization, negative prognostic impact on major depressive disorder, and suicide risk. PDs represent a high burden of disease (which is understood as the impact of a health problem as defined by financial costs, mortality, morbidity, or other indicators), along with individual suffering in terms of diminished health-related quality of life and functional status on the part of the patients, their families, and sometimes even the clinicians (Kramer & Levy, 2016; The World Health Organization Quality of Life Group, 1998). PDs have also been clinically associated with significant public health problems, such as criminal behavior, substance abuse and dependence, suicide, divorce, child abuse, occupational disability, and heavy use of mental and general health care, yet longitudinal studies examining the persistence of such problems for patients with different types of PDs have not been published (Skodol et al., 2005).

PDs reportedly affect roughly 6% of the global population with no significant variations between countries. More than half (51.2%) of people who have been diagnosed with a PD also meet criteria for other mood disorders (Tyrer et al., 2010). PDs have been shown to significantly impact the treatment trajectory of comorbid conditions and are associated with high costs of services to society. Unfortunately, there are large numbers of individuals diagnosed with a PD who do not seek mental health treatment from any health care service provider and thus are not represented among treatment-seeking patients, individuals who reject treatment rather than seek it, or may be in treatment but with a different primary diagnosis (thus not capturing the morbidity of the PD for the specific individual). These variables influence the reliability and generalizability of morbidity studies along with a variable manner in which criteria may be attributed for diagnosis. For example, in determining a diagnosis of Borderline Personality Disorder (BPD), a client has to meet five of nine core established criteria. Agreement between the criteria among different clients is not required, nor is the level of severity. As such, separate individuals can receive the same diagnosis, but by completely separate diagnostic criteria. The existing diagnostic system provides 126

473

ways to establish a diagnosis of BPD (Trull & Durrett, 2005). This example demonstrates the difficulty in establishing homogeneic diagnostic models, criteria, level of severity, diagnostic threshold, functional impact, and evidence-based treatment practices. By extension, the same concerns apply to the other nine PDs addressed in the *Diagnostic and Statistical Manual of Mental Disorders* (5th ed.; *DSM-5*; American Psychiatric Association, 2013).

This chapter is not intended to describe the diagnostic criteria for PDs in explicit detail as that responsibility remains with the authors of the *DSM-5* (APA, 2013). Rather, this chapter is intended to help emerging clinicians conceptualize and apply a family systems framework when working with people who have PDs.

DSM-5 AND FAMILY SYSTEMS

Systems thinking is a conceptual framework that helps to identify and understand patterns of behaviors exhibited within a particular system; notably, the family system. The objective for this chapter is to stimulate further critical considerations of relationships between and within the broad category of PDs and the associated interconnectedness of family systems with respect to these disorders, functions, and dysfunctions. What this means is that when working with an individual who meets the clinical criteria of having a PD, we must consider bidirectional interactions that the individual has with other people and that other people have with him or her; how he or she relates to and with other people and systems; and how connections are made, maintained, or developed between and among contexts. Further, we must consider whether or not a disorder must reside exclusively within an individual or should it be evaluated within the lens of a relationship?

Relational syndromes represent a constellation of behavioral patterns which may be associated with disruption of a family system or relationship that does not necessarily rise to a level of clinical diagnosis but does require clinical attention (M. Wamboldt, Kaslow, & Reiss, 2015).

Systems help us identify who we are as interconnected and interrelated individuals within the familial emotional unit and appreciate that behaviors cannot be understood in isolation from the system. As such, it is important to look at the way a system affects an individual as well as the manner in which an individual is impacted by the system. A framework for treatment of PDs includes connecting problems and psychopathology to specific interventions. Livesley (2012) has proposed a comprehensive three-pronged treatment framework that includes:

1. A distinction between the core or defining features of PD common to all cases and individual differences in problems and personality characteristics that delineate the different forms of disorder;
2. A conceptualization of personality as a loosely organized system based on heritable mechanisms; and
3. A social-cognitive model that represents personality and personality pathology in terms of cognitive-emotional structures derived from adaptive mechanisms. (p. 23)

Livesley's systemic approach dovetails with the treatment principles put forth by Critchfield and Benjamin (2006), which include "(a) the importance of the therapeutic relationship; (b) the focus, frame, and rationale of treatment; (c) flexible tailoring to patient's problems; (d) patient predictors; and (e) support for therapists" (p. 666). In combination, these two frameworks provide guidance to clinicians on how to bring about change within the parameters of "understanding the patient's limits and difficulties inherent in making changes to long-standing personality problems and ways of being" (p. 669). The personality system includes multiple domains, such as cognitive-affective, perceptive, interpersonal, familial, and societal (Magnavita, Levy, Critchfield, & Lebow, 2010, p. 64).

Formalized diagnosis of PDs did not occur in the United States until 1952 with publication of the first edition of the *DSM* (American Psychological Association, 1952, as cited by Coolidge & Segal, 1998). Different perspectives have arisen depending on the intended primary use for the classification, whether for use in research, in clinical settings, for administrative needs, statistical analysis, morbidity studies, and so forth. *DSM-5* (APA, 2013) retained the 10 PDs from *Diagnostic and Statistical Manual of Mental Disorders* (4th ed.; *DSM-IV*; APA, 1994) and *Diagnostic and Statistical Manual of Mental Disorders* (4th ed., text rev.; *DSM-IV-TR*; APA, 2000), and included, for the first time, Section III, which provides a number of diagnostic and assessment resources and notably includes the *Alternative DSM-5 Model for Personality Disorders* (put forth by the *DSM-5* Personality Disorders Work Group). Section III also includes eight conditions that have been identified for further study (p. 783). *DSM-5* was intended to be a paradigm shift in conceptualizing similar disorders with common etiology on a spectrum of severity, to recognize overlap between physical and psychological domains, and to enhance understanding of cultural and developmental life span influences (Norton, 2016). However, with *DSM-5* the long-standing categorical format was retained instead of moving to the proposed dimensional model. Dialogue regarding the relative value of each system continues as the profession moves forward in pursuit of developing the optimal *DSM* format to meet the needs of clinicians, researchers, and statisticians.

Although the genealogy of the *DSM* and *International Statistical Classification of Diseases and Related Health Problems (ICD)* systems may seem at first glance to be unrelated or disconnected to the discussion of PDs, these classification systems provide contextual insight into the evolution of the broad category of PDs, which then moves us toward a better understanding of the specific defining features. An ongoing dialogue exists between clinicians and researchers regarding the separate benefits of working from a categorical perspective versus a dimensional model. The *DSM-5* is written as a categorical model. The categorical model represents each diagnosis as distinctly separate from other diagnoses or health conditions and as such has been criticized as failing to adequately account for comorbidity and other symptom/behavioral overlap between and among narrowly defined categories of diagnoses. Whereas in the dimensional model, the *DSM-5* PDs workgroup identified 11 indicators that, if implemented, could inform the framework of related disorders. These indicators include "shared neural substrates, family traits, genetic risk factors, specific environmental risk factors, biomarkers, temperamental antecedents, abnormalities of emotional or cognitive processing, symptom similarity, course of illness, high comorbidity, and shared treatment response" (APA, 2013, p. 12; Kamphuis & Noordhof, 2009; Livesley, 2007; Widiger, Simonsen, Krueger, Livesley, & Verheul, 2005, as cited in Berghuis, Kamphuis, & Verheul, 2012).

Although an in-depth discussion of the evolution, classification, and criteria of PDs within the *DSM* organizational system is beyond the scope of this discussion, it is important to appreciate that 21 PDs have been identified across the seven versions of the *DSM* and are depicted in Table 18.1 (Coolidge & Segal, 1998, p. 595; personal communication, June 16, 2016). Ten PDs have remained across the past three versions of the *DSM*, suggesting a paradox of stability through change in operational definitions for PDs as a general category.

Spectrum Perspective

Everyone has overt behaviors, which are made up of a unique combination of personality traits. These traits reflect basic conditions in which individuals differ. Personality has been defined by APA as referring "to individual differences in characteristic patterns of thinking, feeling and behaving" (APA, 2016) and may be considered to include: cognitive elements such as thoughts; volitional elements such as willfulness; emotions; and behavioral tendencies or propensities (Family Firm Institute Practitioner, 2014). Culture influences behaviors as well, drawing from micro-level behaviors at the individual and interpersonal

TABLE 18.1 The Evolution of Personality Disorder Diagnoses in the Diagnostic and Statistical Manual of Mental Disorders (DSM)

DSM-I (1952)	DSM-II (1968)	DSM-III (1980)	DSM-III-R (1987)	DSM-IV (1994)	DSM-IV-TR (2000)	DSM-5 (2013)
Paranoid	Paranoid	Paranoid	Paranoid	Paranoid	Paranoid	Paranoid
Schizoid	Schizoid	Schizoid	Schizoid	Schizoid	Schizoid	Schizoid
Antisocial	Antisocial	Antisocial	Antisocial	Antisocial	Antisocial	Antisocial
Emotionally Unstable	—	Borderline	Borderline	Borderline	Borderline	Borderline
Compulsive	Obsessive-compulsive	Compulsive	Obsessive-compulsive	Obsessive-compulsive	Obsessive-compulsive	Obsessive-compulsive
Passive-Aggressive	Passive-Aggressive	Passive-Aggressive	Passive-Aggressive	—	—	—
Cyclothymic	Cyclothymic	—	—	—	—	—
Inadequate	Inadequate	—	—	—	—	—
Dyssocial	—	—	—	—	—	—
Sexual Deviation	—	—	—	—	—	—
Addictions	—	—	—	—	—	—
—	Explosive	—	—	—	—	—
—	Hysterical	Histrionic	Histrionic	Histrionic	Histrionic	Histrionic
—	Asthenic	—	—	—	—	—
—	—	Schizotypal	Schizotypal	Schizotypal	Schizotypal	Schizotypal

(*continued*)

TABLE 18.1 The Evolution of Personality Disorder Diagnoses in the Diagnostic and Statistical Manual of Mental Disorders (DSM) (continued)

DSM-I (1952)	DSM-II (1968)	DSM-III (1980)	DSM-III-R (1987)	DSM-IV (1994)	DSM-IV-TR (2000)	DSM-5 (2013)
—	—	Narcissistic	Narcissistic	Narcissistic	Narcissistic	Narcissistic
—	—	Avoidant	Avoidant	Avoidant	Avoidant	Avoidant
—	—	Dependent	Dependent	Dependent	Dependent	Dependent
			Appendix A	Appendix B	Appendix B	Section III
			Self-Defeating	—	—	—
			Sadistic	—	—	—
			—	Passive-Aggressive	Passive-Aggressive	—
			—	Depressive	Depressive	—

Used with permission from Coolidge and Segal (1998; personal communication, June 16, 2016) .

relationships level to become shared norms and values at the macro level (social environment, environmental context, race, class, gender, and so forth; van Wormer & Besthorn, 2010). Thus, we can appreciate the complex interactions between normal and abnormal; functional and dysfunctional; and the role of odd, eccentric, or quirky behaviors and social mannerisms to account for the significance of various behaviors along a somewhat arbitrary continuum of very healthy to very unhealthy/impaired.

Given the complexity and subjective nature of human behaviors, understanding the distinctions between personality functioning, characteristics, and traits is imperative because simply having odd or extreme traits is not necessarily pathological (Clark & Ro, 2014). Furthermore, having a diagnosis is not necessarily equivalent to the need for treatment of intervention (APA, 2013, p. 648). Distinctions between personality functioning and traits can be empirically challenging as some conceptual overlap exists (Clark & Ro, 2014).

People who have PDs have dysfunctional coping patterns, have distorted perceptions of self and the environment, display characteristics such as indecisiveness, dependence on others' advice, self-defeating behaviors, anxiety and perfectionism, instability, and experience difficulties in interpersonal relationships (Guindon & Giordano, 2012). Sperry (1995) noted that when working with individuals who have PDs, "the goal is to facilitate movement from the PD to a more functional personality style" (as cited by Guindon & Giordano, 2012, p. 407). Within the context of family systems, this can be a complicated task. Reduction and stabilization of dysfunctional behaviors, coping patterns, and characteristics are common treatment goals, rather than being curative. The counselor will need to look at how patterns of interaction are impacted by changes in coping patterns and other dysfunctional behaviors. As with any change, often the system will struggle to maintain equilibrium, even if that equilibrium includes the maintenance of unhealthy interaction patterns. When one family member makes a significant change, the dynamic between family members will shift (Nichols, 2013). The couples and family counselor will consider how best to support the client system in working through these individual and relational changes.

Moving From Behaviors Toward Diagnosis

The broad category of PDs was first introduced on a separate axis (Axis II) into the *Diagnostic and Statistical Manual of Mental Disorders* (3rd ed.; *DSM-III*; APA, 1980) in 1980 in an effort to move forward research and scientific study. In order to draw from scientific evidence, the disorders had to be defined in a manner that was observable and therefore measurable. A listing of specific criteria for each PD had been developed and has been revised over time (beginning with *DSM-III*) to the current language of the *DSM-5* (APA, 2000, 2013). In order to rise to a level of diagnosis for a personality disorder, the client must meet a specific minimum number of criteria and demonstrate functional limitations attributable to the symptoms and behaviors. No single criterion is considered to be essential or hierarchical, but a diagnosis is warranted once the specified number of criteria is met. This diagnostic process includes consideration of the PD definition that if a symptom is no longer endorsed by the client and additional symptoms are not disclosed that rise to a level of "substantial personal and interpersonal distress, functional impairment, and use of mental health resources," then the client no longer meets criteria for the diagnosis (APA, 2000, p. 685; Dixon-Gordon, Turner, & Chapman, 2011; Horne, 2014). It is noted, however, that enduring personality problems do not necessarily constitute having a PD diagnosis (Westen, 1997). Maladaptive personality problems/behaviors that are not severe enough to reach a diagnostic threshold may nonetheless spur clients to seek treatment. A diagnostic threshold can be established if "the disturbance causes clinically significant distress or impairment in social, occupational, or other important areas of functioning" (APA, 2013, p. 648). Guindon and Giordano (2012) suggested that the differences in functioning and need for support depend on where the client is within the holistic course of a mental health disorder. Often the families of these individuals experience significant interpersonal distress due to the maladaptive coping mechanisms and relational dynamics created between and among family members. Conceptualizing both the person with the PD and the family as the identified "client" requires a clinician to consider diagnosis/diagnoses within the context of the relational system.

Clusters

Ten PDs are addressed in *DSM-5* and are grouped into three clusters representing descriptive patterns and similarities within each cluster. Within the 10 patterns are four core features of PDs:

1. Rigid, extreme, and distorted thinking patterns (thoughts)
2. Problematic emotional response patterns (feelings)
3. Impulse control problems (behaviors)
4. Significant interpersonal problems (behaviors)

It is typical for PDs within the same cluster to co-occur and the client must exhibit at least two of these four features, which are common to all PDs (Hoermann, Zupanick, & Dombeck, 2015; Skodol et al., 2005). As noted previously, the specific criteria for each diagnosis are provided within the *DSM-5* and are not a part of this work. However, a brief operational definition follows for each of the 10 PDs.

Cluster A: Individuals who have odd, eccentric behaviors.
Common features in this cluster are social awkwardness and social withdrawal dominated by distorted thinking.

- Paranoid Personality Disorder: Characterized by pervasive distrust and suspicion. This may become problematic when individuals are suspicious of their family members, which may lead to a lack of trust and frustration in the family system.
- Schizoid Personality Disorder: Characterized by pervasive pattern of social detachment and restricted range of emotional expression. The detachment and restricted emotional range may lead to strained or distant familial relationships.
- Schizotypal Personality Disorder: Characterized by pervasive pattern of social and interpersonal limitations. Individuals have reduced capacity for close relationships and are acutely uncomfortable in social settings. They may have odd beliefs such as thinking that they can read other people's thoughts or that their own thoughts have been taken from them (APA, 2013, pp. 649–659; Hoermann, Zupanick, & Dombeck, 2013). Family systems may struggle to compensate for the lack of interpersonal coping mechanisms and the odd thought patterns present in individuals with Schizotypal Personality Disorder.

Cluster B: Impulse control and emotional regulation are hallmarks of this cluster.
Often referred to as *relationship destroyers*, individuals in this cluster are highly dramatic, both emotionally and behaviorally, and are erratic. In the general population, Cluster B Personality Disorders are the most common among individuals who have been diagnosed with PDs.

- Antisocial Personality Disorder: Individuals display pervasive disregard for the rights of other people, and are deceitful and manipulative. They frequently act impulsively without considering the consequences and typically do not have remorse for harm that they cause others. Symptoms may first appear in childhood as a Conduct Disorder. Conduct Disorder is often considered the precursor to Antisocial Personality Disorder. Family members may be fearful of individuals with Antisocial Personality Disorder, thus further complicating existing family dynamics.

- BPD: Individuals display intense and unstable emotions that can shift quickly; have a difficult time in self-regulation; and are often impulsive and engage in risky behaviors and see the world in "all or nothing" terms. This is the most commonly diagnosed PD and has garnered the most research attention. Systemic consequences may include highly volatile interpersonal dynamics and unclear expectations and roles.
- Narcissistic Personality Disorder: Characterized by exaggerated sense of self-worth and powerful sense of entitlement. Individuals have fantasies of unlimited success and power, their superior intelligence, or their stunning beauty. These people believe that they are special and deserve special treatment. In the context of relationships, this disorder can be particularly destructive given the power imbalance that is created between family members.
- Histrionic Personality Disorder: Individuals display excessive emotionality and attention seeking. Their lives are full of drama and they are uncomfortable when they are not the center of attention (APA, 2013, pp. 659–672; Carver, n.d.; Hoermann et al., 2013). Family members may express frustration with the attention-seeking behaviors of individuals with Histrionic Personality Disorder, which may lead to emotional distancing as a protective measure.

Cluster C: Personalities characterized by being anxious and fearful.

Cluster C is considered the anxious, fearful cluster as it includes three personality disorders which share a high level of anxiety and fearful thinking. Further, they typically avoid developing relationships either by being overly clingy, being distant or unconnected, or through rigid control. It is important to note that Obsessive-Compulsive Personality Disorder is *not* the same as Obsessive-Compulsive Disorder, which is a type of anxiety disorder.

- Avoidant Personality Disorder: Individuals are intensely afraid that others will ridicule or reject them, which leads them to avoid social situations or interactions with others. They often have a limited social world and underdeveloped social skills. This lack of social skills can inhibit relational functioning within the family system.
- Dependent Personality Disorder: Individuals have a strong need to be taken care of by other people and are fearful of losing the support of others. These people are clingy and have difficulty in being alone. Family members may engage in enabling patterns that look similar to codependence (Rotunda & Doman, 2001).
- Obsessive-Compulsive Personality Disorder: Individuals are preoccupied with rules, orderliness, perfectionism, and control. They are rigid and inflexible in their approach to things (APA, 2013, pp. 672–682; Hoermann et al., 2013). The rigidity and lack of flexibility may lead to overly rigid boundaries and decreased cohesiveness in the family system.

RELATIONAL AND CULTURAL FEATURES

As with any psychological disorder, relational and cultural features help to contextualize specific clinical diagnoses. PDs do not exist in a vacuum and are reciprocally influenced by both culture and relational patterns.

Relational Features

Relational problems (formerly referenced as V codes; now represented as Z codes) are addressed in the *DSM-5* through *International Classification of Diseases, Tenth Revision, Clinical Modification* (ICD-10-CM; National Center for Health Statistics, 2017) codes. These are used when a relational problem is the focus of clinical attention that is associated with clinically significant impairment of functioning or symptoms among one or more members of the relational unit or impairment of functioning of the relational unit. In using these codes, it is imperative that a primary mental health diagnosis be ruled out. Assessment for relational problems should include probing for symptoms associated with problems in relationships, and a comprehensive history should be completed to rule out a more complicated mental health diagnosis. The comprehensive history should include information regarding prior relationships, prior interventions concerning relationships, current and past work difficulties, and current medical problems.

Examples of Relational Problems

Parent–Child Relational Problem

It may include having difficulty with appropriate discipline in the home, worry about truancy, or other academic problems; overprotection of the child, which limits the child's capacity to grow; suspicion or knowledge of the child's drug or alcohol use; and unresolved parental conflict in divorced or estranged families, resulting in parental alienation syndrome. With respect to PDs, in childhood behaviors related to Oppositional-Defiant Disorder or Conduct Disorder may be present and disruptive to the family in general and between the parent and the child in particular. Adult children may also have parent–child relational problems whether or not they remain living with the parents. **Example:** One difficulty for parents of adult children who have PDs is to temper efforts to guide economic, educational, medication compliance, social activities, adherence to probation or parole conditions, and so forth. Worry stemming from loss of contact when a child runs away from home or otherwise leaves without letting family members know that he or she is alive and safe, whether or not he or she is taking his or her medications (it is likely that he or she is not if he or she has run away), or considering the range of potential consequences of actions common to having limited insight are daily companions of parents and family members of people who have PDs. Although it is common to try to establish boundaries and to restrain from constant worry, it is much easier said than done. "Tough love" is often a component of a behavioral or treatment plan but is often difficult to operationalize.

Bowen's theory would have the parents examine the origins of their separate parenting behaviors by looking at the history of parenting in their respective family of origin. This knowledge can help parents gain some control over their parenting styles and change or shift relationships with their own children.

Child Affected by Parental Relationship Distress

Examples: Parents may present with a primary complaint regarding having difficulty with appropriate discipline in the home or at school. In the course of assessment, the clinician may discover that the parent(s) or others within the family unit are abusive to the child. Conversely, there might be a situation in which the parents are at their wits end in trying to support an angry and out-of-control teenager who may be using drugs or alcohol. There might be worry about a child's truancy from school and the consequences that being suspended or expelled from school would have on the family such as loss of driving or other privileges, invoking a need to keep a closer eye on the child at more frequent intervals to try to ensure that the child is where he or she is supposed to be and is associating with friends who have been vetted by the parents. There could be suspicion or knowledge of the child taking drugs, using alcohol, sniffing aerosols, and so forth. Prescription drug use as well as nonprescription medications may be the child's drug of choice depending on availability. There could be unresolved family conflict exacerbated by parental separation or divorce, remarriage, birth of a planned or unplanned baby, estrangement from other family members, or death of a family member. Again, drawing from Bowen, a close look at multigenerational issues is key as there may be patterns of alcoholism, drug use, legal problems, estrangement or abandonment, or abuse that have not been openly discussed but are being perpetuated within the current family dynamic.

Partner Relational Problem

Examples: Neither partner has problems or concerns that meet the criteria for a mental health condition. There might be physical or sexual abuse of an adult within a family relationship. One of the partners might be engaging in sexually risky behaviors or engaging in behaviors that have caused or contributed to disturbances in an intimate adult relationship. On the other hand, one partner may be demonstrating behaviors of a PD and the other partner is trying to be supportive or trying to maintain stability of the relationship despite what might appear to be a purposeful sabotage of these efforts. People who have PDs often have limited or lack of insight or empathy as to the manner in which their behaviors impact other people.

Sibling Relational Problem

Excessive arguing and/or fighting between siblings; excessive jealousy between siblings. **Example:** There is often significant controversy within the family unit as to "who started it" as the personality-disordered sibling is unlikely to acknowledge responsibility or culpability in stirring up heightened emotions between siblings.

Cultural Features

It is not a new or novel idea that a reciprocal influence exists between culture on mental illness and the impact of mental illness on culture (Montagu, 1961/2006). Shorter (2012) asserted that: "Personality disorders exist not as natural phenomena but as cultural phenomena. As a society we need some way of identifying people who can't quite get it all together." As such, it is critical to explore, assess, and make meaning of the cultural nature of PDs in order to work toward developing multicultural competence. Notably, developing multicultural competency requires purposeful effort beyond reading a book or attending a workshop to become culturally fluent. Rather, development of cultural competency takes time and experience to approach mastery of a new conceptual worldview (Parham, 2002). It is important to keep in mind that even though universal or common behaviors can be found in different cultures, it does not mean that they play the same role everywhere. For example, for African-descent people, "mental illness/disorder criteria is thinking and behaving that is devoid of, opposes, or contradicts own-race maintenance, protection, and development" (Azibo, 2014, p. 42). Azibo further described the harm inherent in providing treatment for a client's presenting problem and then releasing/returning him or her to family/community of origin without addressing own-race maintenance as "incalculable" (p. 42).

The presence of interpersonal relationship problems is the most defining feature of all PDs (Hoermann et al., 2013). This is often referred to as "self-other" disturbance. Where healthy personalities are distinguished by interpersonal flexibility, PDs are characterized by rigid patterns of interpretation and response that are not typically open to (or capable of) reflection, insight, or modulation. For example, a person might experience constantly shifting self-states from being thoughtful and considerate in one moment to being driven by anger, rage, demandingness, and self-destructiveness in the next. Furthermore, it is important to consider that in the therapeutic milieu a therapist may also be considered as an "other."

Measuring the impact of culture on an individual's behavior is professionally challenging. Beyond the experience of the client, these intense and unpredictable behaviors often lead to caregiver strain and frustration by parents, family members, teachers, and therapists. Furthermore, it is essential that practitioners offer culturally responsive caring that takes into consideration the clients' beliefs, priorities, and preferences with respect to how they prefer to manage their health care services (Munoz, 2007). Mental health clinicians must acquire and further develop culturally responsive reflective skills needed to work through the persistent personality puzzles presented by disordered clients as well as to attend to the professional discomfort that comes with learning about and vicariously experiencing privilege and marginalization through clients' lived experiences.

Cultural differences should be considered as possible explanations for "symptoms." Notably, as with the prior comments regarding systems, these cultural factors cannot be viewed in isolation. Rather, they must be viewed within the individual's different and unique viewpoints, family systems, wealth of experiences, and in combination with issues of oppression or privilege that may be attributable to the individual's overall life experiences. All human behaviors stem from the specific context of our individual, unique experiences (Parham, 2002).

Multicultural and Social Justice Competencies

The applicability of diagnostic criteria to culturally specific symptomatology and culture-bound syndromes is not well known and is difficult to determine. Personality symptoms must be assessed in context-specific terms to determine whether or not the manifestations are functional (normal) or dysfunctional for the client's cultural condition as many behaviors are socioculturally determined. It is also noteworthy that the approach used in assessing behaviors and/or symptoms may yield different results and may differ between clinical practitioners. Whether or not traits/behaviors become dysfunctional often depends on the social context. Certain traits may not be considered pathological unless they significantly interfere with functioning (Paris, 1998).

Sue, Arredondo, and McDavis (1992) developed the Multicultural Counseling Competencies, which was operationalized as the original single-lens perspective for multicultural competency. Changes in the world at large have moved the expectations for cultural competence beyond race, ethnicity, and culture. Systemic clinicians must develop *wide lens* or holistic competence in understanding the complexities of an individual's experience. These complexities include (but are not limited to) individual social constructs, such as race, ethnicity, gender, sexual orientation, economic status, religion, spirituality, and disability (Ratts, Singh, Nassar-McMillan, Butler, & McCullough, 2016). Ratts et al. (2016) developed the Multicultural and Social Justice Counseling Competencies, which replaced the original Multicultural Counseling Competencies.

Importance of Diversity and Social Justice in the Helping Profession

Mental health professionals have an ethical obligation to be multiculturally competent and have the disposition to work with a diverse and challenging client population. Understanding (beyond a general working knowledge) of demographic, social, and cultural variables is necessary for appropriate diagnosis and effective psychological service. That said, although it is beyond the scope of any individual to develop a comprehensive mastery of every aspect of culture as significant differences exist within and between the complexity of cultural variables, the average member of the cultural group is able to acquire a good many of them (Montagu, 1961/2006). By extension, mental health professionals can develop cultural content mastery as well.

FAMILY SYSTEMS ASSESSMENTS

Clinicians should make every effort to assess the relational unit or family system when working from a systemic perspective. The following are examples of family systems assessments, which describe ways of addressing systemic concerns that may arise in families where one member has been diagnosed with a PD. This is not intended to represent an exhaustive list of possible assessments or instruments. The clinician should select an appropriate instrument based on the presenting concerns or variables to be assessed.

Theory to Practice

A variety of family systems theories have been discussed throughout this text. Rather than duplicate previous efforts, we discuss a single theory and provide information regarding multiple assessment instruments that are available for use.

Bowen's family systems theory suggests that although there are no magical answers, the systematic approach provides a different way of conceptualizing human problems. For example, individuals cannot be understood in isolation from one another, but rather as a part of their family; as the family is an emotional unit. Bowen uses systems thinking to describe the complex interactions of the (family) unit. A basic assumption of Bowen's theory is that the emotional system affects most human activities and is the principal force in the development of clinical problems (Kerr, 2000). For example, a family might experience marital discord, child abuse/neglect, intimate partner abuse, parent–child relational problems, sibling relational problems, and so forth. Similarly, relationship difficulties might be an inherent part of a PD. M. Z. Wamboldt and Wamboldt (2000) noted that relationships often change as a function of psychological disturbance or disease states.

A system may be further defined as a set of interacting elements. Bowen's focus was on patterns that develop in families in order to defuse anxiety. His theory includes eight interacting concepts necessary for understanding and working with systems: triangles, differentiation of self, nuclear family emotional processes, family projection process, multigenerational transmission process, emotional cutoff, sibling position, and societal emotional process (Brown, 1999; Kerr, 2000).

A brief overview of the interacting concepts follows to help in conceptualizing Bowen's uniquely descriptive terms:

Triangles represent a three-person relationship and are the smallest stable relationship unit. The process of triangulating is the underpinning of Bowen's theory and occurs when the anxiety within a dyad is relieved by a vulnerable third party who either takes sides with one member of the dyad or provides a detour for the anxiety (Brown, 1999; Kerr, 2000).

Differentiation of self refers to the ability to separate feelings and thoughts and the degree to which a person can discern between thoughts and feelings. For example, individual feelings and/or choices are set aside in the interest of creating harmony or less anxiety within the system (Brown, 1999; Kerr, 2000).

Nuclear family emotional processes reflect a multigenerational concept stemming from the notion that individuals repeat in their marital and relationship choices the same patterns of relating that were learned in their family of origin. In this process, four basic relationship patterns are reflected that influence where problems or conflicts develop within a family system. The four basic relationship patterns are identified as marital conflict, dysfunction in one spouse, impairment of one or more children, and emotional distance (Goldberg & Goldberg, 2012; Kerr, 2000).

Family projection process is the primary manner in which parents transmit their emotional problems to a child, potentially impairing the function of one or more of the children and increasing the children's risk of developing clinical symptoms (Kerr, 2000).

In family projection, the children develop symptoms as a result of becoming entangled within the parental relationship anxieties (Brown, 1999).

Multigenerational transmission process refers to family patterns that are repeated across multiple generations. For example, patterns of behavioral dysfunction are transmitted through a variety of mechanisms, including not only child abuse and neglect but also poverty, discrimination, marginalization, and social factors (Magnavita et al., 2010).

Emotional cutoff refers simply to emotional distancing. According to Bowen, all people have some degree of unresolved attachment to their parents. He further described emotional cutoff as "the emotional process between the generations through which people separate themselves from the past in order to start their lives in the present generation" (Bowen, 1978, p. 382, as cited in Titelman, 2003).

Sibling position stems from the notion that people who grow up in the same sibling position within their family of origin predictably have similar characteristics. For example, a first-born female would likely gravitate to a youngest-born male spouse. The characteristics of one position are typically complementary to the other rather than being hierarchal (Kerr, 2000).

Societal emotional process identifies parallels between familial and societal emotional functioning and extends Bowen's understanding of family as an emotional unit to society as an emotional unit (Kerr, 2000; Titelman, 2003, p. 36). This element of Bowen's family systems theory attempts to link his system with societal evolution rather than clinical practice.

Assessment Is Continuous

Assessment is both a product and a process used to understand and predict behaviors. Assessment within a family systems perspective typically includes multiple methods, such as individual and family history interviews, behavioral observations, and use of formal instruments as no single method provides a complete picture. The clinician needs to understand where the family has been, where they are now, and in what direction they want to go (McIntire & Miller, 2006).

Accurate assessment of family relationships and inter/intrapersonal functioning is critical in determining treatment interventions. Assessment methods commonly used in family therapy include observational methods, interviews, self-reports of family interaction, and graphic representations of relationships, such as through the use of genograms. Crosscultural implications to the assessment and diagnosis of PDs provide a basis of understanding.

In contrast to assessing individuals, family counselors focus on assessing the family system. The primary focus of the family system includes assessment of family relationships, patterns, structures, and level of function. Bowen's theory also includes drawing from multigenerational histories to assist the clinician in sorting through patterns and invisible issues that may exist (Titelman, 2013). In addition to its role in planning interventions and treatments, assessment data can be used to evaluate outcomes. Information gleaned through the assessment process can be used to generate hypotheses regarding the nature and cause(s) of the problem(s), family members' perceptions of the problem(s), and potential areas of strength. As such, the assessment process can help to facilitate change. Interestingly, the assessment process for PDs does not attempt to address the causal nature of problematic behaviors.

Now that we have a general understanding of the role of systems and a theoretical orientation to family systems, we can take a look at some of the family systems assessment instruments and processes. Instruments should reflect the importance of culture in the classification of mental disorders generally, and in PDs specifically. Numerous other instruments are available for use depending on the variable(s) that the clinician is interested in assessing.

Guided Interviews

The guided interview is an essential element of the assessment process that can help to identify risk and protective factors and provide context for understanding the family's concerns (Ghanbaripanah & Mustaffa, 2012). The following questions are provided by Erford (2012) as a guideline to assess family-based problems:

- What is the problem as the family sees it?
- Who has defined the problems?
- Who is more involved in the problem than others?
- Who is uninvolved and why?
- How do different views and perceptions of the problem align?
- What experience and discussions have led the family to define the problem in the way that they do?
- What unresolved questions remain?
- What expectations for the future does the family have that are relevant to the present problem?
- Is there any unresolved grief or mourning left over from the past?

Family Systems Assessment Tool

Dickinson et al. (1996) developed the Family Systems Assessment Tool as a self-report measure designed to assess aspects of relationships and family dynamics within a client's family and past experiences with his or her family of origin through a multigenerational family systems theoretical perspective.

Family Systems Stressor-Strength Inventory (FS³I)

The FS³I focuses on "identifying stressful situations that occur within families and the strengths that families use to maintain healthy family function" through assessment of three sections: general family systems stressor, specific family systems stressor, and the family strengths (Haefner, 2014; Mischke-Berkey & Hanson, 1991, p. 319). The focus of this instrument is to evaluate stressful situations that occur within families and the strengths from which family members draw to maintain healthy functioning. Each family member completes the instrument on a separate form prior to an interview with the clinician. The clinician evaluates each family member on general and specific stressful situations and the strengths that he or she has self-identified. Each family member's responses are color-coded along with the clinician's perception score on the quantitative summary, and the clinician synthesizes information from all family members. A family care plan can then be utilized to prioritize diagnoses, set goals, develop prevention/intervention strategies, and evaluate outcomes.

The McMaster Family Assessment Device (FAD)

The McMaster Family Assessment Device (FAD; Epstein, Baldwin, & Bishop, 1983) is a screening device based on the McMaster Model of Family Functioning and contains seven intercorrelated scales that measure problem solving, communication, roles, affective responsiveness, affective involvement, behavior control, and general functioning. The purpose of the FAD is to identify problem areas efficiently and as simply as possible and it is designed to gather information directly from the family members. Any problems that are identified by the FAD should be further assessed in greater detail by attention to significant and relevant biological, psychological, and sociological factors. It is a 53-item paper-and-pencil questionnaire that can be filled out by all family members older than 12 years of age. The 53 items are statements that a person could make regarding his or her family and are rated among four possible responses: strongly agree, agree, disagree, and strongly disagree. An example of items from each of the scales is provided:

- Problem solving: We confront problems involving feelings.
- Communication: We do not talk to each other when we are angry.
- Roles: We discuss who is to do household jobs.
- Affective responsiveness: We are reluctant to show our affection for each other.
- Affective involvement: Our family shows interest in each other only when one can get something out of it.
- Behavior control: Anything goes in our family.
- General functioning: In times of crisis we can turn to each other for support.

The Mental Measurements Yearbook provides a brief synopsis of tests in print. A search using the key words "personality disorders" yielded 22 separate assessments. Clinicians should become familiar with frequently used, evidence-based instruments along with norming processes, validity, and reliability of the instruments. Additionally, clinicians must practice within their scope of practice and receive appropriate training in administering, scoring, and interpreting the test results prior to administering an instrument.

FAMILY SYSTEMS INTERVENTIONS

Evidence over the past few years has supported the notion that *one size doesn't fit all* with respect to working with family systems that are dealing with PDs. Despite the fact that there is likely only one identified patient within the family unit, the entire system is vulnerable to the emotional fallout. Various approaches have been considered to yield similar efficacy outcome measures without significantly differing results across the spectrum of PDs (Livesley, 2012). The overall treatment goal is to "do no harm, and where possible, do good" (Smith, 2005, p. 371).

Among treatment models typically utilized with patients who have been diagnosed with PD, the following five models have been most studied and found to be efficacious for BPD: Dialectical behavioral therapy, transference-focused psychotherapy, mentalization-based treatment, schema-focused therapy, and systems training for emotional predictability and problem solving (Kramer & Levy, 2016). There are several additional treatments for PDs, which are presented as being potentially valid treatment options but which have more limited empirical support such as psychodynamic, humanistic-experiential, dynamic-deconstructive, and interpersonal (Kramer & Levy, 2016). In the integrative model, which has primarily been addressed throughout this chapter, interventions may be purposefully selected from any existing theory or approach so long as they address the patient's need and circumstances based on the case conceptualization (Critchfield, 2012).

Extensive knowledge of theory and practice related to the spectrum of relational disorders, as well as a repertoire of knowledge regarding "personality systematics, which is the study of the interrelationships among the various domains of the personality system," is required of providers to provide ethical and competent services (Magnavita et al., 2010, p. 64). Using an integrated system, however, rather than drawing from a single lens focused on a particular aspect of psychopathology, multiple interventions are purposefully pulled from their respective theoretical frameworks in a manner that might be considered eclectic other than for one key point: interventions are selected based on their targeted therapeutic benefit but without adopting their associated theoretical assumptions (Livesley, 2012, p. 19).

Although the goal of any treatment model is to decrease conflict and to improve communication and caring relationships, low family engagement and retention are significant problems for intervention programs. The results in consequences include diluted public health benefits and frequent no-shows or cancellations, which are costly for clinicians. Keeping families engaged in services can be challenging as individuals who may need services the most receive lower amounts (in terms of frequency and duration), and a wide variety of experiences can interfere with the treatment process leading them to disengage. When asked, family members often relay conflicting time demands, scheduling conflicts, high costs, lack of transportation, and child care as practical obstacles.

Table 18.2 lists interventions in alignment with the corresponding therapeutic needs gleaned from Critchfield (2012). Additional interventions may be gleaned from specific theoretical orientations to address specific client needs.

Therapists' Characteristics

Working with patients who have been diagnosed with PDs has notoriously been viewed as challenging, time-consuming, frustrating, and, for some, unrewarding as these patients are known to frequently present with multiple interaction and regulation problems. These behaviors may stimulate negative reactions, emotional retreat, strained alliances, and feelings of helplessness or burnout for some therapists (Aviram, Brodsky, & Stanley, 2006; Critchfield, 2012; Kramer & Levy, 2016). To that end, it is important to consider characteristics of the therapist that may impact the therapeutic relationship, the course of treatment, and treatment outcomes, as well as protect the therapist.

Kramer and Levy (2016) have noted the importance of the clinician to be *open-minded* and to have an adaptable approach, particularly when working from an integrated theoretical orientation. Fernandez-Alvarez, Clarkin, Salgueiro, and Critchfield (2006) have described that the effective therapist's characteristics when working with personality-disordered clients should be "(a) open-mindedness, flexible, and creative in the treatment approach; (b) be comfortable with long-term treatments requiring emotionally intense relationships; (c) be tolerant of his or her own negative affects; (d) have patience; and (e) have a specific training in the treatment of PDs" (p. 215).

ETHICAL AND LEGAL IMPLICATIONS

Systemic practitioners should be mindful of the ethical guidelines set out by their governing professional organizations. The American Counseling Association (ACA) calls on counselors to

> know and understand the ACA *Code of Ethics* and other applicable ethics codes from professional organizations or certification and licensure bodies of which they are members. Lack of knowledge or misunderstanding of an ethical responsibility is not a defense against a charge of unethical conduct. (2014, Section I.1.a)

Standards of practice are organized around core ethical values of beneficence, nonmaleficence, justice, fidelity, and autonomy. For couple and family counselors, the ACA and the American Association for Marriage and Family Therapy (AAMFT) *Codes of Ethics* should be thoroughly examined and applied to clinical work. In addition to ethical guidelines,

TABLE 18.2 Interventions and Therapeutic Needs	
Intervention	**Therapeutic Need Addressed**
Consistent structure	Abandonment fears, affects dysregulation, internal chaos
Open-ended, validating stance	Shared goals of treatment
Therapist stance	Structures treatment and sets limits on unacceptable behavior, empathy, positive regard, congruence in feelings
Present-centered and problem-focused approach	Reduces symptoms, instills hope, enhances collaboration
Create hierarchy of symptoms	Sequential targeting and prioritizing of behaviors; repeating themes, self-concepts, or beliefs
Summarize interpersonal sequence of wish, response of other, and response of self from patient's relational narratives	Behaviors learned in the past likely predict future behaviors and relating
Adaptive copy process	Treatment can be focused on particular relational history, patterns learned, and thoughts/feelings about the attachment figures being copied
Develop contextually appropriate baseline of relating (with self and others); connect in positive ways with others	Involves ability to be moderately enmeshed with others (protect/trust) as well as to be moderately differentiated from them (affirm/disclose)

Source: Critchfield and Benjamin (2006).

counselors must also be aware of laws and policies at the local, state, and federal level that may impact clinical practice. The treatment of systems in which one or more members has a PD increases the complexity of the clinical course of treatment. Although practitioners need to have a comprehensive understanding of the ethical guidelines and potential legal concerns that may impact their professional work, this section focuses on specific ethical and legal issues that may be more challenging for those working with systems that include individuals who have been diagnosed with a PD.

Identifying the Client

In systemic work, the family or couple system is typically identified as the "client." When working with systems in which a member has been diagnosed with a PD, the couples and family counselor will still frame treatment from a systemic vantage point. Navigating the reimbursement process with third-party payers can orient treatment back to the individual, as most insurance companies do not reimburse unless there is an identified client.

Addressing clinical concerns from a relational standpoint may need to be more fully and intentionally explored when an individual is identified as the "client" for reimbursement purposes. The family or couple can work with the counselor to determine who might participate in the counseling process and how the relational system or family is defined.

Professional Competence

Many clinicians view professional competence as binary; that is, that one is either competent or incompetent. This perspective can lead to inappropriate referrals and lack of insight around continuing education needs. Professional knowledge and understanding are dynamic processes that counselors hone throughout their careers. Competence includes many dimensions and exists along a continuum (Remley & Herlihy, 2007). When working with PDs in the context of relational work, clinicians may feel ill-equipped to navigate treatment. However, with this awareness comes the professional responsibility to expand their foundation of knowledge through reading professional journals and other literature, attending professional development conferences, obtaining supervision, or consulting with colleagues as needed. The ethical requirement for clinical supervision and/or consultation extends beyond that which is required by the state for licensure. Notably, ACA's guidance in Section I.2.c. Consultation is as follows:

> When uncertain about whether a particular situation or course of action may be in violation of the *ACA Code of Ethics*, counselors consult with other counselors who are knowledgeable about ethics and the *ACA Code of Ethics*, with colleagues, or with appropriate authorities, such as the ACA Ethics and Professional Standards Department. (ACA, 2014, Section I.2.c)

Counselors can guide treatment using an ethical decision-making model and conducting a risk–benefit analysis around clinical decisions (Magnavita et al., 2010). Magnavita et al. (2010) suggested determining the course of treatment by first exploring the risks of working with clients without having specialized competence in treating PDs, and the risks of referral to another clinician who does have this specialized competence. Honest evaluation of one's clinical skill set is necessary in completing this type of risk–benefit analysis. Similarly, it is crucial to consider ethical aspects of novel psychotherapeutic treatments and/or interventions as liability and risk management are critical issues (Kramer & Levy, 2016). Although there are a few evidence-based treatment modalities indicated for this population, there is no specific standard for clinical competence beyond adherence to ethical guidelines for general practice (Magnavita et al., 2010). Knowledge and familiarity with the current research base on specific PDs is crucial to counselor competence. In the ACA *Code of Ethics* (2014), counselors

> recognize the need for continuing education to acquire and maintain a reasonable level of awareness of current scientific and professional information in their fields of activity. Counselors maintain their competence in the skills they use, are open to new procedures, and remain informed regarding best practices for working with diverse populations. (ACA, 2014, Section C.2.f)

Nondiscrimination and Appropriate Referral Processes

The AAMFT and ACA codes of ethics specifically address nondiscrimination (AAMFT Standard 1.1; ACA Section C.5). Given the challenging and persistent nature of PDs, many clinicians may find it difficult to determine when they are appropriately referring a client and when they are engaging in discriminatory referral processes. AAMFT Standard 1.10 suggests that clinicians assist clients in "obtaining appropriate therapeutic services if the therapist is unable or unwilling to provide professional help" (AAMFT 2015, Standard 1.10). This standard may be interpreted to suggest that counselors can pick and choose the clients with whom they work. Shiles (2009) suggests that helping professionals may attempt to justify discriminatory referral practices by conceptualizing them as ways of avoiding client harm and working beyond one's scope of competence. However, personal discomfort with a clinical situation is not sufficient reason for referral. Professionals should consider the following questions before referring, according to Shiles (2009, p. 142):

- Based on both my training and professional experience, do I feel competent to work with this client?
- Can I be respectful of my client's beliefs related to his or her presenting concern?
- How might my reaction to this client differ from my reaction to a client with a similar presenting concern, but with different demographic variables?
- Can I expand my competence regarding this issue through reading, supervision, or other professional activities?
- Am I willing to work at expanding my competence, and if not, why?
- Is this an area that the APA regards as essential for competent practice?
- Would referring this client cause more harm than good for this client and for other clients with similar characteristics who are considering counseling?
- Have I exhausted all other options before considering this referral?

As clinicians develop professional and clinical competence, it is important that continued emphasis be placed on learning new skills and gaining the competencies needed to work with a diverse clinical population. This is supported in both the AAMFT *Code of Ethics* and ACA *Code of Ethics*, where counselors are called to maintain competency (AAMFT Standard 3.1) and develop new skills by engaging in continued education (AAMFT Standard 3.10; ACA Section C.2.f). Counselors must intermittently examine their competency around systemic perspectives and their interaction with complex individual clinical concerns.

Lack of Treatment Potency

PDs are known for their resistance to treatment. Historically, the psychodynamic approach to treatment focused on the individual therapeutic framework. As family systems theory gained traction and challenged this intrapsychic paradigm, more emphasis has been placed on individuals in the context of their relational systems. Given the tenacious nature of PDs, therapeutic flexibility becomes essential. Counseling with families over the course of the family life cycle using evidence-based modalities appears to enhance treatment outcome (Magnavita et al., 2010).

Considering the overall lack of treatment potency in general, the evidence base for systemic treatment of PDs is small. Clinicians will be called to make determinations around length of treatment, frequency of sessions, theoretical orientation, and whether or not additional counseling modalities might be beneficial. In the systemic treatment of PDs, it may be useful to include multiple treatment modalities (group, individual, family), and counselors will need to decide how those modalities are delivered concurrently or sequentially.

Boundaries

Awareness of boundaries is especially important in managing clinical relationships with clients diagnosed with PDs. This may be further complicated in relational therapeutic work as multiple family members are involved in the process of counseling. Setting appropriate therapeutic boundaries can be more challenging when working with clients diagnosed with PDs (Magnavita et al., 2010). Boundary issues may include unreasonable demands around therapist accessibility and communication outside of the therapeutic session. As with any clinical relationship, the counselor must consider what is in the best interest of the identified client (the family or couple system), and proceed accordingly while adhering to legal and ethical parameters.

Nonabandonment

As with any clinical situation, counselors do not leave their clients without ensuring continuity of care or appropriate clinical termination (AAMFT, 2015, Standard 1.11; ACA, 2014, Sections A.11d and A.12). Nonabandonment is an especially important consideration in working with PDs in families and couples as these systems can be especially vulnerable to transition and ambiguity. For example, BPD is linked to abandonment and even clinically appropriate referral or termination may be perceived by the client and the client's family system as abandonment (Schmahl et al., 2004).

CASE CONCEPTUALIZATION

In order to understand working with families and PDs and to assist emerging clinicians to further conceptualize a personality-disordered situation through the family systems lens, the authors have developed the case of Demaris, Chad, and Noam—a family impacted primarily by BPD. The complex situation will assist the mental health care provider in considering potential differential diagnoses and comorbid conditions.

Presenting Concerns

Demaris is 36 years old and lives with her husband Chad (45) and infant son Noam (3 months) in a suburban community outside of Chicago, Illinois. They are condo dwellers and enjoy a number of property amenities as a part of their Homeowners' Association (HOA) fees. Demaris and Chad have been together on and off for 3 years prior to their marriage 1 year ago. Demaris has been in and out of counseling since high school where she was initially diagnosed with Attention-Deficit/Hyperactivity Disorder (ADHD). She has had a strong academic career as evidenced by earning high honors in high school and graduating cum laude from her undergraduate program in health care administration. During high school and college, Demaris had numerous and intense short-term relationships and reported feeling more connected to the "new" people in her life than those with whom she had an established history. This pattern of instability in her relationships has been persistent. During her freshman year of college, Demaris threatened suicide by medication overdose during a fight with her roommate. This incident led to the roommate moving out and Demaris resuming counseling at the university wellness center. Demaris requested new counselors three times during her college years, stating that her counselors often ignored her and did not care about her enough to truly help. Demaris claims that she likes to "reinvent" herself, especially during times of stress, and will dye or cut her hair, change her style of dress, and even assume a different accent.

Demaris worked full time as a medical practice office manager until Noam's birth and has been on leave since then. Demaris has a history of impulsive spending and has three credit cards that are maxed out. The family relies on Demaris's income to help pay these credit card bills along with sharing some responsibility for household expenses. Chad works in information technology (IT) at a legal group in downtown Chicago and regularly needs to go in to work early or stay late. Commuting from the suburbs adds substantially to his time away from home as it takes roughly an hour each way by train. Chad is angry and frustrated that Demaris is constantly "up and down" and shares that he often walks on egg-shells around her to avoid setting her off. Chad reports that her emotional outbursts have become more frequent and intense since the baby's birth 3 months ago. Most recently, Demaris became so angry with Chad for coming home from work 20 minutes late without letting her know ahead of time that she left for 2 days, leaving Chad with Noam. Chad had to make arrangements for Noam's care so that he could go to work, and he was unaware of Demaris's whereabouts until she returned home 2 days later.

Concurrent Problems

Demaris gained 20 pounds during her pregnancy and has lost all but five pounds since Noam was born. Although she is not considered overweight, she feels uncomfortable by the changes in her body after giving birth and frequently makes claims that Chad must be cheating on her because he thinks she is fat. Demaris insists that it is only a matter of time before Chad will leave her. Chad is not concerned about Demaris's weight gain and believes that she is using this as a way to manipulate and control his behavior. Chad has experienced heightened anxiety over the past year and believes it is related to Demaris's pregnancy and the stress associated with having a new baby. This fear of abandonment triggers Demaris's emotional outbursts and has become more severe since the birth of her son.

Background History and Stressors

Demaris describes her relationship with her mother as "complicated" and she has not spo-ken with her in a year. As a child, Demaris's mother would often leave for months at a time, leaving Demaris with neighbors or extended family members. Demaris has two older male siblings, both of whom were in junior high at the time she was born and has limited contact with them but considers them to be supportive of her as the perpetual "little sister." Although Chad reports a close relationship with his mother Judy and two younger broth-ers, he is estranged from his father who left the family when Chad was 8 years old. Judy watches Noam when the couple is unable to secure other childcare although she lives more than an hour away from Chad and Demaris. When Demaris left for 2 days, Judy stepped in so that Chad could go to work. Judy believes that Demaris is a bad influence on Chad and has encouraged Chad to file for divorce and sole custody of Noam. The couple has experienced financial stress since the birth of their son and Demaris's leave from work. When Noam was born, Demaris went on a spending spree and opened a new department store credit card that she has already maxed out in addition to the existing three cards. Demaris now has personal credit card debt that is more than $12,000.

Strengths

Although the couple expresses a tumultuous relationship, both Demaris and Chad enjoy spending time together and have a shared interest in music. Demaris shares that her rela-tionship with Chad is the longest and most consistent relationship she has had in her life. Chad admires Demaris's creativity. Chad is an attentive father and enjoys spending time with his infant son. Although they share a common religious background, they do not currently attend church services together. However, Chad is marginally involved with the early morning men's group at church and attends Sunday services one to two times per month.

DSM-5 Impressions and Implications

Demaris is the identified client in this case. Although Demaris was first diagnosed with ADHD Combined Presentation in high school, her inappropriate emotional intensity, persistent relational instability, impulsivity across a variety of contexts, and fear of abandonment have contributed to an updated diagnosis of BPD. The BPD diagnosis was provided during her freshman year in college, following the suicide threat event. This diagnosis is evidenced by her pattern of unstable relationships throughout young adulthood. Due to the level of conflict present in Chad and Demaris's relationship, relationship distress with spouse and high emotional expression level in family were included in the initial diagnostic impression. The financial stress present since Demaris's most recent spending spree and break from work warrants inclusion of unspecified problems related to employment.

Relational Problems

Demaris frequently brings up her belief regarding Chad's lack of care for her and that he will inevitably leave her during arguments. During arguments, Demaris often dares Chad to leave her and "prove her right," which only serves to escalate the interaction. Chad notes that he cares deeply for Demaris but worries that without increasing trust in their relationship, they will not be able to move forward. Chad reports that he and Demaris have days when things are great and then for seemingly no reason Demaris will begin to "pick fights" with him. In these situations, Chad and Demaris enter into a demand–withdraw pattern where Demaris wishes to engage Chad in an argument and Chad attempts to avoid conflict by withdrawing. Chad emphasizes his desire to make things work to support his young family and new son.

Assessments

Chad and Demaris have agreed to seek family counseling in hopes of stabilizing their relationship and to determine if the BPD diagnosis still applies for Demaris and if so, to obtain treatment and intervention to address the behaviors that she exhibits particularly during times of stress. They have chosen to work with Janeesa N. (a licensed marriage and family therapist) as the behavioral health group she belongs to is included in their provider list through their group medical insurance benefits. Janeesa is an African American female who has been working in the group practice for 3 years after earning her master's degree.

Chad and Demaris have received intake materials to complete prior to their first appointment that include a brief family history, history of previous mental health problems and treatment(s) received along with the provider's contact information and date of last service. Additionally, they will each complete the Beck Depression Inventory-II and Beck Anxiety Inventory, the Couples Satisfaction Index, the FS³I, and the McMaster Family Assessment Device. They will also complete the "Readiness Ruler" to assess their readiness for change. Their responses to this instrument will be used during their intake session as part of a conversational approach in motivational interviewing. Demaris will also complete the Connors Adult ADHD Rating Scales (self-report) and Chad will complete the observer's rating scale. The new-patient information packet includes a disclaimer that additional assessments may be used during the course of treatment to assess targeted areas.

Interventions

Following intake and a treatment plan discussion with Chad and Demaris, the recommended treatment approach for this family includes Dialectical Behavioral Therapy for couples. This approach emphasizes reducing negative patterns of interaction and building positive coping skills and constructive interaction patterns (Fruzzetti & Fantozzi, 2008). This approach seeks to establish safety within the relationship and decrease invalidating behaviors (Fruzzetti & Fantozzi, 2008). Both Demaris and Chad would work on skills that contribute to positive interaction patterns, including emotion regulation, self-management, and appropriate expression, validation, and relationship mindfulness (Fruzzetti & Fantozzi, 2008).

Ethical and Legal Implications

Confidentiality is at the center of a sound therapeutic relationship. Beginning the counseling relationship with clear expectations around confidentiality and its limitations is especially important in the context of couples and family counseling. Demaris and Chad should be made aware through the informed consent process how the counselor will maintain confidentiality, and the situations in which confidentiality can be breached in order to prevent imminent harm to the client. Given the relational nature of couples and family work, counselors should consider how they will interact with individual family members and how previously held secrets will be handled in the course of therapy. Due to Demaris's history of making suicidal threats and the general increased risk for suicidality in clients who have been diagnosed with BPD, careful screening and assessment will need to occur to monitor suicide risk. Throughout the counseling process, informed consent should be revisited to provide clear and consistent expectations around the nature of the therapeutic relationship. It should be made clear to Demaris and Chad that any threats of self-harm will be managed through a safety plan and that the counselor will assess risk and proceed accordingly to protect the welfare of individual family members and the family system as a whole.

Clinical boundaries pose another potential ethical challenge with Demaris and Chad given Demaris's history of unrealistic therapeutic expectations. A written agreement may be included as part of the informed consent process outlining the definition of appropriate communication and contact between the counselor and the client. As part of this process, the counselor should include emergency contact information so that the couple is able to contact a provider when the counselor is not on duty.

Given the increased complexity of family systems work, particularly in the context of working with a family system in which one member has a PD diagnosis, ongoing supervision and self-care will be essential for the provider. Regular supervision of challenging clinical cases will support the counselor in providing continuity of care, prevent potential counselor burnout, and mediate the effects of any value conflicts between the client and the counselor.

DISCUSSION

As you continue to reflect on the case study and the overall approach, contemplate these questions:

- What assessment tools would you consider using with Demaris and Chad at the onset of counseling? Why would you choose these specific instruments?
- How would you organize the issues of concern for this couple? Why did you prioritize in this manner?

- What differential diagnosis considerations would you put forward and why?
- What other interventions should be considered for each of the issues of concern that you have identified? What are the therapeutic needs for each intervention that you have suggested?
- What issues from their respective family of origin do you see as manifesting in the current relationship between Chad and Demaris?

SUMMARY

Mental illness represents a significant public health concern. According to the WHO, mental illnesses represent the basis of disability more than any other group of illnesses in developed countries, including cancer and heart disease. Approximately 25% of the adult population in the United States has a mental illness and approximately 50% will develop a mental illness at some point during their lifetimes (Centers for Disease Control and Prevention [CDC], 2011). Of these people, it is anticipated that roughly 6% will develop PDs (Tyrer et al., 2010). These are sobering statistics.

The question then becomes how to best address the mental health needs in our country and throughout the world. The short answer is to conduct more research, find better evidence to drive evidence-based practices, train more clinicians and researchers, and expand basic training to include more direct experience not only in how to treat people who have disordered personalities but also in how to better identify and diagnose specific conditions so that treatment efforts can be better targeted.

Given the tools at hand, what are some next steps? From a holistic perspective, we all have a personality of some type and are in some type of relationship with every situation and every person that we encounter. As such, work related to personality and PDs affects everyone. Yet in the medical model, we focus treatment on the specific case, for example, a broken bone, a heart problem, a head injury, depression, anxiety, posttraumatic stress disorder, oppositional behaviors, and so forth. Two long-standing criticisms of the *DSM* (our primary tool for diagnosis) are that it has failed to attend to matters of relationship assessment, and an ongoing lack of agreement persists between use of the existing categorical model and the proposed alternative dimensional model.

Clinicians and psychotherapeutic researchers are caught between the diagnostic and treatment paradigm that all clients are unique and should be treated accordingly and the relatively limited body of evidence-based practice detailing specific techniques and interventions with respect to working with people who have PDs. Additional training opportunities detailing *what* knowledge is needed in the realm of PD treatment and *how* to acquire a broader knowledge of diverse treatment modalities could bring depth and breadth to services designed to meet the requirements of clients (where they are in the course of their disorder progression) and to hopefully build professional toolboxes for sustained symptom relief and behavior management. Furthermore, the field would benefit from understanding the life span impact of disordered behaviors and impaired functioning within family and external community relationships, including employability, avoiding criminal justice situations resulting from impulsive behaviors, and support for family members who live with and around disordered loved ones.

REFERENCES

American Association for Marriage and Family Therapy. (2015). *AAMFT code of ethics.* Alexandria, VA: Author. Retrieved from http://www.aamft.org/iMIS15/AAMFT/Content/Legal_Ethics/Code_of_Ethics.aspx

American Counseling Association. (2014). *ACA code of ethics*. Alexandria, VA: Author. Retrieved from http://counseling.org/docs/ethics/2014-aca-code-of-ethics.pdf?sfvrsn=4

American Psychiatric Association. (n.d.). History of the *DSM*. Retrieved from https://www.psychiatry.org/psychiatrists/practice/dsm/history-of-the-dsm

American Psychiatric Association. (1980). *Diagnostic and statistical manual of mental disorders* (3rd ed.). Washington, DC: Author.

American Psychiatric Association. (1994). *Diagnostic and statistical manual of mental disorders* (4th ed.). Washington, DC: Author.

American Psychiatric Association. (2000). *Diagnostic and statistical manual of mental disorders* (4th ed., text rev.). Washington, DC: Author.

American Psychiatric Association. (2013). *Diagnostic and statistical manual of mental disorders* (5th ed.). Arlington, VA: American Psychiatric Publishing.

American Psychiatric Association. (2016). Psychological topics: Personality (Adapted from the Encyclopedia of Psychology). Retrieved from http://www.apa.org/topics/personality

Aviram, R., Brodsky, B., & Stanley, B. (2006). Borderline personality disorder, stigma, and treatment implications. *Harvard Review of Psychiatry*, 14(5), 249–256. doi:10.1080/10673220600975121

Azibo, Daudi Ajani y. (November, 2014). The Azibo Nosology II: Epexegesis and 25th anniversary update: 55 culture-focused mental disorders suffered by African-descent people. *The Journal of Pan African Studies*, 7(5), 32–178. Retrieved from http://www.jpanafrican.org/docs/vol7no5/4-Nov-Azibo-Noso.pdf

Berghuis, H., Kamphuis, J., & Verheul, R. (2012). Core features of personality disorder: Differentiating general personality dysfunctioning from personality traits. *Journal of Personality Disorders*, 26(5), 704–716. doi:10.1521/pedi.2012.26.5.704

Brown, J. (1999). Bowen family systems theory and practice: Illustration and critique. *Australian and New Zealand Journal of Family Therapy*, 20(2), 94–103. doi:10.1002/j.1467-8438.1999.tb00363.x

Carver, J. (n.d.). Personality disorders: The controllers, abusers, manipulators, and users in relationships. Retrieved from http://drjoecarver.com/3/miscellaneous2.htm

Centers for Disease Control and Prevention. (2011, September 2). Mental illness surveillance among adults in the United States. *Morbidity and Mortality Weekly Report (MMWR)*, 60(3 Supp.), 1–32.

Clark, L. A., & Ro, E. (2014). Three-pronged assessment and diagnosis of personality disorder and its consequences: Personality functioning, pathological traits, and psychosocial disability. *Personality Disorders: Theory, Research, and Treatment*, 6(1), 55–69. doi:10.1037/per0000063

Coolidge, F., & Segal, D. (1998). Evolution of personality disorder diagnosis in the diagnostic and statistical manual of mental disorders. *Clinical Psychology Review*, 18(5), 585–599. doi:10.1016/S0272-7358(98)00002-6

Critchfield, K. L. (2012). Tailoring common treatment principles to fit individual personalities. *Journal of Personality Disorders*, 26(1), 108–125. doi:10.1521/pedi.2012.26.1.108

Critchfield, K. L., & Benjamin, L. S. (2006). Principles for psychosocial treatment of personality disorder: Summary of the APA Division 12 Task Force/NASPR review. *Journal of Clinical Psychology*, 62(6), 661–674. doi:10.1002/jclp.20255

Dickinson, W. P., deGruy, F. V., Dickinson, L. M., Mullins, H. S., Acker, S., & Gilmer, V. (1996). The family systems assessment tool. *Families, Systems, and Health*, 14(1), 57–71. doi:10.1037/h0089822

Dixon-Gordon, K. L., Turner, B. J., & Chapman, A. L. (2011). Psychotherapy for personality disorders. *International Review of Psychiatry*, 23, 282–302. doi:10.3109/09540261.2011.586992

Epstein, N., Baldwin, L., & Bishop, D. (1983). The McMaster family assessment device. *Journal of Marital and Family Therapy*, 9(2), 171–180. doi:10.1111/j.1752-0606.1983.tb01497

Erford, B. T. (2012). *Assessment for counselors* (2nd ed; Kindle Edition). Belmont, CA: Brooks/Cole, Cengage.

Family Firm Institute Practitioner. (2014, April 23). Balancing personality traits: Capitalizing on the strengths of our "true self." Retrieved from https://ffipractitioner.org/2014/04/23/balancing-personality-traits-capitalizing-on-the-strengths-of-our-true-self

Fernandez-Alvarez, H., Clarkin, J. F., Salgueiro, M. del, C., & Critchfield, K. L. (2006). Participant factors in treating personality disorders. In L. G. Castonguay & L. E. Beutler (Eds.), *Principles of therapeutic change that work* (pp. 203–218). New York, NY: Oxford University Press.

Fruzzetti, A. E., & Fantozzi, B. (2008). Couple therapy and the treatment of borderline personality and related disorders. In A. S. Gurman (Ed.), *Clinical handbook of couple therapy* (4th ed., pp. 567–589). New York, NY: Guilford Press.

Ghanbaripanah, A., & Mustaffa, S. (2012). The review of family assessment in counseling. *International Journal of Fundamental Psychology and Social Services*, 2(2), 32–35. doi:10.1016/j.sbspro.2013.10.189

Goldberg, H., & Goldberg, I. (2012). *Family therapy: An overview* (8th ed.). Belmont, CA: Brooks/Cole Cengage.

Guindon, M. H., & Giordano, F. G. (2012). Career counseling in mental health and private practice settings. In D. Capuzzi & M. Stauffer (Eds.), *Career counseling: Foundations, perspectives, and applications* (2nd ed., pp. 399–428). New York, NY: Routledge.

Haefner, J. (2014). An application of Bowen family systems theory. *Issues in Mental Health Nursing, 35*(11), 835–841. doi:10.3109/01612840.2014.921257

Hoermann, S., Zupanick, C., & Dombeck, M. (2013). The history of the psychiatric diagnostic system. Retrieved from https://www.mentalhelp.net/articles/personality-disorders

Hoermann, S., Zupanick, C., & Dombeck, M. (2015). Personality disorders. Retrieved from https://www.mentalhelp.net/articles/personality-disorders

Horne, G. (2014). Is borderline personality disorder a moral or clinical condition? *Neuroethics, 7,* 215–226. doi:10.1007/s12152-01309199.3

Kerr, M. E. (2000). One family's story: A primer on Bowen theory. Retrieved from http://www.thebowencenter.org

Kramer, U., & Levy, K. (2016). Psychotherapy for personality disorders: Questions of clinical utility. *Journal of Psychotherapy Integration, 26*(3), 338–346.

Livesley, W. J. (2012). Integrated treatment: A conceptual framework for an evidence-based approach to the treatment of personality disorder. *Journal of Personality Disorders, 26*(1), 17–42. doi:10.1521/pedi.2012.26.1.17

Magnavita, J. J., Levy, K. N., Critchfield, K. L., & Lebow, J. L. (2010). Ethical considerations in treatment of personality dysfunction: Using evidence, principles, and clinical judgement. *Professional Psychology: Research and Practice, 41*(1), 64–74. doi:10.1037/a0017733

McIntire, S. A., & Miller, L. A. (2006). *Foundations of psychological testing: A practical approach.* Thousand Oaks, CA: Sage.

Mischke-Berkey, K., & Hanson, S. (1991). Family Systems Stressor-Strength Inventory (FS³I). In K. Mischke-Berkey & S. M. H. Hanson (Eds.), *Pocket guide to family assessment and intervention* (pp. 72–83). St. Louis, MO: C. V. Mosby. doi:10.1016/0738-3991(92)90156-D

Montagu, A. (1961; published online 2006). Culture and mental illness. *American Journal of Psychiatry, 118*(1). 15–23. doi:10.1176/ajp.118.1.15

Munoz, J. P. (2007). Culturally responsive caring in occupational therapy. *Occupational Therapy International, 14*(4), 256–280. doi:10.1002/oti.238

National Center for Health Statistics. (2017). *International classification of diseases, tenth revision, clinical modification.* Retrieved from https://www.cdc.gov/nchs/icd/icd10cm.htm

Nichols, M. P. (2013). *Self in the system: Expanding the limits of family therapy.* New York, NY: Routledge.

Norton, A. (2016). *DSM-5 update for counselors and students.* Retrieved from http://www.anorton.com/DSM5ResourcePage.en.html

Parham, T. A. (2002). *Counseling persons of African descent: Raising the bar of practitioner competence.* Thousand Oaks, CA: Sage.

Paris, J. (1998). Personality disorders in sociocultural perspective. *Journal of Personality Disorders, 12*(4), 289–301. doi:10.1521/pedi.1998.12.4.289

Ratts, M. J., Singh, A. A., Nassar-McMillan, S., Butler, S. K., & McCullough, J. R. (2016). Multicultural and social justice counseling competencies: Guidelines for the counseling profession. *Journal of Multicultural Counseling and Development, 44*(1), 28–48. doi:10.1002/jmcd.12035

Remley, T., & Herlihy, B. (2007). *Ethical, legal, and professional issues in counseling* (2nd ed.). Upper Saddle River, NJ: Pearson.

Rotunda, R. J., & Doman, K. (2001). Partner enabling of substance use disorders: Critical review and future directions. *American Journal of Family Therapy, 29*(4), 257–270. doi:10.1080/01926180152588680

Schmahl, C., Elzinga, B., Ebner, U., Simms, T., Sanislow, C., Vermetten, E., . . . Bremner, J. (2004). Psychophysiological reactivity to traumatic and abandonment scripts in borderline personality and posttraumatic stress disorders: A preliminary report. *Psychiatry Research, 126*(1), 33–42. doi:10.1016/j.psychres.2004.01.005

Shiles, M. (2009). Discriminatory referrals: Uncovering a potential ethical dilemma facing practitioners. *Ethics and Behavior, 19*(2), 142–155. doi:10.1080/10508420902772777

Shorter, E. (2012, December 2). Personality disorders, the DSM, and the future of diagnosis [blog]. Retrieved from http://blog.oup.com/2012/12/personality-disorders-the-dsm-and-the-future-of-diagnosis

Skodol, A. E., Gunderson, J. G., Shea, M. T., McGlashan, T. H., Morey, L. C., Sanislow, C. A., . . . Stout, R. L. (2005). The collaborative longitudinal personality disorders study (CLPS): Overview and implications. *Journal of Personality Disorders, 19*(5), 487–504. doi:10.1521/pedi.2005.19.5.487

Smith, C. M. (2005). Origin and uses of primum non nocere—above all, do no harm! *Journal of Clinical Pharmacology, 45*(4), 371–377. doi:10.1177/0091270004273680

Sue, D. W., Arredondo, P., & McDavis, R. J. (1992). Multicultural counseling competencies and standards: A call to the profession. *Journal of Multicultural Counseling and Development, 20*(2), 64–88. doi:10.1002/j.2161-1912.1992.tb00563.x

Titelman, P. (Ed.). (2003). *Emotional cutoff: Bowen family systems theory perspectives.* Binghamton, NY: Haworth Clinical Practice Press.

Titelman, P. (Ed.). (2013). *Clinical applications of Bowen family systems theory.* New York City, NY: Routledge.

Trull, T. J., & Durrett, C. A. (2005). Categorical and dimensional models of personality. *Annual Review of Clinical Psychology, 1*, 355–380. doi:10.1146/annurev.clinpsy.1.102803.144009

Tyrer, P., Mulder, R., Crawford, M., Newton-Howes, G., Simonsen, E., Ndetei, D., . . . Barrett, B. (2010). Personality disorder: A new global perspective. *World Psychiatry, 9*(1), 56–60. doi:10.1002/j.2051–5545.2010.tb00270.x

van Wormer, K., & Besthorn, F. (2010). *Human behavior and the social environment, macro level* (2nd ed.). Oxford, UK: Oxford University Press.

Wamboldt, M., Kaslow, N., & Reiss, D. (2015). Description of relational processes: Recent changes in *DSM-5* and proposals for *ICD-11. Family Process Institute, 54*(1), 6–16. doi:10.1111/FAMP.12120

Wamboldt, M. Z., & Wamboldt, F. S. (2000). Role of the family in the onset and outcome of childhood disorders: Selected research findings. *Journal of the American Academy of Child and Adolescent Psychiatry, 39*(10), 1212–1219. doi:10.1097/00004583-200010000-00006

Westen, D. (1997). Divergences between clinical and research methods for assessing personality disorders: Implications for research and the evolution of Axis II. *Journal of Psychiatry, 154*(7), 895–903. doi:10.1176/ajp.154.7.895

World Health Organization. (2011). *International statistical classification of diseases and related health problems* (Vol. 2 Instruction Manual, 10th Rev. ed.). Geneva, Switzerland: Author.

World Health Organization Quality of Life Group. (1998). The World Health Organization Quality of Life (WHOQOL) Assessment: Development and general psychometric properties. *Social Science and Medicine, 46*(12), 1569–1585. doi:10.1016/S0277-9536(98)00009-4

SYSTEMS-FOCUSED THERAPY WITH PARAPHILIC DISORDERS

Katarzyna Peoples and Emily Meyer-Stewart

The word *paraphilia* is derived from the Greek language. The term *para* means "around or beside," and *philia* means "love." In literal terms, paraphilia means love that is outside the norm or it can be translated as "abnormal or unnatural affection" (Morrison, 2014, p. 565). Paraphilias specifically refer to sexual arousal and satisfaction other than through behaviors associated with human courtship and genitalia (American Psychiatric Association [APA], 2013b). The term first appeared in reference to early 20th-century ethnographic anthropological research that called for a less medicalized view of sexuality (Janssen, 2014).

We can thank Dr. John Money for popularizing paraphilias as he spent much of his career categorizing paraphilias in the 1970s. Before that, the term *paraphilia* was largely unfamiliar. In 1980, paraphilias made it into the *Diagnostic and Statistical Manual of Mental Disorders* (3rd ed.; *DSM-III*; APA, 1980) as official diagnoses and there have been changes along the way to these categorizations. For instance, is an atypical sexual behavior always a Paraphilic Disorder? Or can a paraphilia be a sexual orientation, like "kink" or "fetish" communities, for example? We discuss the answers to these questions in great detail throughout the chapter.

Let us first be clear that fetishes and kink are *not* the same as paraphilias or Paraphilic Disorders, as they are now termed, even though they are often used interchangeably. We differentiate among these terms in great detail later in the chapter along with giving readers guidelines for distinctive treatment approaches. Since we cite research and other literature written prior to a change in terminology, we refer to "paraphilias" and "Paraphilic Disorders" interchangeably in this chapter. However, clinicians should make the distinction in their practice with clients and refer to the current revised term *Paraphilic Disorder* when a diagnosis is indicated.

DSM-5 AND FAMILY SYSTEMS

Systems theory allows us to understand the connections that either reinforce or add to the disintegration of ourselves and our relationships. By assessing and addressing the client's family, social, and moral influences, we are able to increase our understanding of how best to move forward with a client diagnosed with a Paraphilic Disorder. There is a common thought that systems theory can be used only when working with families, and this thinking has led many counselors to put the systems approach on a shelf, in favor of individually focused theoretical counseling approaches (Smith-Acuña, 2011). Using a systems approach to diagnosing a Paraphilic Disorder, however, allows for less linear thinking and more contextual reasoning, which aides in lowering the number of false positive diagnoses for the paraphilias. Connectivity and attachment style within the family generate distinctive emotional patterns that are greater than what one person could accomplish alone (Chibucos & Leite, 2005; White & Klein, 2008; Whitechurch & Constantine, 2009). It is our belief, therefore, that addressing treatment within a family systems approach is one of the most effective ways to treat Paraphilic Disorders. Currently, we are in the age of the *Diagnostic and Statistical Manual of Mental Disorders* (5th ed.; *DSM-5*; APA, 2013a), where the term *Paraphilia* is changed to *Paraphilic Disorder*. Someone with a Paraphilic Disorder experiences significant distress and impaired functioning from personal sexual interests and sexual arousal outside of the cultural norms established by the family of origin system, current relationship system, ethnicity, or legal system. Just being embarrassed about certain sexual urges or feeling shame does not elicit a Paraphilic Disorder diagnosis. And although the *DSM-5* has opened the door for women to be diagnosed with paraphilic behaviors other than Pedophilic Disorder, almost all people diagnosed and treated for a Paraphilic Disorder are male (Garcia & Thibaut, 2011; Morrison, 2014).

Paraphilic Disorders are defined in the *DSM-5* as emotional disorders caused by sexually arousing fantasies, urges, or behaviors that are recurrent, intense, occurring over a period of at least 6 months. Such disorders cause significant distress individually or across a variety of systems, often having a negative impact on the sufferer's work, social, and/or familial system. The legal system is sometimes involved as well, causing additional problems and monetary costs.

The definition of the *disorder,* aforementioned, stands in contrast to the definition of sexual *variants*, which are nonpathological, atypical, consensual sexual behaviors, not diagnosable as mental illness. This means that although someone may engage in sexual practices outside the norm, he or she may not have a Paraphilic *Disorder* at all. For example, for many years all fetishistic and kinky behaviors were categorized as disorders. In the *DSM-III*, there was no differentiation made between pathology and orientation, meaning if someone practiced atypical sexual behavior, that person was diagnosable as mentally ill. This changed a bit with the *Diagnostic and Statistical Manual of Mental Disorders* (4th ed.; *DSM-IV*; APA, 1994) revisions that stated a paraphilia was a pathology only if it caused distress to the targeted person or sexual interest. This interpretation was still pretty faulty, however. Why? If a person acted horrified at the idea of kink play suggested by his or her partner (e.g., "Hey, let's role play—I'll dress up in your underwear and maybe you can tie me up with this scarf then slap me until I say stop. What do you think?"), the partner suggesting atypical sex play could be diagnosed with a mental illness, and worse. During contentious custody hearings, a spouse could report such atypical sexual behaviors as perverse and deviant acts, causing loss of child custody due to editions of the *DSM* that predated the current fifth edition (Wright, 2014).

Still, there is work to do in future *DSM* revisions with regard to the paraphilias. Research has historically used samples drawn from forensic populations, which is viewed by some as sampling bias (Krueger, 2010; Wollert & Cramer, 2011). Others believe that bias was not overcome during the most recent *DSM* revision of Paraphilic Disorders, citing a lack of diagnostic specifier uniformity and omission of key research in support of new diagnostic categories for sexual and gender identity disorders, as well as significant conflict regarding validity of the paraphilias included in the fifth edition (Balon, 2013; Welch, Klassen, Borisova, & Clothier, 2013). Currently, due to exclusion of a remission specifier for pedophilia, a person with this diagnosis has no hope of full recovery and experiences perpetual legal entanglements (Balon, 2014).

Those diagnosed with a Paraphilic Disorder of one type are often comorbid with another type, meaning that they often exhibit symptoms from two or more Paraphilic Disorders. It is not uncommon to have multiple paraphilic behaviors present even if they are not all diagnosable per *DSM-5* criteria (APA, 2013a; Morrison, 2014). Polyamory is also common among certain nonpathological paraphilic behaviors, with one or more identified primary partners and multiple "play" partners. In family systems parlance, such polyamorous relationships may exhibit a high level of differentiation from family of origin practices while also presenting a level of emotional fusion with multiple partners.

Gender is currently not used as a *DSM-5* diagnostic criterion for the Paraphilic Disorders; however, transvestic disorder no longer restricts the diagnosis to heterosexual men. This shift may see an increase in the number of people diagnosed with transvestic disorder as heterosexual and homosexual men and women who experience significant impairment and/or distress across life domains due to such behaviors can now be diagnosed (APA, 2013b).

Currently, with the *DSM-5* revisions, no paraphilias or kinky behaviors are now regarded as mental disorders in themselves, prompting the question, "Are we missing a large group of people who need treatment but who fear seeking treatment due to perceived or real counselor bias and stigmatization?" This question is addressed in more detail in the subsection on ethics and assessing for bias.

Historically, sexuality has been both demonized and glorified, depending on the cultural context. There has been a fluid shift between viewing uncommon, fringe, or otherwise "abnormal" sexuality as resulting from a disease state or from a place of biological variations on a theme. Viewing sexuality and sexual expression from the lens of pathology is the work of the *DSM*, and it is our work as counselors to change the lens toward normative, albeit atypical variations of sexual expression, if specific parameters for diagnosis are missing (De Block & Adriaens, 2013).

Moving from this broad overview, what, specifically, are the diagnosable Paraphilic Disorders? Are they merely a culturally defined combination of sexual preferences that are frowned upon due to social mores and norms? Is there no longer a clear-cut way of assessing for sexually deviant behaviors? Must counselors have specialized training to work with clients diagnosed with a Paraphilic Disorder? Are all paraphilias pathological? These questions are very much at the forefront of counselor education on diagnosis using the *DSM-5*.

In this chapter, we provide information on the specifics of each paraphilia listed in the *DSM-5*, with a discussion on cultural and family systems implications, assessment and intervention strategies, and legal and ethical guidelines for working with Paraphilic Disorders. We end with a case study for clinical practice in diagnostics and interventions.

Exhibitionistic Disorder

People with Exhibitionistic Disorder get sexually aroused by exposing their genitals to unsuspecting strangers. In other cases, people with this disorder have a strong desire to be observed by others during a sexual activity. Urges are acted on with nonconsenting others and people who suffer from this disorder experience significant distress and have impaired function because of their urges and impulses. In order to meet diagnostic criteria, a person must be distressed or impaired by exhibitionistic behaviors, fantasies, or urges for 6 months or more or cause harm to others. Because of these strict guidelines, many people who engage in exhibitionistic behaviors do not meet criteria for Exhibitionistic Disorder. In fact, the definition for exhibitionistic disorder differs from the definition for the general pattern of behavior of exhibitionism (Zucker, 2013).

Many people with exhibitionistic disorder may masturbate during their exposures or may fantasize about exposing themselves while masturbating. Most of these are men. They may be aware they need to shock or surprise nonconsenting observers in order for them to be sexually aroused. In most cases, the victim of exhibitionistic behavior is an adult female or a child. Exhibitionistic behaviors are often viewed as nuisance behaviors since physical harm is rare and actual sexual contact with a victim is hardly ever pursued.

People who suffer from this disorder usually start exhibiting symptoms during adolescence, but the first exhibitionistic act could occur as early as preadolescence and as late as middle age. Although most people with this disorder are married, they often have troubles in their marriage due to social problems or sexual problems.

More men than women are diagnosed with Exhibitionistic Disorder, and this may be a cultural factor. Western society, along with other cultures, accepts and encourages female exhibitionism. Hence, distress and impaired function may not be factors for many women with exhibitionistic behaviors and tendencies.

Some people with exhibitionistic tendencies want others to watch them perform sexual acts, and they prefer a consenting audience rather than surprising an unsuspecting stranger. Many people with these urges end up in the pornography industry or may make amateur pornographic videos of themselves. They do not usually have distress over their desires and so are not candidates for diagnosis.

Most exhibitionists (diagnosable or not) are married. However, their marriages are often negatively affected by poor social and sexual issues, including frequent sexual dysfunction. Couples working from a systemic perspective are encouraged to jointly take responsibility for the problems in their relationship, which decreases some of the shame associated with treating this disorder.

Frotteuristic Disorder

People who suffer from this disorder have an intense sexual arousal when they touch or rub against nonconsenting people. They may also fantasize about touching or rubbing up against others who are nonconsenting. Usually, people with frotteuristic behaviors rub against others in public settings, such as crowded places like subway systems or buses. In order for people to be diagnosed with frotteuristic disorder, they must experience significant distress or functional impairment over their urges, fantasies, or behaviors for 6 months or more.

People with this disorder are diagnosed when they rub against or touch nonconsenting individuals on three separate occasions or more. They must also exhibit distress, and they could also be diagnosed with this disorder even if they never had any physical contact with others but feel significant distress over their desires and impulses.

People with frotteuristic disorder can exhibit symptoms as early as late adolescence. They might initially rub against their friends, family members, or teachers and feel pleasurable feelings without feeling sexual arousal. This will later progress to sexual arousal, but frotteurism is often pleasurable but nonsexual in the earliest phases of this disorder.

Because the nature of this disorder is engaging with nonconsenting others, legal consequences can occur. Although many people with the disorder are breaking the law, many of these behaviors are seen as nuisance behaviors since they rarely end in physical harm or pursue more invasive sexual acts. Because frotteuristic behaviors are usually conducted in public, crowded places, nonconsenting individuals may just interpret these behaviors as accidental or annoying but not intentional. One can see how many frotteuristic acts may go unreported (Fileborn, 2013) and statistics for people with these behaviors may be grossly distorted. In addition, families and spouses may not be aware of a family member or spouse who suffers from this disorder since people engage in frotteuristic behaviors outside of the home.

Pedophilic Disorder

Pedophilic Disorder is characterized by recurring sexually arousing fantasies, urges, or behaviors that involve prepubescent children or young adolescents (usually younger than 13 years). These urges must persist for 6 months or more and are often understood as biological sexual drives (Berlin, 2011). A person with pedophilia does not have to have acted on these urges to be diagnosed. Pedophilic urges and fantasies must be impairing to the individual or greatly distressing for diagnosis to occur.

This disorder is diagnosed in people who are at least 16 years of age or older and when the child who is the target is 5 years younger than the person diagnosed. Older adolescents (e.g., ages 17 and 18) may not meet diagnostic criteria if they are involved with younger adolescents (around ages 12 or 13). That is not to say that legal issues would not arise from such a relationship.

It is important to note that legal and diagnostic criteria differ substantially with this disorder. Although a person may not meet diagnostic criteria for Pedophilic Disorder, he or she may break laws when involved with younger adolescents (i.e., statutory rape cases) and suffer legal consequences due to those behaviors. It is also important to note that the age ranges under this diagnosis are Western cultural ranges. In other cultures, sexual activity, childbearing, and even marriage are allowed and accepted at younger ages.

Most people who suffer from pedophilic disorder are males. They will be attracted to either young boys or young girls, or even both. Preference is more often toward the opposite sex than the other way around. In most cases when there is an attraction toward a child or offense toward a child, the offending person with pedophilic disorder is usually known to the child. He or she may be a teacher, family member, family friend, and so forth.

Some people with pedophilic disorder or pedophilic urges can be attracted to both children and adults at the same time, whereas others are exclusively attracted to children and have no attraction toward adults. People with pedophilia who have victimized a child are often in denial that an offense happened. In many ways, they think that they are helping the children they victimize by being close to them. Many people with pedophilia choose children whose parents seem unfit or absent in their eyes. In this way, an offending adult feels as if he or she is taking care of the victimized child. Hence, you can see how most offenders are known to the child. They are usually close to the parents as well.

Some people with pedophilic disorder may threaten their victims with violence if they disclose the abuse. Others may detach completely if the child seems as if he or she will disclose the abuse to others. Many offenders feel betrayed by this disclosure when this "special relationship" that developed between the offender and the victimized child is dissolved.

Many people with pedophilia suffer from substance use as well as depression, post-traumatic stress disorder, and anxiety. Most people diagnosed with this disorder have a history of sexual abuse themselves and may feel stuck within a certain age range, often choosing victims in the age range within which they were abused as children. The course of pedophilic disorder is chronic, and perpetrators often have or develop substance abuse or dependence and depression.

This disorder is not easily treated since legal barriers prohibit most diagnosed people who have offended from seeking treatment. Imagine if you knew that you would be arrested if you told your therapist about your problems. Would you seek help? This legal dynamic makes it particularly difficult to seek treatment within a family systems perspective. Offenders and family members may deny child sexual abuse within the home even if there is evidence to substantiate it for fear of legal repercussions. In these situations of not reporting or seeking help for the family, marriages often become toxic and children are even more traumatized.

There may be an association between viewing child pornography and hands-on sexual offenses (Bourke & Hernandez, 2009), but studies differ on this relationship between offenses (Endrass et al., 2009; Kaufman, 2014; Seto, Hanson, & Babchishin, 2011). In any case, viewing child pornography is often a reliable indicator of sexual attraction toward children, but it is also illegal. If a client disclosed this information in therapy, it would have to be reported to legal authorities since therapists are mandated reporters.

Sexual Sadism Disorder

Sexual sadism was listed under the heading of Sociopathic Personality Disturbance, subsection OOO-x63 Sexual Deviation in the *Diagnostic and Statistical Manual of Mental Disorders* (1st ed.; *DSM-1*; APA, 1952). Rape, sexual mutilation, and sexual assault were given as examples of sadistic sexuality and clinicians were encouraged to explore any underlying issues that might suggest a primary personality disorder before giving a diagnosis of sexual sadism. Revisions of the *DSM* through the fifth edition published in 2013 echo the call to consider what else may be underlying the sexually sadistic behaviors presenting in the client. The *DSM-5* goes the furthest in this consideration by suggesting that under certain consensual situations, sexual sadism is not pathological nor diagnosable.

Sexual Sadism Disorder in the *DSM-5* involves a nonconsenting other or others and/or provokes significant distress or impairment for the person who has such desires. The disorder is distinguished from atypical sexual behavior that falls under the banner of *safe, sane, and consensual* sexual kink (Connan, 2010). An important part of this distinction is the level of psychosocial and psychological distress and impairment experienced by those who admit interest and participation in sexually sadistic behaviors. If someone has the interest yet only fantasizes about such desires, and the assessment reveals no history of legal problems associated with victimization, nor intense feelings of regret and shame, Sexual Sadism Disorder is not diagnosable.

The recurrent nature (over a period of 6 months or more) and intensity of sexual arousal based on inflicting physical or psychological suffering on a nonconsenting other and causes distress of impairment warrants diagnosis of Sexual Sadism Disorder. The diagnosis can be given if there is no identified victim when such types of sexually related fantasies or urges are accompanied by clinically recognizable impairment across the domains of social, occupational, and relational functioning (APA, 2013b).

Diagnosis can include the specifier of *In a controlled environment*, wherein the person is residing in a restricted environment, such as a correctional or a residential facility. *In full remission* is also a specifier if there is no acted upon nonconsensual urges nor impairment across social and work systems, nor in other areas of functioning for a period of 5 years or more in a nonrestricted setting. It is noted in the *DSM-5* (APA, 2013a) that consensual sexually sadistic behaviors are not diagnosable per se, so attention to level of dysfunction and intensity of disturbance across system domains is important for the counselor to consider.

Differential diagnoses include other Paraphilic Disorders, certain personality disorders, substance use disorders, and bipolar and related disorders. Comorbidity is linked to those who have been convicted of criminal acts against a nonconsenting other or others and to other mental health diagnoses. Nearly all of the published research papers on sexual sadism using *DSM* criteria for diagnosis were conducted on adult incarcerated males, which may be an indicator of sampling bias for comorbidity (Krueger, 2010). The disorder is differentiated from sexual sadism *orientation*, which is seen in both males and females and first appears in mid to late adolescence.

Use of sexually explicit, sadistic pornographic literature or media may be an indicator to support the diagnosis of sexual sadism disorder, especially if the use of such materials provokes feelings of shame, guilt, or other psychological impairment for the participant.

Sexual Masochism Disorder

Sexual masochism first appeared in the 1968 edition of the *Diagnostic and Statistical Manual of Mental Disorders* (2nd ed.; *DSM-II*; APA, 1968) and was listed as a sexual deviation indicating "coitus performed under bizarre circumstances" (APA, 1968, p. 44). In the *DSM-5*, Sexual Masochism Disorder has diagnostic criteria similar to Sexual Sadism Disorder in that it is a recurrent pattern of intense sexual arousal from behaviors, fantasies, and urges lasting 6 months or longer that cause significant, clinical distress across the domains of work, social relationships, and/or other domains of importance. Although the duration of 6 months or more is typical, the diagnosis can be made if the period of time is less than 6 months if the activities are sustained during a specific period of time. Specifiers include *restriction of breathing* (asphyxiophilia), *controlled environment* (correctional, residential, or other restricted setting), and *full remission* if the client experiences no distress nor impairment across social and work systems, nor in other areas of functioning for a period of 5 years or more in a noninstitutional setting (APA, 2013b).

Sexual Masochism Disorder can also be diagnosed if the behaviors are self-inflicted, and a feature of the disorder is loss of control (Morrison, 2014). Loss of control results in self-inflicted injury and possibly accidental death, as is some cases of autoerotic asphyxiation. Loss of control helps differentiate the *disorder* from the *orientation* in that consensual sadomasochism makes use of words or a word that signals the activity must stop, thereby allowing for control of the duration and intensity of pain received by establishing clearly defined and respected limits (Connan, 2010; Gross, 2006).

The person with sexual masochism disorder achieves arousal from receiving physical and/or psychological practices such as bondage, pain infliction, suffocation, and humiliation rather than inflicting pain, as is the case for sexual sadism disorder. Through the circular process of inflicting or receiving pain, sadism and masochism form a symbiotic role relationship, calling to mind a structural system of behavior wherein one person's behavior directly affects and is grounded in another's behavior so that the system's task is accomplished. It is noted that not all sexually masochistic behaviors are diagnosable so attention to intensity of impairment across system domains is critical for consideration.

Differential diagnoses include other Paraphilic Disorders, substance abuse disorders, and personality disorders, which may also appear as comorbid diagnoses. Age of onset of problematic symptoms is late adolescence. Use of explicit pornographic literature or media portraying acts of humiliation and suffering supports the diagnosis of sexual masochism disorder.

Transvestic Disorder

Transvestism, also referred to as "cross-dressing," has a long history of representation by both men and women across time. Think Joan of Arc. Think Shakespearian actors. Today, transvestism is more or less accepted, depending on geographical location, religious persuasion, and cultural norms, and it may or may not be used for sexual arousal purposes.

Cross-dressing is distinguished from transvestic disorder by way of the disorder's focus on cross-dressing for sexual arousal and by the level of clinically significant impairment and distress across social, occupational, and relationship systems as a result of the behavior. Recurrent, intense sexual arousal that is driven by cross-dressing behaviors, urges, and/or fantasies occurring over the course of 6 months or more is diagnosable as transvestic disorder.

Specifiers include sexual arousal due to certain fabrics or clothing type, such as silk or women's lingerie (*with fetishism*) and sexual arousal at the thought of oneself as female (*with autogynephilia*). A further specifier, *In a Controlled Environment*, can be used when cross-dressing occurs while residing in a restricted setting (i.e., correctional facility, psychiatric hospital, or residential clinic). Systemic clinicians may also use the specifier *In full remission* if symptoms and distress abate for 5 or more years (APA, 2013a).

Heterosexual males are more likely to be diagnosed with transvestic disorder, although a change in wording in the *DSM-5* opens the door of diagnosis to homosexual men and heterosexual and lesbian women (APA, 2013a). Significant distress can result especially for heterosexual married men who often experience marital problems due to the partner's expressed fears, shame, confusion, and judgment of the behavior. A 2011 case study of the personal stories of cross-dressers and their spouses revealed a poignant aspect to the secrecy, relationship impact, and spousal tolerance that surrounds this socially questionable behavior (Hill, 2011).

Often, cross-dressing appears first in childhood, and by puberty males may ejaculate while wearing or fantasizing about wearing women's clothing. Adolescent males and young adults are more likely to present with sexual experiences when cross-dressing, through masturbation or other penile stimulation. Conflict ensues when socially normative heterosexual experiences, such as a desire for marriage, interferes with the ability or willingness to cross-dress. Increased distress is the result and it is at this time that a counselor may first encounter transvestic males. Abatement in cross-dressing behaviors usually proves temporary and is likely to return with time, coupled with secrecy and the likelihood of shame. Intensity of distress surrounding the behavior increases, with noticeable, recurrent patterns of throwing away and then repurchasing women's clothing. Such buy and purge behaviors indicate a potential diagnosis (APA, 2013b).

With age, males experience less or no sexual release as a result of cross-dressing while at the same time experiencing an increase in feelings of well-being while cross-dressing, and lowered levels of distress and impairment across domains. When the level of distress or impairment at cross-dressing is lowered to this degree for a period of 5 or more years, in a noninstitutional environment, full remission is the diagnostic specifier.

Differential diagnosis includes fetishistic disorder and gender dysphoria, and comorbidity is high for other paraphilic behaviors, and especially so for masochistic disorder and fetishistic disorder.

Fetishistic Disorder

In the original Portuguese, *fetish* referred to a magical charm or idol and its use today refers to sexual activity involving an inanimate object or objects for the purpose of sexual arousal (Morrison, 2014). Normative sexual objects, such as dildos and vibrators, are not considered fetish items, but body parts (or missing body parts in some cases) can be. Ears, feet, toes, hair, and arousal at the thought of sex with an amputee all qualify as fetish activity, as well as all other nongenital body parts and the plethora of fetish objects used for sexual arousal and stimulation: shoes, dirty socks, leather, rubber, and silk items, to name a few.

A preference for fetish objects during sexual arousal does not constitute a disorder, however. Similar to all other Paraphilic Disorders, Fetishistic Disorder is present only when, over a period of 6 months or more, a client experiences intense sexual arousal from behaviors, fantasies, and urges due to the use or thoughts of use of fetish items not normative to genital sexual activity, *and* such thoughts and behaviors cause clinically identifiable distress across the domains of social, work, and relationship functioning, *and* the fetish items are not related to cross-dressing or a comorbid diagnosis of transvestism (ACA, 2013).

Research suggests use of fetish items is a way to control sexual behaviors and alleviate internalized anxiety, in that there is predictability in responsiveness to an object, which is questionable with a living sexual partner (Bhugra, Popelyuk, & McMullen, 2010).

Specifiers include body parts (Partialism), nonliving objects, and "other" objects. Environment is also a specifier if the behaviors are absent due to an institutional, controlled environment (e.g., jail, rehab). Full remission is the specifier if, over the period of 5 years or more, the client experiences no distress across domains while living in an uncontrolled environment (home). Comorbidity is high for all other paraphilic behaviors, and males far outnumber women when meeting diagnostic criteria.

Support for a diagnosis can include sexual arousal due to touching, holding, tasting, inserting, smelling or otherwise interacting with the fetish item while masturbating and such activity is persistent across time, often starting in puberty. It is not unusual for those with a fetishistic disorder to have vast collections of items used for sexual arousal and stimulation, other than those typically associated with sadism or masochistic sexual behaviors (e.g., belts, whips, blindfolds) and assessment for such a collection supports the diagnosis. As with all of the Paraphilic Disorders, cultural considerations of the client must be considered during the diagnostic process.

In addition, consideration of how the relationship system is affected by fetishism is important, especially with regard to where, when, and with whom such behaviors are practiced. If the couple is in a polyamorous relationship, for example, rules for engaging in fetishism are likely spelled out and a part of the poly agreement. If, however, fetishism is practiced outside of a monogamous relationship without the knowledge of the spouse or partner, such behaviors are likely to cause significant disruptions to the relationship system, with the possible outcome of divorce, separation, or loss of child custody.

Voyeuristic Disorder

People who suffer from voyeuristic disorder have a desire to spy on nonconsenting people during their private activities. Their urges, fantasies, and behaviors bring them significant distress or impaired functioning for a period of 6 months or more. Usually, voyeuristic individuals get sexually aroused by looking at people undressing or being naked as well as watching them during sexual acts. In most cases, people with this disorder are aware that they are looking at a nonconsenting individual and will not ask for consent to spy on the targeted individual.

Since people with voyeuristic disorder engage in behaviors that are essentially anonymous, diagnosis can be difficult in terms of assessment. Self-report is typically the mode of diagnosis, and the most common symptoms of this disorder are experiencing strong sexual urges or fantasies from watching another person naked with or without consent. Just like in other paraphilias, tendencies do not equal diagnosis. People with this disorder must suffer from significant distress or hindrance to normal functioning because of their voyeuristic tendencies (for 6 months or more), and this is not the case for all people who engage in voyeurism.

People who do not disclose their voyeuristic behavior after being caught spying on nonconsenting individuals usually say that those engagements are accidental or not sexual in nature. According to *DSM-5*, these people (who fail to disclose behaviors and deny having sexual fantasies or continual sexual interest in voyeuristic behaviors) deny feeling of stress and/or social impairment. Interestingly enough, because of this denial, they can be diagnosed with having voyeuristic disorder.

Having a desire to watch others engaging in sexual situations can actually be quite common and not abnormal (Rye & Meaney, 2007). Voyeurism usually starts during the adolescent years or even in early adulthood. When adolescents are caught for voyeuristic behaviors, they are not often arrested since the legal system is pretty lenient with adolescent voyeurs.

Voyeurism becomes pathological when individuals spend a great amount of their time seeking opportunities to spy on nonconsenting individuals involved in private acts. Impairment is evident within voyeuristic disorder since many diagnosable individuals will neglect their responsibilities to seek out voyeuristic opportunities. On many occasions, voyeuristic individuals will masturbate to orgasm during a spy session. However, in most cases, people with voyeuristic disorder will not seek sexual contact with the people they observe. Families and spouses are often not aware of a person's voyeuristic tendencies when someone has a voyeuristic disorder since behaviors are often engaged in outside of the home.

Other Specified Paraphilic Disorder

Clinically recognizable distress across social, work, and relationship system domains due to sexual fantasies, urges, and/or behaviors that are not addressed in the identified diagnostic categories for Paraphilic Disorders fit this diagnostic code. This code includes specifiers for sexual arousal and behaviors that cause significant distress due to thoughts, urges, and sexual activities with animals (zoophilia), corpses (necrophilia), anonymous sexual phone calls (telephone scatologia), body fluids (urophilia, known collectively as "water sports"), enemas (klismaphilia), rape scenarios (paraphilic coercive disorder), feces (urophilia), and sexual satisfaction from dressing in diapers or being treated as a baby (infantilism; ACA, 2013). This list is not exhaustive, since sexual expression comes in various culturally and socially adaptive forms. Such behaviors have high comorbidity with all other Paraphilic Disorders. Include specifiers for environment (institutional settings) and remission (5 or more years of nonsymptomatic sexual behaviors while out of an institutional setting).

Unspecified Paraphilic Disorder

Because of the complexities of human sexual behaviors, it is sometimes difficult to diagnosis a Paraphilic Disorder. Systemic clinicians may encounter clients who present with atypical sexuality and sexual behaviors that are causing significant distress across the domains of social, work, and/or relationship functioning, yet the behaviors do not meet the specifications for diagnosis as outlined in the *DSM-5*. When a counselor is unable to determine if a specific Paraphilic Disorder exists, yet the client is experiencing clinically significant impairment due to atypical sexual fantasies, urges, and/or behaviors, a diagnostic code of F65.9 is applicable.

When in doubt about diagnosing a paraphilia, consider a session wherein the behaviors can be openly discussed with the spouse, partner, or the sexually invested other so that collateral information can be collected for a more specific qualifier, and to rule out differential diagnoses as primary. A discussion of each partner's understanding of what it means to be sexually intimate may reveal differences in perceptions and definitions that can then be worked on during ongoing couple's sessions. A shared perception of what defines sexual intimacy and the recognition that "sexual intimacy is consensual," (Birnie-Porter & Lydon, 2013), may lead to renewed investment in the relationship and clarity for the system.

Remember that the family or relationship system that functions in or around paraphilic behaviors can be a supportive base for treatment options or may serve as a contributing factor in paraphilic behavior morphing into a Paraphilic Disorder (see case study example at the end of this chapter for distinguishing differences). Because all family members bear responsibility for systems dynamics, it is important to consider how each person contributes to maintaining the status quo, whether through silence, denial, or full awareness of ongoing paraphilic behaviors and what this means to systemic function and dysfunction (Hentsch-Cowles & Brock, 2013).

RELATIONAL AND CULTURAL FEATURES

Turning from the particulars of diagnostic criteria for the Paraphilic Disorders, we now draw your attention to relational and cultural factors that have an impact on the etiology of the disorder. We start with a brief discussion of the research on neurological and biological factors of interest.

Etiological understanding of the paraphilias is still limited and continued research is needed on nonforensic populations and women, who present with paraphilic behavior significantly less than men (Garcia & Thibaut, 2011). There is commonality in the neurological responses of those with chemical addiction and in those with intense sexual arousal: the involvement of the pleasure–reward pathway (mesolimbic dopamine system corridor; Keane, 2004). Once the pleasure pathway becomes involved in a behavior, the likelihood of a person returning to that behavior is increased and, over time, pleasure-seeking behaviors are escalated, amped up so to speak, to compensate for a decrease in the release of dopamine that results over time. Repetitive paraphilic behaviors usually start in adolescence and histories of paraphilic clients bear out the idea that the search for increasingly more intense sexual arousal and release is part of the dynamic of such behaviors. This progression is led by a simple concept: the anticipatory incentive of a pleasure payoff (Berner & Briken, 2012).

Rahman and Symeonides (2008) looked at the impact of fraternal birth order and non-right handedness on the likelihood of paraphilic behavior choices. Although these factors seem somewhat disparate with regard to paraphilias, the researchers demonstrated statistical significance between non-right handedness, number of older male siblings, and increased paraphilic sexual interests in their sample of 200 nonincarcerated males.

What does such seemingly disconnected research mean for counselors diagnosing Paraphilic Disorders using a systems approach? Simply that the paraphilias are, indeed, complex diagnostic categories, rich with potential for misunderstanding if we look only at biological and neurological factors in the etiology of the conditions. Hence, our next focus is the impact of relationships and culture on the development of paraphilic behaviors. You will quickly find that questions arise that call for an introspective counseling stance.

Although family upbringing, attachment style, and historical context all have an impact on the way sexuality is expressed, culture is by far one of the most influential factors in determining whether a certain behavior is pathological. Human sexuality is, in all cases, a part of social life, and all social life is governed by norms, inferred rules of behavior, and status quo. The rules in societies differ in terms of sexuality. What is consent? What is homosexuality? What are gender roles? What is premarital sex? All of these questions can be answered differently depending on the culture of the group you might be asking. Dictated laws about sexual behaviors also differ across cultures. Age of consent is one particular law that grossly differs depending on the country one might visit and can even differ within a country. In the United States, for example, the age of consent ranges from 16 to 18, depending on which state or district (Washington, DC's age of consent is 16 years old). This is important information when determining whether a behavior is problematic (i.e., pathological) or merely a preference.

The Role of Family

Children learn about sexuality through observation of sex roles and by direct teaching from their primary caregivers, media, and peer relationships. The family system, however, has the largest impact on how individuals express their sexuality and sexual behaviors as they grow through adolescence and into adulthood. Families differ tremendously in terms of how they express and deal with sexuality and sexuality is especially affected by religious views, geography, and historical context. Think about your own family and upbringing. Were you raised in an era known for its sexually liberal views or sexually conservative views (e.g., 1950s America versus 1970s America)? Were sexual messages based on religious beliefs as normed by the state or world region where your parents lived or where you were raised? What were your family's views on homosexuality? What about birth control? What did your family think about premarital sex? What about cohabitation or polyamory? Was nudity acceptable in your household? What did your family teach you about the purpose of sex? Was this an acceptable practice in your family's value system? Were there instances when males/females or older/younger children were treated differently? How do you think your experiences have shaped you today? If you interviewed three other people and asked them the same questions, you would most likely get completely different answers. In this way, you might be better able to see how differently "normal" is viewed in terms of sexual behavior just from family upbringing.

Assessing a client's family of origin views on sexuality is not a routine practice for many counselors, but it should be. When family background and systemic contexts are ignored, problems due to family upbringing (e.g., parent–child problems, sibling rivalry, other parent–child problems, other specified problems related to upbringing) can often be missed by counselors. Therein, counselors can quickly also miss opportunities to fully understand their clients.

The Role of Culture

Let us now expand our conversation of differing sexual norms to social cultures, niche group cultures, religious cultures, county, state, country cultures, and so forth. A sexual behavior that is accepted in one group may be shunned in another. From microculture to macroculture, sexual norms change along with laws and ethical guidelines. Is exhibitionism pathological? It can be, as it is dependent on gender and context in our Western culture. Exhibitionistic women do not often have problems in our culture when they sexually expose various body parts in dance clubs. Men might be arrested if they acted in similar exhibitionistic ways. What about pedophilia? Isn't that always pathological? Not necessarily, since cultural context greatly influences such things as age of consent. Remember that the age of sexual consent ranges from 16 to 18 in the United States, and it is as low as 12 in India and Mexico (Anagol, 2016; UNICEF, 2016).

Transvestism is also a matter of cultural and historical interpretation. Women dress in men's clothing routinely in Western culture without a problem and cross-dressing "ladyboys" are common in Tokyo, taking on various roles in society such as entertainers, tribe leaders, shamans, and models. Many traditional Native American societies respected and valued androgynous cross-dressers, referred to as Two-Spirits. They were viewed as spiritual members of the society, often interchanging male and female roles, sexual practices, and clothing. Early European settlers and religious orders were quick to condemn, demonize, and "convert" Two-Spirits, who often resorted to suicide as a result (Williams, 2016). Whether accepted, revered, outcast, or feared, it is clear that geography and culture played a large part in shaping historical and current views on transvestism.

With all of the varying cultural factors contributing to our understanding, one can easily get confused on how to assess for pathology in an effective way. Although some countries may have clearly defined cultural parameters, helping clients in our Western culture presents more challenges. The United States has long been known as the "melting pot," accepting a wide range of people from various cultural backgrounds, races, and religions, and counselors are ethically mandated to consider cultural and relational norms when determining if a client has a problem with a paraphilic behavior. Although some rules about sexual problematic behavior are clear in our society, like laws surrounding child endangerment, others are a bit more murky. Hence, assessment of a paraphilic "disorder" is often complicated, changing from one situation to the next, requiring careful consideration of multiple factors and systems.

FAMILY SYSTEMS ASSESSMENTS

Since its first appearance in 1952, the *DSM* has shifted to meet changes in cultural normative behaviors that are now considered preferential rather than pathological. The removal of homosexuality as a mental disorder from the *DSM* in 1973 is the best example of this shift toward acceptance of a new cultural norm for sexuality. Such a shift has allowed for increased family understanding and support of a behavior that was, until very recently, considered a sexually deviant perversion. Moral, social, and familial definitions of sexuality continue to evolve, and use of a systemic approach creating a connective thread throughout the various systems involved in the diagnosis of a Paraphilic Disorder is helpful (see Figure 19.1).

It is clear that the initial assessment is of utmost importance in establishing the level of social functioning and emotional distress of clients who present with paraphilic behaviors. The overriding rule of thumb in defining whether pathology is present is "hostility and the incapacity for consensual sexuality" (Berner & Briken, 2012, p. 130).

Assessing whether an individual has a *Paraphilic Disorder* versus a *sexual lifestyle* or *orientation* can present some challenges for counselors. Yes, guidelines in the *DSM-5* tell us that impairment and distress are key factors, but how can a counselor identify "distress" for a client? What about a client denying having a problem? Many people who suffer from Paraphilic Disorders will not seek help, and if they do, they are often referred for treatment involuntarily. They may be referred through the legal system, through the school system, or because of a troubled marriage on the brink of divorce or custody disputes. When such individuals enter treatment, they may try to present their sexual behaviors as

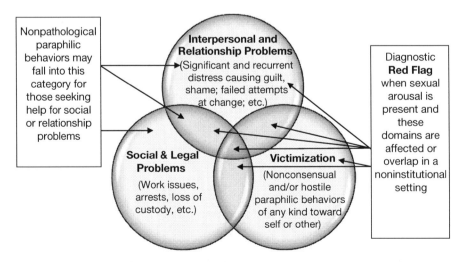

FIGURE 19.1 Systemic view of paraphilias and diagnosis potential.
Source: Figure created by Emily Meyer-Stewart.

acceptable and orthodox for various reasons—denial, shame, ignorance, and fear of stigmatization or legal repercussions are just a few reasons for a client's inaccurate testimonials. Even when counselors get the entire truth from clients, there are still some significant challenges in making a diagnosis. Some questions for the counselor to keep in mind during assessments are: Is what I'm hearing a Paraphilic Disorder or a paraphilic lifestyle choice since the client is accepting of the sexual behavior? Is the client's relationship or marriage in trouble because of paraphilic sexual behaviors? Have I taken a look at how the client's personal values, culture, and religious beliefs are at play (Kleinplatz & Moser, 2004)?

One very clear-cut diagnostic red flag for diagnosis is victimization of self and/or others. If, for example, a client with an attraction toward children is arrested for child pornography, the diagnosis is clearly made (pedophilic disorder) due to the illegal nature of the behavior, and treatment can begin with a well-defined treatment plan: avoid any sexual behaviors involving children.

Now consider sexual sadism and sexual masochism as diagnoses. If a client routinely engages in consensual sexual bondage behaviors with his or her spouse, is it pathological? What about if that client widows and later marries a spouse who does not want to engage in bondage sexual play? Does the client's need or desire to engage in bondage become pathological? What if the marriage suffers because of the client's sexual preferences? Does a paraphilia then become pathological? As a counselor, you can see how "distress" can change as life dynamics change, and it can be very confusing to pinpoint problematic behavior. After all, who has the problem in such a scenario, the client who wants to engage in bondage sexual play or the spouse who may have rigid sexual boundaries? Either spouse might have the problem depending on relational and cultural norms.

In addition to having confusion over who might have the problem, a counselor may wonder what the best treatment intervention might be. Should the client work on ceasing bondage behaviors or should the spouse work on incorporating bondage into their sex life? What does the couple want, and what if they want different things? How does a counselor decide where to draw the line between what is acceptable sexual behavior and pathological conduct? In our experience of working with clients who engage in paraphilic activities, determination of pathology is made by asking two simple questions: "Is there consent?" and "Is there a victim?"

Is There Consent?

Consent is defined as permission for something to happen or agreement to do something (Merriam-Webster, 2016). When counselors work with clients who are engaging in paraphilic activities, the first thing that should be asked when determining if behaviors are pathological is whether the sexual target has given consent. If no consent was given by the person who is the sexual interest, the client's sexual behavior can be assessed as problematic and opens the door to diagnosis. Age of consent, of course, is also a factor here. In Western society, a child cannot give consent under a certain age.

Is There a Victim?

A victim is someone who is harmed, injured, or killed as a result of a crime, accident, or other event or action (Merriam-Webster, 2014). Is there a victim of a client's sexual behaviors? If there is, the paraphilia is pathological. Just to be clear, "victim" can also include the person with the paraphilia. If a person is in great distress because of having a paraphilia and cannot perform basic duties at work and/or if the sexual activity caused significant personal harm to the person, then he or she is a victim of the Paraphilic Disorder. Significant harm can result, for example, during autoerotic asphyxiation or when objects inserted into or used upon one's own sexual organs cause physical damage needing medical attention and/or repair. As a result, the emergency room may be the first place that a spouse or invested sexual partner discovers his or her partner is practicing paraphilic behaviors since use of certain fetish and sadomasochistic sexual practices can lead to physical harm or even death due to asphyxiation. Hospital staff assigned to such admissions would do well to consider referring these patients to a practitioner familiar with family systems assessments and cognitive behavioral treatment modalities that can identify and modify sexual practices that are harmful physically and psychologically (Gladding, 2015).

Assessment Tools

A variety of assessment tools are available in helping the counselor understand a client's attitudes regarding sexuality and sexual expression. When determining if a paraphilic behavior is a disorder or merely atypical sexual behavior, such assessments can provide additional insight and treatment direction for the counselor. Use of the Adult Attachment Interview (George, Kaplan, & Main, 1996) provides an excellent starting point in assessing family constellations and will identify attachment style. This information will help the counselor support the client through transformative change, as the counselor becomes the secure base from which the client can explore experiences and learn how to tolerate, assess, and communicate difficult feelings related to those experiences (Wallin, 2007).

An additional tool is the BARE: the *Brief Accessibility, Responsiveness, and Engagement* Scale (Sandberg, Busby, Johnson, & Yoshida, 2012) that measures attachment behaviors in couples, focusing on "a systemic perspective on relationship functioning" (2012, p. 524). Knowing how each individual in the relationship perceives partner accessibility, responsiveness, and engagement can allow for increased communication and understanding about these and other attachment issues that are reflected in the family or relationship system. In addition to the Adult Attachment Interview, we suggest the following assessment tools that deal specifically with sexuality. This is by no means an exhaustive list of all psychosexual assessment tools, but a few we selected to give you an overview of what is possible to assess with an instrument. Use of these individual assessments for increased understanding of relationship and systemic functioning is helpful for the individual seeking treatment, for treatment planning, and as aides to rule out or corroborate differential diagnosis.

Attitudes to Sex Questionnaire

A Likert-scaled tool to measure such items as personal willpower, belief in God, intelligence, and a general belief in ability to overcoming problems related to fetishism, pedophilia, sexual sadism, and voyeurism (Twohig & Furnham, 1998). Couples can gain insight and understanding into the sexual wants and desires of their partner, based on a broad range of predecessors, such as moral beliefs and upbringing. Sharing the results in an emotionally safe couple's counseling session can be beneficial.

Multiple Paraphilic Interests Scale

A rating scale tool to measure paraphilic interest and criminality. This is a lengthy multi-itemed scale entailing 96 pages, capturing specific behavioral information across various domains and time (Smallbone & Wortley, 2004). This scale is best used with an individual since the information may cause the counselor to take on the role of mandated reporter, in the case of known and identified victims who may be revealed. This assessment tool is an aide in understanding the generational attitudes and family of origin–learned patterns of dysfunction, since it works back through time to childhood and considers trauma, violence, and sexual abuse to which the client may have been exposed or have been a victim.

Paraphilias Scale

A Likert-scaled tool to measure sexual arousal, attitude, and occasion of thoughts involving paraphilic behaviors (Seto, Lalumiere, Harris, & Chivers, 2012). Because the disclosure of thoughts about sexual violence can be disruptive to the couple's relationship, and since the thoughts are not determinate of behavior, it is best to use this tool with the identified client and for the purpose of gaining clinical insight and awareness into the level of dysfunction resulting from the paraphilic behavior.

Sexual Behaviors and Desires Measure

A scaled measurement tool for assessing willingness to participate in various sexual activities, including paraphilic behaviors (Reese-Weber & McBride, 2015). Couples who may be searching for ways to develop sexual intimacy through atypical sexual behaviors would benefit from taking this assessment and sharing the results in a counseling session. This is also a way to assess if the relationship system can tolerate atypical sexual behaviors or if the behaviors are considered too disruptive to the system.

Assessing the Impact of Paraphilic Disorders on the Family

Now that we have determined how to assess whether a paraphilia is a problem, let us move forward in assessing Paraphilic Disorders through a family systems perspective. Many characteristics must be considered within the family systems lens to assess a pathology: (a) Assessing Paraphilia as a Pathology or a Lifestyle; (b) Assessing How Behavior Has an Impact on the Sexual Relationship; and (c) Assessing How Family Is Affected by Paraphilic Behaviors. In using a systems lens for diagnosis and in treatment, the entire family system is reviewed so that the influence of and emotional problems generated in partners and spouses are addressed (Hentsch-Cowles & Brock, 2013).

We address each of these general assessment guidelines in detail so that we can highlight the family systems assessment approach. It is assumed that a clinician would also complete a detailed formal assessment of the family, including a detailed sexual history of all sexual behaviors from childhood to present day.

Assessing Paraphilic Disorders as a Pathology or a Lifestyle

When a person is distressed over his or her partner because he or she likes to engage in sexual paraphilic behavior, it can be difficult to assess whether the paraphilic urges of said partner are pathological. How can a clinician assess this within a family systems lens? After all, we are taking the entire family into account so what is a pathology and what is lifestyle that might need to be worked out?

Previously, we addressed the two questions a counselor needs to ask in order to determine whether he or she is dealing with a pathology or a lifestyle choice: "Is there a victim?" and "Is there consent?" Although these two questions are the core of determining pathology, it is important to note that they may not always determine a specific paraphilia. For example, a father who molests his young daughter absolutely qualifies for a pathological label, needs treatment, and can suffer legal consequences. However, he may not meet criteria for pedophilic disorder since he may not have recurring sexually arousing fantasies, urges, or behaviors involving prepubescent children for 6 months or more. Regardless, family treatment needs to occur for all family members because of the molestation that occurred. Treatment may vary depending on whether a person has molested a child or if a person has pedophilic disorder and has molested a child, but pathology exists in either situation.

For the sake of the rest of this discussion, we assume that a paraphilia exists within a family dynamic in order to illustrate how to assess appropriately. What a clinician needs to correctly determine is whether a paraphilia is a disorder (i.e., pathology) or an orientation (or lifestyle choice). To that end, use of a narrative approach to collecting information from each person in the system is beneficial for the clinician as well to those present in session as it allows for increased understanding and insight about family of origin influences on sexuality and current levels of function and dysfunction due to these factors (Smith-Acuña, 2011).

Assessing Consent

Assessing whether there is consent involved with a Paraphilic Disorder is straightforward. If a sexual interest or target did not give consent to the sexual behavior being exhibited, pathology exists. This rule applies to all nonconsensual sexual behaviors, from coercive behaviors such as sexually violating children to nuisance behaviors such as rubbing up against people in subway systems. If a husband acts on a sexual urge with his wife in the bedroom, and the wife does not consent to the behavior, but the husband sexually acts out anyway, it is a confirmation that the husband has a pathology.

Assessing Victimization

Determining a victim can be more difficult at times, but a simple way of assessing victimization is to determine whether *anyone is* harmed by the sexual behavior, including the person with the paraphilia. For example, if a person is downloading bondage images at work because he or she has a compulsion to do this and cannot wait to go online within more appropriate environments, like home, there are plenty of victims. The person with the paraphilia may lose a job. The family may suffer financially because of the job loss. One can even argue that the person's boss is victimized, paying an employee for a job not done. Another victim scenario is if a person with a paraphilia cannot enjoy sex with another person in any other way except engaging in a certain paraphilic activity. In such a scenario, there are victims—the person with the paraphilia and the sexual partner if one exists at that time.

If both questions of consent and victimhood are met with a resounding "no," a clinician can, in most cases, safely assume that the paraphilia is not a pathology. Many people who are into kink or fetishistic behaviors enjoy these behaviors within a functional sexual relationship and utilize these behaviors as a way of connecting with their sexual partners. For many people, kinky sexual play is just another form of intimacy and enjoyed with no problem to the relationship. But what if a paraphilia is not pathological but is definitely a problem in a sexual relationship? Now that is a common problem that necessitates further discussion. Let us move forward to that.

Assessing How Behavior Has an Impact on the Sexual Relationship

After asking the two pathology questions of consent and victimization, a clinician will know whether a paraphilia is a disorder or a lifestyle choice. Depending on the assessment, treatment will differ drastically. If a paraphilia is assessed as a disorder, a client should meet the criteria within the *DSM-5* guidelines and treatment can begin helping the client change or avoid destructive patterns. If any sexual behavior involving a child is discovered, a clinician, of course, needs to report that information to the proper authorities under mandated reporter requirements. In most cases, the state will take over the treatment process with state-approved clinicians to treat individuals who have sexually offended against a child or have been involved with any sexual activity involving children.

But what if a clinician has determined that the paraphilia is *not* a disorder but a life-style choice *and* the sexual partner is distressed by that lifestyle choice? In essence, the marriage suffers because the sex life suffers. Partner A wants to get a little kinky in the bedroom to spice things up after a few years in marriage and Partner B is disgusted by Partner A's sexual desires. Partner B says "no way, no how." Partner A feels rejected, frustrated, and resentful. The marriage suffers because of the emotional backlash from the sexual decision Partner B made for both partners. In such a situation, it is safe to conclude that Partner A's paraphilia is not pathological, but the sexual relationship is certainly suffering because of the paraphilia. To complicate things even more, once sexual preferences are acquired, they are really challenging to alter. In essence, after some time of repeating certain behaviors, individuals solidify their preferences into a sexual template of sorts (Carnes, 2010). This can create a big problem when a couple cannot or will not work together to merge differing sexual preferences. In certain terms, the couple is suffering from sexual incompatibility, and a family systems lens is most effective for assessing this problematic situation.

In systems theory, family members are understood to relate to one another through interdependence patterns and those relations affect other members (Chibucos & Leite, 2005). Hence, one person influences the other person and as one person acts, another person is affected by those actions (Whitechurch & Constantine, 2009). In marriage, one partner's decision about the relationship is always a decision for both. For example, if a wife does not want to have sex with her husband, she is making the decision for both of them to not have sex. By looking at this undeniable series of actions and reactions, one can see why family systems approaches are so effective in assessing paraphilias.

Although many problems with paraphilic tendencies start in the bedroom, they most often stem out to other parts of the family system. In the example stated previously, Partner A and B's sexual incompatibility did not only affect their sex life. Resentment developed in Partner A because of Partner B's rigid stance against engaging in any kinky sexual play. Now the problem is emotional, and that touches everything in Partner A's and B's lives, including the family system.

Assessing How Family Is affected by Paraphilic Behaviors

In family systems theory, it is understood that all members of a family take full responsibility for what is going on in the relationship (Collins & Collins, 2012), which is very different from the victim-perpetrator model that restricts recovery when dealing with sexual issues (Shursen, Brock, & Jennings, 2008). In a recent study, researchers used genograms to map paraphilias, and their selected families contained clusters of paraphilias within their family systems. Many individuals carry unresolved issues from their childhoods, and therefore, problematic sexual behaviors and patterns are commonly traced across generations of families (Brown, 2001). This demonstrates that families do, in fact, share symptoms, confirming that a family systems lens is most appropriate for assessing paraphilias.

All family members learn to cope with problematic sexual problems in their own ways as they come up. Unfortunately, their coping mechanisms are often dysfunctional (Carnes, 1989.) Many families have periods of time when they may be dysfunctional because of stressful circumstances or traumas. For example, a death in the family may elicit some dysfunctional coping mechanisms. However, after a time, healthy families usually return to a functional state after the trauma or crisis passes.

Dysfunctional families have problems that are ongoing and chronic. Children do not get their needs met appropriately, and negative parental patterns are common. When assessing the impact of paraphilic behaviors on the family, a counselor needs to understand the difference between function and dysfunction in a family unit. After all, many families are unique and not all family units have the same messages around sexual norms. Although a family may be more open sexually, it may function in a healthy way. Another family that is more rigid may function healthfully as well. Therefore, it is not productive to focus solely on sexual behaviors when assessing the impact paraphilic behavior may have on the family. The focus needs to be more global. The question to be answered is, "Is this a healthy and functional family unit?"

Function Versus Dysfunction

Attachment theory, first understood through the 40-year collaborative work of John Bowlby and Mary Ainsworth, plays an important role in understanding how family connectedness or disconnectedness affects relationship and intimacy function or dysfunction across the life span. Researchers have considered this impact and the conclusions drawn are not surprising: attachment style is related to psychological adjustment in all areas of functioning, including sexual behaviors (Bogaert & Sadava, 2002; Conde, Figueiredo, & Bifulco, 2011; Péloquin, Bigras, Brassard, & Godbout, 2014).

In addition, anxiously or avoidantly attached adults are negatively affected in the areas of dysfunctional relationship beliefs (Kilmann, Finch, Parnell, & Downer, 2013), commitment struggles (Coy & Miller, 2014), and couple bonding (Sandberg et al., 2012). As may be expected when one thinks about the implications of avoidant attachment styles, each of these studies supported a related hypothesis around negative intimacy outcomes and avoidant attachment. Insecurely attached individuals are more likely to identify with risky sexual practices and are less choosy when it comes to sexual partnering. Since both risky sexuality and less discrimination when seeking a sexual partner are attributes of certain paraphilic behaviors, it seems important to consider a client's attachment style during the assessment process. (For additional reading and understanding of attachment theory and its use and effectiveness in the counseling room, we recommend Wallin's 2007 *Attachment in Psychotherapy* as a starting point.)

Functional, securely attached families are certainly not perfect, however, and may exhibit dysfunctional behaviors from time to time, yet they carry the trait of being what Winnicott (1953), in his work on attachment, referred to as "good enough." They may yell, misunderstand one another, there may be tension and anger, and triangulation, but these unproductive behaviors are not chronic in functional family systems. Rules are clear and consistent yet flexible when appropriate. Messages from parents are explicit. Family members feel free to interact and ask for attention when needed. Family members are allowed to be individuals and encouraged to pursue their individual needs. Boundaries are respected. There is no emotional, physical, verbal, or sexual abuse among any family members, and parents are dependable. Children and parents all function within their appropriate roles. Children are not expected to be parents, and parents do not act like children. Mistakes are expected and dealt with appropriately, whereas perfection is viewed as unattainable.

Although many families may miss the mark on some of the functional family criteria from time to time, they meet all functional expectations on a consistent basis. Dysfunctional families do not. Some parents may not do enough for their children, leaving them to parent themselves. For example, a couple that attends swingers' clubs together while their children are left alone night after night by themselves may have a harmony in their sexual lives, but are sorely suffering as parental units and breeding dysfunction in their family system. Other parents may overcompensate with the raising of their children, never allowing their children to be autonomous and learn on their own. For example, a father may have a great deal of shame about his desire to dress in female clothing, and, due to that, he forbids his son to engage in any activities that may seem "girly."

Abusive parents always cause dysfunction in a family system, and abuse can be emotional, verbal, physical, sexual, or a combination. Verbal abusive parents can be super critical or insulting, and might criticize their children's intellect, abilities, looks, or basic conditions. Although some verbally and emotionally abusive parents are direct, others might be more passive-aggressive and may disguise put-downs with humor. Physically abusive parents create dysfunction since they create an environment of fear, leaving a child with feelings of anger, sadness, distrust, and feeling unsafe. Sexual abuse may be the most blatant example of family dysfunction, leaving children with tremendous emotional consequences.

Questionnaire for Use in Family Assessment

Once a counselor can identify the differences between function and dysfunction within a family unit, assessment of how a paraphilia affects the family is more easily evaluated. The following simple questionnaire can be used as a guide when assessing the effects of paraphilic tendencies on a family. Asking these questions as part of the family assessment can reveal the origins and current levels of family functioning:

- What are the family rules?
- Can rules be changed if needed?
- How do parents communicate what is expected to children?
- How do family members ask for attention when they need it?
- How do family members express individuality?
- How does the family view mistakes?
- Do parents operate within parental roles? How?
- How do children operate within the family? What are their responsibilities?
- Is there any abuse (emotional, verbal, physical, or sexual)?
- What are the messages about sex and how are they communicated in the family?

Mallory conducted a study to "examine how parent-child sexual communication (frequency, quality and type of messages) influences the development of sexual attitudes (idealistic and pessimistic) and in turn couples sexual communication" (Mallory, 2016, p. 2) and his appendix section includes various scales to use when assessing what was communicated about sexuality via the family of origin.

FAMILY SYSTEMS INTERVENTIONS

When using family systems interventions, family members are understood to all contribute to the problem at hand. Each family member works through individual issues with a focus on showing how his or her behaviors have an effect on the rest of the family unit. All members of the family are seen as being connected to each other through their network of interwoven relationships. When all family members begin to work together, they see how their individual roles have an effect on the roles of others within their family system. Once family members recognize how their actions affect one another, they can then begin to make more positive changes that are beneficial to the family as a whole (Bowen, 1978).

Incorporating medications as part of family systems treatment may or may not be appropriate depending on the situations and symptomatology of the person with paraphilic tendencies. For some with a Paraphilic Disorder, medication may be a requirement of family members, especially if the Paraphilic Disorder is diagnosed in an adolescent family member. Counselors must work collaboratively with a referral to a psychiatrist for medication need assessment and follow-up medication checks, on a case-by-case basis. Selective serotonin reuptake inhibitors and tricyclic antidepressants as well as hormone treatment with estrogen and/or progesterone are part of a pharmacological approach to treatment. However, these types of treatments are considered to be a "minefield of ethical issues" (Garcia & Thibaut, 2011, p. 784) and should be used only under the care and direction of a psychiatrist trained in ethical pharmacological treatment delivery for Paraphilic Disorders.

Guidry and Saleh (2004) offer 10 nonmedication interventions for counselors working with paraphilic sex offenders who present with comorbid psychiatric diagnoses. Although we must be clear that not everyone with a Paraphilic Disorder is a sexual offender, the incidence of psychiatric comorbidity is high for all of the paraphilias and therefore, a somewhat reworked overview of the Guidry–Saleh interventions is appropriate and useful when considering how best to help clients and their families or invested others. The following suggestions, based on the clinical interventions of Guidry and Saleh, can be used in an individual session or in a small group of the client's family members or significant others:

- Provide psychoeducation on how to manage symptoms of the co-occurring psychiatric disorder (e.g., depression, anxiety) if any are present.
- Encourage the client's acceptance of personal responsibility for paraphilic behaviors. We would add that an aid to this is use of in-session language and goals for out-of-session behaviors that reflect personal responsibility for overall mental and physical health as they relate to the paraphilic behavior (I chose . . . I decided . . . , etc., rather than blaming language and shame-based behaviors).
- Invite family or supportive others into session, keeping the group small (3–4 at most), and only when appropriate and helpful for the identified client's treatment.
- Using a dialogical, collaborative stance, increase insight and awareness into the repetitive cycle of paraphilic sexual behaviors as in a "chain of events" determination.
- Identify and actively address feelings of shame and social stigmatization of a Paraphilic Disorder that may accompany the family and the identified client.
- Be aware of the cultural, intellectual, and developmental issues that may be present for the client and the client's family. Create a list of client and family strengths, weaknesses, and learning styles so that these can be considered when planning innovative or creative in-session activities and out-of-session coping skills strategies.
- Review the initial assessment for clues on the client's socialization in childhood and adolescence (was he or she in foster care, a runaway?). Use this information to increase understanding and potential negative life schemas and cognitive distortions so that these can be addressed in session with psychoeducation and evidence-based cognitive behavioral interventions.
- If a limited capacity for empathy is identified in the client due to a psychological diagnosis (e.g., depression, anxiety, or narcissism), work on increasing an appreciation for and understanding of the identified victim (self, other, family) using various creative and cognitive approaches.
- Cast a wide net in addressing all potential areas for increased self-efficacy, personal responsibility, coping techniques, and awareness of self and other, and use these to cultivate overall improvement in functioning across social, family, and occupational domains.
- Develop a plan to prevent relapse that identifies triggers and skills for relapse avoidance.

Education

Educating family members is one of the most important first steps of treating problems attributed to paraphilic tendencies. After a counselor has determined whether a paraphilia is a disorder or a lifestyle choice, educating the family should be the very next step. Families may need to learn about the symptoms of a Paraphilic Disorder and how to best support a family member trying to decrease or eliminate paraphilic behaviors. If families are dealing with a lifestyle choice or orientation, they may need to be educated about sexual norms and how they can work together to incorporate a new but not necessarily understood paraphilic behavior into their lives. As families are educated, they can learn how to support each other through some difficult changes and work together to overcome challenges.

Educating yourself as a clinician is also important. Several organizations such as the National Coalition for Sexual Freedom in the United States, and Pink Therapy in the United Kingdom have a goal to educate clinicians with specific training in awareness, knowledge, and skills when working with clients with paraphilic behavior.

ETHICAL AND LEGAL IMPLICATIONS

By this point in our discussion, you are likely realizing that even though diagnosing a Paraphilic Disorder can be challenging, there are skills worth learning and tools worth using to help you in using a holistic, contextual systems approach to working with clients. Although we have already mentioned a few ethical and legal areas that surface with the Paraphilic Disorders prior to this section, we delineate the major ethical and legal implications here.

One specific area of ethics to which we now turn our attention is most important when beginning a counseling relationship with someone with paraphilic tendencies: counselor awareness of personal beliefs, assumptions, and biases toward those who have paraphilic urges or engage in paraphilic behaviors.

Addressing Personal Biases

As a profession, we are called to the practice of self-awareness via various ethical codes that govern our education and licensing. "Know Thyself" is a call to personal understanding of how our own background, religious views, cultural heritage, attachment style, and attitudes have an impact on our ability to be effective, empathic counselors. When personal beliefs and biases go unaddressed, a counseling relationship can quickly become ineffective or, even worse, destructive. We strongly suggest that counselors complete a self-assessment on their own biases when beginning to work with this population. Otherwise, bias can turn into stigmatization and pathologizing of atypical sexual behaviors in clients (Ford & Hendrick, 2003; Hoff & Sprott, 2009; Kelsey, Stiles, Spiller, & Diekhoff, 2013; Laska, 2013; Lawrence & Love-Crowell, 2008; Yost, 2010).

Mandated Reporting

Every counselor is a mandated reporter and must know the reporting laws of the state in which he or she practices. This is particularly important when working with Paraphilic Disorders. Since sexual trauma or abuse, past or present, is somewhat of a staple conversation when working with this population, counselors may confront some murky scenarios that may or may not mandate reporting. First and foremost, counselors must assess whether there is a violation at all. (See sections on "Assessing Consent" and "Assessing Victimization" for guidance.) If a violation has occurred, counselors would then assess whether the offense required a report to legal authorities or if it should be addressed confidentially with the client through counseling.

Although suspected child abuse or any sexual activity involving a child is always reportable, it is not always clear. What about a case that is 20 years old and was never reported? Suppose your client told you that he experienced sexual abuse as a child that he never reported. Now he still sees his abuser and is retraumatized every time. What are the legal and ethical implications of such a scenario?

Many states are not clear on child abuse reporting and how far in the past their legal mandates extend. Although there may be clear child abuse in a client's past that was never reported, a legal report may not be mandated depending on a state's statutes of limitations (if those are clear in the first place). Furthermore, in the age of online therapy, abuse might have happened across state lines, further confusing the responsibilities of a mandated reporter.

When legal guidelines fail to clearly communicate responsibilities to counselors, they must depend even harder on the ethical principles of *fidelity* (Am I being trustworthy?), *beneficence* (Am I doing what is best?), and *nonmaleficence* (Am I not causing harm?). Even more so, it is important to find out what the client needs during these times. In most cases, a client will want to process the abuse and talk about the large range of emotions attached to such a trauma. After all, that was probably the biggest reason the subject was highlighted in the first place.

Because bringing up such sensitive information was probably a difficult thing, a counselor needs to be respectful, reassuring, and have control over any personal reactions to hearing difficult and, perhaps, shocking information. Based on the session (or sessions) of disclosure, counselors should let their clients guide them as they express their wishes and needs. Only then can counselors make better decisions about what the next steps should be, in collaboration with their clients.

Counselors do not need to investigate or substantiate their clients' claims. Their job should be only to help clients clarify issues on their own as they come to terms with what is going on with them interpersonally. If a client should ask a counselor to seek legal remediation for any scenario that does not require legal action, clinical supervision should be the first step in the process. Although a clinician can document a client's reported distress and discuss future treatment goals, it is often recommended that counselors avoid requests to participate in advocate situations within the legal system or help clients confront perpetrators.

Finally, counselors must respect their clients' wishes when legal guidelines are unclear. If they do not, they can put their clients at risk across a wide range of circumstances. When in doubt, counselors should seek supervision, and always focus their attentions on their client's well-being. The ACA is clear about its focus on client well-being, stating that "[t]he primary responsibility of counselors is to respect the dignity and promote the welfare of clients" (ACA, 2014, Section A.1.a) while always making use of an ethical decision-making model (Section I.1.b). Both of these concepts are reiterated in the 2015 American Association for Marriage and Family Therapy (2015) *Code of Ethics*.

CASE CONCEPTUALIZATION

In this case conceptualization, we introduce you to James, a man who is struggling with his paraphilic behaviors and tendencies. As you read over this case, you will have an opportunity to see how spouses are so closely affected and how people with paraphilias may not consistently be diagnosed with Paraphilic Disorders even though they may cause them significant problems. Lastly, we will challenge you with some questions about this case and ask what you would do in a situation such as this if you were James's clinician. Use the information you have learned in this chapter to guide you in your decision-making process.

Presenting Concerns

James is a 65-year-old married White male who is seeking treatment for relationship dysfunction he is facing in his second marriage. James is currently working a recovery program for alcohol use disorder, now in full-remission (he has been sober for 6 years). His first wife died from breast cancer, and 3 years later he met Anna. Five years ago, James and

Anna were married, and he considered his marriage to be happy and stable. James and Anna hit their first marriage crisis 2 weeks ago when Anna discovered James's subscription to a hard-core Bondage and Submission, Sadism, and Masochism (BDSM) site on their credit card bill. When Anna looked up the site, she saw various disturbing sexually explicit images of women being bound and gagged. She was horrified and told James that she wanted a divorce. She was not going to be married to a "pervert and abuser of women." When James pleaded for her to forgive him and told her that he would get counseling for his problem, Anna agreed on the condition that he would never bring "this smut into the house again." James agreed to Anna's terms, cancelled his subscription, and called a counselor to help "fix him."

Concurrent Problems

Prior to requesting treatment now, James had never thought he had a problem with his BDSM urges. Although he had some shame about seeking pleasure through pain as an adolescent, he attributed it to his family's sexual rigidity and not that there was anything wrong with him. James had previous treatment for his alcohol abuse and admitted that he was an "alcoholic" but never felt he needed treatment for his paraphilic urges.

Background History and Stressors

James filled out a detailed background history on his childhood upbringing, family environment, and sexual experiences at the start of his counseling session. He described having a "sexually rigid" family environment. James's parents were staunch Catholics, and sex was not something that was thought about as pleasurable or recreational. At the age of 7, James's father walked in on him playing with his penis in his bedroom as he was getting dressed for church. He immediately yelled at James to "Stop that sinful behavior!" and made an appointment with their family doctor so that James could be treated for his perversions. At the doctor's office, James was "treated" with "shocking devices" to his penis in an effort to dull the urge to seek pleasure "down there." James remembers being really frightened at the time, but after a few days, he started intentionally hurting his genital area to produce pain "because it felt good in some weird way." He started with mild pressure of his hand on his penis and later started to use tools like clothes pins and some of his father's tools to intensify the pain and pleasure that he felt. By the time he was a late teen, he often included alcohol in the mix of pleasure and pain.

As James became an adult, his fondness of creating pain to seek pleasure became more sexualized. He participated in rough sexual play with girlfriends, and masturbation usually had a pain element associated with it. He enjoyed having sex without any pain associations, but he got the most pleasure when he was able to feel some kind of pain or pressure to his genitals or anus.

James met his wife Julie when he was 33, and they married a year later. He and Julie were able to enjoy the use of alcohol for relaxation and prior to sexual activities. James and Julie both enjoyed rough sexual play, and through their years of marriage, they engaged in many BDSM activities together including, tying up, whipping, gagging, orgasm control, psychological games, anal play, and other impact play. James said they got "really rough" from time to time, but they always used a "safe word." He described fantasies of their kinky sexual experiences in which he refused to stop despite her use of a safe word, but these thoughts were never acted upon, nor did it cause him any internal conflict. Overall, they enjoyed their sex life together immensely.

After James's wife passed away from cancer, his use of alcohol increased to the point of his recognition that he needed to enter a 28-day inpatient rehabilitation program for recovery. His grief and use of alcohol as a coping tool were addressed in rehab and he reports no relapse after entering a recovery program 5 years ago. He met Anna at a recovery meeting, and they fell in love very quickly. James said that his sex life with Anna was fulfilling but very "vanilla" (i.e., no kinky activities were present in their sexual activities). He remembers wondering if a few drinks would help them both relax so that kink could be introduced into their sexual relationship, but he never discussed this thought with Anna and he did not relapse with alcohol despite the urge to use.

After 2 years of marriage, James started to have stronger urges for feeling pain during his intimate time with Anna. When he asked Anna to smack his butt "really hard" during sex, Anna became very angry with James, telling him "no way!" and ending the sex session immediately saying he better go to Sex Addicts Anonymous meetings. James was embarrassed by Anna's disdain and suggestion to attend a new kind of recovery program, as he did not view himself as a sex addict nor to have inappropriate sexual desires. He never suggested any kind of rough sex play with her again, nor did he attend the suggested recovery program. Instead, he started looking online at "lighter bondage sites" until he progressed to "hard-core BDSM sites" in a matter of 3 years. He usually imagined himself receiving pain from a willing partner, but he was also sexually excited by images of women being bound and gagged.

Strengths

James did not feel any guilt or shame over his sexual urges or behaviors nor did he relapse into alcohol use. His continued abstinence from using alcohol as a coping mechanism showed that he responded to treatment directives well to manage current stressors in his life. James also showed that he had an awareness of his destructive behaviors in his relationship with Anna since he felt badly about hiding his sexual activities from Anna. He was aware that he was hiding sexual behaviors that Anna probably would not agree with and that his "mild BDSM habit" had increased to "something disgusting," as Anna put it. James never cheated on his first wife, and stated that he certainly did not plan on cheating on Anna, showing his ability to commit to a long-term partner despite significant stressors.

DSM-5 Impressions and Implications

James showed many masochistic tendencies as he was sexually aroused by behaviors, fantasies, and urges of bondage and pain infliction, and he enjoyed being the receiver of pain rather than the giver. He did meet criteria for a comorbid diagnosis of alcohol use disorder, sustained remission. However, James did not meet criteria for Sexual Masochism Disorder since his behaviors, fantasies, or urges did not cause him any significant, clinical distress across the domains of work, social relationships, and/or in other domains of importance. His marriage was distressed because of Anna's difficulties with James's behaviors and urges and not due to James's paraphilic tendencies alone. Also, since James was able to engage in a functional sexual relationship with Anna without the need to engage in masochistic activities, he did not meet any criteria for loss of control.

Relational Problems

Due to his marriage to Anna, someone who did not engage in any BDSM activities and did not approve of such sexual behaviors, James experienced significant problems in his marriage (problems in relationship with spouse or partner). Although James did not feel guilt or shame about his sexual urges, he did feel like he was the problem in the relationship. Anna thought he was "disgusting" and did not understand why James had these urges or how they could be pleasurable. Her disdain for James paraphilic urges became the primary problem in their marriage. When James was married to his first wife, they shared the same sexual desires and engaged in paraphilic behaviors together in a way that worked well for their marriage. After he married Anna, those sexual behaviors stopped for a few years but James's sexual urges reignited after some time. When he tried to incorporate some masochistic behaviors into his sex life with Anna, he felt embarrassed for the first time after being rejected. Instead of discussing this incident with Anna to try to come to some resolution, James started engaging in secretive sexual behavior that satisfied his masochistic urges. This hiding behavior quickly turned into a "dirty little secret" and left Anna feeling betrayed, confused, and angry when she found out about James's "underground life." Although James did not meet criteria for Sexual Masochism Disorder, he certainly created a problem because of his masochistic tendencies and behaviors.

Assessments

Three assessment tools that might be helpful for gaining more information about James's condition and situation are the Attitudes to Sex Questionaire (Twohig & Furnham, 1998), the Paraphilias Scale (Seto et al., 2012), and the Sexual Behaviors and Desires Measure (Reese-Weber & McBride, 2015). Although James does not meet criteria for any Paraphilic Disorder, these assessments would be helpful tools in helping James identify problematic areas in his life that he may not have identified through his background history. Assessment tools should always be used in conjunction with a therapeutic conversation and in the context of what is going on in the client's life at that time.

Assessing Consent and Victimization

In James's case, there was no evidence of either lack of consent or victimization. Throughout his history and in his current position, James did not engage in any sexual behavior without consent from his sexual partner. His first wife engaged consensually with James during BDSM activities, and they designated a "safe word" to stop any sexual activity if either of them felt uncomfortable at any time, and he did not act upon his sexual fantasy of ignoring her safe word. James disclosed this information privately, and stated he did not share this information with his current wife. James's current wife, Anna, stated that she never felt coerced or violated at any point during their sexual time together.

No victim was identified in James's case. Although Anna was hurt and felt betrayed over the discovery that James subscribed to a BDSM site, James stopped the behavior immediately after he found out about Anna's distress and sought help. He did not continue the behavior despite Anna's disapproval. James was able to enjoy sex with Anna without engaging in paraphilic behaviors, therefore further demonstrating the lack of victims in his case.

Assessing How Behavior Has an Impact on the Sexual Relationship

It was determined that James's paraphilia is not a disorder but a lifestyle choice or atypical sexual orientation. However, the complexity of James's case lies in the fact that his wife Anna is distressed over his tendencies and their marriage is suffering. James and Anna, in some areas of their sexual relationship, are incompatible. James likes kink and Anna refuses such activities. Furthermore, Anna has decided for *both partners* that they will not be engaging in any BDSM activities. Although James came in to see the counselor with hopes of squelching his sexual tendencies, he will quickly find out that this request is often improbable as he has engaged in sexually masochistic activities for most of his life. After some time, his feelings of panic, guilt, and remorse may turn to resentment and anger toward Anna.

Assessing How Family Is Affected by Paraphilic Behaviors

James and Anna had a very functional marriage for the first few years of their relationship together. After James was sexually rejected by Anna, some dysfunction started to creep in. James felt like he could not express himself to Anna and felt "shamed" by Anna's abrupt rejection to his sexual suggestion. In order to cope, he created a secret sexual life where he engaged in secretive sexual behaviors in the online environment. Just like he learned in his family to hide his sexual masochistic urges, James hid from Anna and engaged in masochistic behaviors in secret. The family rule seemed to be: "Don't talk about kinky sex and certainly don't engage in it." James did not feel like the rule could be changed, but he never approached this subject with Anna so no discussion was ever had about how they might come to a working agreement in their sexual life. James did not feel like he could slip or make a mistake after he was found out. His initial request to "be fixed" was from the fear that Anna would leave him if he acted on his masochistic urges in any way.

Interventions

After James met with his counselor for a number of sessions to discuss his background, assess for Paraphilic Disorder, and talk about treatment goals, he was encouraged to bring Anna in for sessions on an ongoing basis. Anna agreed to come consistently, and marriage counseling began.

James and Anna both met with the counselor together to discuss their concerns and their goals in marriage counseling. They talked about what they both wanted in their marriage and the problems they needed to overcome. Initially, Anna just wanted James to "get fixed" and stop engaging in any masochistic sexual behaviors. After some education about Paraphilic Disorders versus paraphilic orientations, Anna felt less anxiety about James's desires but did not have any interest in engaging in "hard-core" BDSM activities at any point.

Anna and James realized how their behaviors affected one another and that any sexual decision one partner made was a decision for both of them. They learned how to communicate more openly about their sexual wants and needs as well as their relationship engagements in general.

James did not have any symptoms that required medication treatment, but both were informed that if they felt that medication was needed for any reason that they should discuss this in counseling and an appropriate referral would be made to assess that need at that time.

James was encouraged to take personal responsibility for his secretive behavior, whereas Anna was able to discuss how she had been hurt by James's actions. James, in turn, had the opportunity to tell Anna about his past and how masochistic tendencies had been a large part of most of his life. Although he knew that Anna did not want to engage in any hard-core BDSM activities, the couple was able to take small steps toward a compromise. Anna was nervous about trying new sexual behaviors with James, but she told him what she might be comfortable with to begin. Anna was also able to talk about the sexual messages she received growing up and how they had an impact on her sexual "rigidity" today. She was also honest about her own feelings of loss of control with chemical addiction prior to her own recovery 10 years ago and her fears of feeling out of control in sexual situations.

James and Anna continued to address their sexual issues and relationship issues in counseling week to week and eventually moved to every other week and then monthly. Although they had many areas to address and a lot of work to do together to become "sexually compatible," they were off to a good start. Regularly scheduled sessions kept them on task with treatment goals and allowed them to address challenging areas as they surfaced.

Ethical and Legal Implications

First and foremost, the counselor must have an understanding of his or her own sexual bias, preferences, and attitudes so that the client's best interests are not lost in a personal agenda. Suggested assessments designed to increase counselor self-awareness are the Comfort and Willingness Scale to Address Client Sexuality Scale, developed by Harris and Hays (2008), and the Attitudes about Sadomasochism Scale (Yost, 2010). Each can be used to address the ACA *Code of Ethics*, Sections A.4.a and A.4.b (2014).

Based on the guidelines given previously, there is no evidence of either lack of consent or victimization with regard to James's atypical sexual orientation toward BDSM. No child or under-aged adolescent was involved in any of James's activities and, therefore, there is no ethical mandate to report his activities.

DISCUSSION

As you continue to reflect on the case study and the overall approach, contemplate these questions:

- Since James's marriage is suffering due to James's paraphilic tendencies and behaviors, why would James's condition meet criteria for *significant distress* in the *DSM-5*?
- If Anna stated that James violated her consent at one time during sexual play, would James's masochistic "orientation" or "lifestyle choice" become a "disorder"? Why or why not?
- Since James, by self-report, has an identified diagnosis of alcoholism (in remission for 5 years), what is the counselor's responsibility in establishing if a current substance use disorder is also having an impact on his marriage with Anna?
- At what point should the counselor refer Anna for individual counselor sessions, if at all?
- Since James experienced sexual arousal when fantasizing about not listening to his first wife's "safe word," what is the appropriate counseling response? Is it a good idea to bring this information into the couple's work? Why or why not?

SUMMARY

Paraphilias are conditions that can be exhibited as disorders or orientations, and it takes a skilled and open-minded clinician to differentiate between the two. Although many people will have significant distress due to their paraphilic tendencies, there are many others that embrace paraphilic urges and behaviors and create lifestyles that work for them and their sexual partners. It is vitally important for counselors to listen to their clients about their situations, assess their wants and needs, identify whether there are significant stressors, and find out if there are any victims associated with paraphilic behaviors before giving Paraphilic Disorder diagnoses or identifying pathologies or dysfunctions. Although many families may experience dysfunction in their lifetimes, not all families are dysfunctional, so completing a full family assessment is essential for properly working with this population. Cultural norms are also incredibly important to take into account when working with paraphilias since norms can range drastically from one culture to the next. Although many therapeutic approaches exist in the treatment of Paraphilic Disorders, a family systems approach is most recommended because it focuses on personal responsibility in relation to others within a family dynamic. Although one person may have paraphilic urges, all family members are affected and contribute to the problems within the family. Finally, ethical and legal issues can occur regularly when treating this population, especially within the realm of personal biases and mandated reporting so that counselors should regularly assess their value systems and keep their clients central in their decision-making practices.

REFERENCES

American Association for Marriage and Family Therapy. (2015). *AAMFT code of ethics*. Alexandria, VA: Author.

American Counseling Association. (2014). *ACA code of ethics*. Alexandria, VA: Author.

American Psychiatric Association. (1952) *Diagnostic and statistical manual of mental disorders* (1st ed.) Washington, DC: American Psychiatric Association Mental Hospital Service.

American Psychiatric Association. (1968). *Diagnostic and statistical manual of mental disorders* (2nd ed.). Washington, DC: Author.

American Psychiatric Association. (1980). *Diagnostic and statistical manual of mental disorders* (3rd ed.). Washington, DC: Author.

American Psychiatric Association. (1994). *Diagnostic and statistical manual of mental disorders* (4th ed.). Washington, DC: Author.

American Psychiatric Association. (2013a). *Diagnostic and statistical manual of mental disorders* (5th ed.). Arlington, VA: American Psychiatric Publishing.

American Psychiatric Association. (2013b). *Paraphilic Disorders*. Retrieved from http://www.psychiatry .org/FileLibrary/Psychiatrists/Practice/DSM/APA_DSM-5-Paraphilic-Disorders.pdf

Anagol, P. (2016). Age of consent and child marriage in India. In N. Naples, R. C. Hoogland, M. Wickrama-singhe, W. C. A. Wong (Eds.). *The Wiley Blackwell encyclopedia of gender and sexuality studies*. Hoboken, NJ: Wiley-Blackwell. doi:10.1002/9781118663219.wbegss558

Balon, R. (2013). Controversies in the diagnosis and treatment of paraphilias. *Journal of Sex and Marital Therapy, 39*, 7–20.

Balon, R. (2014). Politics of diagnostic criteria: Specifiers of pedophilic disorder in DSM-5. *Archives of Sexual Behaviors, 43*, 1235–1236.

Berlin, F. S. (2011). Pedophilia: Criminal mindset or mental disorder? A conceptual review. *American Journal of Forensic Psychiatry, 32*, 3–26.

Berner, W., & Briken, P. (2012). Pleasure seeking and the aspect of longing for an object in perversion: A neuropsychoanalytical perspective. *American Journal of Psychotherapy, 66*(2), 129–150.

Bhugra, D., Popelyuk, D., & McMullen, I. (2010). Paraphilias across cultures: Contexts and controversies. *Journal of Sex Research, 47*(2–3), 242–256.

Birnie-Porter, C., & Lydon, J. E. (2013). A prototype approach to understanding sexual intimacy through its relationship to intimacy. *Journal of the International Association for Relationship Research, 20*, 236–258.

Bogaert, A. F., & Sadava, S. (2002). Adult attachment and sexual behavior. *Personal Relationships, 9*, 191–204.

Bourke, M. L., & Hernandez, A. E. (2009). The "Butner Study" redux: A report on the incidence of hands-on child victimization by child pornography offenders. *Journal of Family Violence, 24*, 183–191.

Bowen, M. (1978). *Family therapy in clinical practice*. New York, NY: Jason Aaronson.

Brown, E. M. (2001). *Patterns of infidelity and their treatment*. Philadelphia, PA: Brunner-Routledge.

Carnes, P. (1989). *Contrary to love: Helping the sexual addict*. Center City, MN: Hazelden.

Carnes, P. (2010). *Facing the shadows: Starting sexual and relationship recovery*. Carefree, AZ: Gentle Path Press.

Chibucos, T. R., & Leite, R. W. (2005). *Readings in family theory*. Thousand Oaks, CA: Sage.

Collins, P. C., & Collins, G. N. (2012). *A couple's guide to sexual addiction: A step-by-step plan to rebuild trust and restore intimacy*. Avon, MA: Adams Media.

Conde, A., Figueiredo, B., & Bifulco, A. (2011). Attachment style and psychological adjustment in couples. *Attachment and Human Development, 13*(3), 271–291.

Connan, S. (2010). A kink in the process. *Therapy Today, 6,* 10–15. Retrieved from http://www.therapy today.net

Consent [Def. 1]. (2016). In *Merriam-Webster's online dictionary* (11th ed.). Springfield, MA: Merriam-Webster.

Coy, J. S., & Miller, M. M. (2014). Intimate partners who struggle with formal commitments: Attachment styles, major challenges, and clinical implications. *American Journal of Family Therapy, 42,* 232–242.

De Block, A., & Adriaens, P. R. (2013). Pathologizing sexual deviance: A history. *Journal of Sex Research, 50*(3–4), 276–298.

Endrass, J., Urbaniok, F., Hammermeister, L. C., Benz, C., Elbert, T., Laubacher, A., Rossegger, A. (2009). The consumption of internet child pornography and violent sexual offending. *BMC Psychiatry, 9,* 43. Retrieved from http://biomedcentral.com/1471-244X/9/43

Fileborn, B. (2013). ACSSA Resource Sheet. Australia: The Australian Institute of Family Studies.

Ford, M. P., & Hendrick, S. S. (2003). Therapists' sexual values for self and clients: Implications for practice and training. *Professional Psychology: Research and Practice, 34*(1), 80–87.

Garcia, F. D., & Thibaut, F. (2011). Current concepts in the pharmacotherapy of paraphilias. *Drugs, 71*(6), 771–790.

George, C., Kaplan, N., & Main, M. (1996). *Adult attachment interview protocol* (3rd ed.). Unpublished manuscript, University of California at Berkeley.

Gladding, S. T. (2015). *Family therapy: History, theory, and practice.* Boston, MA: Pearson.

Gross, B. (2006). The pleasure of pain. *The Forensic Examiner, 15,* 56–61.

Guidry, L. L., & Saleh, F. M. (2004). Clinical considerations of paraphilic sex offenders with comorbid psychiatric conditions. *Sexual Addiction and Compulsivity, 1,* 21–34.

Harris, S. M., & Hays, K. W. (2008). Family therapist comfort with and willingness to discuss client sexuality. *Journal of Marital and Family Therapy, 34*(2), 239–250.

Hentsch-Cowles, G., & Brock, L. J. (2013). A systemic review of the literature on the role of the partner of the sex addict, treatment models, and a call for research for systems theory model in treating the partner. *Sexual Addiction and Compulsivity, 20,* 323–335.

Hill, R. (2011). We share a sacred secret: Gender, domesticity, and containment in transvestia's histories and letters from crossdressers and their wives. *Journal of Social History, 44*(3), 729–750.

Hoff, G., & Sprott, R. A. (2009). Therapy experiences of clients with BDSM sexualities: Listening to a stigmatized sexuality. *Electronic Journal of Human Sexuality, 12,* no pages noted.

Janssen, D. F. (2014). How to "ascertain" paraphilia? An etymological hint. *Archives of Sexual Behavior, 43,* 1245–1246.

Kaufman, A. (2014). The Butner study: A report on the fraudulent execution of the Adam Walsh Act by the Federal Bureau of Prisons (BOP). Retrieved from http://cfcamerica.org

Keane, H. (2004). Disorders of desire: Addiction and problems of intimacy. *Journal of Medical Humanities, 25*(3), 189–204.

Kelsey, K., Stiles, B. L., Spiller, L., & Diekhoff, G. M. (2013). Assessment of therapists' attitudes towards BDSM. *Psychology and Sexuality, 4*(3), 255–267.

Kilmann, P. R., Finch, H., Parnell, M. M., & Downer, J. T. (2013). Partner attachment and interpersonal characteristics. *Journal of Sex and Marital Therapy, 39,* 144–159.

Kleinplatz, P., & Moser, C. (2004). Toward clinical guidelines for working with BDSM clients. *Contemporary Sexuality, 38*(6), 3–4.

Krueger, R. B. (2010). The DSM diagnostic criteria for sexual sadism. *Archives of Sexual Behavior, 39,* 325–345.

Laska, R. S. (2013). *Surrendering safely: Increasing clinicians' understandings of kink* (St. Catherine University Libraries, Master of Social Work Clinical Research Papers, Paper 222). Retrieved from http://sophia .stkate.edu/msw_papers/222

Lawrence, A. A., & Love-Crowell, J. (2008). Psychotherapists' experience with clients who engage in consensual sadomasochism: A qualitative study. *Journal of Sex and Marital Therapy, 34,* 67–85.

Mallory, A. B. S. (2016). *Family sexual communication and sexual attitudes: Understanding the influence on couple's sexual communication* (Master's thesis). Retrieved from http://krex.k-state.edu/dspace/bitstream/ handle/2097/32652/AllenMallory2016.pdf?sequence=3&isAllowed=y

Morrison, J. (2014). *DSM-5 made easy: The clinician's guide to diagnosis.* New York, NY: Guilford Press.

Péloquin, K., Bigras, N., Brassard, A., & Godbout, N. (2014). Perceiving that one's partner is supportive moderates the associations among attachment insecurity and psychosexual variables. *Canadian Journal of Human Sexuality, 23*(3), 178–188.

Rahman, Q., & Symeonides, D. J. (2008). Neurodevelopmental correlates of paraphilic sexual interest in men. *Archives of Sexual Behavior, 37*, 166–172.

Reese-Weber, M., & McBride, D. M. (2015). *Sexual behaviors and desires measure* [PsycTESTS database record]. Washington, DC: American Psychological Association.

Rye, B. J., & Meaney, G. J. (2007). It is good as long as we do not get caught. *International Journal of Sexual Health, 19*(1), 47–56.

Sandberg, J. G., Busby, D. M., Johnson, S. M., & Yoshida, K. (2012). The Brief Accessibility, Responsiveness, and Engagement (BARE) Scale: A tool for measuring attachment behavior in couple relationships. *Family Process, 51*(4), 512–526.

Seto, M. C., Hanson, R. K., & Babchishin, K. M. (2011). Contact sexual offending by men with online sexual offenses. *Sex Abuse, 23*, 124–145.

Seto, M. C., Lalumiere, M. L., Harris, G. T., & Chivers, M. L. (2012). *Paraphilias scale* [PsycTESTS database record]. Washington, DC: American Psychological Association.

Shursen, A., Brock, L. J., & Jennings, G. (2008). Differentiation & intimacy in sex offender relationships. *Sexual Addiction and Compulsivity, 15*, 14–22.

Smallbone, S. W., & Wortley, R. K. (2004). *Multiple paraphilic interests scale* [PsycTESTS database record]. Washington, DC: American Psychological Association.

Smith-Acuña, S. (2011). *Systems theory in action: Applications to individual, couples, and family therapy.* Hoboken, NJ: Wiley.

Twohig, F., & Furnham, A. (1998). *Attitudes to sex questionnaire* [PsycTESTS database record]. Washington, DC: American Psychological Association.

UNICEF. (2016). *Age of consent.* Retrieved from http://www.unicef.org/rightsite/433_457.htm#to_have_sex

Victim [Def. 1]. (2016). In *Merriam-Webster's online dictionary* (11th ed.). Springfield, MA: Merriam-Webster.

Wallin, D. (2007). *Attachment in psychotherapy.* New York, NY: Guilford Press.

Welch, S., Klassen, C., Borisova, O., & Clothier, H. (2013). The DSM-5 controversies: How should psychologists respond? *Canadian Psychology, 54*(3), 166–175.

White, J. M., & Klein, D. M. (2008). *Family theories* (3rd ed.). Los Angeles, CA: Sage.

Whitechurch, G. G., & Constantine, L. L. (2009). Systems theory. In P. Boss, W. J. Doherty, R. LaRossa, W. R. Schumm, & S. K. Steinmetz (Eds.), *Sourcebook of family theories and methods: A contextual approach* (pp. 225–254). New York, NY: Springer.

Williams, W. (2016). *The two-spirit people of indigenous North Americans.* Retrieved from http://www.firstpeople.us/articles/the-two-spirit-people-of-indigenous-north-americans.html

Winnicott, D. (1953). Transitional objects and transitional phenomena. *International Journal of Psychoanalysis, 34*, 89–97.

Wollert, R., & Cramer, E. (2011). Sampling extreme groups invalidates research on the paraphilias: Implications for DSM-5 and sex offender risk assessments. *Behavioral Science Law, 29*, 554–565.

Wright, S. (2014). Kinky parents and child custody: The effect of the DSM-5 differentiation between the paraphilias and Paraphilic Disorders. *Archives of Sexual Behavior, 43*, 1257–1258.

Yost, M. R. (2010). Development and validation of the attitudes about sadomasochism scale. *Journal of Sex Research, 47*(1), 79–91.

Zucker, K. (2013). DSM-5: Call for commentaries on gender dysphoria, sexual dysfunctions, and Paraphilic Disorders. *Archives of Sexual Behavior, 42*(5), 669–674.

INDEX

Made in United States
Troutdale, OR
08/10/2023

11974913R10317